ENGINEERED
WORK MEASUREMENT

SECOND EDITION 1965

ENGINEERED WORK MEASUREMENT

The principles, techniques, and data of Methods-Time Measurement, modern Time and Motion Study, and related Applications Engineering data

DELMAR W. KARGER, B.S.E.E., M.S.Gen.E., P.E.
Dean, School of Management
Rensselaer Polytechnic Institute
Troy, New York

FRANKLIN H. BAYHA, B.S.M.E., P.E.
Research Associate (I.E.)
The University of Michigan
Ann Arbor, Michigan

Second Printing

INDUSTRIAL PRESS INC., 200 Madison Ave., New York, N.Y.

Foreword

The status of work study has undergone a considerable change over the years. Originally, Frederick W. Taylor used it as a means of replacing guesswork and estimate by facts as he developed his ideas on the scientific management of industry. The work measurement aspects of his work attracted the greatest amount of public attention. The social, ethical, and moral rightness of work measurement became a controversial issue of the day, culminating in a full scale Congressional investigation of scientific management in 1912.

The contemporary work of Frank B. and Lillian M. Gilbreth in the field of motion study brought new and original ideas on the role of method in productivity. Because it was new, it also provoked controversy although less intense than that engendered by work measurement. The Gilbreths contributed a deeper understanding of work, methods, and fatigue than had hitherto existed and above all a greater understanding of the importance of the human element in all work study.

During the pioneer era, brilliant work study installations were made by Taylor, the Gilbreths, and their associates, installations which aroused great interest on the part of management for what these procedures could contribute to the ever-present task of reducing costs and increasing productivity. Although there were two schools of thought as to whether the main emphasis should be placed on time study or on motion study, the procedures began to receive increasing acceptance on the part of the more progressive leaders of business and industry.

Unfortunately for the orderly progress of work study, World War I came along and with it an unprecedented demand for increased production. The record which had been compiled by the application of time and motion study in bringing about increased production, although not yet extensive, was sufficient to cause managements to turn towards work study in important numbers. So sudden was the increased demand that there were not enough qualified time and motion study practitioners to meet it. The demand continued, however, and presented to unqualified practitioners the opportunity to capitalize on it. Self-styled efficiency experts sprang up overnight. They had no difficulty in selling their services to management, for management was in the mood to buy. What they did, however, was all but disastrous. By applying unskillfully a powerful tool which they understood but poorly, if at all, they presently aroused the antagonism of both management and labor. Their monumental failures with time and motion study and wage incentives reduced the regard in which these procedures were held to a low point. Managers, whose hopes for these procedures had been destroyed, were not inclined to try again. Workers lost confidence in the benefits the procedures were said to bring to them and wanted no more of them. It was a dark moment in the history of work study and one from which a long period of recovery was necessary.

But it is impossible to keep a sound idea submerged for any length of time, no matter how badly it may have been mishandled. During the interval between World War I and World War II, an increasing number of sound work study installations were made by well-qualified practitioners. These demonstrated beyond question what a properly engineered installation could do for a company. It was no coincidence that in industry after industry, the leading companies were those who used work study procedures the most extensively.

During this period, the work study procedures themselves underwent considerable development. Emphasis swung more and more from work measurement to methods study although both were recognized as being necessary to each other. Research was undertaken to develop procedures capable of doing an ever-better job of methods improvement and work measurement. General understanding of the procedures also grew. Partly this was due to the application experience of a growing number of people in industry. Partly it was due to the colleges and universities, who by adding work study courses to their curricula, turned out an increasingly large number of graduates with at least an appreciation-level knowledge of the field. A gradual increase in books and articles dealing with work study subjects also made its contribution to increase in understanding.

As a result of all this, when World War II came along and brought another great surge in the demand for increased productivity, industry was better prepared. Managers, many of them former time and motion study men, knew better what constituted sound work study practices. Many trained practitioners were available. Even more important, perhaps, was the fact that adequate training courses were available so that the work study force could be and was expanded in a fairly short time. Work study was applied extensively and in the majority of cases soundly. The result was a tremendous increase in productivity which contributed importantly to the outcome of the war.

The war, of course, brought many changes. It stimulated research in the work study field just as it did in so many other fields. New procedures were developed and improved application practices for the older procedures came into being.

In addition, the attitude of labor towards work study became much more receptive. That work study resulted in increased production was beyond question. The need for increased production was equally evident, especially to the men and women who had sons and daughters in the armed forces. Training courses at the appreciation level were widely given which took much of the mystery out of work study and removed fears of the procedures based on lack of understanding. The War Production Board, too, made an important contribution. Under the wise guidance of men with an extensive background in the work study field, an understanding of the principles on which methods improvement, work measurement, and wage incentives should be based was widely spread. The Board insisted upon cooperation between management and unions whenever new installations were made and saw to it that both groups understood and accepted the work study practices which would best meet the needs of their particular situation.

It should not be inferred, however, that all things were satisfactory in the work study field during the war period. Many distortions of sound practice were countenanced in order to meet temporary conditions. Certain managements, for example, feeling that they had somehow to get around the restrictions imposed by the wartime freezing of wages in order to attract or hold the needed workers used distortions of their wage incentive systems as a means of providing higher take-home pay. Labor, too, in some instances, used its strength and the confusions of the times to force distortions that were to its immediate but not longrun advantage. The resulting misapplications tended to make certain installations appear unsound and probably slowed down the general progress of work study to a certain extent.

But these distortions were temporary disturbances which while perhaps serious in their effect on an individual company could not permanently stay the advance of work study. In the post war period, work study spread not only in the United States of America, but especially in the war-ravaged countries of the Western world. There the need for increased productivity was beyond question. Production in unprecedented amount was necessary to replace the destructions of war if the people were to survive. So work study know-how was sent abroad under the technical assistance program sponsored by the United States government. It gave great impetus to the installation of work study methods, particularly in Western Europe.

And presently the work study practices which had been so freely exported returned to the United States, often reinforced and improved by sound research and engineering work done abroad. The very term work study that is used so freely in this book was first brought into general use in Great Britain by Mr. Russell Currie, C.B.E., of Imperial Chemical Industries Limited, to express to his management the basic purpose of all of the techniques and procedures which had been developed for the purpose of increasing productivity and reducing costs.

The techniques and procedures, in the meantime, multiplied further during the post war period. The literature also multiplied as many experienced practitioners and teachers of work study methods contributed their ideas and thinking to the general advancement of the art. Each book and article which is produced adds to the general understanding of work study and what it can do and thus is to be welcomed by those who believe that increased productivity and increased standards of material well-being are inseparable.

So it is with the pages that follow. There will be found a reflection of the impact that work study developments have had on two men who have lived through several decades of work study application. As practical men in daily contact with the work study application problems faced by the dynamic industry of which they were a part, they have had the opportunity to test and use many of the procedures which are a part of work study. Their description of these procedures, colored as it is by firsthand practical experience with them, provides an unusually useful guide to their successful application.

Because of its practical flavor, the book will encourage practicality in approach to all who study it carefully. Of necessity, it describes in some detail the procedures which it advocates. It does so, however, from the standpoint of those who have used them to solve the practical problems with which they have been confronted. The book reports no new research done by the authors themselves and advocates no untested ideas which they may hold. Instead, patiently and painstakingly, it tells the reader step by step what he must know and do to handle a work study assignment acceptably under a wide variety of conditions.

The authors support the procedures they advocate in no uncertain terms, although at the same time they recognize that other procedures, properly used, may be equally acceptable. They endeavor to integrate the older time and motion study practices with some of the newer developments, particularly in the field of predetermined motion times and thus arrive at a combined procedure which is more complete than either of its parts.

In total, they depict in practical terms the current evolution of work study. The book thus presents a valuable summarization of the influences of the past on the practices of the present to the serious student of work study and its use by management.

H. B. MAYNARD

Pittsburgh, Pa.
September 1, 1957

Preface to the First Edition

The aim of the authors in writing this book has been to further the attainment of scientific management by promoting competent work measurement in all its forms. This aim seemed to require most a unified text encompassing all essential principles, data, and techniques of Methods-Time Measurement, modern Time and Motion Study, and related Applications Engineering data. At present, such information can be obtained only from diverse sources and authorities. Included here are all the essential facts required to develop labor standards and better manufacturing methods with either Methods-Time Measurement or Time and Motion Study.

We have tried to make this text equally appealing to practicing engineers, engineering and business students, consulting organizations, and colleges with industrial engineering curricula. Meeting their diverse needs necessitated a very practical approach coupled with an adequate presentation of the important theoretical aspects of work measurement and a constructive point of view.

While conceding that proper application of most predetermined time systems will ordinarily measure manual motions satisfactorily, the authors feel that Methods-Time Measurement is the best approach available today. With many others, they believe, primarily due to the continuing research of the MTM Association, MTM will mature into the only predetermined time system universally recognized and applied. Active usage of MTM has already spread beyond the United States boundaries into Canada, France, Holland, England, Sweden, Switzerland, Japan, and many other foreign countries. Its inclusion as a required subject in many industrial engineering college courses is another indication of its general acceptance.

The MTM portion of this text, particularly Chapters 1 through 20, has been reviewed by the MTM Association for Standards and Research for conformity with official interpretations and for inclusion of the topics considered essential to adequate MTM training. This portion has been incorporated into a training manual used at The Magnavox Company in a course approved by the MTM Association.

The authors gratefully acknowledge their general indebtedness to the Board of Directors of the MTM Association for authorizing the review and their particular gratitude to Mr. Richard F. Stoll, Executive Secretary, and to Mr. Alfred H. Walter, Chairman of the Training Committee and Consulting Engineer of A. T. Kearney & Company, for their patience and cooperation in performing this official review. Their suggestions were most helpful.

The Magnavox Company is also due grateful recognition for encouraging the authors as members of its staff. It was through Magnavox support of the MTM Association as a Sustaining Member that the authors became thoroughly acquainted with MTM.

Public acknowledgment of everyone who helped and encouraged us in this work would be very difficult. However, special thanks are due Dr. H. B. Maynard, President, Methods Engineering Council of Pittsburgh, Pennsylvania; Mr. John M. Allderige, Technical Advisor, Industrial Engineering Division, Eastman Kodak Company; and Mrs. Icel C. Bauserman, Secretary, who devotedly typed the manuscript and was a source of other vital help. Finally, the kind indulgence of Mrs. Karger and Mrs. Bayha for the many hours spent apart from our families can never be repaid.

DELMAR W. KARGER
FRANKLIN H. BAYHA

Fort Wayne, Indiana, 1957

Preface to the Second Edition

Having stressed the dynamic nature of work measurement in the very successful First Edition, it is not surprising that the authors have found it necessary to update and revise every portion of this text. Expansion of old material and the addition of much vital new material have been achieved while retaining the effective basic format of the chapters. Recently defined knowledge evolving from the study of human factors, the social sciences, etc. has been incorporated.

The reader interested in MTM will find much additional information and many newer interpretations in every chapter — many have received major revisions. Research data developed both in the United States and abroad since the publication of the First Edition has been included. Noteworthy is the new supplementary, more detailed data on Apply Pressure and Position.

Also included are initial results of the Learning Curve Research Project at the University of Michigan sponsored by the MTM Association for Standards and Research. These enable the approximate prediction of the time an operator requires to learn a given sequence of MTM elements well enough to meet the MTM performance standard. The prediction of learning time has been much discussed at many technical meetings, but up to now the discussion has been somewhat academic. However, these results comprise the first practical prediction system ever to be established!

Finally, for the MTM reader, this provides the most complete and up-to-date coverage available on the subject, both theory and application. The text is recognized by the MTM Association by approval of its usage for recognized Application Training Courses.

The treatment of traditional time and motion study as well as the more recent statistical techniques also has been enhanced by the presentation of much new material. The integrated approach to predetermined times and the traditional methods of time determination has been strengthened.

The remarks included in the Preface to the First Edition can be reinforced by the comment that the intimate experiences and connections we have enjoyed during the interim with all aspects of MTM, the MTM Association, the MTM research at the University of Michigan, and the work measurement field in general all serve to confirm our previous statements.

Our personal thanks and professional respect for direct aid in this revision could be extended to many, including our critical readers. However, special gratitude is due to: Mr. Richard F. Stoll, Executive Secretary, and Mr. John E. Mabry, Staff Industrial Engineer, of the U.S.-Canada MTM Association; Dr. Walton M. Hancock, Professor and Chairman of the Department of Industrial Engineering, University of Michigan; Mr. James A. Foulke, Dr. Richard C. Jelinek, and Mr. Karl G. Bartscht of the Industrial Engineering staff at the University of Michigan; and our erstwhile Editor-in-Chief, Mr. Holbrook L. Horton of The Industrial Press. We are also most happy to repeat our encomiums to Mrs. Bayha and Mrs. Karger for their patience, constancy, and inspiration during our literary efforts.

FRANKLIN H. BAYHA   DELMAR W. KARGER
Ann Arbor, Michigan   *1965*   *Troy, New York*

Contents

CONTENTS

PART I

Introduction and Background

CHAPTER I

Origins — A Brief History of Scientific Management and Work Measurement

The search for a better way to do things has progressed since the birth of mankind. The inventor of the wheel, undoubtedly, was motivated by a desire to eliminate some of the hard work involved in dragging things about on a sled or travois. Better methods were thus early allied with the benefit and welfare of human individuals. Indeed man's self interest demands more efficient, less fatiguing procedures by which to do work.

Industry, from its earliest beginnings, has always been concerned in some degree with manufacturing methods. The interest is greatest during periods of low profit and severe competition. When such urgency for reducing costs by finding better methods and establishing sound work measurement subsides, there is a tendency to be satisfied with existing conditions. This situation, generally existing during times of high profit, is a major factor in economic downswings. Thus, capital, management, and labor, which constitute industry, each has a profound stake in an ongoing effort to find and institute better methods.

In the 19th and the early part of this century, Taylor, Gantt, the Gilbreths, Emerson, and others originated the scientific management concept. They introduced and developed many new principles of management together with techniques designed to systematize and standardize the planning, operation, and control of industry. Basic to the implementing of many of these progressive steps was the establishment of an adequate basis for work measurement. The evolution of better methods has been rapid ever since.

Frederick W. Taylor is generally known as the Father of Scientific Management. He was responsible for the first definitive approach to work measurement.

3

In 1885, Mr. Taylor was made a foreman of the Midvale Steel Company near Philadelphia. In common with any other foreman, he was held responsible for the amount of production turned out by his department. Because his men were not producing nearly as much as he believed fair to the company, he assumed the task of doing everything possible to raise the productivity of his department to what he envisioned as a satisfactory level of performance. Taylor had the firm conviction that high productivity was the only firm foundation for material prosperity.

Dr. Taylor followed the time-proven approach of experimenting with new procedures, noting the results, and then drawing conclusions. He developed a simple principle which underlies the operation of modern industry. It is summarized by him as follows: "The greatest production results when each worker is given a definite task to be performed in a definite time in a definite manner." This is axiomatic in progressive concerns today.

The definite task usually is assigned by management in the form of a job process or job description. The definite time and definite manner portions of Taylor's Principle involve measurement. Measurement and control are two of the three elements with which management must be concerned. The third is planning. Planning is thought in advance of action—a most important element, since control merely corrects after-the-fact, that is after variance from the standard set by measurement has been noted and analyzed. This reference to the three elements of management provides a proper perspective on measurement. Obviously, measurement is both necessary and important as a basis of corrective action or as a datum for planning. Taylor recognized that he must find some way to measure the performance of production workers if he was to manage them on a sound basis.

Dr. Taylor at first measured his workers' performances and established production levels or operation times from the resulting past performance records. He later found such measurements and the production goals established on ordinary historical performance records to be unreliable because they were based on the same poor performance that he had noted originally.

His next step in the development of work measurement was to use a stop watch to establish the time to perform a given operation. He was not the first to use a stop watch to time elements of an operation. We know of one instance as early as 1760 when M. Coulomb used a watch to time operation elements for industrial planning purposes. Dr. Taylor, however, developed a complete technique for standardizing performance times by using a stop watch together with a specific method of operation. Taylor's full description of time study was a part of his discussion on "The Present State of the Art of Industrial Management" for a Subcommittee on Administration of the ASME[1] as follows:

[1] *Transactions,* ASME, vol. 34, 1912, pp. 1199, 1200.

The analytical work of time study is as follows:

(a) Divide the work of a man performing any job into simple elementary movements.

(b) Pick out all useless movements and discard them.

(c) Study, one after another, just how each of several skilled workmen makes each elementary movement, and with the aid of a stop watch select the quickest and best method of making each elementary movement known in the trade.

(d) Describe, record, and index each elementary movement, with its proper time, so that it can be quickly found.

(e) Study and record the percentage which must be added to the actual working time of a good workman to cover unavoidable delays, interruptions, and minor accidents, etc.

(f) Study and record the percentage which must be added to cover the newness of a good workman to a job, the first few times that he does it. (This percentage is quite large on jobs made up of a large number of different elements composing a long sequence infrequently repeated. This factor grows smaller, however, as the work consists of a smaller number of different elements in a sequence that is more frequently repeated.)

(g) Study and record the percentage of time that must be allowed for rest, and the intervals at which the rest must be taken, in order to offset physical fatigue.

The constructive work of time study is as follows:

(h) Add together into various groups such combinations of elementary movements as are frequently used in the same sequence in the trade, and record and index these groups so that they can be readily found.

(i) From these several records, it is comparatively easy to select the proper series of motions which should be used by a workman in making any particular article, and by summing the times of these movements and adding proper percentage allowances, to find the proper time for doing almost any class of work.

(j) The analysis of a piece of work into its elements almost always reveals the fact that many of the conditions surrounding and accompanying the work are defective; for instance, that improper tools are used, that the machines used in connection with it need perfecting, that the sanitary conditions are bad, etc. And knowledge so obtained leads frequently to constructive work of a high order, to the standardization of tools and conditions, to the invention of superior methods and machines.

From the 1912 date of the Taylor summary, one can see that Time Study is not a new technique. His summary is as valid today as when it was originally penned.

Soon after Taylor began his work, Mr. Frank B. Gilbreth left the construction field in which he had been a successful building contractor to devote his time to the study of methods as they are related to scientific management. The story of Gilbreth's discovery, on his first day as a bricklayer's apprentice, of the many different methods used by bricklayers for the simple task of laying a brick is known to everyone familiar with the

field of industrial engineering. This simple discovery, plus the encouragement of his wife, Dr. Lillian M. Gilbreth, finally provided the incentive to
give up his profitable business so he could devote his time to promoting
scientific management and conducting research and application work in the
field of motion study. The Gilbreths made many detailed laboratory studies
of motions and methods before they eventually developed the micromotion
study procedure that forms the basis for much that is covered in this text
on Work Measurement.

Both Taylor and Gilbreth won many followers who saw fundamental
differences in the procedures developed by these two outstanding men. At
length, two groups of practitioners developed who considered themselves
irrevocably opposed to each other. This lasted roughly from 1910 to
1930. One group was known as the Time Study group, the other as the
Motion Study group.

In general, the Time Study group could see nothing realistic or practical in the laboratory approach of the Gilbreths, while the Motion Study
group felt their adversaries were unscientific and crude in their work.
Neither group grasped the fundamental truth that motions take time and
both ideas are uniquely interdependent.

Eventually, the groups became better acquainted and found that they
really differed little in their fundamental approaches. This ultimately
resulted in combining the best features of both procedures into what is
now known as "Methods Engineering." Before entering a general discussion of Methods Engineering, a more detailed look at the acknowledged
shortcomings of Time Study is advisable, since they become involved in
Methods Engineering as well.

Mr. Robert Franklin Hoxie made a thorough study of Scientific Management for the United States Commission on Industrial Relations[2] in
1914. He lists 17 factors in Time Study practice at that time which could
be varied subject to human will. These factors were as true in 1914 as
they are today:

(1) The general attitude, ideals, and purposes of the management and the
consequent general instruction given to the time study man;
(2) The character, intelligence, training, and ideals of the time study man;
(3) The degree to which the job to be timed and all its appurtenances have
been studied and standardized looking to uniform conditions in its
performance for all the workers;
(4) The amount of change thus made from old methods and conditions of
performance, e.g., the order of performance, the motions eliminated,
and the degree of habituation of the workers to the old and the new
situation when the task is set;
(5) The mode of selection of the workers to be timed and their speed and
skill relative to the other members of the group;

[2] Robert Franklin Hoxie, *Scientific Management and Labor*, D. Appleton & Company, 1921, pp. 46, 47.

(6) The relative number of workers timed and the number of readings considered sufficient to secure the result desired;

(7) The atmospheric conditions, time of day, time of year, the mental and physical condition of the workers when timed, and the judgment exercised in reducing these matters to the "normal";

(8) The character and amount of special instruction and special training given the selected workers before timing them;

(9) The instructions given to them by the time study man as to care and speed, etc., to be maintained during the timing process;

(10) The attitude of the time study man toward the workers being timed and the secret motives and aims of the workers themselves;

(11) The judgment of the time study man as to the pace maintained under timing relative to the "proper," "normal," or maximum speed which should be demanded;

(12) The checks on the actual results used by the time study man in this connection;

(13) The method and mechanism used for observing and recording times and the degree of accuracy with which actual results are caught and put down;

(14) The judgment exercised by the time study man in respect to the retention or elimination of possibly inaccurate or "abnormally" high or low readings;

(15) The method used in summing up the elementary readings to get the "necessary" elementary time;

(16) The method employed in determining how much should be added to the "necessary time" as a human allowance; and

(17) The method of determining the machine allowance.

Time Study practice today is still open to active criticism on each of the 17 factors listed by Mr. Hoxie. That such criticism is of a crucial nature is affirmed by serious strikes, files of grievances, and other positive evidence of time study failure due to one or more of the foregoing factors. Evidence of failure is not always as tangible as a grievance. On the surface, things often seem to be proceeding in a wonderful manner. However, there may be hidden losses due to production control failures, standard cost systems apparently working improperly, and other similar under-the-surface indicators of difficulty.

In order to combat the above listed shortcomings, industrial engineers have developed a reasonably uniform concept of normal pace; time study personnel have been trained to exercise proper judgment; and statistics have been used to validate the accuracy of time studies, etc. All of these have helped to build faith in time study as a recognized and accepted yardstick of measurement. The fact still remains, however, that time study is a very rough measure which in no way compares to a vernier caliper or micrometer as to accuracy.

In the early development of the steam engine, designers worked with cylinders ⅜ inch or more out of round; and it was a real accomplishment when they finally produced a 57-inch cylinder true within the thickness of an old shilling. Today, designers work in terms of millionths of an inch.

However, whether they work to the thickness of an old shilling or to millionths of an inch, they still must deal with tolerances. Of course, as methods of production have improved, acceptable tolerances in terms of total measurement have been much reduced.

In a similar vein, as production methods have been refined and the work volume per worker has increased, standards of work measurement must be more precise. The preciseness of measurement and the tolerance inherent in normal time study procedure were at one time acceptable, but they are rapidly becoming unacceptable in many applications. For example, it is not unusual today to find one or more production workers filling key operational positions in a partially automated production system. Obviously, management must know precisely what to expect of the worker under such a circumstance.

Taylor recognized the relationship existing between methods and time. It was one of his chief reasons for subdividing an operation into such time study elements as "pick up piece," "place piece in jig," and the like. In a very real sense, the early disagreements would have been avoided by closer study of his works.

Frank and Lillian Gilbreth refined Taylor's concept of work elements by further subdivision into "therblig" elements of Transport Empty, Transport Loaded, Grasp, Use, Assemble, etc. In addition, they also contributed toward method improvements by establishing the currently well conceived and generally accepted principles of motion economy, plus the previously mentioned micromotion technique. The therblig classifications emphasized primarily a better understanding of the *composition* of normal industrial operations from the operator's standpoint. They were not developed with great concern for the absolute performance times for the therblig elements, but rather primarily to provide a methods improvement tool. They did, however, lead to a classification of elements adequate for what is known today as *predetermined time standards*. This important development will be treated separately in Chapter 3.

While these are the origins of the scientific management concept and of work measurement, the reader should never forget that this is a dynamic world. It is a world of increasingly rapid change and development primarily due to the continually increasing amount of effort spent on research and development in almost every field of endeavor, including work measurement.

CHAPTER 2

Orientation—Human Factors in Modern Business

Human factors have a great and dominant effect on the business world. Especially in a rapidly advancing technology, they loom as large or larger in the final decisions of good management as do the purely technical aspects of a given problem or situation. Guidance and measurement of human performance are thus necessary and important. For these reasons, study of the specific factors underlying the behavior of workers is a very practical and fruitful pursuit.

The foregoing statements very naturally generate questions such as the following: What is the aim and purpose of work measurement? Of what productive or practical value is the result of gaging human labor? Why should work be measured? Can society as a whole and/or individually reap any genuine benefit from analysis of work content and measuring of the performance of workers? On what assignable cause did the just fame and honor which accrued to Taylor, the Gilbreths, and other pioneers of this area of knowledge depend and derive?

These and hosts of similar questions invariably arise when industrial engineers deal with people both new to and familiar with the arts and sciences of work measurement. They deserve candid, satisfying answers lest the erroneous impression be promoted that there is something mysterious and ulterior about the whole subject. This chapter will concentrate on these queries, since they all have a certain common aspect which is most easily termed Human Factors in Modern Business.

That many value judgments are inherent in the above list of questions is readily apparent to the reader. In every sphere of human activity, the presence of values and the choosing of those by which to govern personal action is unavoidable. This is especially true when the field of an art or a science deals directly with people rather than factual data concerning things.

The measurement of human performance is inseparably bound up with the many personal factors affecting human action—the "human equation" cannot be ignored. By orienting the reader in respect to questions such as those in the beginning of this chapter, and the major psychological and physiological factors, the authors hope to provide clues or answers that will increase the professional capabilities of any person measuring or directing human performance.

Not only are the various "human equation" factors involved in the determination of human performance, but these same factors must be understood by the person(s) directing and/or using work measurement. These various factors or variables affecting human performance will be outlined later in this chapter.

THE AIM OF WORK MEASUREMENT

Work measurement offers one of the most reliable avenues or aids used by Scientific Management to achieve the benefits of increased production at lower cost for the advantage of everyone. The aim of work measurement is thus to aid scientific management. Examining the two concepts of *scientific* and *management* separately and in greater detail will render the essentials clearer.

The Scientific Method is generally understood to mean the application in a systematic manner of expert knowledge and skill. Management can be defined as the art of controlling and/or directing human activity to specific goals. Scientific Management, therefore, consists of directing human activity toward specific goals with maximum reliance on expert knowledge in a systematic way.

Scientific Method

This section will discuss how the scientific method used by Scientific Management is developed and applied as opposed to the purely subjective procedures that are often used in other activities involving human endeavors.

It is generally recognized that while true knowledge about anything must be based on facts, the actions of people as a whole are governed by mixtures of fact and opinion. That part of an action or reaction which is based on fact is more likely to be an objective kind of thing, whereas that part resting on opinion tends to be subjective in nature and hence influenced by personal feelings. Thus, personal effects which seem likely to result from compliance with the acts and orders of others have a definite influence on the actions of people.

While it is necessary for leaders to utilize their own subjective skills to phrase orders and achieve practical results in directing people, the practice of leadership as an art tends to be unproductive in establishing what is the right approach rather than the expedient one for a given situation. Scientific managers, on the other hand, do not rely solely on subjective control; rather they utilize all possible objective data to help choose the right course of action. More unbiased thinking about work problems, greater reliance on factual data, and increasing use of objective attitudes of all types will engender less error in actions than subjective procedures because the basis of action then rests on demonstrable fact rather than hasty or ill-considered opinion. It is this orientation that historically has been called the scientific attitude.

Good work study techniques deal in facts, not in personalities. Facts about the human being involved in work situations permit the use of objective skills, while avoiding the prejudicial effects accompanying efforts to form an opinion or feeling about the same human being. In this respect, the scientific approach tends to be impersonal.

Remember, however, that objective skills are properly employed to get the right answers; implementing those answers requires the use and understanding of many subjective techniques based on enlightened opinion. The role of objectivity thus becomes one of providing the enlightenment needed to promote justice in subjective action. The complete elimination of all subjective elements in decision-making never will be possible, however, since our total knowledge of human action always will be limited to some extent. This truism should serve as a caution to both beginners and experienced industrial engineers. That is, people have a natural tendency to become so enamoured of quantitative measurement techniques that they fail to recognize the necessity for supplementing such techniques by subjective approaches, especially when evaluating such a difficult-to-measure item as human performance. This failing is particularly acute when quantitative measurement is being applied to a departmental unit as a whole.

Another attribute required of scientific procedure, since it basically proceeds on fact rather than opinion, is that a means of determining facts must exist. It must also be established that the facts discovered are meaningful and useful. The scientist essentially determines the facts by measurement. The meaning of the measurement is established by validation of the procedures used to determine these facts. Work studies, therefore, to be objective, must involve both adequate measurement and validation in order that the resulting facts can permit necessary subjective application without fear of gross error.

Measurement itself includes two major problems. First, is the matter

amenable to measurement?   Second, do the measurements taken accord
with actual performance in the changing fabric of existing life?   Perhaps
the major contribution of Taylor and the Gilbreths was a reproducible
demonstration that the performance of human beings can be measured.
To some extent, they also achieved validation of the reported results of
their studies.   Since their time, however, the means of measurement have
become increasingly finer and revalidation has been necessary.   The finer
means of measurement in modern time study, motion study, and predetermined time systems will be fully explained in this volume.   The work of
revalidation has been most notable in the field of predetermined times.
However, this work will not be complete until more widespread knowledge
and application of such techniques permit the evolution of even more
scientific procedures.   The study of work measurement, being concerned
with human activity, is closely allied with such other human sciences as
economics, biology, sociology, physiology, psychology, and philosophy.
Indeed, the work analyst must rely heavily on his knowledge in the related
fields to achieve his facts as well as to validate them.

Management Control

The aim of work measurement, although it might be very scientific,
would be barren in the practical sense if it were not integral with good
management.   Such management consists in understanding and directing
the actions of human beings in such a way that the environment of the
enterprise is controlled rather than the result of impulse.   Management
as the directive aspect of work measurement utilizes the factual data resulting from scientific evaluation to produce useful, harmonious results from
and among all agents in productive activities.

The agents of production are men, materials, and machines.   It is axiomatic in business that each of these constituents merit specialized attention,
in order that a proper balance among them may result in the profits which
are the lifeblood of financial existence.   Seasoned executives commonly
place *men* at the pinnacle of the trio, since business exists by and for the
social ends of men.   Other fields of engineering have made monumental
contributions to modern knowledge of materials and machines; the rise
of industrial engineering to achieve similar status regarding the human
element in production has been a relatively recent phenomenon.   Work
measurement, in its better forms, has been the greatest single impetus
toward attainment of major industrial engineering achievements.

Control is thus a prime necessity for management, as was mentioned in
Chapter 1.   Whether such control is good or bad depends most directly on
the degree of objectivity which executives exercise in deciding courses and
modes of action.   Good managers apply their subjective skills only after
objective facts pertinent to the problem at hand have been obtained from

scientific measurement of all variables in the productive activity. This is most important, since control in the basic sense is exercised primarily to correct deviations from the standard or norm.

Obtaining maximum human performance consistent with recognized social responsibilities, such as guarding against exploitation of workers, is of prime importance in any business. This involves not only the man at the machine but also workers in such other functions as supervision, accounting, engineering, sales, and general offices. Human capacity is governed by and responsive to knowable laws similar in many respects to the physical, chemical, and mathematical laws which comprise the foundations of all engineering facts and procedures. Personnel departments have grown to meet the need for human control in industry, and they comprise a strong arm of management. Their success, however, must derive from factual data regarding human activity. Industrial engineering departments, with work measurement as their most potent tool, thus are a logical connection between the personnel department and other functional groups on which the management depends for sound courses of action to follow. A work analyst thus combines the viewpoints of both engineers and workers in the fields of human relations to a higher degree than any other individual found in industry.

Scientific Management

To attain maximum performance within the limits discussed, work evaluators must follow a well-defined procedure. The first step in this procedure involves determining the equipment, tools, workplace, and other physical conditions best suited for the task at hand. The next logical step is to utilize these in the best way possible, which means deciding the exact method or process to be followed by the human operator. A detailed knowledge of human capabilities is vital to this second step. When this approach is practiced by competent analysts, and the resulting method put into action with appropriate worker training and enlightened supervision, the attainment of the maximum in human performance becomes possible.

The Gilbreths were particularly concerned with the human phases of work study which permit maximum performance for the social benefit of all groups. Their work delved deeply into the capacity of human bodies in thought, motion, and direction. Establishing work methods involves decisions regarding such scientific topics as, for example, the time for the eye to recognize objects or the possible simultaneous motions of which the body members are capable. In its entirety, the field of work measurement involves knowledge in all the branches of engineering and mechanical skills related to the task being studied. It also intimately involves all fields of knowledge regarding the human operator.

This text, as it attempts to promote the aims of work measurement, essentially concerns itself with two major concepts. First, what are the motion capabilities of the human body? Secondly, what is the time required to perform these bodily functions? The laws or principles governing human motion must include both answers as well as due appreciation for moral and ethical values by which human activities are guided and limited.

THE VALUE OF ANALYZING WORK

So far, the presence and need for knowledge of the laws and principles governing human motions are evident. If the aims of work measurement are realized, what value do they then have in the social structure? The trend toward more extensive use of work measurement is unmistakable; it is typical of modern observers to wish to know what desirable results will accrue from this trend. Or, to state the question in everyday language, what good is this business, anyway?

One obvious factor is that by setting a goal for the production worker, the degree of attainment provides a yardstick for measurement of performance. It will thereby indicate when there is need for corrective action and the area in which it will be most wisely applied. The unequal degree of motivation and ability of workers in an enterprise obviously makes this approach desirable.

Work measurement tends to remove purely opinionated or prejudicial treatment of a given individual on the payroll. Not only will it show up good or bad performance; but, as later outlined in this book, it will help locate the true source of most performance difficulty. In many cases, competent usage of the technique of work measurement will also materially aid in determining the proper solution to a given work performance problem.

Not only is it desirable to set standards for gaging performance and thereby make it possible to approach the higher attainment; but experience has also amply demonstrated that financially rewarding the worker for performance above standard on some proportional basis can result in an average of 20 to 30 per cent increase in productivity. Usually this is done on a direct percentage basis—that is, 120 per cent output for a given time yields 120 per cent of the basic pay for that period. Therefore, another value of work measurement can be direct financial benefit to the worker. His company, in turn, will enhance its financial status by having more return per unit of investment in that worker's job. Ultimately, this can be reflected in lower prices to the consumer for merchandise at the same level of quality.

Human output directly affects production control, materials control, and the functioning of the personnel department. The problems here involve determination of the number, kind, and quality of employees required to

meet schedules.   Superior results in such management decisions can evolve
from adequate usage of work measurement.   Conversely, the possible level
of production or amount of materials required for the available labor force
and equipment can be more accurately prescribed when the productivity
per worker is known.   The personnel functions are directly affected in
either event.

Hosts of such specific examples which illustrate the value of work study
could be cited.   On the manufacturing floor, aggressive application of the
principles being presented in this book have been of major importance in

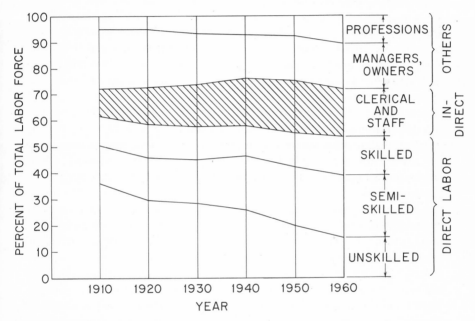

Fig. 1.   Skill distribution in United States labor force.   (Based on data of U. S.
Bureau of Census and U. S. Bureau of Labor Statistics.)

the continuing rise of productivity per factory or direct labor employee.
This has resulted in a steady decrease in the proportion of direct labor in
the total labor force, with a corresponding rise in indirect labor, as shown
by Fig. 1.   The significant trends for the 50-year period covered in Fig. 1
are numerically as follows:

DIRECT LABOR   8.5% decrease from 62.4% to 53.9%
INDIRECT LABOR   7.5% *increase* from 10.2% to 17.7%
OTHERS   1.0% *increase* from 27.4% to 28.4%

For the novice to labor evaluation, it is well to deviate here to explain
the meaning of direct and indirect labor.   Direct labor, sometimes termed
prime labor, is loosely defined as all labor directly expended in building or

making the product. Each plant has its own interpretation. Some include such service labor and supporting personnel as inspection, receiving stores, shipping, materials handling, repair, testing, relief operators, instructors, etc., while others do not so classify such workers. Indirect labor is generally defined as all labor not directly expended in producing the physical output. Texts on cost accounting will yield any additional information desired regarding these definitions.

It was with direct labor that Taylor, the Gilbreths, and the early work measurement pioneers were concerned. The growth of indirect personnel illustrated in Fig. 1 has tended to focus more attention on work measurement in the office. Since most factories have long utilized work measurement techniques in the direct labor areas and therefore have a lesser potential for further improvement, it is with the indirect labor force in most industries and governmental agencies where the greatest chance for labor reduction lies. More on office work measurement will be found later in this text.

One should not assume from Fig. 1 or the preceding discussion that work measurement is the only factor influencing the labor ratios shown. Another major causative factor is automation. Until about 1955 most automation had been applied to direct labor on the factory floor. However, note in Fig. 1 that the *proportion* of office workers in the labor force actually declined by 2.5 per cent in the 1950–1960 decade. Office work automation as typified by electronic computers, automatic data processing devices, and allied equipment has not only become common but is rapidly increasing in application. In fact, such automation even has invaded the engineering field to the stage where computers are used to generate designs, write specifications, perform information searches, plot curves, solve equations, and for many further uses beyond mere computation. However, all this does not negate the statement that work measurement is needed in the indirect labor area—actually it reinforces this need to assure proper usage of office automation.

The need is further reinforced by the data plot in Fig. 2, which shows the rapid expansion of all indirect labor in the face of only 50 per cent increase in direct labor from 1920 to 1963. Even though skilled workers are included with white-collar workers in this plot, the doubling of the total is unmistakably clear. Note also the tripling in professional and managerial as well as the doubling in service workers. While these groups normally are not expected to perform against time standards, many beneficial results are increasingly resulting from the application of other industrial engineering approaches to the problem of increasing their efficiency. Also, it should be noted that the white-collar worker is more and more frequently being evaluated against clerical time standards, even though the conditions of their application differs from the situation found with direct labor. As much of the decline in the relative number of direct laborers in the skilled, semi-skilled, and unskilled classes has resulted from work measurement, so now and in the years ahead the "paperwork monster" will necessitate similar results from clerical work measurement in conjunction with office automation.

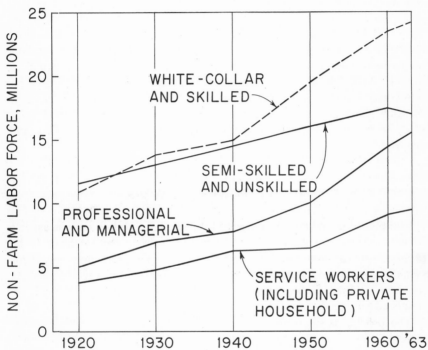

Fig. 2.   Change in United States non-farm civilian labor force by occupation.   (Based on data of U.S. Bureau of Census and U.S. Bureau of Labor statistics.)

The general importance of work measurement to business and industry in terms of managements' relations with workers under their charge is so obvious as to require little elaboration. This is reflected by a representative random sampling survey in 22 American cities of 497 industrial plants which had 100 or more employees. It was conducted in 1959 by the management consulting firm of Stewart, Dougall & Associates for the MTM Association for Standards and Research. Two-thirds of the respondents used some form of work measurement. While only 53 percent of the plants with less than 200 employees used work measurement, it was used by 81 percent of those having 500 or more employees.

It is important to stress that inattention to the human factors by managers and supervisors can be more destructive of good will and productivity in industry than any other single factor. Leaders are human themselves and should exercise due humility and fairness in their social responsibility. They must implement work study results, and will therefore appreciate any measurement technique which inherently allows due emphasis on the human factors.

Even the consumer gains values from usage of work measurement, although they are often so intangible as to resist discussion and definition. Just as the consumer indirectly "dictates" the production situation and its corresponding effect on workers, the workers in turn directly affect the price, quality, and quantity of consumer goods that create the buyer's environment. No one lives in a vacuum in any social structure, his actions may exert wider influence than he dreams or knows; the individual, in turn, is molded by reverse action of society upon himself. Good production conditions and prosperity enhance the lives of all members of society; therefore, any aid to creating these desirable ends, such as good work study techniques, is a commendable activity worthy of strengthening and growth.

MUSCLE POWER AT WORK

The preceding material has oriented the reader regarding various aspects of work measurement that should always remain in the forefront as he progressively masters the content of this book. He must, however, focus his attention on the human body as a very efficient and marvelous machine in order to achieve the goals of work study which are the benefits just discussed.

The product is the *result* of work, not the *work*. Work itself is energy directed toward a physical object for the purpose of shaping, altering, forming, or transforming it into a condition in which its utility commands the buying power of a consumer. That energy can result from mechanical, chemical, electrical, or human action. Other fields of engineering deal adequately with all but human energy; this source of power is the exclusive province of work study analysts. From what has been said earlier, it is easy to see that industrial engineers are responsible for designing effective usage (methods) for what is perhaps the most complex power source of all, as well as the most precious—the human body. Not only is the direct power of the human body used to shape a product but even when mechanical, chemical, electrical, and other forms of energy are used, they are always directed and/or aided by humans.

Business exists as an activity because the owners desire to make a profit while rendering service to society, and a concern will survive only by satisfying this desire. To achieve or maximize profits, the industrial engineer must know how to obtain maximum performance from the human machine.   Yes—for many practical purposes of work study, the worker must be regarded as a muscle machine.   *Under no circumstances, however, can or should the social, physical, and other aspects of the human worker be ignored.*

Human labor is expensive, yet it is the agent of production which adds the greatest value to the finished product.   It not only is responsible for its own output, but must govern and control the materials and machines as well.   Higher degrees of skill are even more expensive, and workers possessing them are hardest to find and hold on the job.   The need for analysis of this cost is, therefore, obvious.   No enterprise could profitably ignore this major factor in product cost.

In observing and evaluating operators as muscle machines, human relations problems are simplified rather than aggravated.   The work analyst judges or measures the worker only with respect to the performance of his muscles, he does not directly delve into personal affairs or other private concerns of the worker in an attempt to achieve a total picture of the entire nature of the worker.   He must indeed understand people and know well how to cooperate and guide them into better work habits; but such matters are the *art* of work study, the *science* of work study is restricted to impersonal measurement techniques.

The *art* of work study is equally important as the *science* and much of the knowledge relating to this will either be covered or mentioned in such a manner that the proper area of study can be readily consulted in additional reference books.   However, since the *art* of any subject can be described only partially by writing or talking about it, there is a largely personal element in mastering it which can be acquired only by direct experience and practice.

Finally, it is important to note that people all differ in many ways, including the physiological behavior which their muscles exhibit.   A creditable concept to allow for this factor has been developed by industrial engineers, and this is the concept of the "average worker."   Now no human likes to admit to being just average, although he believes average men exist.   The novice, especially, experiences difficulty in forming the correct concept of an average worker.   With perseverance, experience, and unbiased examination of many workers, however, he soon develops the concept and matches it with that held by acknowledged work analysts. There are definite aids to this that will be discussed under performance rating.   The real problem is not achieving agreement with an individual analyst, but rather in formulating a clear definition which distinguishes the average worker in a way that is acceptable to work analysts, other employees, and the general public.   This is a psychological problem beyond the scope of this book, but the industrial engineering profession has recognized it and is taking steps toward achieving this desirable goal.

VARIABLES AFFECTING HUMAN OUTPUT

In order to understand the worker as a muscle machine, the specific factors influencing individual output and their relative importance must be considered. Figure 3 represents the consensus of many competent industrial engineers, and the listings made are a synthesis of many sources. Reference to this figure in the following discussion will make the text clear.

The result of the application of human energy is *production*. The amount produced depends directly on motions and the time these motions consume. Since the time required to perform a given motion under set conditions is later demonstrated to be essentially a constant for the average worker, it follows that the *motions used* are the largest single factor determining the amount of output that can be anticipated. The *motion speed* is subject to natural limits, and it is thus less effective in predicting the net output. It can be readily demonstrated in a number of ways that these statements are true. For example, the style of penmanship employed more directly determines the time required to write a letter than does the swiftness of the fingers alone, composing time not being considered. As a matter of fact, a writer can greatly increase his writing speed by adopting a simpler style of penmanship even though he makes no effort to write faster. *Method* is understood by industrial engineers to connote the motions used when speaking of a manual operation and with tooling eliminated as a consideration. When motion speed is broken into its components, the industrial engineer believes they are *effort, skill,* and *conditions*.

Effort is defined as the "will to work," the drive or impetus behind the motions of the worker.

Skill is defined as the proficiency with which a given method can be followed by an operator. It should be noted that the work measurement definition of skill does not denote the common meaning of the term. Skill in the common sense concerns the possession by a worker of the ability to perform difficult tasks easily. In the parlance of work analysts, however, a janitor can be just as skilled as a watchmaker, provided each is following a *prescribed* set of motions with equal facility and ease.

Conditions is defined as those factors in a productive situation which are external to the worker himself, but affect his performance.

Since changes in the variables underlying methods will frequently double or triple output, a great deal more than can be accomplished by altering effort alone, there is little doubt that its prescription is a prime responsibility of good management, and its enforcement is the mark of good supervision. For example, mechanization of an assembly line, with the related

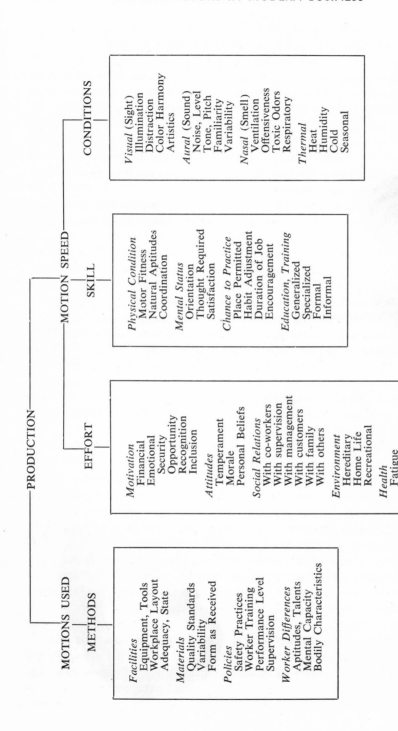

Fig. 3. Variables determining productive output.

changes in the motions used by the remaining operators, can well create wider markets and therefore new jobs. This facility change would not be possible, however, without the necessary approval and capital investment of the management. Effort, on the other hand, cannot be arbitrarily or easily increased because it is basically controlled by the worker himself. Indeed, haste in working may lead to economic waste and other undesirable effects, so that the increase of effort must be attended with a good deal of judgment and understanding on the part of operators, executives, and supervisors. It can be changed by good management, but the change is more subtle and less obvious both as to means and net amount. The worker must be sold before he will cooperate.

In order to clarify more fully the reasons behind these statements, the basic variables behind the factors influencing production are next discussed.

Methods

This major factor in production by operators depends on four main variables: (1) The facilities provided; (2) the materials being worked; (3) the differences between workers; and (4) the policies of the company regarding the way tasks are to be done.

Facilities include the machines and major apparatus under manual or other worker control and the other working tools he is provided with to do his task. The manner in which these are oriented and located will affect the motions he can use, and will therefore create limits on the method which can be used. The adequacy of the facilities for the work to be done and the state of repair, lubrication, and operating ease will likewise contribute to better or inferior methods.

When determining the motions to be prescribed, an analyst must examine the materials being worked. This includes the states in which they come to the worker and leave his work station, the variation of dimensions or other measurable characteristics, and the quality standards under which the receipt and forwarding of materials are permitted. Since these material factors all have a bearing on the amount and kind of work to be performed, it is obvious that they influence the methods employed.

Company policies often place restrictions on the choice of method. The safety requirements of some tasks overrule any other consideration in setting up the manner in which the work is to be done. Training of the workers to use certain standardized methods may prevent other methods from being considered. High levels of performance in general denote that good methods are being followed and, conversely, low performance levels indicate the use of bad methods. The closeness and quality of supervision affects the possible choice of motions, particularly when the foremen are following policies on method rigidly advocated by the company.

Reference to works in differential psychology will prove to anyone doubting it that there are genuine differences between people which may decidedly affect the methods of which they are capable. The work analyst must therefore be cautious that he prescribes motions and sequences of motions of which average operators are capable. He cannot, however, hope to tailor the job to any and all persons who might wish to perform it, nor would this be desirable. Special aptitudes, or superior talents for certain kinds of variations of work will enable the owner to outshine his fellows regardless of a prescribed method. Lack of normal aptitude will make it difficult for a worker to measure up to the task. Increasingly, as machines and work methods and products become more complex, the mental capacity of a given worker to know and to use knowledge and intelligence in his work is becoming more important. This must be given attention when setting the job conditions. Different methods may make possible complex production whereas poor and/or older methods would fail to accomplish the task because they confuse and/or frustrate the worker. Bodily characteristics peculiarly adapt some workers to use methods aiding output whereas an average operator might find them difficult. The understanding of average bodily behavior will help the analyst select practical methods that avoid undue demands over and above the powers of average workers.

Effort

The "work readiness," or willingness of an employee to expend his energy in effective work, is a complex of human behavior worthy of close attention by industrial engineers. Lack of this attention has historically been the root of many production floor problems, management difficulties, work stoppages, union friction, and disastrous strikes. Management increasingly is recognizing its fair share in the problem of providing the psychological climate in which its personnel can and will put forth their best efforts. Much of the bargaining material with which unions deal concerns this factor of productive output.

Typically, people work because of financial motivation. When their minimum monetary needs are slightly exceeded, however, they discover the desire for additional satisfactions such as better light, ventilation, safety, relief from excessive fatigue, understanding, recognition, and encouragement by supervisors, etc. The hue and cry for security has been prominent since the early 1930's in many fields of life. People want the chance to realize the opportunities for self-improvement and advancement that arise in the normal course of their tasks—in fact, engineers rate the type of job and the opportunity for professional growth almost as high as salary. Recognition will increase effort, as is attested by such present-day industrial activities as clubs, newspapers, company awards, personal letters from the executives, and the old "pat on the back"—the standby of the foremen of

Taylor's days. Workers like to feel included in the group and will strive to produce better when they believe they "belong." The use of motivation by all parties concerned in a productive enterprise has indeed graduated from theoretical to practical emphasis in recent years.

The effort an operator makes also results from his attitudes. His temperament must be consonant with the task and his co-workers before his effort will be more than lackadaisical. High morale in the shop tends to increase effort. A person working in a tolerant economic and religious climate that permits and aids human freedom will tend toward excellent effort; the reverse is true under environments of despotism and suppression. The maintenance and improvement of employee attitudes thus are realistic goals which aid in raising output through extra effort.

For a man to show his best efforts, he must be happy in the social sense. All of the people with whom he comes into contact both at work and away have an influence in this respect. Disappointing or frustrating social relations, whether of the brief or long-lasting type, are destructive of working effort. Carefree and satisfying activities with other people keep the worker attuned to the need and value of doing a fair day's work. Common courtesy between employees often makes the difference between good and poor effort in a factory.

His job is but one part of a worker's total environment. Some people are by nature, or family custom, lazy and indifferent to appeals to increase their effort. The hereditary energy of other types of people is such as to assure that they will hardly ever fail to put everything they have into the work at hand. Most folks are somewhere between, but even hereditary factors permit change by intelligent management seeking to benefit from higher effort levels.

Difficulty at home may likewise militate against good job performance, whereas a happy home life usually is the hallmark of a good worker. Conditions at home are being given more and more consideration by management. Prospective employees, particularly executives, are now often being thoroughly investigated concerning this item. Counsellors are also often provided to help solve these and other general problems of the employees.

Modern industry has recognized the needs of employees in recreational activities by providing such opportunities within company groups, and by generally encouraging private recreation. Sports, entertainment, and cultural pursuits help fit a worker to try to give fair output.

For humanitarian, as well as legal and practical reasons, the importance of health has induced management to provide many medical services and much related advice to their personnel. Rest periods and refreshment privileges promote recovery from fatigue, which is the arch-enemy of good effort. Healthful surroundings and provision for nutritional lunches are also such aids. Continued public campaigns to employ the handicapped call attention to the fact that such workers are also capable of work effort justifying their employment. Temporary handicaps of health, such as colds, injuries, diseases, and discomfort are obviously given attention because they tend to reduce effort and therefore result in a loss of profitable output.

Skill

Just as other engineers must select the proper controls and governing devices to assure the correct performance of complex production machinery, the industrial engineer finds it essential to smooth production by devising ways in which the human power at his disposal may be made responsive, flexible, and dependable regarding demands. In no small degree, he achieves these goals by his adept handling of the question of skill. While it is first important to have available the appropriate capabilities for a given task, it is of equal importance that the correct and smooth functioning of muscles be obtained. The worker must, in other words, be *able* to follow a given method; but he must also be induced to *use* the method which the industrial engineer has carefully determined to be the most efficient for accomplishment of the work at hand. As is true for mechanical or electrical controls, however, he must know the limiting behavior and variation of skill to wisely prescribe and enforce methods in production.

A worker is most capable of following directions—methods—when he is in excellent physical condition. His reflexes and other evidences of motor fitness are a gage of the responsiveness of his nervous system, much as the sensitiveness of temperature controls are judged by the tolerance of setting they will control. Natural aptitudes may either be beneficial or detrimental to successful action of muscles in a given task. Coordination, or the lack of it, may make the difference between a master craftsman or a duffer working with the same tools. The work analyst must, therefore, either fit his methods to the available human power or else recommend the correct human capabilities for a desired method.

When instituting a new method, or revising existing methods, the industrial engineer must consider the mental status and equipment of the worker. Every effort must be made to assure that the workers are properly oriented to the method, since a good beginning is half the battle. Whether the workers on the task are capable of exerting the required thought will often decide which method will be most practical; however, the actual "think time" in most productive jobs is usually far less than most persons suspect or realize. This is especially true for many quasi-professional jobs not ordinarily found on a factory floor. Some employees love to think, others shun the appearance of being intellectual. It is generally true, on the other hand, that when satisfaction from a job well done or pride of workmanship result from following a prescribed method, the mental problems of method enforcement tend to dissolve. Sensible appeal to this factor is thus a good industrial engineering procedure promoting increased skill.

To follow a given method, much depends on the opportunity for practice given the operator. Skill cannot be consciously varied by the worker over a short span of time or training, but long practice and special training in a work technique can greatly enhance his skill. Whether this is done in a place in which embarrassment for errors might result or at a location permitting worry-free experimentation might often determine the success of the method chosen. Old habits must often be revised, new ones developed, or advantage must be taken of existing work habits to maximize the cost-saving potentialities of a new method. Workers tend to prolong jobs of short-run duration by evasion of methods and refusal to practice the motions required, while long-run jobs tend to promote cooperation in this respect. Encouragement to practice, and during the course of practice, will often result in attainment of the method when inattention to this factor would destroy its value or even negate the advantages of an improved way of doing things. Industry meets these challenges with training schools, vestibule schools, or utilization of training personnel on the shop floor; the work analyst must fit his efforts into the particular policy on practice of new methods which prevails in his plant situation.

Finally, the education and training of workers enter into the problem of skill and its relation to work methods. ⎰Workers cannot be expected to perform skillfully on tasks which their background has not fitted them to do.⎱ Likewise, a watchmaker might well enthusiastically follow the set method for assembling a complex control device, but balk and procrastinate when expected to grind gates off rough iron castings. The skill of a worker must be complemented by the method to assure compliance, and the variety and length of education or training he has along a given line influences the work analyst in deciding the proper motions and task sequences which will take advantage of the skills available.

Conditions

The questions of effort and skill, as is readily apparent from the preceding discussion, largely revolve around human capacities and relationships. However, people also work in conditions or surroundings which, while not primarily composed of human factors, do have a direct bearing on their productiveness. It devolves upon management to enhance the working environment in order that the speed of motions may be maintained and improved. *The important factor in the following conditions is not what their absolute value might be, but whether one condition or another is normal and the best that can be provided for the work being done*. People will adapt themselves to an amazing range of conditions and react normally as long as they feel that humane and just consideration in adjusting those conditions has been taken by the management.

Conditions basically affect the sense mechanisms of the human machine. To adequately consider conditions thus implies that the impact of the surroundings on the sensual apparatus is involved. Motions are bound up with mental action through the sense of touch, but this is an internal relation which cannot be effectively changed through changing of the surroundings alone; the previous discussion suggested ways to achieve this kind of human control. The senses of sight, sound, smell, and thermal comfort are amenable to a degree of control by changes in the surroundings directly, thus being affected by external or mechanical control.

Visual perception is aided by the correct kind and amount of illumination, and much expert data and advice on this subject is available. Reduction of distraction of the eyes can be achieved by shielding flashes, drawing the sight of the worker to the more important areas by effective workroom design, and/or proper use of color and similar strategies. The effect of harmonious and contrasting colors in workrooms has been given much study, and specific rules are obtainable from experts on the subject. Work has even been done on enhancing the artistic appeal of surroundings so that they contribute to better output. Related to this is the modern industrial architecture which differs widely from that of early industrial buildings. The aim of all these efforts is to induce the operator to keep his eyes focused on his work, while affording him restful and uplifting vistas when he does look away.

The assault of noise in modern industry on the aural senses can be terrific, as witness the ear troubles often found among industrial workers in steel mills, machine shops, transportation centers, and even many offices. The noise level alone is not entirely to blame for this. Sounds might be loud, but of such tone and pitch as to not displease or distract the worker. On the other hand, much trouble can be caused by even low intensity noises that are dissonant, rasping, whining, or gruff. Public address systems are often misused in this way. Familiar sounds, such as the music played at intervals during the workday, help combat the strain caused by unusual noises which shock the listener. Acoustical treatment of work spaces is also being employed for such purposes so as to reduce the aural fatigue associated with highly variable or high frequency noises. With modern acoustics providing so many relieving methods, management can ill afford to lose production because of sound problems within the work surroundings. The industrial engineer can do much to recognize noise troubles and suggest their elimination.

The problems of nasal irritation are closely allied with health and safety areas of work study. The supply of fresh air directly aids or inhibits production. Toxic odors should be kept below safe physiological levels. Offensive smells, although not necessarily dangerous, are usually undesirable as related to good working conditions. The presence within work areas of agents which cause such respiratory troubles as colds, sinus attacks, dry throats, and allergic reactions should also be discovered and eliminated where possible. Alert management can do much to promote higher production by attending to the nasal problems.

Finally, thermal conditions can either engender productiveness or inefficiency by their effects on the workers. Extremes of heat or cold should either be avoided, or action taken to make them tolerable. The dress of workers may often be dictated by the temperature usual to their tasks. Providing protective clothing where dangers to the body and/or ordinary dress exist and providing temperature control to permit working in light clothing will aid human output. Humidity must be kept appropriate to the temperature, or else fans and other moisture and/or heat combating devices must be employed to assure worker comfort. Modern heating and air conditioning has progressed to the stage where a good thermal environment will pay for itself in the extra production it makes possible. Seasonal and cyclic weather variations, while most vital to outdoor workers, also affect the personnel who work indoors. They enter and leave from seasonal extremes or sometimes must frequently pass in and out of doors in their normal task routines. Good conditions in this respect will help maintain the work pace, and the work analyst can recommend changes in jobs which will help to minimize interference to production from thermal variations.

SUMMARY

It is hoped that the reader has been brought to the conclusion that human factors abound in modern business and that the problems of fully utilizing the human machine invade every realm of the business enterprise.

Much talk and discussion is heard these days regarding new and strange concepts in the field of industrial management and management engineering. Consider such popular topics as: Automation, Changeable Work Centers, Cybernetics, Automatic Computers, Electronic Business Machines, the Automatic Factory, Operations Research, Mathematical Programming. Surely there are human factors here! The drive for guaranteed annual wages reflects this truism. As the future becomes today, the problems of management become increasingly complex.

In past years, much was heard about mechanization. Today it is called automation. New machines or mechanized lines are introduced only if they yield cheaper and better products. Such expensive equipment is often paced by the worker.　What he can do and how to secure his best performance to effectively use the machine must obviously be known in advance.　Automatic and manually controlled operations are frequently installed in a complex series of operations, the slowest of which may be either fully automatic, fully manual, or a combination of both.　Obviously, the limits of human performance must be known to even design and cost such an installation, to say nothing of operating it.

Electronic computers, high-speed printers, and complex business machines are being introduced into offices for the same reasons that expensive machines were—and are now—being installed in the factory—to make most efficient use of expensive and hard-to-get skilled labor.　Better and more reliable products often accompany this trend.　The same human factors governing the factory situation apply equally to office situations.

Human engineering is now less advanced than engineering of materials and machines.　This gap must be closed—indeed effective use of engineering strides in non-human fields has in many cases reached a barrier due to lack of knowledge of the human machine.

The value of studying work measurement should now be crystal clear to the reader.　Agreement is also likely with a statement made early in this chapter that aptly sums it:

Work measurement offers one of the most reliable avenues or aids to scientific management to achieve the benefits of increased production at lower cost for the advantage of everyone.

CHAPTER 3

Predetermined Time Systems—
Development and Comparison

The story of the beginnings of work measurement and some of the associated problems were given in Chapter 1 to set the scene for the development of predetermined time systems. Because of the basic need to understand the human equation in work measurement, the factors with which it deals, and to orient the reader to the true nature of the aims of work measurement, Chapter 2 covered this area of information by elaborating on scientific management and the variables influencing human output. The reader is now in a position to understand the transition from traditional techniques of time study and motion study to the newer procedures of methods engineering and predetermined time systems being used by scientific management.

Essential details on how to take and apply time and motion studies, combining both the Taylor and Gilbreth viewpoints, have not yet been given; these will comprise a later major topic.

To resume the history of work measurement, a period of adjustment followed World War I. The economy began to expand, and boomed for almost the entire 1920 decade. The pressure of the times, together with political and social trends toward optimism and satiation of desires, caused an ever-increasing demand for goods and services of every description. Industry grew rapidly, but not wisely. This, in turn, generated a demand for the application of the promising approaches of work measurement in order that profits might survive in spite of increasing financial pressure, competition, and inflation. Another significant trend was the rising influence and power of labor unions.

Reliable work analysts of both the time study and motion study groups were enlisted to solve such problems with the hope of quick answers and certain results. However, it became increasingly apparent that the answers of work measurement were neither quick nor easy. Good analysis took patient, long hours of qualified effort and, in addition, areas of uncertainty persisted. The truism that *there is no substitute for good management* was discovered. Work study was no panacea, in fact its application without scientific management was dangerous.

As often happens in human affairs, charlatans or well-intentioned but ignorant persons stepped into this situation which was ripe for exploitation. "Salesmen" with little real understanding of either management or work measurement grabbed stop watches, "pat" analysis reports, newly created jargon, and other deceptive paraphernalia and took to the "pickins." The companies served benefited little, and true professional management and/or industrial engineering was seriously damaged. Thus evolved the era of the "Efficiency Expert" that damaged the good repute of work measurement, alienated workers and their unions, and bred other undesirable effects which still partially persist. Work study's promise and its promotion of managerial competence seemingly failed its first real test, resulting in public discredit and distaste for the whole approach; progress was dealt a hard blow.

What went wrong? Obviously, adequate and reliable work measurement is a professional activity of high caliber. It is no plaything to be exploited by the uninitiated or untrained person working without professional restraints. While the lack of professional approach caused most of the trouble, something else evidently proved a hindrance to those who remained in every sense professional in conduct. The more astute practitioners began at this point to seriously analyze the nature of work measurement itself. This is a typical reaction toward progress in any field of human endeavor. Initial tools serve until natural processes of curiosity, or calamity, engender a closer scrutiny that finally reveals faults in the older techniques. Keen minds then evolve better answers to the basic problems. Finer, sharper tools emerge after critical thinking reveals them.

The shortcomings of both time study and motion study as separate entities were elaborated in the first chapter. Now old tools are not necessarily invalid, but are usually proper for the kind of job they were intended to do *provided they are wisely and correctly used*.

The basic precepts of the pioneers themselves pointed the way to salvation. Dr. Taylor insisted that:

(1) The right operator be found to permit reliable study.
(2) The correct tools should be properly used by the operator.
(3) The operator should use the proper *motions* during performance.
(4) Only then should a stop watch be employed to find the task *time*.
(5) No value could accrue from the study unless it was followed by teaching and enforcing the use of the method on which the time was taken.

To these guiding lights, the Gilbreths added several other ideas:

(1) If the best and least involved *motions* are used for a task, the *time* required will automatically be minimal.

(2) Performance times are subject to natural variation and the laws of probability; out of the range of times for a given motion, the most useful value is the mean time. The average operator is most numerous.

(3) No work study or other means of specifying job content is adequately done unless the human factors have been considered and humane answers found. Cooperation is superior to coercion.

(4) Human beings differ markedly in many ways; but, in the statistical sense, there are points of similarity between all people which permit the discovery of laws of behavior that can predict actions with calculated reliability. The physiological mechanism involved in motion performance is such a point of likeness.

Any sound evolution must build upon and borrow from the precedents in its own field. Sound ideas never grow useless; rather newer ideas, to be sound, must include the use and understanding of the older ideas. This is as true of work measurement as it is of any other kind of tool or field of human endeavor. The ideas of Taylor, father of time study, and the Gilbreths, parents of motion study, given above did not deserve the division and disunity that occurred in work measurement. Often in human affairs, the middle course proves wisest. Logically, then, attention should properly be given to *both* the *motions* and the elapsed *times* involved in work performance if major benefits are to result from any form of work measurement. This principle is followed in today's methods engineering, and it is the avenue to all predetermined time systems having a sound, scientific basis.

The basic key to all predetermined time systems is the fact that variations in the times required to perform the same motion are essentially small for different workers who have had adequate practice. Mathematical relationships can therefore be established between motions and times subject to predictable statistical limits. The credit for first stating this key is generally attributed to Mr. A. B. Segur, who wrote in *Manufacturing Industry* during 1927 as follows:

Within practical limits, the time required for all experts to perform true fundamental motions is a constant.

The desirability of predetermining both the most basic motions and the time they require for an average operator was indirectly acknowledged almost from the beginning of work measurement. Many noted analysts achieved a degree of success by amassing large amounts of standard data for typical jobs, assuming that the same data would permit method establishment and setting of task times on similar jobs. The work of Carl Barth, Harrington Emerson, The Industrial Management Society, and Ralph M. Barnes typified this approach. They focused the problem sufficiently to specify that, when basic human motions have been gaged in terms of method effect and mean performance times, a practical set of work study data has been achieved.

A word of caution is appropriate, however. Neither stop watch time study nor motion study with therbligs have been superseded. In current methods engineering practice either or both procedures are often used as the soundest approach to the most practical solution of a particular problem involving methods work and the establishment of labor standards. Similarly, informed industrial engineers properly use both the more traditional techniques and predetermined time systems to develop standard data that will efficiently meet the need for rapid standards specification.

It is obvious that only the manual, or operator-controlled, part of work cycles is evaluated by predetermined time systems. The time required by process-controlled elements must still be found with the aid of a timing device. Process time is that consumed when the machine, material characteristics, or other physical or chemical changes (not themselves dependent on an operator's manual motions) control the working time—only timing devices will measure it directly. The stop watch is far from obsolete, it must merely be used in a different manner.

DEVELOPMENT OF PREDETERMINED TIMES

Predetermined time systems were rather slow in development. Only about three of them, notably MTA (Motion-Time Analysis), Work Factor, and MTS (Motion Time Standards) trace their usage into the 1930–1940 era. Possibly, this was in part due to the effects of the depression and its aftermath. The bad taste left by the "efficiency experts" also undoubtedly left its effect. Industrial engineers had to expend much of their energy and thought to overcome this bad reputation, which hindered profitable usage of their time in developing new approaches to surmount the hostile surroundings and in regaining acceptance by managers.

This situation did not continue. The 1940's brought a rapid war mobilization with shortages of material and manpower. There was little time in which to achieve the necessary tremendous increases in productivity. Business was forced to pay closer attention to all types of labor-saving devices and managerial controls. The patient efforts of qualified industrial engineers had also, by then, overcome much of the bad reputation of the past.

Several more of the better known predetermined time systems, including MTM, originated during this period. The pace of production and economic pressure continued after the war, in response to the hunger of demand created by years of non-availability of necessities, luxuries, and investment-type production. During the entire decade, however, management avoided the errors made in the "efficiency era" that thrived under similar economic conditions.   This is to the credit of both managers and wiser practitioners of work measurement.

Then, from 1950 to the present time, the predetermined time systems already established continued a healthy growth as competition reappeared. The remaining systems also came into existence since then.   It is interesting to note that typically human differences in interpretation as to the significance of various aspects of the new concept of predetermined times led to a degree of divergence of systems.   Thus arose a new need—the need to attain more universal agreement on one or several of the more prominent systems.   Only then could the traditional factional disputes that had plagued conventional time study and motion study be averted.   The cycle of development had been completed and had begun another round.

This review of the history of work measurement is vital to proper insight into the various work study systems and procedures.

CHARACTERISTICS OF PREDETERMINED TIME SYSTEMS

Time study and motion study groups long ago learned to ask and answer "What? Why? How? When? and Who?" when analyzing operations. Applying this five-point attack to the subject of work measurement aids in properly considering the characteristics of a predetermined time system. The results of such analysis are as follows:

What?

Work measurement is a management tool based on the use of scientific principles with the aim of ascertaining both the cost of labor in productive situations and procedures by which that cost might be effectively reduced. To achieve both these aims, it is essential to determine both the motion and time characteristics of the work situation under study.   The specific method must be set before the time can be determined.

Why?

The answer to this question in any field borders closely on the philosophical structure of the field itself.   The previous chapter elaborated on this question.   To restate it briefly, work measurement offers one of the most reliable avenues or aids used by scientific management to achieve the benefits of increased production at lower cost for the advantage of everyone.

How?

The earliest answer here was "Put a watch on it."   The next reply was "Analyze and classify the motions in minutest detail."   Both schools agreed "Let's arrive at universal standards upon which all can build in unanimity their undisputable answer to any given problem of work measurement." But where this goal was agreed, wide diversity prevailed as to the means of achievement. Most of the remainder of this book will be devoted to answering this question, as it remains the crux of work study development toward the common ideal of all scientific managers.

When?

Work measurement should be used in all times and places in which a reasonable likelihood exists that productive improvements will accrue in greater amount than the cost of measuring the work. More specific facts on this general statement will be found threaded throughout this book, although the greatest concentration of answers appear in the section on *Applications Engineering.*

Who?

The more advanced forms of work measurement should be practiced only by properly trained and qualified persons acting under appropriate management direction. The less involved forms should be utilized by every member of the managerial force in particular, and this extends as well to every worker who would be proud of the quality and effectiveness of his work. Further remarks on this matter will be found in the closing chapters of this book.

The answers to these questions permit a clear definition of predetermined time systems and analysis of their characteristics. The historical background and human aspects of work measurement make possible a better understanding of the subject. This book presents a major emphasis on Methods-Time Measurement; the value and comprehension of this system tends to be enhanced when the history of work measurement and knowledge concerning predetermined time systems is clearly known.

While the authors believe and will attempt in the remainder of this text to indicate the superiority of MTM as a predetermined time system, their definite endorsement of the whole concept of predetermined times extends to the other systems as well. No criticism is made with derogation aforethought, rather honest personal observations will be given. Each system has some feature or combination of facets which commends it and contributes a worthwhile aspect to the subject as a whole. As the future will likely prove, unanimity can most easily thrive when a spirit of cooperative professionalism prompts work analysts as they search for the ultimate system.

Definition

A predetermined time system is an organized body of information, procedures, and techniques employed in the study and evaluation of work elements performed by human power in terms of the method or motions used, their general and specific nature, the conditions under which they occur, and the application of prestandardized or predetermined times which their performance requires.

Note several salient features of this definition which adequately cover the many systems now known. They specifically concern human energy expended as work, and do not measure process time, as mentioned earlier. It is necessary to confine the attention, for one given study or evaluation, to one specific method at a time. The true essence of a particular motion and its relation to other motions must be clearly understood. The context in which the motions are performed will affect their analysis and performance time. And finally, the time, or range of times, which is assigned to a given motion has been determined in advance; the standardized data promotes uniformity and universality in application.

Predetermined Time Systems—Aims and Ideals

For a field as broad and varied as work measurement, it is difficult to formulate a set of aims and ideals that could be the basis for a technique satisfactory to all concerned. The dangers of over-elaboration are as great as those of over-simplification; however, the authors feel that the following discussion will point out the more important criteria tor predetermined time systems in general. Since these criteria are admittedly ideal, it is readily conceded that no single system will completely satisfy all of them.

1. The approach and usage of a system must be professional in the best sense of that term. Salesmanship of the system is a necessity, but this should be done with befitting dignity and taste. Industrial engineers, being concerned with the design of procedures and controls for the interaction of people, materials, and machines, have a responsibility in the design sense that is just as real as the honesty of a civil engineer who uses an adequate factor of safety to design a bridge. Human lives are affected, as are the economy and natural resources. For these reasons, the professional aspects surrounding a predetermined time system merit prime attention in evaluating the system.

2. The system must be based on sound concepts with heavy reliance on the fields of physiology and psychology. Competent personnel should follow known and accepted scientific and mathematical rules while developing the data which comprises the working portion of the system.

3. The desirability of validating the data both by the developers and independent efforts is self evident. Such validation is not likely to occur

unless the methodology and background data are made available to the public. Publicity increases the chance for further validation and for providing convincing evidence of the correctness of the data—both being essential to public trust and confidence in the system.

4. Some form of training control will insure that misuse of a system through partial or improper understanding will not engender a repetition of the "efficiency expert" era. A good predetermined time system provides an agency or procedure by which training in the system can be properly controlled. Such training should be available to the public subject to limits of qualification and ability. It could also be further safeguarded by means of testing, continuing publication of new data, interchange of data between practitioners, and circulation among practitioners of application experiences with the system.

Such training control is hard to achieve. One approach used to achieve it is to limit the publication of data and procedural methods. However, this could produce other bad effects. Therefore, the authors believe that the agency for training control preferably should be administered separately from the information and data sources of the system. This independent agency should work mainly on a level of professional endorsement, the lack of which would deter use of the system by untrained people. It should, upon proper request, certify the adequacy of the training courses and the knowledge of trainees to allow interested parties to ascertain the competence of practitioners seeking to apply the system to their own operations. Admittedly, this is not the strongest form of training control. The individual's opinion concerning the emphasis this ideal deserves will determine his ranking of this with the other ideals expressed or which he may desire to subtract from, or add to, those expressed in this text.

Its application by inexperienced and incompetent persons can and will damage the repute of any system. In a sense, this was one of the basic faults of conventional time study that is only now being counteracted by more professional attention to its features. It was so easy to set a stopwatch on a task without adequate knowledge and interpretation of the reading taken that many of the laity of work measurement wrought sore difficulties for those qualified and able to use the stopwatch correctly. Once a system becomes universally known and accepted, however, the problem lessens because the majority of the practicing industrial engineers will have been properly trained in its theory and application in adequate college courses.

5. The working form of a good predetermined time system must be practical and practicable to make it adaptable to the solution of many types of work-study problems. It must be applicable to a wide range

of variation in work content, industrial practices, and workers' skills. Lack of these features will tend to hinder beneficial results it might otherwise attain, and limit its effectiveness as a major tool of work design.

6. A good system is easy to use. Analysts will become discouraged if their constructive time becomes occupied by an ever-increasing mass of details. Techniques with this fault will be discarded for more workable ones. The specific feature of predetermined time systems most directly bearing on this problem is the fineness of division of the motions classified. These divisions must be detailed enough to account adequately for all practical variations without exceeding the tolerance of the analyst for details. On the other hand, rather fine subdivisions are proper to a good system, especially if they are amenable to synthesis into larger categories which do not violate the limits of workability noted.

7. Actual work situations are dynamic, changing with the times and new technologies. A good predetermined time system should be maintained in a dynamic condition to meet the challenge of change. Truly valid data, for the methods of determination used, will not subsequently be shown to be incorrect. A system should, however, be flexible enough to employ improved means of data determination and to permit being brought up to date as the occasion demands. This feature suggests that the advocates of the system should carry forward a continuing program of research, seeking new basic knowledge and further substantiation of existing knowledge. Such a requirement is basic to all engineering; it must certainly be met by such a new branch as industrial engineering in which much remains to be discovered and applied.

Though a predetermined time system might be soundly conceived and initiated, lack of development will hinder it from maintaining its acceptable status. It will fail to meet new requirements imposed by new inventions or procedures that affect work content and methods. Even so enduring a structure as a beautiful palace will fall into disuse and ruin without proper maintenance and updating to such modern devices as electricity, running water, central heating, and the like.

8. A good system has a practical emphasis. It must give correct answers for actual work situations. The best means of assuring this facet for predetermined times concerns the use of the two main data sources. Laboratory data results from controlled conditions; it should properly be used only for isolation of the variables, their nature, their interrelationships, and approximate numerical limits they normally exhibit. For the actual application data, however, reliance must be placed on industrial samples of sufficient scope, range, and size to permit valid conclusions. Industrial

data inherently show the behavior of motions under actual operating conditions; such data may be confidently applied to achieve correct answers for practical aims.

9. Another ideal of predetermined time systems is universality. Acceptance must be broad, not confined to limits of special industries, or geographical boundaries. It should perform equally well in diverse operations, foreign countries, and in the hands of anyone properly trained. Regardless of the merits of a predetermined time system, limited acceptance for any reason will vitiate its usefulness in solving the many work-study problems demanding prompt attention. This generally results from inadequate or unfavorable publicity, lack of professional "selling," or custody of the system by persons inept at using the multiplicity of channels for advantageous public communication. A skilled craftsman may be using a superior type of micrometer, but if nobody believes his measurements, the instrument is of little worth in his work.

The data should be preserved in some definite physical form, such as motion pictures, punched cards or tape, magnetic tape, etc. to permit reexamination at a later date; thus, anyone who approaches the system without prejudice can evaluate such evidence.

Many of these ideals of predetermined time systems are difficult to attain fully in human situations. These standards, however, do provide a gage which could be used to measure any given system. It is conceded that no existing system is likely to meet all of these criteria.

The fact that a system does not entirely meet a given ideal does not imply a reduction in its value. It is also important to emphasize the fact that systems other than Methods-Time Measurement should not be judged by these ideals based solely upon the meager information concerning them contained in this chapter. The authors' knowledge concerning some of them is limited due to a lack of published material. What has been endeavored, at a minimum effort, is to indicate the identity of some of the more important systems and a few of the facts concerning them—so that the student, engineer, or manager could, if he so desired, further investigate one or more of the other systems. The authors readily concede that valid data can be developed using predetermined time systems other than Methods-Time Measurement. While they personally believe the Methods-Time Measurement system to be superior from an over-all viewpoint, it is admitted that it probably does not excel in every single aspect.

Under no circumstances would the authors imply or advise that anyone, or any firm, consider the abandonment of one system for another if they are getting satisfactory results from it—since the better known systems generally yield valid and usable labor standards that provide an excellent medium for analyzing and improving manual work.

MAJOR PREDETERMINED TIME SYSTEMS

Many predetermined time systems have been formulated since the debut of the first. Some were and are maintained by private industry for internal usage. Others were semi-public and later gained restricted support. Yet others, of which MTM is a notable example, have become widely known and used because all their data have been made public information. The last groups have proved most hardy, simply because human beings tend to react against restrictions on their minds or efforts. Obviously, fairer evaluation of their worth is possible because more is known of them. Significantly, the published material on all systems has increased greatly subsequent to the first edition of this text. The features of various systems, as next listed, can be evaluated by the reader by reference to the guides established earlier in this chapter.

Motion-Time Analysis

MTA, as the abbreviation for this system is known, was the first and is the oldest system. Mr. A. B. Segur constructed it on the foundation of the principle of predetermined times which he stated. It features well-defined motion categories based on physiological principles, variable time bases for possible variations in the motions, distinct rules of usage, and an approach to motion combinations. The system is apparently sound, as attested by its long lifespan, and has been fruitful in cost evaluation for many firms.

The A. B. Segur Company administers the system, reserving the training and answers to inquiries to its own jurisdiction. Therefore, while general opinion holds that MTA is valid, unanimity of opinion by work analysts is difficult. Criticism might be undeserved simply because they cannot find the facts without agreeing to the secrecy required of all trainees. This situation has recently been alleviated by publication of some of the data and procedures.*

Work measurement is unquestionably much indebted to Mr. Segur for many of the basic concepts of predetermined times; he pioneered in this service among the groups who studied with him. Indirectly, he also demonstrated the value of public dissemination of the source, data, and validation of a system.

Work-Factor

Work-Factor is the trade-mark which identifies the consultant services and predetermined time system of the Work-Factor Company. The Work-Factor system, like MTA, has many advocates. Mr. Joseph H. Quick

---

Industrial Engineering Handbook, edited by H. B. Maynard, McGraw-Hill Book Co., 1956, 2nd Edition 1963.

and associates founded it on accumulations of stop watch studies, plus motion pictures and photographic studies, over a long period at the Radio Corporation of America. The Work-Factor states that the system has been revised and refined several times to generalize its acceptability to all lines of work and to increase its universality. According to recent publications*, there have been some changes or additions to the basic tables indicating the presence of refinement effort and an effort to further standardize the rules and procedures for using the data. This firm has established a strong training control by teaching and disclosing the complete procedures only to industrial groups as an integral part of an over-all service they render their clientele.

Work-Factor has several sets of data. One is detailed for fine analysis, another encompasses broader elements for quick rough analysis work, and a third is further abbreviated for quick analysis. The accuracy of answers required and study time limitations dictate which set of data to apply to a given situation. The detailed data permits a high degree of methods correction work by one skilled in its usage. The data, however, is difficult to apply without the training the company provides or equivalent information from another source. Interpretation is important to success with the system. The company does maintain, however, regional clientele groups which exchange information and usage experiences.

This system recognizes the motion variables of distance, weight, degree of control, and body member acting. The distance and body member are handled directly by table headings, but a rather specialized approach is used to account for the effects of weight and degree of control. A variable number of "work factors" is assigned to a motion for the latter two variables, and time increases are proportional to the applicable number of work factors. The degree of control is divided, for purposes of finding the number of work factors to be used, into four categories—steering or directional control, precaution or care, change of direction, and manner of motion termination. Combinations of these with weight categories yield from one to four work factors. With the basic values, therefore, a range of five performance times can be applied for a given body member to act through a certain distance. Another feature of Work-Factor is a workable manner of accounting for combinations of motions involving more than one body member.

Knowledge of the system spreads chiefly by individuals in the groups trained who subsequently relocate in other companies, since they generally like the methodology of the system and continue to apply it. Its original success was in the electronic industry and in other industries

* *Industrial Engineering Handbook,* edited by H. B. Maynard, McGraw-Hill Book Co., 1956, 2nd Edition 1963 and *Work-Factor Time Standards* by Quick, Duncan, and Malcolm, McGraw-Hill Book Co., 1962.

employing relatively small, light hand assembly. This tends to show that fine manual sequences and/or assembly operations are amenable to systematic study by predetermined time systems.

General Electric

This famous concern has several private systems of predetermined times. One is dubbed the "Get and Place" system and is used for estimating and preproduction standards purposes. Its motion categories include large sequences of motions, and the variation in applicable times is minimal.

Another is known as MTS, for Motion Time Standards, and roughly corresponds to the detailed type of Work-Factor Data. Finer motion subdivisions and a larger range of times makes it useful for production standards. Provisions also exist for the degree of control used and for motion combinations.

A third system, of more recent origin, is known as DMT.* Dimensional Motion Times were formulated by Mr. Helmut C. Geppinger at Bridgeport, Connecticut. The principle of the system is that the time it takes to perform previously standardized operations on parts with standardized designs bears a relationship to the dimensions of the part. The part is thus measured in certain dimensions and a time for producing it assigned by reference to standard data tables.

General Electric has always been known for its policy of training its employees. While training in these systems was therefore confined to that group, the company made no particular attempt to bar spreading of the techniques or information. Indeed, this would be difficult to do when personnel relocated. Their systems have thus become semi-public, and are sometimes used by others when they find the data serves their purposes adequately.

The source and data for these systems (except DMT) have not been publicly circulated; but it is common knowledge that usage of time study, data from other systems, and adaptation of data to General Electric operating policies was made a part of them. They are, essentially, a synthesis of data that has been oriented to company usage.

Holmes

Mr. Walter G. Holmes, while employed at Timkin-Detroit Axle Company, developed a set of time data that assigned values to body motions and the basic therbligs in essentially unchanged form. He included this in the text *Applied Time and Motion Study* by W. G. Holmes, Ronald Press Co., rev. 1945.

---

* *Dimensional Motion Times* by H. C. Geppinger, John Wiley & Sons, Inc., 1955.

Methods-Time Measurement

Since complete information on this system is a major purpose of this text, no elaboration will be added at this point. The next chapter deals specifically with its origin and early development, and the following one with the MTM Association for Standards and Research (and its international affiliates) which now administer the system.

Mundel

Professor Marvin E. Mundel has helped to develop several predetermined time systems. One of these was published fully in the *Journal of Industrial Engineering* (Vol. IV, No. 4, February 1944). This system, developed with associates—principally Dr. Irwin P. Lazarus—while under contract to U. S. Army Ordnance, is called OPAPT for *Ordnance Predetermined Approximate Performance Times.* It is used in ordnance depots as a uniform work study practice.

A unique feature of the data published is a wide range of times assignable to various distances of motion and degrees of control exercised. The analysis of positioning motions is particularly acute and detailed. The exposition of the times allowed is developed from the basic equations for velocity and acceleration, with the full source of values shown. A compensating factor table to adjust resulting standards to operating conditions is another feature. The complete presentation of the data in this manner is a commendable professional service.

The so-called Mundel System apparently has worked well under the requirements of Army Ordnance, and availability of the data makes testing of it in other situations easy.

Basic Motion Timestudy

This system was developed by the Canadian consulting engineering firm of J. D. Woods and Gordon, Ltd. It was published rather fully in the *Journal of Industrial Engineering.* The data is frankly acknowledged to be a revision of Methods-Time Measurement, adding features of several of the other predetermined systems. Their aim was to achieve easier application and closer differentiation of times than they felt was possible with MTM. Many work study personnel have expressed the opinion that it is basically an individualistic interpretation of MTM and is therefore not a distinctly new creation. The classification of motions was changed somewhat and a different set of time data applied, but full validation of the changes is not possible from the information published However, additional material published later* does increase the available knowledge pertaining to BMT.

---

* *Basic Motion Timestudy* by Bailey and Presgrave, McGraw-Hill Book Co., 1958.

SUMMARY

It can readily be seen that each of the systems discussed has several features to commend it. No single system can be said to be superior in all respects to all others. Rather, the thought here has been that the best of these systems, or a new system as yet unfounded, all contain features that approach the ideals laid down in this chapter. It is fairly certain, as well, that the ultimate system will draw its format and features heavily from the systems known today.

The variety of these systems, and the number of them, all attest in a positive way that the departure from traditional time study and motion study as discrete entities has brought the industrial engineer closer to the ideal form of work measurement.

To illustrate the extent of predetermined time system usage at the present time, further reference to the survey of American industry by Stewart, Dougall & Associates cited in Chapter 2 will be helpful. It disclosed that in the plants utilizing work measurement (two-thirds of the sample), 56 per cent of them use a predetermined time system, and over half of the latter group use it as their prime work measurement tool, i.e. in a full-fledged manner. Table 1 presents an analysis of the group making full-fledged use of a predetermined time system. It will be noted that MTM is used twice as often as any other single system.

Table I.   Analysis of Full-fledged Predetermined Time System (PTS) Usage
(Adapted from data in survey by Stewart, Dougall & Associates)

Predetermined Time System being used Full-fledged	No. of Plants Reporting			Percentages of Plants Surveyed			
	Size of Plant, employees		Totals	Based on 96 using PTS fully	Based on 185 using PTS some	Based on 331 using Work Measurement	Based on 497 total in survey *
	100–499	500 +					
MTM	22	14	36	37.5	19.5	10.9	7.2
W-F	7	6	13	13.5	7.0	3.9	2.6
MTA	10	3	13	13.5	7.0	3.9	2.6
BMT	7	5	12	12.5	6.5	3.6	2.4
DMT	3	1	4	4.2	2.2	1.2	0.8
Own System	10	4	14	14.6	7.6	4.2	2.8
21 Others	17	8	25	26.0	13.5	7.6	5.0
Total Replies	76	41	117	121.8	63.3	35.3	23.4
Plant Totals	58	38	96	100.0	100.0	100.0	100.0
Multiple Reply Factor	1.31	1.08	1.22	1.218	0.633	0.353	0.234

* Includes 50 plants not replying at all.

Predetermined time system development will now tend, hopefully, toward the growth of synthesis and compromise which ultimately will produce the universal, unanimous system alluded to earlier. The individual systems, especially MTM, provide a sound basis on which to build this ultimate system. Professional attitudes on the part of all work analysts now are more essential than ever.

The personal opinion of the authors is that Methods-Time Measurement accords best with the ideals of work measurement stated in this chapter. Specific comments and reasons for this opinion will be given with reference to those ideals. It is felt that, until continuing research and application of predetermined times amasses a convincing weight of conclusive evidence, tentative agreement on the best existing system is a desirable goal. This goal is one of the aims for which this text has been prepared, both in its original version and in this revised second edition.

CHAPTER 4

Methods-Time Measurement—
A New Approach

Methods-Time Measurement is the only predetermined time system whose entire data (including the research) has been made completely available to the general public. It was developed at Methods Engineering Council, Pittsburgh, Pennsylvania, by Messrs. Harold B. Maynard, Gustave J. Stegemerten, and John L. Schwab following preliminary study at Westinghouse Electric Corporation. They merit commendation for their high ethics and the unselfish discharge of their professional responsibilities in making the results of their work completely available.

These men further aided the development of scientific management by founding, with others, a non-profit research and development organization known as the MTM Association for Standards and Research. They assigned all their data and development rights to this association.

The above factors are primarily responsible for Methods-Time Measurement being the pre-eminent predetermined time system for work study and measurement. The authors contend that it fully qualifies Methods-Time Measurement as providing a basis of agreement for all practitioners on a single and universally recognized predetermined time system. Why this opinion is held is easy to understand after the material in the preceding chapters is digested. In this chapter and the next, specific proof is offered that Methods-Time Measurement best meets the predetermined time system ideals. Frank statement of these aims at the beginning of intensive study of Methods-Time Measurement should serve to orient the reader and allow his complete appraisal of the facts.

An authoritative account of the origination of Methods-Time Measurement has been published in a text by the discoverers of the system.[1] Their text, the first one published concerning any predetermined time system, was

[1] *Methods-Time Measurement* by Maynard, Stegemerten and Schwab, McGraw-Hill Book Co., Inc., 1948.

in itself a unique venture in the field of work measurement. It played a leading role in bringing MTM to its present state of development.

A principal aim of the present text is, therefore, to carry forward this effort by:

1. Presenting additional fundamental information that will aid MTM practitioners.
2. Providing practical application data and approaches to the many problems encountered by MTM practitioners. The authors, with professional experience obtained primarily in industry, present this material against the background where MTM will normally be used.
3. Integrating MTM fundamentals with the older forms of work study and work measurement (motion study and time study). Only by such integration can work study and work measurement achieve its proper goals and aims.

For those who are unfamiliar with MTM, a recounting of its development will show the capabilities of the originators and the firm basis on which the MTM procedural structure rests.

During 1940, a large group of time study men completed a methods improvement program conducted by Methods Engineering Council, a management consulting firm, headed by H. B. Maynard, whose reputation in the profession is one of world-wide recognition. Founded by Maynard in 1934, the organization name gives recognition to the fact that its founder first coined the words "methods engineer" and that the firm was primarily doing methods evaluation and methods improvement work. Under his guidance the company expanded and grew in a few short years until it was in 1940 already working for companies, large and small, in the United States, as well as in many foreign lands. But in these years they put great emphasis on training, believing that "show-how" for its clients was as important as "know-how." As a result, the men who were trained achieved substantial cost reductions. However, the inventors of MTM, in making an analysis of these results, became convinced that the cost reductions were actually the result of methods correction rather than an outgrowth of true methods engineering.

Maynard, Stegemerten, and Schwab therefore searched for a means by which good methods might be established in advance of production. They deduced that, if operators learned the best method as they began a new task, the need and possibility of marked improvements later would be lessened. Training costs would also be lower. This would be a boon to managers plagued by production problems, labor difficulties, lack of training guides, and a paucity of usable knowledge for correct methods establishment prior to starting production.

They decided to study common industrial operations and endeavor to develop "Methods Formulas." Their initial choice was to investigate sensitive drill press operations. They intended to extend the same approach into other areas if they were successful in finding such suitable formulas in their first effort, so that there would result eventually a body of information which had been desired by even the earliest of work analysts. The findings of the research on sensitive drill press operations surprised even the researchers, since they were able to expand the results into the first predetermined time system to gain general public acceptance and usage. They found that truly basic motions had been isolated and valid times had been established for these motions after trials on other types of work.

It is a cardinal rule of good research that the data should be preserved and compiled in the most convenient, economical form possible that will permit future reference, validation, and extension of the data. To comply with these rules the originators of MTM decided to film the operations, accurately record and explain all data taken from the film, and validate their conclusions by testing under actual production situations. In addition, it was a traditional approach—the Gilbreths had relied heavily on film as a research medium. The major difference in the analytical approach of Maynard, Stegemerten, and Schwab from that of the Gilbreths was that they were also disciples of the work measurement school which believed that a basic connection existed between time and motion and that they fortunately discovered the key by which such equivalence could be demonstrated and evaluated.

Having decided to analyze the drilling operations from the standpoints of both time and motions used, the researchers next reasoned that only one thing prevented the films from being both a time study and a motion study in reproducible, easy-to-review form. This was the question of the performance level of the operator. Obviously, when a constant speed or regulated camera and projector are employed, each frame of film represents a measurable time lapse dependent directly on the speeds involved. This time lapse, however, would not necessarily equal the normal time needed for the motion being observed. In order to find the normal time from the film frames, the operator's performance level must be agreed upon and a correction factor applied to the running time of each film frame to determine the normal elapsed time for the motion—or portion of motion—viewed in that frame. Frame counts are therefore a means of finding the time—if the performance rating question can be solved.

Performance rating will be discussed in detail later in this text; but some information is needed here, since valid time standards rely on finding the time for an *average* operator employing a consistent method with *average* skill and effort under *average* conditions. Any particular operator being studied may vary from this norm. His actual performance time must be adjusted if the time is to be used in the development of a standard meeting the above requirements. Such adjusted actual times are referred to as "leveled" times.

Many conceptions as to how to establish the norm and judge operation performance against this norm have been developed. Complete agreement among work analysts has been difficult to attain. Probably the best approach, and the one having the widest acceptance, was establisned by the Society for the Advancement of Management. The SAM rating films generally produce agreement on what comprises normal performance and provide a means for sharpening judgment of variations from the norm. The judgment, based on the over-all performance observed, does not attempt to isolate factors for component variables.

Another system of performance rating having wide acceptance was developed earlier by Lowry, Maynard, and Stegemerten, often called the LMS system. This system accounts specifically for the effort, skill, conditions, and consistency in a work situation based on a given method. It uses specially developed numerical percentage factors to evaluate the increase or decrease from normal exhibited by an operator. It, too, yields a satisfactory conception of normal and provides time study analysts with a usable and generally satisfactory means of rating performances.

The MTM originators took a practical approach to the stumbling block of standard time measurement—the problem of finding what constitutes a standard of normal performance. First, while actual shop runs of drilling operations were being photographed, several seasoned raters used the LMS system independently for the various parts of the operation and for the operation as a whole. Second, the film was later analyzed for the motion content of the operation in question. Third, the consensus of ratings was applied to the frame counts to yield normal motion times.

This general rating procedure also is used by the MTM Association in its continuing research program. Essentially, then, everyone who applies the MTM data times to motions equivalent to the well-defined categories set up by the MTM system tacitly agrees to the ratings of the original observers as constituting a standard of normal. This means that all persons who properly apply MTM are using the same yardstick.

Actually, no means of measurement is absolute, as Einstein well demonstrated in his Theory of Relativity. Rather it will be *relative to an accepted standard* against which the measurement could actually or potentially be checked at any time. The standard itself is usually a defined quantity or an artificial amount against which all other measurements in the same units, or equivalent units, are gaged by implication. This is true of all such common measurements as the inch, foot, yard, etc. In effect, therefore, the MTM measurement is at least a usable common standard reference measure.

The rating procedure used obviously did not result in absolute answers —that is, they were not necessarily precise. When analysts correctly apply the data in the established manner, however, their results will be accurately consistent. Any experienced work study analyst knows very well that consistency is a bigger problem than precision. MTM has provided a way to achieve complete consistency by setting up once and for all—whether it is precise or not—a norm or standard against which all measurements of motion times may confidently be made.

Although the originators of MTM do not make this claim, the utilization of experienced raters working under the men who developed the rating system employed would tend to assure that the data produced was precise as well as accurate. Since then, virtually every conceivable type of industrial operation and many non-industrial tasks have been adequately measured with MTM. The authors of this text feel that in the practical sense— particularly since multitudes of stop watch checks in many industries and diverse operations have confirmed MTM times—the MTM data is both sufficiently accurate *and* precise. A pure scientist might not be satisfied with this statement, but engineers are practical scientists who must produce workable designs and profitable answers to fit a dynamic environment in which the human element exerts an effect equal to or greater than the technical elements.

Having solved the performance level problem in the manner described, Maynard, Stegemerten, and Schwab were then in a position to follow the normal engineering procedures of definition, analysis, conclusion, and verification described in the technical factor section of this chapter.

DEFINITION OF METHODS–TIME MEASUREMENT

The official definition of MTM has been unchanged since the originators first embodied it in this form:

Methods-time measurement is a procedure which analyzes any manual operation or method into the basic motions required to perform it and assigns to each motion a predetermined time standard which is determined by the nature of the motion and the conditions under which it is made.[2]

The wording of this definition is precise and carries a number of meanings deserving explanation.

The hyphenation of Methods-Time is a definite, descriptive part of the system because it constantly reminds MTM users of an important fact. This is the connection between the method of doing a task and the time that task will require. It correctly implies that methods work must *precede* the setting of task times, since the time and method are integrally related

[2] By permission from *Methods-Time Measurement* by Maynard, Stegemerten and Schwab. Copyright, 1948, McGraw-Hill Book Co., Inc.

and time of itself is meaningless for a task unless it is set in conjunction with a definite, identifiable method.

A method, in this sense, consists of a set or sequence of motions logically performed in a definite order to produce the desired effect on the workpiece or the placement of the body members. The physical behavior imparted to objects will depend on the work done by the human mechanism, and many variables exist on which the characteristics of the work and its duration depend. When these factors have all been properly analyzed and any needed corrective action taken, a *method* has been established. Only then can a reliable *time* for the task be assigned.

Methods-Time Measurement is an analytical procedure. The procedurized analysis must be accomplished if the time required for the motions made is to be established. Definite steps must be followed, as shown later in this text, to make successful usage of the time data. Analysis cannot be circumvented if successful results are to accrue from either the method or the time standpoints. The analysis designed into the MTM system inherently aids its user to arrive at better methods and lower times for a given task. The system is thus internally cohesive, in that each motion itself yields clues to methods improvements, in addition to the improvements indicated by the motions considered as a chain of integral links in the method concerned. This feature is almost unique in work measurement systems.

The measurement is restricted to manual portions of the method. The term manual is used in a dual sense in MTM. It refers alike to the hands alone and also to other portions of the body and/or body members.

The major body subdivisions, physiologically, are the trunk or torso and all members attached thereto. The hips, legs, and feet are appendages used mostly for support, carriage, and transport of the trunk. Their actions are included under Body Motions. The neck and head contain most of the major sense organs, of which the eyes have the most useful function in work performance. Eye motions are a separate category of MTM motions that require analysis. The remaining body members—the shoulders, arms, wrists, hands, and fingers are usually categorized as manual members. The major portion of the MTM system has oeen associated with these latter manual members of the body since they are the most used body members.

The next concept of the MTM definition is that, following analysis of the manual actions into basic motions, a pre-established time value which does not permit interpretation by the analyst is assigned to each motion. MTM provides a true standard for each basic motion encountered. It will consistently produce reliable time measurements when used by competent analysts. This is the main concept of any predetermined time system and meets the test of clarity and practicality.

The time assigned to each motion does not depend on the operator; it is for the average operator in the universally varying distribution. The times are mean values which will gage the performance of any operator, either the average or the exceptional performer at either extreme of the probability curve. The element of analyst judgment is eliminated in this respect and the established times are therefore objective.

Finally, the time does depend, however, on both the true nature of the motion in question and the conditions of performance imposed on the motion by all other agencies besides the operator involved in the situation. This will become clearer as each motion is exhaustively discussed in separate chapters.

Although, as noted earlier, the primary official definition of MTM has never changed, the MTM Association in 1958 adopted the following sub-definitions to emphasize and clarify it:[3]

1. *Methods* — time: The specific method must be established before the time can be determined.
2. *Manual* operation: This means the normal operation performed by people, and excludes operations controlled by equipment and process such as welding time and machining time.
3. *Basic* motion: This refers to the finger, hand, and arm motions; eye motions; and the body, leg, and foot motions shown on the data card.
4. *Nature* of the motion: The times for specific basic motions are affected by the degree of control or accuracy involved.
5. *Conditions:* The times for specific basic motions are affected by the conditions of the objects, such as jumbled, small, flat; by the restrictions imposed upon the path of the motion; and by the degree of care or precision that must be exercised.

These statements constitute a concise summary of the preceding discussion in official format.

TECHNICAL ASPECTS OF ORIGINAL RESEARCH

With the basic approach to tneir "Methods Formulas" determined, the originators of MTM were ready to accumulate the needed data on film and then to analyze the film for the motion-time information being sought. At first they tried the conventional micromotion technique of element subdivision using therbligs (Gilbreth elements). The work sequences in the drilling operations were listed in therbligs along with the leveled times (actual times adjusted by the concepts defined earlier) from the films. The trial plots of this data resulted in a meaningless scatter, showing the need for further element subdivision to permit curve drawing. After checking

[3] By permission from *Journal of Methods-Time Measurement,* Vol. 4, No. 4, MTM Association for Standards and Research, Ann Arbor, Michigan, Nov.-Dec. 1958.

the actual shop conditions to assure that the data itself was correct, they began to redefine the elements — thus originating the MTM elements.[4]

The new definitions were in terms of basic motions with readily identified starting and ending points. These motions were classified as to type and another plotting trial showed highly meaningful data had been achieved. Other operations studied in this manner yielded further data which correlated with the original studies. Instead of specialized "Methods Formulas", the originators discovered they now had a predetermined time system documented by many feet of motion picture film with performance ratings coded to the film and record sheets of all the pertinent data. The principal technical factors connected with this work are next discussed.

Time Units

The time represented by one motion picture frame naturally depended on the speed at which the film was exposed. Constant speed equipment was used to assure uniform time increments for each frame. By applying the performance rating in percentage terms, it was then possible to find the average time consumed by an average operator in the frame in question.

However, it was of practical necessity to assign time values in units which had the dual advantages of easy usage and yielded numerical results that could readily be used to supply the input to cost systems. Most industries rely on decimal minutes or decimal hours for their measurement and subsequent costing of labor. Time units such as these, however, would have been difficult to use because of the fact that many of the basic motions were very short in elapsed time of performance and many zeros would have been needed between the decimal point and the first significant digit.

This is clearly illustrated by the film speed times expressed in commonly used time units. Since the film speed used in the original research was 16 frames per second, each frame covered an unrated elapsed time of 0.0625 seconds, 0.0010417 minutes, or 0.00001737 hours.

The obvious way to avoid such unwieldy time units was to recognize that units are arbitrary by nature—the necessity for conversion to other desired units being the only real limitation. Maynard, Stegemerten, and Schwab invented a new time unit known as the Time Measurement Unit and assigned 0.00001 hours as the value of one Time Measurement Unit. Since most wages are in dollars per hour, the TMU can be multiplied by the hourly rate and the decimal point then shifted five places to the left

---

[4] The reader should realize that this account of the original MTM research is greatly condensed. A complete chronology can be found in the speech "Dividends from Research" by Prof. D. W. Karger which is part of the *Proceedings* of the 1963 International MTM Conference at New York City, available from the MTM Association, Ann Arbor, Michigan.

to find the cost of labor directly. Also the hours required to produce 100 motions (or pieces) can be found by shifting the decimal two places to the left.

As a result of the unit chosen, the following time conversions will be valid:

1 TMU equals 0.00001 hours	1 Hour equals 100,000 TMU
equals 0.0006 minutes	1 Minute equals 1,667 TMU
equals 0.036 seconds	1 Second equals 27.8 TMU

Under these conditions, one unrated film frame at the research speed was equal to 1.737 TMU. No motion time less than this value could be set from the film. This proved to be the principal limit on the precision of the original data. When other film speeds, such as the faster speeds used in later MTM research sponsored by the MTM Association, are used to get a finer time determination, it is merely necessary to find the new per frame time in TMU to easily fit the new data into the present MTM system. Precision then becomes a matter of film speeds and control of the filming mechanisms; on the other hand, accuracy is inherent in the film frames themselves. The main chance for error is in the performance rating factor applied; but even here consistency is possible if the researchers are experienced in rating techniques and can agree with other raters about the operation on the film. Recently, MTM research sophistication has been increased by the usage of such devices as electronic data collectors in conjunction with extremely sensitive transducers, punched card equipment, and computers.

Motion Definition

While it is necessary to have a definite per frame time which can be corrected to average by a rating procedure, only half of the name Methods-Time has been considered. Since the time for a given motion depends on the frame count for that motion, definitive identification points for the motion must be established. These points must permit both good methods work as well as description. However, measurement points in turn depend on the content specified or defined for a given motion. It was in determining the true basic motions, their names, and the precise content of the motions that Maynard, Stegemerten, and Schwab did perhaps the most creative work involved in discovering MTM. From the great mass of data which they had previously analyzed and isolated, exploratory plots were made of variables seeming most basic. The truly basic motions as found in MTM were finally brought to light by applied original thinking.

The basic motions and definitions are a subject which deserve more detail than can be compressed adequately into this chapter; indeed, each motion comprises a separate chapter in the Fundamentals section of this

Table I. Film Frame Measuring Points for Various Motions

MOTION	BEGINNING FRAME	ENDING FRAME
Reach	One preceding first frame in which noticeable motion occurs.	One in which noticeable motion has ceased or that marks the start of the next basic motion following.
Move	Same as for Reach	Same as for Reach
Turn	Same as for Reach	Same as for Reach
Apply Pressure	One in which preceding motion clearly ceased.	One in which next motion clearly begins.
Grasp	Frame next after completion of preceding motion (Reach)	One in which next motion starts.
Position	Frame next after completion of preceding motion (Move)	Ensuing Release was included in frame count of original research, then the Release time was deducted to find Position time total. Ending point for position-release combination was the one in which the next motion (Reach) began.
Release	Frame next after completion of preceding motion (Move or Position)	One in which next motion (Reach) began. This was also checked by noting the frames covered by the finger motions of release.
Disengage	Frame next after completion of preceding motion (usually a Reach). Grasp time was included in frame count of original research, then the Grasp time was deducted to find the net Disengage time.	One in which the recoil or reflex action ended.
Walking	No frame counts used, rather controlled condition time study.	
Body	A combination of MTM and time study was employed.	

text. It is of interest here, however, to delineate the measuring points on the films that were actually used in the original and all subsequent research. This has been done in the very important Table 1 to show exactly whence the motion categories used in MTM evolved, a useful set of facts for anyone desiring to check the data for his own satisfaction or other reasons. Reference to this table will be instructive when studying the motion chapters.

One unclarified point remains. How can an observer tell when a motion has begun or ceased when using the frame count techniques just presented? The answer to this question cannot be stated adequately in a simple manner, although the reader likely will be satisfied with an indication of the nature of this task; anyone who has done micromotion work and attempted film analysis will more fully appreciate the high degree of skill and judgment demanded by the technical aspects of identifying motion breakpoints from film frames. MTM Research Report 107 entitled "A Research Methods Manual" provides many of the technical details and, in particular, describes a projection plotting method which reveals clearly the periods of stoppage or minimum velocity between motions. The laws of motion, as well as technical principles of photography, also enter the problem. For example, the speed of the motion relative to the shutter speed of the camera and the sensitivity of the film emulsion will influence the clarity of the images; and blurs in film frames yield various types of clues, depending on the status of a number of conditional scientific factors pertinent to the operation at the point where a given frame occurs. The kind and duration of motions adjacent, as well as overlapping conditions between motions, also enter the analysis. It is, therefore, stated for the satisfaction of the reader that definite, reliable, and scientific means exist by which researchers can find the proper frame at which a motion begins and ends. Such means were carefully utilized in both the initial development and subsequent additions to the MTM data.

How the motions, and their related times, were isolated should now be clear to the reader. Distance measurements, when needed, were found either by direct measurement, use of a calibrated background in the picture, or a special projection technique that depends on lens ratios to decrease the error of distance estimation. These are accepted research means for distance determination.

CONCLUSIONS OF THE ORIGINAL RESEARCH

With the aid of a shorthand coding system for the motions, described fully in the motion chapters to follow, the research results were summarized and condensed into a handy-sized data card. The original data card may be seen in the text by Maynard, Stegemerten, and Schwab. Most of their results, however, form an integral portion of the newer data card information presented in each motion chapter in the present text. An official current data card is enclosed in the pocket at the rear of this text.

Their conclusions also included specific rules for measurement, usage, and appropriate cautions vital to application of the data on the card. Such rules arose because the originators fully recognized that the application of the data would necessarily occur without the wealth of background experience they had gained and habituated from their research work. In other words, they took pains to build practicality into their system so that the benefits of research would not be lost due to poor presentation and indecision during usage.

Verification of the Data

A variety of statistical, mathematical, and graphical techniques were applied to the data and plots to assure that no gross error had occurred during the analysis of films or the subsequent efforts described. It is a tribute to the pains and care taken by Maynard, Stegemerten, and Schwab that research later conducted by many other people only in rare instances revealed differences greater than one film frame at the film speed of the original research. Such accuracy was due to consistent, professional application of scientific research principles, not to fortuitous chance.

Test usage of the data was next made on actual production problems in real industrial situations by Methods Engineering Council personnel for several years. The phenomenal success of the data (reported in many magazine articles) prompted the inventors to write their text and to will to the public domain the basic discoveries they had made. No other predetermined time system has such a record of its data sources, procedures used, or public information on verification of the data contained in the system. The professional attitude and attainment of these pioneers of MTM is now beyond question.

PROFESSIONAL ASPECTS

It is valuable to recount the professional factors that promote the superiority of the MTM system.

The data is fully reproducible. The evidence exists in relatively permanent form on film that is available for future study. No secrecy shrouds the methodology and procedures used.

The systematic manner in which the original research was conducted and recorded built a good foundation for further research. The possibility of such research was promoted by the full disclosure of all aspects of the data to the public. That such additional research of verification and extension is in active progress today has proved a real source of vitality and strength for the MTM system.

VALIDATION

The research was verified by Maynard, Stegemerten, and Schwab. Validation, however, was possible only by an independent, unbiased source. Such validation followed quickly on publication of the MTM textbook by the inventors. Cornell University conducted such an independent investigation and reported it for the Management Division of the American Society of Mechanical Engineers at the annual meeting held in New York City during November 26 to December 1, 1950. A copy of this report, paper number 50-A-88, can be obtained from the A.S.M.E.

The Cornell project was concerned with the reproducibility by independent study of the data for a system of elemental motion-time data. Methods-Time Measurement was chosen for study because its full data, with a complete discussion of element definitions, was available. To achieve greater understanding of the system, and some competence in its use, one of the persons conducting the project took a training course in MTM prior to completion of the study.

Cornell carefully stated that the information developed from the study was pertinent to only the MTM system, and that their selection of MTM for study should in no way be interpreted as invalidating any other system. It was clearly explained that other systems differ fundamentally in two respects. First, the classification of motions into which elements are subdivided differ both in content and separation points. Second, the performance level on which motion times are based differs between systems. Consequently, correct comparison of one system with another is difficult, if not impossible.

Regarding the second reason given above, traditional industrial engineering has always employed two basic concepts of average daily performance. These are the high task and low task standards. The accepted meaning of low task is the maintenance of such working pace as could be sustained throughout the day under day work payment conditions. High task, contrarily, implies that the pace of work sustained throughout the day would be that usually found under incentive payment conditions. The MTM system, for example, is based on a low task standard. The performance rating system used relies on a concept of normal pace that matches day work conditions Other predetermined time systems, however, employ varying or different normal pace concepts. This is a further reason why direct contrast and comparison of systems is technically difficult.

The method of study and analysis used by Cornell paralleled that of MTM's founders. This involved detailed analysis of motion pictures of actual industrial operations. Cornell's films were taken in a variety of industries represented by eight companies on operations ranging from small riveted assemblies to complex machine handling. Only incentive operations were included. With a minimum of disturbance at the work-place, a small electric camera was utilized at 1,000 frames per minute. Each frame of film thus represented 0.001 minutes of elapsed time. In most cases at least two analysts used the LMS rating system to level for skill, effort, and conditions.

Cornell's film analysis in terms of MTM elements are summarized below. Their recorded times were leveled to average operator performance. While only a limited amount of data was collected for each element, we quote the conclusions of the report as follows:

The data collected so far appears to point toward the practicability of defining work elements in terms of fundamental elements of motion common to a wide range of industrial activity and the establishment of standards of time for these elements which are reproducible within smaller limits than those normal to current time study practice. In summary for all elements, the check studies have consistently ranged within approximately plus or minus one percent of the MTM times. For individual elements, time differences between check times and MTM times in the order of 0.1 to 0.5 TMU's (0.00006 to 0.0003 minutes) are not uncommon and, as evidenced in the data in this paper, a few are larger. While some of these time differences do represent five percent to ten percent differences in time for specific elements and in isolated cases as much as twenty percent, they are not considered serious in application since any standard is made up of a composite of a number of elements, the majority of which are well within plus or minus five percent. No reason is now apparent why continued study should not result in reconciling the differences which do exist. In some instances further data may alter the check time as pointed out before; in some, modification in the MTM times may be desirable; and in some instances, it is entirely possible that new elements or sub-classes of existing elements may be necessary.

Of equal importance to the subject of validation, but not usually recognized, is the fact that the independent research sponsored by the MTM Association at the University of Michigan has reproduced a major portion of the original MTM data. While the specific research projects are selected by the sponsor, the university has full control of the projects and publishes the results in research reports written by its staff. This research has caused only minor additions and changes to the MTM studied by Cornell. The fundamentals and most of the system have remained unchanged.

The mere fact that many of the shortcomings of time study have been overcome in Methods-Time Measurement alone justifies the use of this or a similar system. In addition, such a system has other corollary benefits as follows:

1. The importance of method is emphasized
2. Methods and equipment can be designed on a scientific basis
3. Time standards will be consistent from job to job
4. Standards can be set in advance of production
5. The ability to set standards in advance of production makes possible

more accurate costing of products and the development of more accurate production planning

6. The time required to derive standard data is greatly reduced
7. Methods are precisely and accurately described
8. Grievance cases can be settled on a basis of fact rather than on opinions.

Once the reader begins an active study of Methods-Time Measurement in later chapters of this text, it will become quite evident that the use of the system emphasizes the importance of method. In fact the system cannot be applied without considering various methods and precisely defining the one finally to be used.

PRACTICAL ASPECTS

It has been stated that methods and equipment could be designed on a scientific basis when MTM is utilized. This means that jobs can be introduced in a manner such that many of the changes now ordinarily expected as a result of subsequent methods improvement will be avoided.

It is still common to find a new job installed on the basis of a general study, with the equipment, tools, and methods specified according to someone's opinion as to what is right. Such opinion results mainly from past experience. The net result is that subsequent methods improvement and motion study work under the name of "work simplification" often accomplish remarkable cost and/or personnel reductions which often disturb the operators and the supervision. Recognition of the need for better measurement of the method and time factors involved in alleviating such problems led directly to the development of MTM.

Through the use of MTM, effective methods can be established prior to the start of an operation. This means that training costs will be incurred only on the original method since normal method deficiencies can be eliminated and the need for retraining thereby reduced. In addition, both operators and supervision will be mentally conditioned to learn the originally specified method as quickly as possible. It certainly will help eliminate many of the human problems now encountered.

The statements concerning proper establishment of methods prior to the start of production in no way rule out the use of Methods-Time Measurement for improving existing methods. If it can be used successfully to establish proper methods prior to the start of production, it is obvious that it can be used to improve existing methods that have developed haphazardly.

The use of a single basis to establish time standards for all manual motions obviously promotes time standards that will be consistently accurate from one operation to another. It likewise means that grievance cases concerning time standards can be settled on a factual basis rather than by opinion. These two assets will do much to avoid some of the problems presently encountered with time standards established on the basis of time study alone. Not only will grievances be minimized; but, when they do occur, they can be settled on a factual basis.

To eliminate unnecessary time studies or MTM studies, repetitive operations in a given industry are normally defined and a time standard developed to cover the work described in the definition. When these operations are later encountered, the industrial engineer merely needs to find the proper definition with its time standard and copy them on his process form. Such definitions and related time standards are known as Standard Data.

Establishing standard data by means of time study necessitates many studies to properly validate the correctness of the data. In general, standard data can be derived with MTM with much less work because only one adequate study need be made. Further studies will not change the correct standard time, hence the over-all effort required to derive standard data for most situations is less with MTM than with time study. More will be said concerning such standard data in a later chapter.

SUMMARY

Methods-Time Measurement has provided industrial and management engineers with a much needed basic tool. Like any tool, it can be refined and improved through additional research and development. This is being done with MTM through a research program dating from the time of its creation.

The authors believe that many other systems probably will satisfactorily measure manual motions when properly applied. But they feel that Methods-Time Measurement is the best system today; and even if it were not, the continuing research of the MTM Association would assure its achieving such pre-eminence in the future.

Industrial engineering and management, as professions, truly are genuinely indebted to Maynard, Stegemerten, and Schwab for a forward step of incalculable value. Also, as Dr. Lillian M. Gilbreth observed in the feature address of the First Annual MTM Conference in 1952 at New York, perhaps the supreme attainment of Methods-Time Measurement is its inspired solutions to the human aspects of work measurement.

The MTM Association for Standards and Research

For quite some time after Maynard, Stegemerten, and Schwab discovered the basic principles of MTM and isolated the technical data, they continued to check and validate their results. The next logical step was to apply it under the usual competitive conditions prevailing in management consulting work. Accordingly, Methods Engineering Council engineers were trained and applied MTM in a wide variety of situations. The results were surprisingly good, as was attested by articles in leading magazines and technical trade journals. However, the demands from industry and the general industrial engineering profession for information and data on MTM brought about the full realization that a truly basic system of predetermined times could not easily be confined to arbitrary bounds of availability or restricted to the purview of only a few practitioners.

To meet this condition, the originators published their textbook in 1948. It was also considered wise, initially, to train other firms of management consultants which could be authorized to provide MTM services similar to those offered by Methods Engineering Council. Some of the outstanding firms of industrial engineers who had personnel trained for this purpose included the Serge A. Birn Company; A. T. Kearney & Company; Benjamin Borchardt & Associates; Bigelow, Kent, Willard & Company; Bruce Payne & Associates, Inc.; and George H. Elliott & Company. These firms did a fine professional job that served to further whet the appetite of their clients for Methods-Time Measurement. Again, the demand became too great to meet with existing methods of dissemination. Control problems also increased. The fact that such competitive firms cooperated so well on a common task of this kind was, however, a unique development in the work measurement field that tended to inspire public confidence in the technique and basic data of MTM.

A whole new approach was indicated to those concerned with the problem of benefiting industry with MTM while avoiding misuse of the system that would create "efficiency expert" damage to it. Something new, organizationally, was essential to the system. Accordingly, a group of seven practicing consultants met with Dr. Lillian M. Gilbreth and Prof. Harry J. Loberg of Cornell University in January of 1951 at New York City to discuss the condition and to find ways of meeting it. Out of this cooperative approach evolved the present MTM Association for Standards and Research. This body became the U.S.-Canada forerunner of the present nine Cooperating National Associations and the International MTM Directorate, which are described later.

The best description of the founding of the MTM Association was made by its first president,* Dr. Harold B. Maynard, in the keynote address of the First Annual MTM Conference at New York City in October of 1952 as follows:

Experience has shown that when an MTM practitioner gains confidence in his ability to apply the procedure, he very often develops the urge to improve upon it. When he encounters an unusual motion sequence for the first time, he is quite likely to want to invent one or more new motion classifications and assign tentative time standards to them. If he then checks with a stop watch and finds that they seem to work out all right — which they often do if they are a very small part of the total cycle time — he concludes that he has added to the development of the MTM procedure, and he uses his new motion classifications thereafter without further checking.

This is, of course, a highly unscientific way of developing the MTM procedure. Unless some kind of control is introduced, it can only result in producing as many different varieties of MTM as there are practicing engineers. Furthermore in most cases, the addition of new motion classifications is completely unnecessary. Experience has already shown that the solution to most application problems lies in learning how to apply existing motion classifications and standards properly, rather than in inventing something new.

The matter of control is not difficult to handle, however, once the need for it is recognized. In our own organization in the early days of MTM, we discovered quite unexpectedly one day during a discussion of the application problems which our staff had encountered, that each man had added new motion classifications (all different) or had developed new interpretations of existing motion classifications (also all different) until we were well on our way to having a completely unstandardized procedure.

Obviously this would never do. We, therefore, developed carefully written descriptions of standard motion-classification interpretations and application practices, and we insisted that they be followed to the letter. We admitted that every word in these descriptions might not be correct at first, and we encouraged our engineers to challenge anything which they believed to be wrong. But each point challenged was checked by further research. If it was found to

---

*Subsequent presidents for successive two-year terms have been: Seth L. Winslow, John A. Willard, Benjamin Borchardt, Prof. Delmar W. Karger, Clive H. VanHorne, Thomas R. Gockel, and T. Blair Evans.

be wrong it was changed, but not until then was the engineer allowed to deviate from the former standard practice. When a new standard practice was approved, all engineers were immediately required to adopt it.

Under this kind of self-imposed discipline, we quickly corrected any initial errors in our application practices and achieved consistency among our own staff. But while this solved our own problem, it did not solve the problems which were rapidly being generated by a growing number of practitioners who were not under our control. We wanted the procedure to be used, for we had a belief in the important contribution which it could make to industry, but we did not want it abused. Too many variations could cause inconsistencies, arguments, weakened faith in the procedure, and all manner of unpleasant consequences. What to do?

The problem was discussed in January of 1951 by a small group of management consultants who were either using MTM professionally at that time or were planning to use it. They recognized the need of bringing both the development and the application of the MTM procedure under control and considered various means of accomplishing this. The result of these discussions was the formation of the MTM Association for Standards and Research whose first Annual Conference we are attending today.

The aims and purposes of the MTM Association stated in its By-Laws are as follows:

To widen acceptance for the proper use of MTM.

To conduct basic and applied research in the field of methods-time measurement. To encourage and stimulate members and other organizations—both commercial and academic—and individuals to conduct similar research and to coordinate the work done by them.

To establish standards and by all possible means to sustain the high quality of work done by all organizations and individuals in their use of MTM.

To compile all available information pertaining to the development and application of methods-time measurement and to provide members with this information at frequent intervals.

A concise summary of each By-Law affords a cohesive structure for the remainder of this chapter—they become, respectively, the following section headings: (1) to widen acceptance, (2) to conduct research, (3) to establish standards, and (4) to provide information. These goals clearly express the dynamic intentions of the MTM Association which have been fulfilled successfully, as attested by the remainder of this chapter.

TO WIDEN ACCEPTANCE

The MTM Association achieves the goals of wider acceptance and proper usage of MTM through the organization of its membership and the efforts they unselfishly donate toward attaining these goals. The total membership is an impressive list of important individuals, industrial organizations, consulting firms, and governmental agencies who find that the many services provided by the association adequately serve their common interest in MTM.

There are a number of membership types, as follows:

A. *Honorary Members*—This highest form of membership recognizes persons who have made outstanding contributions to MTM and work measurement. Presently so honored are Dr. Lillian M. Gilbreth and Dr. Harold B. Maynard, both active in association affairs and universally accorded pre-eminence.

B. *Individual Members*—These are of two classes, as follows:

1. *Academic Members*—Such members comprise persons on the academic staffs of colleges and universities having a working knowledge of MTM and an interest in its welfare. Normally they participate in association activities to bring the educational influence to bear on questions of training and high professional standards. Usually they are privileged to attend training courses of management counsel members without payment of any fee. Most importantly, they influence future industrial engineers favorably toward MTM and its sound usage.

2. *Subscribing Members*—Individuals within companies and firms who belong to the association may for a nominal cost obtain all the data, literature, and information pertaining to MTM. Their subscription supports the association program and assures a wider audience of the benefits of MTM.

C. *Organizational Members*—These belong to either of the following classes:

1. *Industrial or Institutional*—All of the dues of this class of membership are used to sustain the research activity of the association. The class includes both industrial and service firms, along with various agencies and departments of governmental bodies. Because these groups most directly represent the application interests of the total membership, their participation is highly valued in promoting the usage and integrity of the MTM techniques.

2. *Management Counsel*—The majority of fees from this membership class supports the actual costs of the administrative and operating activities of the association. The class includes consultants engaged in training engineers in MTM and installing the MTM system in industrial and other firms. The interests of this class of membership extend into all phases and areas of the association, with particular emphasis on the maintenance of qualified application and training in the MTM system.

D. *Chapter Members*—Chapters are groups of people within a geographical area or region who have affiliated to learn more about

MTM, exchange experiences with its application, and further acceptance of the MTM techniques. Such membership affords a means of contact between these individuals and the association, particularly when other forms of membership are not available to them. They hold their own meetings and discussions for mutual benefit at the local level.

E. *Cooperating National Associations*—Providing a reciprocal representation between the U.S.-Canada association and similar national associations in many other countries of the world, this form of affiliation unites the international efforts in the field and assures equal status between the associations in terms of qualifications and practices. It also provides a mechanism through which foreign groups can achieve growth into national associations with full rights of sovereignty and authority over their own affairs.

The faith of the MTM Association founders in the growth of MTM is attested by the existence of 9 cooperating national associations and a current membership in the U.S.-Canada association of approximately 120 major industrial concerns and 18 governmental agencies, 17 management counsel firms, four continental chapters, two honorary members, 14 academic members, and 62 subscribing members. Figure 1 shows the geographical distribution of the 153 organizational and 78 individual members within the continental bounds of the United States of America and the Dominion of Canada. The worldwide distribution of the remaining membership is depicted in Figure 2, according to the following identity and location key:

Map Code	*Organization Identity*	*Geographical Location*
1	MTM Association for Standards and Research	Ann Arbor, Michigan, U.S.A.
1A	Industrial	Medellin, Colombia, S.A.
1B	Industrial	Santa Fe, Argentina, S. A.
1C	Industrial	Buenos Aires, Argentina, S.A.
1D	Industrial	Buenos Aires, Argentina, S.A.
1E	Industrial	Transvaal, South Africa
1F	Consultant	Melbourne, Australia
1G	Consultant	Melbourne, Australia
2	United Kingdom MTM Association	Manchester, England
3	l'Association MTM Française	Paris, France
4	Deutsche MTM-Vereinigung	Wuppertal-Barmen, West Germany
5	Nederlands MTM Genootschap	Den Haag, Holland
6	Nippon MTM Association	Tokyo, Japan
7	MTM-Selskapet A/L	Oslo, Norway
8	Svenska MTM-Föreningen	Stockholm, Sweden
9	MTM Association of Switzerland	Zurich, Switzerland

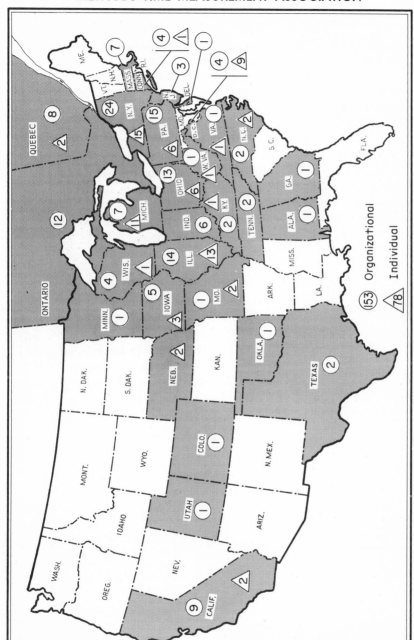

Fig. 1. Membership distribution (Jan. 1964) of MTM Association for Standards and Research in United States of America and Dominion of Canada—Organizational and Individual.

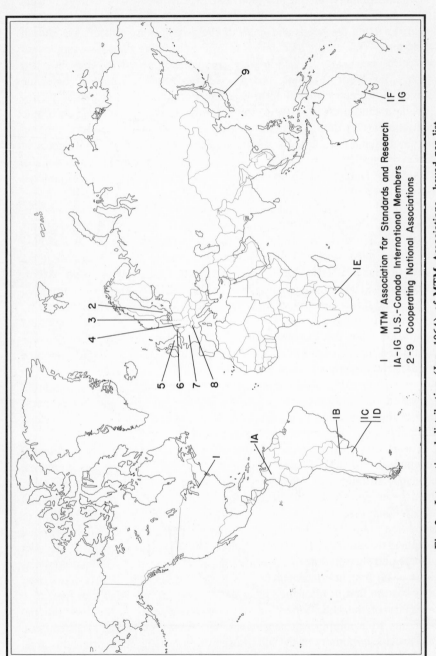

Fig. 2. International distribution (Jan. 1964) of MTM Associations—keyed per list in text.

I   MTM Association for Standards and Research
IA–IG U.S.–Canada International Members
2–9   Cooperating National Associations

Organizationally, all the national associations consist of unpaid officers and committee members who generously donate their time and expenses toward meeting the needs and goals of the association. Officers are chosen by majority vote of the association membership. The only paid employees are those necessary to handle the volume of paperwork and business matters involved. For the U.S.-Canada association, these include the Executive Secretary, a Staff Industrial Engineer, and the office staff. They provide a central clearing house for administration; produce and distribute such supplies as data cards, training and data manuals, research reports, etc.; and facilitate essential communication among the various members of the association. The annual budget of this association approximates $100,000. This is met by dues and nominal charges for services rendered to members and the general public.

Originally, the offices and research activity of the U.S.-Canada association were located in Pittsburgh, Pennsylvania. There, several assistants aided the Executive Secretary in research work in addition to handling other required services. The offices were moved to Ann Arbor, Michigan (now at Suite 101-B Huron Towers, 2200 Fuller Road, Ann Arbor, Michigan 48104) during September of 1953. This move also involved shifting the direct research activity from the association to the Engineering Research Institute at the University of Michigan, utilizing a project supervisor from the Department of Industrial Engineering. Later it was contracted through the Office of Research Administration, under complete administrative authority of the Department of Industrial Engineering. The university provides highly competent, objective, and unbiased research. However, the study projects proceed under the guidance and full cooperation of the association in matters of priority, changes to the MTM system, and public dissemination of the research results.

The international aspects of MTM further illustrate its ever widening acceptance. Its utility soon caused it to spread into foreign countries, primarily through the activities of the management counsel members of the association. As a result of MTM usage abroad, eight additional national associations (see Fig. 2) have developed and others are in process of formation. At Paris, France in 1957 the national associations banded together to establish the International MTM Directorate, with its own officers and the mission of coordinating the Cooperating National Associations. The first international president was Dr. Harold B. Maynard, who also was the first head of the U.S.-Canada association. Also, the Executive Secretary of the U.S.-Canada association was elected as the International Secretary to accomplish the business of the International MTM Directorate and provide continuity of the MTM organizations from their original source.

Another indicator of the recognition of MTM resulting from the high professional standards maintained by the national associations is the membership of the U.S.-Canada association in CIPM. Financed largely by a federal government agency, the Council for International Progress in Management (CIPM) is the U.S.A. representative in the Comité International de l'Organisation Scientifique (CIOS)—the world's foremost management organization of 39 countries which has headquarters in Geneva, Switzerland. The rosters of CIOS and CIPM include many of the most eminent scientific and engineering societies of the world.

All of the MTM national associations and the international directorate function through numerous committees cooperating with their executive offices to provide the many membership services and achieve MTM goals. All committee members donate their time and expenses to further the cause of work measurement standards and research on a high professional basis. Unknown thousands of man-hours and dollars have been expended in this unselfish way by interested individuals and firms toward the advancement of MTM and the various associations. Typical of these committees are the standing committees of the MTM Association for Standards and Research, as follows:

1. *MEMBERSHIP.* This committee promotes the growth of the association by recruiting qualified new members. It also performs the contact functions between prospects and other committees concerned with new applicants. One of its subcommittees is the Chapter Membership Committee, which concerns itself with matters peculiar to chapter membership and activity. Another is the Academic Relations Committee, whose province is affairs pertaining to the academic membership and liaison with academic organizations.

2. *INTERNATIONAL SERVICE.* Special problems connected with the spread of MTM in and to foreign lands comprise the work of this group. Their success is attested by outstanding progress previously cited in the interest and use of MTM by our neighbors abroad. A major contribution of this committee was the establishment in 1957 of the International MTM Directorate to coordinate international MTM activities.

3. *CONFERENCE.* This committee annually conducts under MTM Association sponsorship a national MTM Conference at which outstanding speakers deal with MTM research, development, application, and relationships with other professions and sciences. Attendance at these conventions provides a favorable climate for the interchange of experiences and information on MTM problems by interested parties from virtually the entire U.S.-Canada region and many foreign countries. The entire proceedings of many past conferences are available to the public at nominal cost. A wealth of history, data, and valuable information is thus made available to benefit anyone inquiring into the many facets of the MTM system. On the international level, the directorate has held three International MTM Conferences of similar nature at Paris, the Hague, and New York City.

4. *PUBLIC RELATIONS.* The important function of maintaining a proper public image for the MTM system and the MTM Association is entrusted to this committee. It encourages dignified publicity in the mass media, provides acceptable publicity standards, examines publicity for conformance to these standards, and explores new avenues for presenting the MTM story to the general public. It also is directly responsible for the issuance and control of publications of the association in harmony with the best interests of MTM, work measurement generally, and the membership of the association.

5. *RESEARCH.* This committee establishes basic MTM research projects and recommends their priority to the Board of Directors for official decision, reviews and publishes all of the findings, and provides guidance to the projects in all their phases. Besides direct involvement in the sponsored research at the University of Michigan, it secures and coordinates research in MTM on a cooperative basis with industrial firms and membership groups. The direct research expenditures have been substantial, as graphically portrayed in Figure 3. This display does not account for

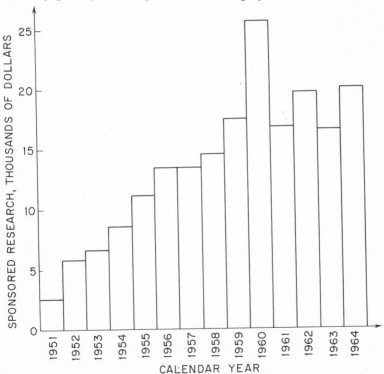

Fig. 3.   Direct expenditures for basic MTM Research by MTM Association for Standards and Research—1951 to 1964.

the expenses of the research committee members or any allocation of charges for work performed by the Executive Secretary or the association staff. All officers and committee members of the association donate their time and pay their own expenses in this professional effort. The research budget responds to the growing demand engendered by the excellent results from completed projects. Many projects on validation, extension, and origination of MTM data are being considered to assure the dynamic development of MTM into a universally accepted predetermined time system which will reduce controversy and promote professional practices in work measurement.

6. *APPLIED RESEARCH*. This relatively new committee deals with the problem of research into the application of MTM, in order to promote the development of more productive ways in which to utilize the MTM system. As a supporting activity to the basic research program of the Association, it is responsible for developing new application tools and procedures based on the MTM data resulting from basic research. A distinct advancement in this area has resulted from the work of the Applied Research Implementation Subcommittee, which has developed the highly useful form of standard data called General Purpose Data (MTM-GPD). Further work is being done on Special Purpose Data and the computerizing of both forms of standard data for membership usage. Another aim of this committee is to promote cooperative research by other organizations within the scope of association interest.

7. *TRAINING*. This very important committee comprises qualified MTM instructors licensed by the association. It recommends the content and methods to be employed in training courses, reviews instructional materials submitted by members desiring course approval, assures conformance of training courses by periodic review and by testing of the attendees on request, writes and revises training course examinations, and establishes norms for grading and evaluating the examinations. Also, a uniform Application Training Course Manual and practice film loops have been developed as training aids for the membership. It is largely through the activities of this committee that organizational members can be assured that their training and staff meet the high minimum standards of the association.

8. *QUALIFICATIONS*. The activities of this committee are related to those of the Training Committee. This group operates in every possible way to assure that Licensed MTM Instructors are professionally qualified to practice and teach MTM. They prepare the written and oral examinations used to qualify instructors and personally conduct the examinations. Also, they develop instructor training courses for the association.

9. *PRACTICES*. The MTM Association has instituted and upholds a Code of Ethical Practice which incorporates the Code of Ethics of the Asso-

ciation of Consulting Management Engineers and ethical standards maintained by other responsible engineering groups. This committee is charged with maintaining the moral and ethical standards of the membership. No better evidence of the professional attitude of the MTM Association can be offered than the existence of this committee.

10. *NOMINATING.* The Nominating Committee selects qualified candidates for MTM Association offices, to be elected by majority vote of the membership, who will further the best interests and goals of the association.

11. *ADMINISTRATION AND POLICY PLANNING.* The task of this committee is to guide the administration of association activities and business affairs. It determines and establishes operating policies which will achieve the stated goals of the association while safeguarding the interests of all its members. Evaluating the effectiveness of association efforts and practices is included in the scope of its duties.

The preceding description of the membership and the way it is organized to attain the association goals leads directly to consideration of the research and standards activities involved in these goals.

TO CONDUCT RESEARCH

The aim of conducting basic and applied MTM research is so crucial to the MTM Association that it was made a part of the corporate name. This aim is extended beyond the immediate membership by a continuing effort to act as a clearing house and coordinating agency for all research pertinent to its field of interest.

A. *Basic Research*—As mentioned earlier, the basic MTM research is now being done in the Department of Industrial Engineering at the University of Michigan. The role of the Research Committee of the MTM Association also has been noted. This research represents fundamental progress in the work measurement area of industrial engineering, and its success has been achieved to a large extent by utilizing the many resources available to the academic staff of the university.

All of the basic research projects are divided into two phases—the laboratory phase and the industrial phase. When a project is originated, the first step is to complete, and often to write a report concerning, a library study of all pertinent literature and information concerning the topic of the research. After this study, experimental investigations are conducted in the laboratory to determine the basic concepts and principles involved, relationships between the various elements and factors, the broad physical and time parameters of the problem, the statistical validity of the experimental data, etc. Normally a report is issued at the conclusion of the laboratory study. The time data developed in this phase is not used to modify or supplement existing MTM data.

When the laboratory study is done, the research team then moves into a representative group of industrial plants and studies actual production operations as performed by regular production workers under existing conditions. The resulting time data is leveled where appropriate and statistically analyzed to develop valid basic MTM data, which is the only kind used to modify or supplement existing data in the MTM system. At the end of the industrial study, a formal research report is written which ordinarily covers both the laboratory study and the industrial study. The results and any new data are then tested in many actual applications by the membership before being considered for inclusion in the basic MTM data.

Evidence of the fruitfulness of this approach is the following list of formal research reports available from the Executive Secretary of the MTM Association:*

R.R. 101 "Preliminary Research Report on Disengage" by Erik Biel-Nielsen and Andrews M. Lang, Pittsburgh, Pennsylvania, February 1951.
Tentative results of a preliminary study of this motion are presented and discussed analytically.

R.R. 102 "A Research Report on Standards for Reading Operations" by Andrews M. Lang, Pittsburgh, Pennsylvania, July 1951.
A summary of the work by other authorities studying reading speed is the basis for an MTM approach to reading times. Other eye motions are also discussed to some extent.

R.R. 104 "An MTM Analysis of Performance Rating Systems" by Andrews M. Lang, Pittsburgh, Pennsylvania, April 1952.
Various rating systems are analyzed and evaluated from an MTM standpoint.

R.R. 105 "A Study of Simultaneous Motions" by David L. Raphael and Grant C. Clapper, Pittsburgh, Pennsylvania, September 1952.
An extensive mass of data on this topic resulted from a major research endeavor that revealed many answers previously unavailable to work analysts. It is perhaps the best practical treatise extant on this subject today.

R. R. 106 "An Analysis of Short Reaches and Moves" by David L. Raphael, Ann Arbor, Michigan, September 1953.
Specific attention to short distances in these elements was devoted toward data revision and validation based on very high-speed film work that yielded significant results and information not earlier known concerning Reach and Move.

R.R. 107 "A Research Methods Manual" by David L. Raphael, Ann Arbor, Michigan, April 1954.
Effective and comprehensive means of conducting research projects

* In the remainder of this textbook, reference to these reports will be given in the following manner: "R.R. 105 (see Ch. 5)." In this way, repetition of long titles and source credits will be minimized to this location.

in time and motion study as used by the MTM research activity are fully revealed to aid others in research and inform the public on the MTM method of obtaining data.

R.R. 108 "A Study of Arm Movements Involving Weight" by David L. Raphael, Ann Arbor, Michigan, March 1955.

Another field of time and motion study lacking validated study was exhaustively researched and resulted in practical MTM data of fundamental importance to all work analysts. Many related variables also were evaluated.

R.R. 109 "A Study of Positioning Movements: I. The General Characteristics; II. Special Studies Supplement" by David L. Raphael, Ann Arbor, Michigan, 1957.

The laboratory phase of an extensive investigation of the components and total behavior of these motions is included in this report. Besides definitively isolating their true nature, the study covered several other aspects of positioning movements from an analytical viewpoint.

RR. 110 "A Study of Positioning Movements: III. Application to Industrial Work Measurement" by David L. Raphael, Ann Arbor, Michigan, November 1957.

The relation of the laboratory study of these elements to the industrial environment was explored in this report. Improved analysis techniques and time values resulted from statistically validated industrial data.

R.R. 111 "Industrial Research on the MTM Element Apply Pressure" by James A. Foulke and Walton M. Hancock, Ann Arbor, Michigan, December 1960.

Based on exhaustive laboratory research (not published as a formal research report) which firmly established the constituents of this element, the industrial phase is here reported. It contains the numerical data and application procedures for Apply Pressure elements.

R.R. 112 "Learning Curve Research on Short-Cycle Operations: Phase I. Laboratory Experiments" by Walton M. Hancock and James A. Foulke, Ann Arbor, Michigan, 1963.

Dealing with one of the most fundamental aspects of human work measurement, this study on learning curves is the first of a series aimed at developing better tools for predicting operator performance.

The original and much of the subsequent MTM research was based on the careful analysis of motion picture film at various camera speeds. This means of study proved cumbersome and slow as the research requirements became more sophisticated. Therefore, a major portion of the research activity during 1960 and 1961 (note increase of costs in Figure 3) was devoted to developing an Electronic Data Collector (EDC). This device permits the handling of large volumes of data, a characteristic result of work measurement research. Also, the portable feature of EDC permits its use both in the laboratory and in the factory. Transducers in the work area are used as sensing devices to activate electronic counters. The EDC registers time and automatically records it on paper tape in units of 100 millionths of an hour. The punched paper tape is converted into punched cards for machine analysis and storage. The data are analyzed by computers at the University of Michigan, which print out the results in various forms including graphical displays. Motion picture cameras, instead of being the primary means of data recording, now are used to supplement the EDC data and to provide a visual record of the experiments. To give the reader some concept of the vast amounts of data collected in a research project, it is helpful to mention that over 100 million bits of information was recorded in only one portion of the laboratory phase of a recent research project.

While the story of basic MTM research up to this point has been impressive, it is probable that future progress will be accelerated as the US.-Canada effort continues while the other Cooperating National Associations begin to publish the results of their researches and also make substantial contributions to the over-all fund of knowledge. Besides becoming even more sophisticated in utilizing advanced technology, future research also will be characterized by a greater reliance on the social and behavioral sciences. The authors firmly believe that the MTM system will essentially supplant all proprietary predetermined time systems as a result of this openly revealed research activity.

B. *Applied Research*—The nature of applied research in the usage of MTM data has been indicated in the description of the Applied Research Committee of the MTM Association. This has become a major effort of the association, with a full-time Staff Industrial Engineer now accomplishing much of the work with the committee. The recently developed General Purpose Data (MTM-GPD) and the accompanying manuals, data control procedures, and application approaches have enjoyed a tremendous reception by industrial users. It enables profitable improvement of operations with minimization of engineering effort, while always retaining a directly traceable relationship to the basic MTM foundation.

To date, two volumes of the "MTM-GPD General Purpose Data Manual" have been released: Vol. I-Basic Level Data and Vol. II-Multipurpose Level Data. Current development concerns Special Purpose Data and computer programs for automatic processing of both of these types of standard data.

C. *Cooperative Research*—Another aspect of MTM research is the work conducted by industrial organizations cooperating with the association and the sharing of research experiences with academic personnel at other institutions of higher learning. In every case, this research either fulfills a direct need of association programs or provides feedback data which serves to guide, corroborate, or indicate new avenues for the MTM system.

One direct instance of cooperative research is that carried out under auspices of the Research Committee in the industrial study phase of the basic MTM research program. Another is the validation phase of basic research following the issuance of the formal report. A third, under authority of the Applied Research Committee, occurs during the development of applied standard data such as that exemplified by MTM-GPD.

The cooperative research with academic personnel is essentially indirect in nature. One way in which it is accomplished is by participation of persons from institutions other than the University of Michigan on MTM Association committees, where the sharing of knowledge and techniques becomes integral with the research projects. Another path utilizes professional inquiries or consultation during which research results are interchanged. Sometimes this is by direct personal contacts, or it can occur during MTM Conferences or as a result of someone responding to publications of the association.

Cooperative research of this nature helps to keep the MTM system sound from both a theoretical and a practical viewpoint. It completes the feedback loop needed in the information system essential to a well-rounded research.

D. *International Research*—The fourth form of research included in the MTM system is that conducted by foreign associations. The International MTM Directorate is charged with coordinating the efforts of the Cooperating National Associations in the area of research and the assimilation of all appropriate research into the MTM data. At least one of the foreign associations has a research program comparable to the U.S.-Canada effort in amount of expenditure. National associations publish the results of this research in a manner similar to the U.S.-Canada association, especially where the research is to be considered on the international level and where the basic MTM system may be affected. For example, the Swedish association has completed two projects which have been published in the *Journal of Methods-Time Measurement* as follows:

R.C.R. No. 1 "Frequency of Occurrence of Basic MTM Motions" by Ulf Åberg, Svenska MTM-Föreningen, Stockholm, Sweden, August 1962.
> This investigation explored the frequency distribution of basic elements in actual industrial environments on production jobs differing greatly as to type and difficulty. It provides a quantitative measure of the importance of each motion for training and application purposes. Also, the results can guide future research.

This report was published in Vol. VIII, No. 5 of the MTM Journal for July-August 1963.

R.C.R. No. 2 "Sequence of Motions in Manual Workshop Production" by Ulf Åberg, Svenska MTM-Föreningen, Stockholm, Sweden, July 1963.
> Of direct value in applied research as well as in training, this treatise determined a typical distribution of motion sequences in a large

sample of industrial context. The results influence the building block concept which is a part of MTM-GPD and help in the construction of statistical models of the motion-sequence population.
This report was published in Vol. IX, No. 2 of the MTM Journal for November–December 1963.

Many other international researches as yet unpublished indicate that the rate of increase of MTM knowledge will be large in the foreseeable future.

TO ESTABLISH STANDARDS

Another major facet of the MTM Association program is emphasized in its official name—the establishing of standards both for MTM motions and for their qualified application. The motion and time standards themselves are the heart of the MTM system. However, it is essential to their success that the training and qualification of the persons using them also is gaged by accepted standards. Otherwise, confidence in the system and assurance that it has been properly used will be lacking and impair MTM application.

Before discussing the standards themselves, it is well to consider several statements which help to clarify the subject. The motion standards appear as official MTM Association publications, all of which are subject to various forms of control that assure the accuracy and validity of the standards. In terms of the using personnel, the MTM Association recognizes by its procedures two general groups—Certified MTM Applicators and Licensed MTM Instructors. Each group must be trained and qualified by somewhat differing procedures to achieve this recognition.

A. *Motion Standards*—At this point, it is premature to discuss the motion data itself; but explanation of two fundamental kinds of data is in order.

To work analysts facing the task of defining and quantifying production operations, a dual need is at once apparent. They must be able to subdivide the work into entities as small as is demanded to differentiate between the variables affecting the work. Conversely, they must be able to reassemble the work components into data blocks of such size as will retain the ability to discriminate, yet large enough to make the data application economical. Otherwise, the cost of their own effort will nullify the gains obtained from the analysis.

The first kind of motion data is called *micro* (for microscopic) data. It is exemplified by the basic or detailed MTM data. The standards for this data are the province of the Research Committee and are determined by the basic research program previously described.

The second kind of motion data is called *macro* (for macroscopic) data.

The MTM-GPD data is this kind. The Applied Research Committee of the MTM Association establishes these standards as a result of the applied research activity noted in an earlier section.

For *both* kinds of motion data, the MTM Association has definite procedures and requirements by which the accepted standards are safeguarded.

B. *Training Standards*—If the users of MTM are not properly trained, they will cause far more trouble than poorly trained time study men. Such men can ruin the future of all pre-determined time system usage in a plant, including the use of standard data. It is very unwise for individuals, departments, or companies to let their reputation be ruined by improper training or an unsound standards installation. Each plant possesses its own peculiarities; what is of major importance in one may be of only minor importance in another. Each installation, therefore, will in most cases vary both in details and in major aspects. Establishing an MTM program involves far more than merely reading this text and then starting to use the techniques and procedures.

The amount of time and effort involved in properly learning the MTM procedure depends on the education, background experience, and intelligence of the individual. The training course requirements, therefore, directly reflect the problems of the individuals taking the course. The principal factors involved in learning MTM are:

1. An understanding of the factors affecting worker output,
2. Technical information and details pertaining to the work study technique,
3. Application data and knowledge which will aid wise use of the technique,
4. Information which will broaden understanding of the technique and its use,
5. Proper appreciation of the human relations factors involved in MTM usage.

Naturally, the extent to which each of these considerations will be elaborated and detailed in any given course will vary according to the type of audience being trained. In general, there will be two types of personnel involved in MTM training courses.

The first type can advantageously be given at least an abbreviated MTM training. They are organization personnel who need enough knowledge to cooperate with and to provide information needed by the MTM analysts. One group of such people comprises those who render decisions or give technical advice to the work analyst. This includes top management, engineering, accounting, and similar staff personnel. Another category of such trainees are those who implement study results or who supervise the rates that are based on study results. This includes such personnel as department heads, foremen, supervisors, group leaders, and perhaps leading operators. In fact, in some cases a company may find it desirable to give a certain amount of information to even the operators themselves.

All of these people are generally given what is known as an MTM Appreciation Course. It is up to the instructor and his company to devise standards for such courses, or to arrange such training with qualified consulting firms; the MTM Association does not provide standards for such courses, although members of the association can be of great assistance in relating their experience with similar courses.

A good MTM Appreciation Course will provide general knowledge of the basic science and present simplified versions of the MTM technique. It will be of distinct value to students and to the company. It will pave the way on the production floor for acceptance of the MTM technique. The resulting confidence in MTM results will be necessary to reap maximum benefit from the program. The cooperation of the trainees and company officials with MTM analysts working on production problems will be enhanced by the ability to intelligently discuss questions on standards and methods together. Supervisors thus trained can also make rough comparisons of several manual methods being considered as alternatives.

Probably the best result of such a course will be the increased methods-consciousness of the supervisory staff with attendant work simplification and cost reduction accomplishments by those most able to achieve them. The course will obviously be a short one confined mainly to simplified versions of MTM data, and will thus be similar to methods and work simplification courses already common in all industry today. The degree of competence and general knowledge already existing among the supervisory staff will determine the need and urgency for such a course.

The second type of person given MTM training is anyone who will directly apply the MTM technique to determine labor standards or for other management purposes. These individuals will generally be industrial engineers, methods men, standards men, or other similar technical personnel. This type of trainee will require as much detailed information as it is possible to give in the time available for training. They should, therefore, be given what is generally known as the MTM Application Training Course. Such a course should be taught in a manner closely resembling a college level course in applied engineering, and formal proof of competence by testing or other means should be required of the enrollees. At the end of such a course, recognition through the issuance of a company diploma aids morale. MTM Association approval can also be secured if the course, instructor, and student meet its standards. According to the MTM Association, the minimum content of an MTM Application Training Course must include the following:

1. Introductory background to MTM emphasizing previous techniques, their limitations and the evolution of MTM

2. Outline of MTM concept of average performance and its close relation to universal concepts of normal

3. All basic elements of MTM should be defined and discussed in detail including special applications, such as eye times, cranking motions, and printing and writing times. This should include training in the use of standard symbols and conventions

4. Simultaneous, combined and limiting motions

5. MTM application techniques including the recording of data:
   a. By observation
   b. By visualization

6. The use of MTM in analyzing, comparing and improving methods

7. The use of MTM in analyzing and improving the effectiveness of machines and equipment

8. The use of MTM in cost estimating

9. The use of simplified versions of MTM data

10. The use of MTM as an aid in operator and supervisory training

11. The use of MTM in developing standard data and time formulas

12. The use of MTM in product design

13. Using MTM to develop a methods conscious organization

14. Periodic review of the work of each session.

The MTM Association also has this to say about the length of course, etc.:

Proper coverage of the foregoing subjects will require a minimum of one hundred and five class hours excluding text reading time by the trainee but including time for class problems and application sessions. It is recommended that this be spread over a period of three weeks. Where it is condensed into less than three weeks it is recommended that close attention be given to the caliber of men being trained.

The training course used to certify an employee of an Organizational Member (if they wish to become Licensed MTM Instructors at a later date) should include a minimum of two weeks of guided application training or the equivalent by a Licensed MTM Instructor of an Organizational Member.

To meet these training standards obviously requires a qualified instructor. The adequacy of course content and instruction can be virtually assured if the course is approved by the MTM Association. In addition to approving course content, the association provides training materials, licenses MTM instructors, and certifies MTM applicators. There are two general methods of obtaining this approval. The first is to engage a Management Counsel Member of the association to effect the training and installation. The second is to qualify an instructor and obtain course approval with the MTM Association for the company, which must for this purpose become an Organizational Member of the association itself. These two methods are next considered.

The services of a qualified consultant will provide training of the highest caliber and will automatically permit approval of the MTM program. He will not only administer the approved examination to trainees, but will generally provide better guided application practice for them than a new company instructor is initially capable of doing. Since this guided practice will be done on the company problems, concurrent benefits such as methods improvements will accrue from the consultant's broader knowledge and experience. Oftentimes, he can save training time and expense by simultaneously conducting the MTM Application Training Course and the MTM Appreciation Courses for the company. This, in turn, may speed the usage phase of the MTM installation.

If the self-installation method is to be used, a word of caution is in order. The one feature of either the MTM Application Training Course or the MTM Appreciation Course common to both is the need to tailor or adapt them to the company and the group being trained. The steps in self-installation may be found in Figure 4. If these steps are conscientiously

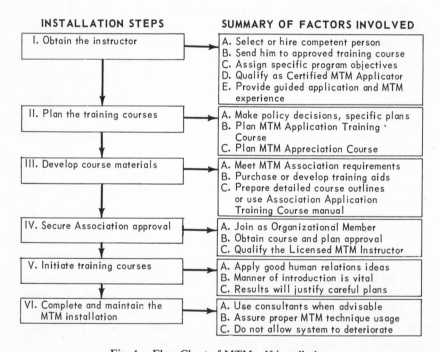

Fig. 4.   Flow Chart of MTM self-installation.

followed, the resulting conformance to MTM training standards will prove a boon to the progress from the MTM program.

Before leaving the subject of MTM training, mention must be made of training courses and materials provided by the MTM Association. First is the instructor training course under the auspices of the Qualifications

Committee, which is given periodically in response to demand for it. This course prepares trainees to meet Licensed MTM Instructor criteria upon passing their examination. A second effort is providing materials for refresher courses. These may cover either the applicator or instructor level. They normally are given by association members in the same location and on the day preceding the annual MTM Conference. Attendance is by advance registration. Finally, for users of the MTM-GPD manuals, periodic users' seminars are conducted by the association. In all of these training courses, there is no question of meeting the training standards because of the instructing personnel and the sponsorship.

C. *Qualification Standards*—All of the preceding material on MTM training has a bearing on the qualification standards of the MTM Association. Each of the qualification categories can be related to training and membership.

The standards for Certified MTM Applicator which result in the issuance of an identification card are determined by the Training Committee. To get an applicator card, the trainee must have been given an approved MTM Application Training Course by a Licensed MTM Instructor and pass a comprehensive written examination which is graded by the association staff. Note that an approved course and instructor requires that either a Management Counsel Member of the association must have given the training, or the company must have become an Organizational Member of the association and qualified one of their staff as a Licensed MTM Instructor. Refresher courses are periodically required to maintain current status of the applicator card for the individual.

The standards for Licensed MTM Instructor include those for Certified MTM Applicator and additional stiff requirements determined by the Qualifications Committee of the MTM Association. They include submission and analysis of a specified type and number of MTM studies taken by the applicant as evidence of proficiency, and an all-day examination by a special committee which gives a more difficult written test and an oral test. Successful completion of these requirements leads to a special diploma, which must be maintained by periodic refresher courses. This assures all concerned that he is well qualified to present MTM courses, and to perform his vital function in implementing an MTM program. It also is the final stamp of approval by the MTM Association of the company MTM program and plans.

Standards for the release of an MTM-GPD manual to a company or other organization are set by the Board of Directors of the MTM Association. The organization must be a member of the association and its staff must include at least one Certified MTM Applicator and one Licensed MTM Instructor, or there must be definite arrangements for the aid of a qualified instructor from outside of the company.

TO PROVIDE INFORMATION

Publications and other informative materials and training aids all help attain the stated goal of the MTM Association to provide its membership with complete information regarding all phases of MTM data and practice. Also, MTM conferences, seminars, and chapter meetings are other sources of knowledge for persons interested in the MTM system.

As noted earlier, the association training and data manuals are available to the membership under special lease conditions connected with training and qualification requirements. All other published materials are sent to the membership as part of their dues privileges. Training aids and supplies are available at nominal prices as well. In addition, except for the manuals, much of the published materials are available to the general public for very reasonable costs. Included in the items available are:

1. *MTM Data Cards*—The working technical data and MTM time values all are published on heavy stock to be a working tool in application practice. Cards are available for Detailed (Basic) MTM Data, Condensed MTM Data, and General Purpose Data (MTM-GPD). Quantity discounts encourage obtaining cards for each person who has occasion to write motion patterns or MTM analyses.

2. *MTM Data Analysis Sheets*—Printed form pads for both basic and MTM-GPD analysis can be obtained. Space is provided to record the job conditions and the motion pattern. Summary forms for totaling elements and conversion calculations also can be purchased.

3. *MTM Research Reports*—These monographs are the formal reports of basic MTM research. A list of currently available reports has been given earlier in this chapter.

4. *MTM Research Reporter*—Progress reports on the current status of basic research are published in newsletter format to keep the membership informed.

5. *Application Training Supplements*—As each basic research project is finished, a tract is published to show how MTM training is affected. The data included supplements the training manual and the data card.

6. *Training Manuals*—The "MTM-ATC Application Training Course Manual" contains all the data and information needed to present an MTM Application Training Course. It also serves as an official reference for those who have completed training. This manual is available only under special lease conditions. Supplements are issued periodically to keep the manuals in the field current.

7. *Training Aids*—To conduct an MTM course, training aids to afford analysis practice and solving of MTM problems are required. These materials are available in kit form and separately to meet the demands of the training manual instructional needs, and to provide uniform materials for the courses.

8. *Film Loops*—For training course, refresher course, and analysis practice purposes, a set of continuous 16 mm. film loops of actual industrial operations with accompanying MTM pattern analyses and operation data can be either purchased or rented.

9. *MTM-GPD Data Manuals*—The "MTM-GPD General Purpose Data Manual" comprises two volumes of source data on this standard data system. Volume I covers the "Basic Level Data" and Volume II contains the "Multipurpose Level Data." Additional volumes will be made available as the MTM-GPD data is enlarged. These volumes are available only under special lease conditions. Supplements are issued periodically to keep the manuals in the field current.

10. *MTM-GPD Master Deck*—A punched card deck may be obtained which contains a master listing of MTM-GPD elements for automatic data processing.

11. *MTM Journal*—The "Journal of Methods-Time Measurement" is a comprehensive MTM periodical published five times annually. It supersedes the former "MTM Newsletter" and "MTM Bulletin" and includes technical aspects, application developments, and general news items about the MTM system. Subscriptions are open to the general public, and provide the best means of obtaining initial awareness of the MTM system or of continuing contact with developments.

12. *MTM Conference Proceedings*—Most of the past annual MTM Conferences are completely reported in a booklet form. These volumes contain all the technical papers and speeches delivered at each conference, comprising a very valuable source of MTM information for the general public.

Besides these publications and materials, the many seminars, technical papers, speeches, and articles in technical periodicals by members of the association and others are a useful source of MTM information. In many cases reprints and passout sheets are available from the responsible party to anyone interested on request. The MTM literature is now very extensive.

SUMMARY

The authors of this text have been privileged to serve in many capacities in MTM Association activities. They can personally affirm that the existence, modus operandi, membership composition, and services which comprise the complex known as the MTM Association for Standards and Research are excellent. It has been a major force in making MTM pre-eminent among predetermined time systems.

Honest evaluation of the story presented in this chapter, along with that previously given, should induce the reader to agree that Methods-Time Measurement accords best with the ideals enumerated for predetermined time systems.

PART II

Fundamentals of MTM

CHAPTER 6

Basic Concepts and Performance Rating

This chapter is concerned with the basic concepts, terminology, and procedures of work measurement as used by industrial engineers. It will provide the necessary background material for proper understanding of the motion chapters which follow.

GENERAL APPROACHES

Three general approaches to time study of a given task or work operation and the related establishment of labor standards are possible in ordinary industrial situations, namely, Direct Observation, Visualization, and Data Synthesis. Each of these will be discussed separately.

Direct Observation

In this approach, the analyst relies on his physical senses—often aided by various measuring devices—to view and record the actual job events as they occur. Time study principally utilizes this approach. Predetermined time systems may employ either it or the next general approach.

Rather well-defined rules of procedure and operating customs have developed over the years to bolster the effectiveness of this study procedure. Indeed, it is the one most familiar to the general public.

Inherently, several features of this approach merit the attention of an analyst deciding the general mode of work study he will employ in analyzing a given task. A principal advantage involves the fact that direct physical evidence of any sort regarding human activity bears greatest weight with the persons affected; it is relatively easy to convince the operator and others that the job has been analyzed in accordance with established procedures. There may not be agreement with the validity of the procedures, but the fact that they were applied cannot successfully be disputed. Secondly, as compared with the other approaches next to be discussed, direct observation requires less engineering knowledge and human skill on the part of the analyst. These are minimal when time study is used and are significantly greater when using a predetermined time system, since both time study and the predetermined system must be known and applied in this latter approach.

When using time study rather than a good predetermined time system such as MTM, there are several distinct disadvantages. First, it permits the most latitude for the worker to influence the study results by conscious or unobtrusive action. Second, when using time study, the data taken is limited in that it inherently shows *only* what *one* operator has done during *one* occasion and with the result reflecting the skill, effort, conditions, and consistency that prevailed during the particular study. To determine the true meaning of the data taken, the analyst must rely on techniques which historically permit endless arguments by persons who do not agree with the analyst's interpretations.

Visualization

When motions and/or time values are determined solely by mental efforts of the analyst, tempered and aided by his knowledge and experience of work study and the particular task being studied, the procedure of visualization is being utilized. Unquestionably, this requires a higher order of ability and perspicacity in the analyst. Indirect reliance on the results of direct observations made in the past may help him, but no direct physical measurements on the job itself are generally taken during the analysis. Traditional time study techniques do not materially satisfy the requirement imposed by this approach; indeed, most of the predetermined time systems were largely developed to satisfy the many occasions in which visualization is the only advisable and/or practical means of ascertaining work content and time allowance.

Debatable features of this method are the reliability of the data so developed, the validity of the analyst's judgment, and the extent to which variables actually present in the task concerned were recognized and/or properly evaluated. Sometimes only the end results of visualized analyses are recorded; this fosters disputes with discontented parties to the study as well as doubt in the mind of the analyst himself when he must later review or revise his visualized answers. However, when the rules of most predetermined time systems are honestly followed, the resulting body of detailed, recorded information reduces controversy regarding the correctness of the method and the related time values.

Another important disadvantage of visualization is that all process timing involved in the task must be found through direct observation (which cannot be done if the task is not being performed) or be estimated.

The estimation can often be quite erroneous, unless guidance data or historical records based on observations are available to reduce the chance of error. In addition, the worker will more readily accept observation standards whereas he might be reluctant to accept visualized standards unless he has been conditioned to their usage and sold on the fairness of the approach.

It is also true that the direct observation approach may be utilized on almost any job being performed without extensive prior knowledge of it, while visualization cannot possibly be successful without a good deal of prior knowledge concerning the work to be done. Usage of this approach demands professional attitudes and knowledge of a high order, and it should not be employed by the inexperienced industrial engineer. The major obvious advantage of visualization is that definitive methods and time standards can be established prior to introduction of the job into the shop. A second important advantage is that the job need not be running for work study on it to be accomplished. Direct observations, conversely, require that the job be instituted and running in the plant before study is possible.

Data Synthesis

The truly competent industrial engineer knows how to avail himself of other more advanced techniques that utilize data from the two approaches previously described. He employs both observations and visualization in combination with mathematical and graphical engineering techniques— this approach is known as data synthesis. Adequate standard data, necessary direct observation, and correct visualization are unified into a concerted attack on the motions, times, and variables of which a given work operation is composed. It is readily apparent that this is the highest order of professional approach to work study.

The preceding comparison of these three approaches to the study of a given task or work operation has been made with a dual purpose. First, the terms defined in this chapter apply equally well to all of the approaches described. Secondly, the ramifications of each approach in terms of the involved procedures are covered in different places in this text. Direct observation facets are discussed in this chapter and the first chapter of Part III. The means by which visualization is achieved are presented in the MTM information and its application. Lastly, the usage of data synthesis is elaborated in Parts III and IV which emphasize the combined usage of MTM and time study.

WORK STUDY BASICS

According to Dr. Taylor's definition of time study and Mr. Hoxie's critique of time study in Chapter 1, the basic approach of observation study is as follows:

A. Break down or divide the job into elemental operations
B. Time each element by means of a stop watch or other specialized timing device
C. Evaluate the level of performance exhibited by the operator
D. Modify the observed times in accordance with the performance level
E. Add any allowances needed to compensate for fatigue, personal time, and unavoidable delays. The latter are termed management delays by some work measurement practitioners
F. Complete the time allotted by applying the variances needed to account for actual operating conditions not evaluated during the study directly.

Effecting these steps achieves the purpose of determining the over-all time required by an average operator working with average skill and effort under average conditions to perform the studied task. Note that, with MTM and other predetermined time systems, steps B, C, and D are replaced by a procedure subject to less controversy. Note further that steps E and F are subjects of a later chapter of this text, since they can be evaluated by such procedures as all-day time studies or work sampling (ratio delay) techniques which are topics in their own right.

Allied with each of the steps enumerated above, a large body of terminology has developed upon which industrial engineers can agree. The American Society of Mechanical Engineers, for instance, has available a publication containing a complete glossary with definitions of such terms. Company policies often place restrictions on or dictate interpretations of standard definitions, so it is .futile to attempt to list exhaustively all the terms germane to work measurement. Instead, the more common terms of most frequent usage will be defined so that their general meaning will be readily recognized when the term is encountered at other places in this text.

Elemental Operations

Consistent with the observer's ability to read the time and record the data (that is, the necessary eye time, writing time, and limits of the physical senses used to catch the breakpoints), a task being studied must be divided into relatively short, distinct components. These components are called *study elements*. The necessity for such division will be outlined in detail later. However, one major reason is that both practical "common sense" and scientific requirements in the study of any operation or phenomenon demand procedures which permit separate evaluation of each component part and/or variable involved.

Elements must be readily identifiable as to starting and stopping points. Breakpoints during observation can be keyed to sounds, the condition of the workpiece, or any other distinctive mark which appears recurrently each time the work cycle repeats.

The length of elements chosen can be varied depending on the purpose of the study and the accuracy of results desired by the analyst. This is not true of MTM elemental motions, since they are as basic as possible with their duration and content being limited regardless of the purpose of the study. Many MTM elements are so short that a time study analyst could not time or even see them without special techniques and equipment not ordinarily available in industry.

Observed Time

When elements are subjected to study using a timing device, the elapsed time indicated by the device is termed *observed time*. Note that this duration of time reflects the combined effects of all variables present in the study situation of which a given element is a part. It provides no way to isolate what proportion of the elapsed time is due to either productive motions or inherent characteristics in the task that might not repeat in all cycles. Likewise, variables generally pertinent to the job might be missing while the timing device is in operation. Therefore, the observed time cannot be used as a work standard without correction for all variables that will bring the elapsed time back to a normal time. These corrections may be small or large; but a 5 to 25 per cent adjustment can easily occur.

Operator Rating

This subject will be fully detailed in this chapter. However, it may be briefly explained by reference to Chapter 2 of this text. During the timing of a job, the operator exerts a major effect on the time it takes to do the work. This effect may increase or decrease the time that will be shown on the timing device from that which would normally be required by an average operator devoting average skill and effort consistently under average job conditions. An *operator rating* is thus an attempt to evaluate in quantitative measure the time effect of the qualitative behavior of the operator. Obviously rating factors, ordinarily expressed in per cent of average performance, are inherently difficult to define, since a dynamic human behavior is being gaged in numerical terms. Many rating systems have been devised to help determine the exact time value for a given performance situation.

Application of Rating Factor

The practical usage of rating is as follows. The observed times for a given element are summed and averaged to find the mean time—often called *average raw time*. The mean time for each element or the sum of the mean times of all applicable elements is then multiplied by the rating factor to correct for the human variables; this resulting product is known by most time study people as *select time*. Select time is, in a sense, the time picked as an average corrected performance time for the element and/or over-all operation; it may be used for further computations as though no human variation would further affect the job in question. In speaking of time standards, industrial engineers usually have in mind the select time, or at least they base their thinking regarding time standards on the select time. The MTM card, for instance, contains select times for motions. Another common name for *select time* is *normal time*.

Allowances

No operator can be expected to perform throughout the day at a rate determined by the total select time for his job. Reduced personal efficiency due to fatigue, permitted time away from the work for personal needs, and small time delays due to such things as listening to the supervisor, time signals, and the like are all termed *operator allowances*. A combined percentage factor, or separate factors for each allowance, is usually applied to the select time to yield the *allowed time*. Allowed time is the average cycle time which the operator may be actually expected to attain throughout the day. Various analysts disagree on the relative value or constancy of these allowances, but opinion is almost unanimous that they total 10 to 15 per cent in the ordinary range of tasks and industries. The MTM data card times (select TMU) are therefore usually modified by the engineer during application by such a factor to obtain allowed times for the operating elements and the task as a whole.

Variances

Among the ways in which management uses the results of time study are direct control of the work process, instruction of the operator, preparation of process sheets, determination of personnel required to maintain production and meet schedules, and calculation of the cost of labor per unit of product.

Routed time is usually labor time which is charged to the job for cost accounting purposes. When multiplied by appropriate hourly wage rates, routed times become the input to cost accounting and pricing systems. Routed time is developed from the application of *variances* to the allowed time.

Variances are a means of adjusting the results of work study for the effect of miscellaneous variables. Some of these variables are the amount of supporting labor and burden which the management wishes to charge against the individual jobs in a plant. Other allowances or variances adjust the standard to reflect the time required for new operators to learn the task, to cover the loss of productive time in change-over from job to job, etc. The nature, amount, and manner of applying variances will be covered in a later chapter.

PERFORMANCE RATING

The basic approaches of two main schools of thought in regard to leveling, or rating the operator's performance, were mentioned in Chapter 4. These are the "speed rating" technique as used with the SAM rating films and the LMS system developed by Lowry, Maynard, and Stegemerten at Westinghouse which ascribes numerical weights to skill, effort, conditions, and consistency as found during a study. The SAM procedure attempts to judge only the over-all performance, whereas the LMS system treats the human variables in a work situation separately. Both techniques, of course, rely on gaging the performance variables in relation to a mental concept of average performance that is held by the rater. Actually, the SAM system now enjoys the widest usage.

Since the original MTM time values were leveled by the LMS system, it is appropriate to study this system in detail. Complete data by the originators, two of whom also participated in inventing MTM, may be found in the text "Time and Motion Study" published by the McGraw-Hill Company. Each variable of the LMS system will be separately discussed, following which the combination of ratings for each variable into a usable leveling factor will be shown.

It is advantageous for the work study analyst to understand thoroughly the LMS system, even though he may not employ it. *Knowledge of the extent to which the variables discussed qualitatively in Chapter 2 affect the productivity of a worker quantitatively helps the analyst make a more precise total evaluation.* This basic advantage of the LMS system should not be overlooked, even though the SAM system is simpler.

Skill

Skill, in the restricted sense of proficiency at following a given method, cannot be varied at the will of the operator over a short time span. It is the basic aptitude of the individual for the given operation. Practice or training can increase it or it may be temporarily curtailed due to illness, dissipation, worry, excessive fatigue, and similar causes.

According to authorities in psychology, there is a wide range of manual dexterity between the best and poorest individuals. Basic manual dexterity as a characteristic of an individual has been studied by many psychologists and standard tests are available for measuring this aspect of the human machine.

Since skill involves manual dexterity most directly, it is logical to expect a like ratio in the worker population. However, the screening of applicants by employment departments, limitation of workers to appropriate job categories, normal attrition of layoffs and discharges which tend to reduce the number of poorer workers, and other modern personnel policies tend to reduce this range in industry. It actually falls in about a 1.5 to 1 ratio.

Skill *of the degree ordinarily met in industry* has been classified in the LMS system into six categories. Note the implication that wider extremes of skill might be found in the total working population, which would also include besides industry the agricultural, distributive, governmental, social service, and other important segments of the complete economy. Comparative definitions have been developed to delineate as clearly and distinctly as possible the characteristics of each category. Individuals in a given category will usually exhibit a preponderance of the given characteristics for that level of skill, although departure on specific items may well be possible and present.

Poor Skill:

1. Cannot coordinate mind and hands
2. Movements appear clumsy and awkward
3. Seems uncertain of proper sequence of operation
4. Untrained on operation
5. Misfit
6. Hesitates
7. Errors occur frequently
8. Shows lack of self-confidence
9. Unable to think for himself

Fair Skill:

1. Only partially trained on operation
2. Fairly familiar with equipment and surroundings
3. Work shows some effect of forward planning
4. Does not have full self-confidence
5. A misfit who has been on job for a long time
6. Knows what he is doing but somewhat clumsy and uncertain
7. Loses some time due to own blunders
8. Can equal output of poor man with less effort
9. Usually does not hesitate

Average Skill:

1. Self-confident
2. Appears a little slow in motions
3. Work shows effects of some forward planning
4. Proficient at the work
5. Follows sequence of operations without appreciable hesitation
6. Coordinates mind and hands reasonably well
7. Appears to be fully trained and therefore knows the job
8. Works with reasonable accuracy
9. Work is satisfactory

Good Skill:

1. Work of adequate to excellent quality
2. Appears noticeably better than ordinary run of men
3. Can instruct others less skilled
4. Markedly proficient
5. Requires little supervision
6. No hesitation
7. Works at steady pace
8. Motions well coordinated
9. Quick in motions

Excellent Skill:

1. Self-confident
2. Possesses high natural aptitude for the work performed
3. Thoroughly trained
4. Works accurately with little measuring or checking
5. Works without errors in action or sequence
6. Takes full advantage of equipment
7. Works fast without sacrificing quality
8. Performance is fast and smooth
9. Works rhythmically and with coordination

Super Skill:

1. Naturally suited to the work
2. The operator of excellent skill perfected
3. Appears to be super trained
4. Motions are so quick and smooth that they are hard to follow
5. Work has machine-like appearance and action
6. Elements of operation blend into each other
7. Appears not to think about what he is doing
8. Conspicuously an outstanding worker

The descriptions illustrate that the key factors in judging skill involve hesitations, precision of movement, interruptions due to errors or improper performance, self-confidence, coordination, rhythm, apparent training and the like.

Effort

Effort—the "work readiness" or drive of a worker to expend his energy —is a variable which the operator can control at will. The effect on effort of various human attributes discussed earlier are not as great as generally supposed. Only a 25 to 30 per cent spread between the slowest and fastest workers was found to be attributable to effort alone by Lowry, Maynard, and Stegemerten. Naturally, slow workers—unless other human factors loom larger—tend to be eliminated whereas excessive effort by even the most conscientious worker cannot be maintained over long periods of time without harm to himself.

Good managers do not desire or encourage the "speed-up" which labor unions decry, rather they achieve most of their production increases by attention to motion-saving methods and mechanization. On the other hand, a worker must be worthy of his hire, and practical management must have the right to rid their organizations of shirkers.

Workers sometimes attempt to "fool" the work analyst by deliberate pacing of their work while under study, but the vast majority of employees are honest and try to be fair in this respect. Indeed, some workers tend to give better effort while being studied than they would normally exert.

As was done for skill factors, six ranges of effort were isolated and defined. The key characteristics outlined permit ready reference and identification of the effort level.

Poor Effort:

1. Kills time
2. Shows definite lack of work interest
3. Resents suggestions
4. Appears lazy and works slowly
5. Makes unnecessary trips for tools and supplies
6. Makes extra motions
7. Maintains poor housekeeping at workplace
8. May purposely use wrong or poor tool
9. Degrades workplace lay-out
10. Purposely uses poor set-up
11. Does work much more accurately than necessary

Fair Effort:

1. Accepts suggestions grudgingly
2. Attention appears to wander from work
3. Fair, rather than poor, effect usually results from late hours, dissipation, or mental worries
4. Puts some energy into work
5. Uses methods that deviate only slightly from those considered proper
6. Does not always use best tools
7. Appears purposely somewhat ignorant of the work at hand
8. Somewhat too accurate
9. Fairly systematic
10. Does not plan ahead

Average Effort:

1. Better than fair; poorer than good
2. Appears to be holding back
3. Works steadily
4. Accepts suggestions; but makes none
5. Maintains a good set-up
6. Plans ahead
7. Follows a good method or that prescribed by process

Good Effort:

1. Works with rhythm
2. Idle time is minor or non-existent
3. Conscientious about his work
4. Interested in his work
5. Works at a good pace that can be maintained throughout the day
6. Actions indicate faith in time-study man
7. Readily accepts advice and suggestions
8. Makes suggestions for improvement of operation
9. Maintains good order at workplace
10. Uses proper tools
11. Keeps tools in good condition

Excellent Effort:

1. Obviously works fast
2. The motions are often more economical than an ordinary operator would use
3. Keenly interested in work
4. Makes many suggestions
5. Obviously glad to get advice and suggestions
6. Generally has good confidence in time-study man; however, a rare exception is that he may also be scared
7. Probably could not keep up effort more than a few days
8. Proud of his superiority
9. False motions at a minimum
10. Works systematically
11. Motions blend into each other

Excessive Effort:

1. Extends his pace to unreasonable limit
2. Best effort from every standpoint but that of health
3. Could not maintain pace throughout day

It is noteworthy that, while skill and effort are evaluated separately in this rating system, the levels of skill and effort tend to complement each other rather than being contrasting. Poorly skilled workers attempting to compensate by excessive effort usually interfere with what little skill they possess and this appears as fumbles, false starts, and frustration. A highly skillful worker, however, appears to work with deceptive ease; every motion counts and produces useful effects on the workpiece. Operators with higher levels of skill can reduce their effort successfully without losing effectiveness. It is usual, however, for poor effort and poor skill to combine and for high skill and high effort to coexist when training has been adequate.

Conditions

Industrial conditions today are generally such that the great majority of time studies will be rated as involving average conditions. A variation of 15 per cent is about the maximum that can be ascribed to the range between poor and ideal conditions. Again, six classes of conditions have been segregated: poor, fair, average, good, excellent, and ideal. The important aspect for the analyst to note is the relative departure from what are usual conditions prevailing in the workspace concerned. It is again appropriate to call the reader's attention to Chapter 2, where the effect of the surroundings of the worker are discussed in quite some detail.

Notice that effort and skill are attributes of the worker himself, whereas the job conditions are external influences on his output. The conditions rating factors have nothing to do with the method employed, functioning of machinery, propriety of tools used, sharpness of tools, and similar considerations. Such matters are subjects for separate attention by conscientious and cost-conscious managers. They relate specifically to tools and methods, having no relation to the concepts gaged as conditions in the leveling procedure.

Consistency

As is true of any series of numerical observations, the elemental times taken during a time study exhibit a variability that can be subjected to statistical analyses of various kinds. Such variation has little to do with the operator, so long as he is giving average performance. It is noticeable, however, that attempts by a worker to influence the time taken will result in inconsistent variation of the elemental times read from a watch. Obviously, the analyst must make an effort to reduce the effect of this ranging of times on a standard.

According to the LMS rating system, the range of inconsistency for valid readings will not exceed about 8 per cent from low to high range. Six classes of consistency have been assigned to adjust for acceptable variation: poor, fair, average, good, excellent, and perfect.

The work analyst can best determine the consistency while he is summarizing the study away from the workplace. If no variation exists in the readings for each element, consistency is perfect; such times are very unlikely to be encountered often and the standard should be increased to recognize this fact. Process- or machine-controlled elements are the only ones in which perfect consistency is not unexpected. Poor consistency is apparent when the times range widely from the mean reading in a random manner. Most studies have average consistency, which means that the readings are very close but have some high and low variations from the average observed time.

Occasionally, serious variations in readings are found in study elements. These variations are often caused by non-repetitive or non-productive events which a properly made study should include to permit adjustment of the standard. Another standard procedure is to strike out from consideration in the averaging of element times any readings that are obviously incorrect or influenced strongly by extraneous factors. The remaining readings are then judged as to consistency.

When judging the consistency, the nature of the work elements should be taken into account. Simple operations such as "move lever," "toss part into container," and the like, should show little or no variation. More complex elements such as "obtain lockwasher from parts pan" and "fit shaft into bearing" will obviously show greater variation.

The skill of the operator should also be considered. Highly skilled workers normally work more consistently than poor employees. In fact, highly skilled operators, providing parts fit properly, etc., will work with good to perfect consistency unless they deliberately attempt to show a poor performance.

Performance Rating Data

The factors in human behavior that affect productivity were discussed in detail in Chapter 2; to this point in this chapter, more specific comments have been added that shed quantitative light on the subject. What remains, therefore, is to see the numerical factors assigned in the LMS system and to learn how to combine them to provide a useful rating factor. This rating factor applied to the mean value of the observed times will then yield the select time desired for any given element.

During the development of the LMS system, some 175 men made comparison studies at every opportunity available for approximately a year's time. In this manner, the effect of varying degrees of skill, effort, conditions, and consistency were evaluated. When the results of these studies were first published in 1927, the leveling factors had been used successfully in many industrial organizations.

When considering the numerical data, remember that it measures the typical industrial worker and that the range of variation will be more limited than might be found in the population as a whole. Many workers in the fields of agriculture, commerce, transportation, government, and distribution probably work differently; inclusion of these groups might materially increase the range and lower the level of job activity considered as normal in this system. However, the values apparently cover adequately the industrial situation, since the LMS system has been used in widely dispersed geographical and political locations with rather uniform success.

The ratings factors for the LMS system are shown in Table 1. The data is used in the following manner: Each level of performance under one of the four major factors corresponds to the descriptions in the preceding text. These categories are coded by letters and numbers for ease of usage. When the time study man is observing the operator, he notes with the code symbols the effort, skill, and conditions for each element and/or the

Table I. Performance Rating Data—LMS System

FACTOR ⟶		SKILL	EFFORT	CONDITIONS	CONSISTENCY
Category	Code	Additive Percentage Values			
SUPER	A1 A A2	+.15 +.140 +.13			
EXCESSIVE	A1 A A2		+.13 +.125 +.12		
IDEAL	A			+.06	
PERFECT	A				+.04
EXCELLENT	B1 B B2	+.11 +.095 +.08	+.10 +.090 +.08	+.04	+.03
GOOD	C1 C C2	+.06 +.045 +.03	+.05 +.035 +.02	+.02	+.01
AVERAGE	D	.00	.00	.00	.00
FAIR	E1 E E2	−.05 −.075 −.10	−.04 −.060 −.08	−.03	−.02
POOR	F1 F F2	−.16 −.190 −.22	−.12 −.145 −.17	−.07	−.04

job as a whole. Later, when summarizing the study, he also assigns a consistency rating.

The numerical rating for each of the factors is then added *algebraically* to the nominal 100 per cent to produce a finished rating. Whether this composite value is one that applies to an element or an entire job, the procedure is the same. Note, however, that for skill and effort more than one value is given for each category. Actually the letter and number combinations are the LMS data as it appears in most published sources and on many time study forms; but the LMS system also contains the intermediate values for those who would rather use the letters only. To employ the double symbols, an analyst must judge whether the high (1) or low (2) range of the category in question is appropriate.

As an example of how the table is used, suppose a time study element was rated according to the descriptive definitions in this chapter as B1A2C and a rating of B was assigned for consistency during the study summary.

The combined rating for the element is then B1A2CB for skill, effort, conditions, and consistency in that order. It is conventional to write the symbols in this order. The per cent rating would result as follows:

B1	Skill	+0.11	(Excellent)
A2	Effort	+0.12	(Excessive)
C	Conditions	+0.02	(Good)
B	Consistency	+0.03	(Excellent)
		1.00	
	Total LMS Rating	1.28 or 128%	

Further examples are:

Fair Skill	E1	−0.05
Good Effort	C2	+0.02
Fair Conditions	E	−0.03
Good Consistency	C	+0.01
		1.00
Total LMS Rating		0.95
		or 95%

Fair Skill	E	−0.075
Poor Effort	F	−0.145
Average Conditions	D	0.00
Fair Consistency	E	−0.02
		1.00
Total LMS Rating		0.76
		or 76%

It is notable that the maximum combination of skill and effort in the table shows a value of $+0.28$ or 128 per cent. Conversely, the minimum combination has a value of -0.39 or 61 per cent. By division, the spread between the best and worst effect the operator can produce is better than 2 to 1. Such differences ordinarily are not likely to be seen in industrial operations. It is important to emphasize, however, that even this spread in productive output can be greatly exceeded by methods changes. It is not uncommon to devise methods by which average operators can triple or quadruple their output at the same performance level; this, obviously, is not possible due to the operator alone.

The time study observer may sometimes note changes in the performance level during the course of the study. Since conditions remain relatively constant, and the worker cannot vary his skill level consciously during the study without departing from the method under study, such changes are normally due to the operator's effort or the use of motions which really constitute a different method. Such variations should be noted in the space for remarks on the study sheet and keyed to the time observations to permit intelligent interpretation or correction later.

Evaluating skill, effort, and conditions as separate items makes it possible to apply LMS leveling factors to a one- or few-cycle study. Although timing of only one or a few cycles is not a good time study practice, practical conditions sometimes necessitate the procedure. For instance, limited parts availability, lack of time for an intensive study, the desire for indications of the over-all time in a hurry, and like situations may require that only one cycle or a few cycles can be timed. If the factors could not be evaluated separately, no such leveling would be possible.

On this score, a note about the SAM rating procedure—the more popular rating system—is in order. As explained earlier, this method of rating judges over-all operator performance in relation to what is considered average in the given plant under the conditions involved. This makes it feasible to rate not only the average observed time for each element of the operation, but also each observed time for the element. Of course, this would normally be carrying the SAM procedure to an unwarranted extreme; but it can be done validly and is sometimes helpful in analyzing a particular operation.

The Concept of Average

Before any rating procedure will permit the equating of one man's time study values to that of another observer, a proper concept of average must be established upon which all industrial engineers can agree. Both men must have the same concept of what constitutes average performance.

One way of achieving this is to pair a novice and a veteran rater to study a variety of operations. Their ratings, upon comparison back in the office or privately on the factory floor, will show whether the novice has the proper concept of average. The novice can then, with the help of such comparisons and practice, adjust his mental concept to agree with that of the more experienced rater.

A better method is to utilize, by purchase or rental, some of the performance rating films obtainable from the Society for Advancement of Management, universities, private industrial firms, or consulting engineering firms. The mere fact that a man is experienced is no guarantee that he can level correctly. Rating films are excellent for training both the novice and the experienced time study analyst. The scheme of pairing can then be used as a supplement to these rating films if the experienced man has proven that he can consistently level correctly.

The Society for Advancement of Management presently has available two sets of rating films. The first set contains 7 reels covering manufacturing operations and 1 reel of clerical and laboratory operations. The second set of 4 rating films is devoted entirely to clerical operations. SAM is also developing a new set of rating films devoted to the general area of production which should be available in the near future. The SAM* rating films are provided with a set of standardized instructions and standard rating values which account for the allowances and per cent of attainment expected in the particular plant situation. A graphical scheme (see Fig. 1)

* The films referenced above can be rented or purchased from the Society for Advancement of Management, 16 W. 40th Street, New York, N. Y. 10018. The films are 16 mm and are supplied complete with the "correct" ratings developed by consensus of many raters.

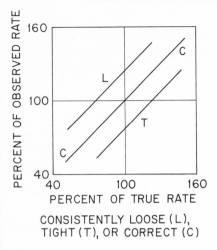

CONSISTENTLY LOOSE (L),
TIGHT (T), OR CORRECT (C)

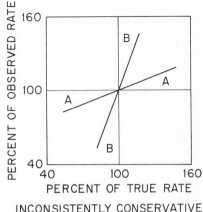

INCONSISTENTLY CONSERVATIVE
(A) OR LIBERAL (B), BUT
NORMAL AT 100% FOR BOTH

Fig. 1.   Rating plots based on SAM rating films.   The five general possibilities are shown.

also permits plotting of the ratings made by the film viewers in such a way that it is easy to see whether the observer is rating "tight," "correct," or "loose." "Tight" means that a man rates too low and would thus allow too little time for fairness to the operator. "Loose" means that the rater's generosity to the operator would be reflected in too much time allowed for the operation—this is unfair to the management. For the best interests of both management and worker, it is essential that the performance rater achieves "correct" ratings of a task.

The greatest sin for a rater is to be inconsistent. When he is "consistently tight" or "consistently loose," it is possible to adjust his readings when he knows his degree of error. When he is inconsistent, however, it is difficult, if not impossible, to reconcile his final time data with an objective standard.

In actual practice, the industrial engineer leaving college to enter industry will normally start working in a plant where time study is already established and the department has a firm policy on the rating procedure to be employed. This may be the LMS system, the SAM system, or a private procedure. In any case, the novice should be given training in the particular system in usage when he begins his work at the plant. Only then can his rating ability and concept of average qualify him to amass times for standard data or any other management purpose.

One remaining method of achieving an average concept has arisen since the usage of MTM has become widespread. This consists of standardizing an operation and setting a reliable MTM rate on it; this time comprises the time required of a 100 per cent operator before the addition of any time allowances. The stop watch will then show accurately the true actual time, and by division the true performance level, which will enable a crosscheck of the performance rating made by either new or experienced time study men.

A second MTM approach to leveling is to establish one element of the study so that it includes the motions defined in a standard MTM motion category. The actual time taken by the operator to perform this element can then be compared (divided) by the MTM time (detailed data) to obtain a performance rating of the operator for that element of the study. If the operator's consistency is average to excellent it would then be reasonable to expect the regular time study rating of the operator to compare closely to this element rating.

CHAPTER 7

Reach

Definition[1]

REACH[2] is the basic hand or finger motion employed when the **predominant purpose** is to move the hand or fingers to a destination.

1. Reach is performed only by the fingers or hand. Moving the foot to a trip lever would **not** be classified as a reach.

2. The hand may be carrying an object and the motion still will be classified as a reach provided the predominant purpose is only to move the hand or fingers and not the object. An example would be the "reach" for an eraser while the performer is still holding chalk in the same hand.

3. Short reaches can be performed by moving only the fingers; longer reaches involve motion of the hand, forearm, and upper arm.

The predominant purpose of the motion is the deciding factor in classifying it as a reach. Holding or palming a light, small item such as a screwdriver, pliers, or scissors while moving the hand does not justify classifying the motion as a move rather than a reach. For example, in the needle trades, a scissors is often held in the palm of the hand while other opera-

[1] From "MTM Basic Specifications" prepared by the 1957 Training Committee of the MTM Association. The main definition and the numbered sub-definitions are considered integral parts of the complete specification for each motion. These data are derived from Vol. V, No. 4 of the *Journal of Methods-Time Measurement* for November–December 1958 and are used by permission of the MTM Association for Standards and Research. To save repetition of this footnote in subsequent chapters of this text, reference is made to this source and this footnote by the following notation: From "MTM Basic Specifications" (Footnote 1, Chapter 7).

[2] The reader will probably recognize that this is basically the same motion as the Gilbreth Basic Element or Therblig called Transport Empty. The similarity of the other MTM basic elements to Therbligs is also interesting to one familiar with that motion study system.

tions such as reaching from the cloth on the working area in front of the operator to a bin containing pins are performed. The motion to the bin should be classified as a reach if the predominant purpose is to get the hand in a position to pick up some pins for the next operation.

The analysis and investigation conducted as part of the development of the Methods-Time Measurement procedure, and subsequent research performed under the auspices of the MTM Association for Standards and Research, has definitely shown that the major influencing factor on the time to make the motion is the predominant purpose and not the fact that a small object is carried in the hand.

It is likewise obvious from a practical viewpoint that the palming of a large, heavy, or clumsy object would have an influence on the motion and would, therefore, change the classification to a move (see next chapter).

This is just one example of the type of distinction that must be made on a practical basis when Methods-Time Measurement is applied. Definite rules to substitute for trained judgment cannot be set down for every specific case that may be encountered. The more experience the well-trained analyst gains, the more likely he is to make correct decisions on the classification of the various movements required in the performance of the work. At best, he must rely on such guiding principles as those in this text.

KINDS OF REACHES

There are five cases or classifications of Reach separately identified in the MTM procedure. They are identified by letters of the alphabet as follows: A, B, C, D, and E.

Case "A" Reach

Case A Reach may be defined as follows:

Reach for an object in a fixed location or for an object in the other hand or on which the other hand rests.

An example of reaching for an object in a fixed location is that of an operator of a punch press reaching for the trip buttons. The example infers that "fixed location" means that the object must be bolted down or be located in exactly the same place each and every time. However, from the required practical viewpoint of the MTM analyst, "fixed" refers to the mental certainty of the object's location and not that it is stationary or bolted down (although such cases could also fulfill the condition).

Practice will help "fix" an object's location in an operator's mind. This is explained by recognizing the function of "kinesthetic sense" which is the *apparent* ability of the muscles to feel the near presence of an object without the visual aid of the operator's eyes. Actually, this "kinesthetic sense" is a capacity of the mind which allows it to almost automatically direct the muscles to return to a location fixed in memory by frequent previous experiences with relative orientations of an object and the body. A popular name for this ability which seems to describe what occurs is "muscle memory."

From a practical viewpoint, all operators who can qualify for factory work can also learn to make Case A Reaches in the time allotted by the MTM procedure. This, of course, will require sufficient practice to reduce the visual or mental control in performing the reach from the conscious to the automatic level. Because of their greater skill, however, better operators will tend to make reaches to single objects which may vary slightly from cycle to cycle in the time allotted for a Case A Reach. The second type of motion just mentioned is normally identified as a Case B Reach.

The above facts could mean that, on highly repetitive work, a classification decision might sometimes be made which seems to conflict with the definition. For example, in a plant having workers who are generally above average in skill due to selection techniques and where the work is highly repetitive, it may be desirable to classify some motions as Case A, which by rote definition may be strictly Case B, if practical observation shows them obviously to be Case A as proved by a time check. In such event, the Case A time is the correct one to use.

One should not make such decisions contrary to the defined limits unless sufficient data is available to justify such procedure. Perhaps clarity on this point is best achieved by mentioning that the two types of occasion when a motion must be classified are: (1) when the motion is being visualized and (2) when a motion has been observed. Remember then that the classification decision hinges on the fact that the standard method prescription should be for the average operator working with average skill and average effort under the average *prevailing* conditions.

In the instance cited above, the skill and repetition constantly prevailing *would* justify the specification of a Case A Reach.

If the other hand is already holding or is resting on the object being reached for, the latter portion of the Case A definition begins to apply. "Kinesthetic sense" goes into action and, as far as the operator's mind is concerned, he has a mental certainty of the object's location. This mental certainty, however, does not apply in this manner unless the object is being held by the other hand within three inches of the grasping point. Actually, a reach ending anywhere within three inches of the body (e.g. cigarette in lips) would justify the Case A analysis for Reach. This is an important point to remember, since the data developed to date indicates that three inches is the practical limit for this "Kinesthetic sense" to operate properly. Of course, exceptions to the 3-inch rule can be found (e.g. a baseball bat in the hand of a professional player) where the grasp point can be further than three inches from the other hand, yet the reach will be made consistently.

Case "B" Reach

This case of Reach may be defined as follows:

Reach for a single object in a location that may vary slightly from cycle to cycle.

The Case B Reach is the reach most commonly encountered in industry. These reaches are also usually easy to identify.

Examples of such reaches are most numerous and some typical illustrations are:

1. Reaching for a paint mask lying anywhere on a stand, prior to painting the part
2. Reaching for a pair of pliers, resting someplace on the work table, which are used for a portion of each work cycle
3. Reaching for a lone pencil loose in one's pocket.

The variance in location normally is understood to be one to two inches; however, the size of the object and other factors need to be taken into consideration from a practical point of view. A variance of two inches for a small part might be of considerably more importance than a variance of three or four inches for a large part. This is because of the need for greater visual and muscular control to direct the hand to the reach destination.

Mention was made in the previous section that unusual operators often convert timewise a Case B Reach into a Case A Reach if they have had sufficient practice. The analyst should be careful not to classify Case B Reaches as Case A Reaches unless very special consideration indicates that such action is the correct approach. It certainly is not intended to be the usual approach.

Conversely, as discussed under the definition of Case A Reach in the previous section, a reach to a part on which the operator's other hand is resting is a Case B Reach unless the point of grasp is within three inches of the resting hand.

Case "C" Reach

The Case C Reach is defined as follows:

Reach for an object in a group of objects which are jumbled so that search and select occur.

It should definitely be understood that it makes no difference whether the objects jumbled together are all of the same kind or whether they are different. The main thing is that they must be jumbled into a pile so that search and select occur. Reaching for a single object would rarely be classified as a Case C Reach, by its very definition.

The time for the Case C Reach is longer per distance moved than for any other case of reach except D, which consumes exactly the same time per inch of reach. One of the reasons affecting the length of time is the necessity for the eyes and the mind to select which object is to be grasped out of the pile, before grasping action can occur. That is, in addition to the required muscular control, both visual and mental control are necessary. This mind and eye action slows down the rate of hand travel and extends the time before grasp action begins, which is actually at the end of the reach time.

Another illustration of the practical decisions which must be made by the analyst is where an operator reaches for a rivet in a pan full of rivets. It may be that the operator usually grasps several with a normal grasp and then allows all but one to sift through his fingers before the move motion takes the hand out of the area of the tote pan. Practical research has shown that, in many cases, the reach is not slowed down to the time shown for a Case C Reach but that the actual time is closer to the value for a Case B Reach. This indicates that a Case C Reach may not always apply to all jumbled piles.

The problem of stock depletions will puzzle some analysts. By this it is meant that, as stock is depleted from a tote pan, the operator is reaching toward only a few parts with reaches logically classified as Case B Reaches. The effect of this can for all practical purposes be ignored; one should always classify the motions for the normal occurrence. If the variations are of enough importance, separate consideration must be given to them. This effect will be discussed to some extent in Chapter 23.

Case "D" Reach

A Case D Reach is defined as follows:

Reach for a very small object or where an accurate grasp is required.

An excellent example of a Case D Reach would be reaching for a little piece of broken glass. The glass, being both small and having sharp edges, requires an accurate grasp to prevent injury to the fingers.

When a very small, hard-to-grasp object is reached to, it is obvious that the time of reach per unit of distance is extended due to the necessity of controlling the motion accurately, particularly the latter portion of the reach. The same effect is encountered where a very accurate grasp is required in order to prevent damage to fragile or polished parts.

Because of the above effects, the time for a Case D Reach was found to be greater than for a Case A or B Reach. In fact, it was found to be identical with the time for a Case C Reach. Remember that the MTM time values were established by research and should be used whether we can fully explain each one or not.

If the operator is reaching to a very small part that is also jumbled with many small parts, only the method description is affected by the decision to classify the reach as either C or D. The analyst should make this decision to best fit the most important characteristic of the operation. However, specification of an R—C directly to one part would never be incorrect where small parts are jumbled together.

In any event, if the above type of problem is encountered, do not allow two reach times, since one identical value suffices.

Case "E" Reach

Case E Reach is defined as follows:

Reach to an indefinite location to get the hand in position for body balance, for the next motion, or out of the way.

Examples of Case E Reaches are numerous. If a heavy object is lifted with one hand, the other hand and arm are often extended out from the body in order to provide body balance. The arm extension is a Case E Reach. Carrying a chunk of ice at your side with an ice tong is almost always an occasion for extending your other arm in an outward direction to provide body balance.

After an operator feeding a punch press has loaded the material into the die, his next motion, following release of the material, is obviously a Case E Reach—getting his hand and arm out of the way of the ram— unless the reach were to the activating device (normally Case A). Moving the hand out of a dangerous area is a Case E Reach which could be dubbed the "safety reach." Such cases could be limiting; that is, subsequent motions could not or should not be performed until the "safety reach" has been completed. Safety directors often make this motion a required and an automatic one by installing "pull guards" on the press equipment.

Another example of a Case E Reach—that of getting tne hand into position for the next motion—would be where a hand is moved in the general direction of the next required motion. This usually occurs while the other hand or some other body member is performing a limiting motion (the one consuming the greater amount of time). After the limiting motion is completed, the hand making the Case E Reach then continues on, usually with some other case of reach.   The practical effect of this is to reduce effectively the chargeable distance of the latter reach.

It is often true that a Case E Reach is made with one hand while the other hand is performing a limiting operation.   In other words, the other hand actually consumes the larger amount of time, and therefore, the Case E Reach need be considered only for methods description.   Frequently, this type of Case E Reach is not shown in the motion pattern, as a time-saving convenience.

A final kind of Case E Reach is one where the fingers only are moved off or out of the way of an object.   In this case, the distance reached is measured by the travel of the fingertip(s).   Normal MTM Case 1 Release motions (see Chap. 13) actually are very short Case E Reaches by the fingers.   However, if the fingertip travel is an inch or more, the reach should be recorded as a Case E Reach of the proper distance and the time allowed, unless it is limited by other motions.   Sequences of such reaches frequently occur when dropping a handful of small parts over a tote pan.

General

We have now considered the five cases of Reach identified in the MTM procedure.   The MTM analyst may find that the following word association will assist in identifying the five cases of Reach.

> Case A Reach—Automatic
> Case B Reach—By Itself
> Case C Reach—Crowded and Choose
> Case D Reach—Diminutive or Dangerous
> Case E Reach—Ease or Extricate

TYPE OF MOTION

In making start-stop motions, such as normal Reaches or Moves, MTM research has revealed that the body member or members go through a period of acceleration to a maximum velocity, that this velocity is maintained through a portion of the motion and that the body member or members are finally decelerated to a stop.   This is quite logical by analogy to the action of an automobile between starting and stopping points.   However, as some critics of MTM point out, the time (Time = Distance ÷ Velocity) to perform a given motion *can be* influenced by the motion preceding or following it.   That this is not a valid criticism of MTM is easily seen by (1) the motion classification descriptions and also by (2) the provision in MTM for consideration of the Type of Motion as given in this section.

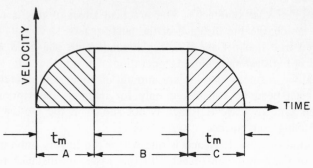

Fig. 1. Type I Motion.

Type I Motion

For identification purposes, the MTM procedure has labeled the condition where the hand is moving at neither the beginning nor at the end of the element as a Type I Motion. Graphically, it can be portrayed as shown in Fig. 1. The meaning of the symbols shown is as follows:

t_m = Time of acceleration or deceleration (they are assumed to be practically equally divided for most conditions)

A = Acceleration period of the motion (time for one "m" value)

B = Constant velocity period of the motion

C = Deceleration period of the motion (time for one "m" value)

Type II Motion

A Type II Motion is identified as having the hand in motion at either the beginning or at the end of the work element. Graphically, it is portrayed as shown in Fig. 2.

It is obvious that by eliminating either a period of acceleration or a period of deceleration from the Type I Motion, the distance traveled by the hand will be greater for a given amount of time. Conversely, for a given amount of distance to be traveled, the time required will be less for a Type II Motion than for a Type I Motion because of the elimination of either an acceleration period or a deceleration period.

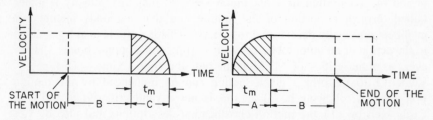

Fig. 2. Type II Motion. (*Left*) Hand in motion at start only. (*Right*) Hand in motion at end only.

It should also be apparent that for Case C or Case D Reaches, the hand cannot be in motion at the end of the element. This is because during a Case C Reach, search and select occurs, and for a Case D Reach a very accurate grasp is required at the end.

Type III Motion

In this type of motion, according to MTM procedure, the hand is in motion at both the beginning and the end of the work element. Graphically, it is portrayed as shown in Fig. 3.

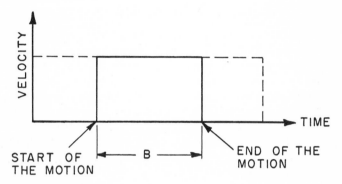

Fig. 3. Type III Motion. Hand is in motion both at the start and at the end of the work element.

The velocity of hand travel is for all practical purposes constant, and the curve described by relating velocity and time is a straight line.

This type of motion is never present during Case C or Case D Reaches because the hand cannot be in motion at the end of the element, as mentioned previously.

General Remarks on Types of Motion

MTM research has evaluated the effect of acceleration and deceleration on the various cases of reach. This information is shown on the data card.

The effect of eliminating one period of acceleration or deceleration is presented in the data card information for Case A and Case B Reaches. In order to establish the time values for Type II Motions for other than Case A Reaches and Case B Reaches, and for all Type III Motions, a set of formulae are given later in this chapter. Basically, those formulas depend on subtraction to find the time required for one acceleration period—or its equivalent, one deceleration period. Table 1 shows these values of "m" for both Case A and Case B Reaches. It also shows the range through which this value varies with distance.

MTM research showed that the "m" value for the Case B Reach is applicable for all other cases except the Case A Reach. This latter reach is the fastest possible, and it also has shorter acceleration and/or deceleration periods than are required for a Case B Reach.

Table I. Value of "m" in TMU for Case A and Case B Reaches

CASE OF REACH	REACH DISTANCE, INCHES																			
	1	2	3	4	5	6	7	8	9	10	12	14	16	18	20	22	24	26	28	30
	Value of "m" in TMU																			
A	.2	.5	.8	1.2	1.2	1.3	1.3	1.4	1.4	1.4	1.5	1.6	1.7	1.8	1.8	1.9	2.0	2.1	2.2	2.2
B	.2	1.3	1.7	2.1	2.8	2.9	2.8	2.9	2.9	2.9	2.8	2.9	2.9	2.8	2.8	2.8	2.7	2.7	2.7	2.6

The assumption is made, when developing times for Type II and Type III Reaches exceeding a 30-inch distance, that the "m" value listed in Table 1 for 30 inches will govern beyond that distance. This is because the time curve has become essentially a straight line with uniform slope when the 30-inch value has been reached in the plot of reach times.

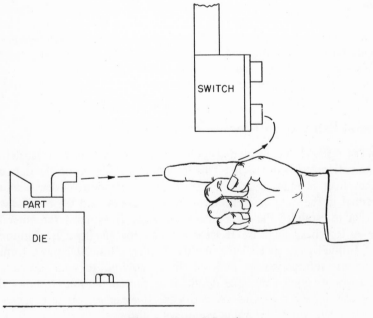

Fig. 4. Type I Reach.

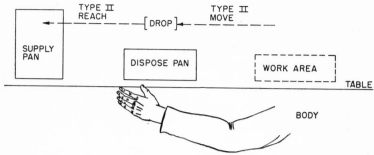

Fig. 5.   Type II Reach.

An example of Type I Motion would be where a punch press operator has just finished placing the part in the die and reaches toward the side to the trip button. The hand is stationary at both the beginning and at the end of the reach. It is illustrated in Fig. 4.

A typical example of a Type II Motion would be where drop delivery into a tote-pan is used and the operator keeps his hand in motion while reaching for a part in another tote-pan as preparation for the next assembly operation. See Fig. 5.

An example of a Type III Motion would be where an assembly operator employs drop delivery into a tote-pan, then reaches his hand to a part lying on a smooth workbench surface and employs what is known as a contact grasp when his hand reaches the part, then slides the part along the workbench in the same continuous arc in which the hand was moving at the moment of contact. For this type of motion, there was no period of acceleration from the moment the part was dropped nor any deceleration up to the point where the part was contacted with the hand or fingers. Motion after contact is normally classified as a move. See Fig. 6.

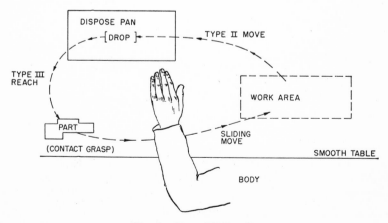

Fig. 6.   Type III Reach.

CHANGE IN DIRECTION

If a very sharp change in direction occurs during a reach motion, it will affect the time for the reach. The change must be abrupt enough to necessitate an appreciable amount of muscular control. A change in direction will affect the time for the reach if a turn of approximately 90 degrees or more is made in a radius of no more than six inches.

An example of this type of situation would be where an assembly operator reaches in over the edge of an assembly frame preparatory to doing work at the bottom corner nearest the operator. This is illustrated in Fig. 7.

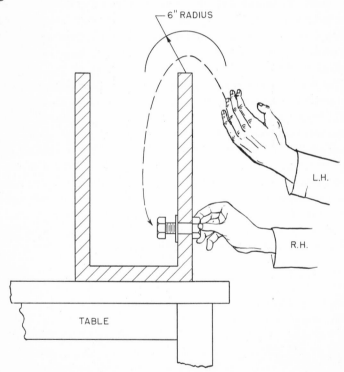

Fig. 7. Change of direction. If the nut were within 3 inches of the right hand, the left hand would be making an R—Acᴅ.

The Case A Reach is the only one slowed enough by a change in direction to consider the time effect as a separate item in the application of the MTM data. This is accounted for by assigning such Case A Reaches the time value for a Case B Reach of the same length. All other cases of reach are affected by other factors to such an extent that the change in direction effect can be neglected.

DATA CARD INFORMATION

As previously indicated, the MTM analyst utilizes a data card containing all of the required information. The data for Reach is reproduced in Table 2, which shows the MTM reach time data (Table 1 on the card) in the form currently approved by the MTM Association.

No portion of the entire official MTM data card will be changed except by the following steps:

1. The Board of Directors of a national MTM association initiates a research project.
2. Research is conducted in the library and the laboratory
3. An industrial research is carried out to confirm the conclusions of the laboratory study and to develop practical MTM time data
4. A research report is published and distributed after each portion of the study
5. Interested parties test the research data in industrial applications and submit the results for appraisal
6. The proper agencies of the MTM Association concerned evaluate all data from whatever source
7. Any MTM data changes deemed appropriate are developed and submitted for approval to the Board of Directors of the national MTM association responsible for the project
8. The International MTM Directorate considers national association proposals and promulgates any data changes which are valid and desirable
9. The official MTM data card is revised.

Every step in this process is subject to review by appropriate individuals, committees, or other groups. Their action may necessitate further study before the project or data changes can proceed. Also, a national association can issue supplemental data and specify various "rules of thumb" for cautious tentative usage as a means of further extensive trial before the final steps of the revision process are completed. Obviously, this careful procedure requires considerable time and effort. It would be bad practice to change data which has satisfactorily met the needs of thousands of application situations without sufficient cause. Because of this procedure, however, one can rely on the official MTM Data Card. Also, such research and the required revision procedures assure the MTM analyst of even better data in the future.

The time values for Reach Case A in motion and Reach Case B in motion at distances of 3 inches or under, Reach Case C for ¾ inch or less, and for Reach Case B in motion for distances of 20 inches and greater have been obtained by extrapolation from existing research data. Because of this, they are shown in light-faced type in Table 2 and on the MTM data card. The hand in motion values for Case A and Case B Reaches can be used directly for Type II Motions, as the "m" values are already subtracted from the basic time.

Table 2. Time Data for Reach
(MTM Data Card Table I—Reach—R)

Distance Moved Inches	Time TMU				Hand In Motion		CASE AND DESCRIPTION
	A	B	C or D	E	A	B	
¾ or less	2.0	2.0	2.0	2.0	1.6	1.6	**A** Reach to object in fixed location, or to object in other hand or on which other hand rests.
1	2.5	2.5	3.6	2.4	2.3	2.3	
2	4.0	4.0	5.9	3.8	3.5	2.7	
3	5.3	5.3	7.3	5.3	4.5	3.6	**B** Reach to single object in location which may vary slightly from cycle to cycle.
4	6.1	6.4	8.4	6.8	4.9	4.3	
5	6.5	7.8	9.4	7.4	5.3	5.0	
6	7.0	8.6	10.1	8.0	5.7	5.7	
7	7.4	9.3	10.8	8.7	6.1	6.5	**C** Reach to object jumbled with other objects in a group so that search and select occur.
8	7.9	10.1	11.5	9.3	6.5	7.2	
9	8.3	10.8	12.2	9.9	6.9	7.9	
10	8.7	11.5	12.9	10.5	7.3	8.6	
12	9.6	12.9	14.2	11.8	8.1	10.1	
14	10.5	14.4	15.6	13.0	8.9	11.5	**D** Reach to a very small object or where accurate grasp is required.
16	11.4	15.8	17.0	14.2	9.7	12.9	
18	12.3	17.2	18.4	15.5	10.5	14.4	
20	13.1	18.6	19.8	16.7	11.3	15.8	
22	14.0	20.1	21.2	18.0	12.1	17.3	**E** Reach to indefinite location to get hand in position for body balance or next motion or out of way.
24	14.9	21.5	22.5	19.2	12.9	18.8	
26	15.8	22.9	23.9	20.4	13.7	20.2	
28	16.7	24.4	25.3	21.7	14.5	21.7	
30	17.5	25.8	26.7	22.9	15.3	23.2	

A research report on *Short Reaches and Moves*[3] is available for help where needed. It includes data which was fully validated and then incorporated on the revised MTM card in March, 1955. The information given in this text agrees with that data. It represents closer evaluation of the shorter Reaches by running film at four times the speed used in developing the original data. This research revised the values for Reach Case A at 3 inches or less, Case B at 4 inches or less, Case E at 1 inch, Case A in motion at 3 inches or less, and Case B in motion at 2 inches or less. It is also the original source for the values at ¾ inches or less.

Note that the times are 2.0 TMU for all reaches ¾ inches or less. In the research on Short Reaches and Moves, it was discovered that this is apparently the minimum performance time for any human motion. It is apparently due to the physiological limits of human reaction time. This time minimum also seems to be independent of the degree of control involved in the motion in question. Isolation of this interesting fact is another original contribution by MTM research to basic motion data.

[3] R.R. 106 (See Ch. 5).

The data card, plus the information previously given, plus practical working rules which follow in the later portions of this chapter will enable one to establish time values for the various kinds of reaches encountered in the home, office, and factory.

THE SHORTHAND OF REACH

In order for the analyst to write down efficiently the various motions required, he must utilize a type of shorthand. This shorthand for the element reach is outlined in the following material.

Reach

Each time the work element reach is encountered, the engineer will indicate on his study sheet the capital letter R denoting Reach.

Distance of Reach

The distance in inches that the operator Reaches is noted following the letter R. All distances are expressed in inches when using the official data card values. Decimals or fractions are to be rounded off to the nearest whole number, unless they are less than one inch. For indicating distances under one inch, fractions may be used when the distance has been accurately measured and notation of this fact is desirable. In the more general case where the analyst knows the distance is ¾ inch or less, but the fraction is not known or easily determined, use of a small case f will suffice.

Example: R12 denoting a Reach of 12 inches
R⅝ showing a ⅝-inch finger Reach
Rf indicating a short Reach under ¾ inch, precise distance not known.

Case of Reach

The case of Reach is identified by the letters A, B, C, D, and E, and is noted following the distance.

Example: R12A denoting a Reach of 12 inches to a single object in a "fixed" location.

Type of Motion

Type I Motion, where the hand is not moving at either the beginning or the end of the Reach, requires no particular identification since it is the standard or most often encountered situation. The example of R12A illustrates this.

Type II Motion, where the hand is moving at either the beginning or the end of Reach, does require special identification. The lower case letter "m" denoting motion is placed either before the R denoting reach or after the letter denoting the case of reach. If it is placed before, it means that the hand is moving at the start of the motion; if it is placed after the case of reach, it denotes that the hand continued moving at the end of the reach.

Example: mR12A denotes that a Case A Reach of 12 inches occurred when the hand was already in motion at the start of the reach.

Type III Motion, where the hand is moving at both the beginning and the end of Reach, is identified by placing the lower case letter "m" both before the R and after the letter denoting the case of Reach.

Example: mR12Bm indicates the hand was in motion at both the beginning and the end of the Reach.

Change in Direction

A change in direction is denoted by placing the *small* capital letters CD to the right of the letter denoting the case of Reach. This is used for Case A Reaches only, to show that the time value used is that for a Case B Reach (see previous explanation).

Example: R12ACD

For other cases of reach, this symbol is not needed because the time is not materially affected by change in direction.

PRACTICAL WORKING RULES

The previous information has defined Reach, the various cases and types of reach, special conditions encountered, etc. The material which now follows contains additional practical rules of application, an interpretation of the data card, and other information which will be of value to the MTM analyst.

Measurement of Distance

The distance reached should generally be measured with a flexible steel rule. If one makes several sample Reaches and observes them closely, it will be noticed that the hand does not normally travel in a straight line but rather in an arc or with a curved motion. The curved path represents the distance that should be used in applying the MTM data. It is for this reason that a flexible steel rule is better for measurement purposes than, for example, a yardstick.

Distances should be measured and not estimated, unless one has had a great deal of practice in estimating distances and can do so quite accurately. All fractions or decimals should be rounded off to the nearest inch except those of ¾ inch or less. For these extremely short distances

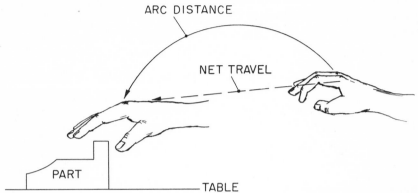

Fig. 8. Distance measurement. The inches of arc distance traversed by the index knuckle, as shown, is the chargeable distance of the Reach. It is improper to use the straight line net travel as Reach distance.

the minimum time of 2.0 TMU applies and the distance is normally indicated as an f (stands for fractional). The value for 1 inch applies to all distances over ¾ inch up to 1½ inches. This is a "rule of thumb" for short distances.

A practical reference point of measurement on the hand is the knuckle of the index finger. Figure 8 illustrates the proper method of making a measurement of Reach for an ordinary situation. In measuring short finger Reaches, the finger nail is an easy point from which to obtain dimensions of movement.

It has been found that the average person can Reach a maximum length, *horizontally,* of only 24 inches directly away from the body without making assisting body movements. If a radially forward horizontal Reach exceeds this distance, it can generally be assumed that some body movement was employed. The symbol and time for a 24-inch Reach would, therefore, be used in this event. Maximum arc distance for a move involving lateral motion with the arm extended could, naturally, exceed this. Shorter persons, of course, cannot Reach even 24 inches, whereas tall persons with long arms could Reach an even greater distance without supporting body movements. In defining the length of reach, one should specify the distance proper for the average operator, not the exceptional one. This principle of accounting for the average operator holds for specifying *any* MTM motion or motion combination.

Figure 9 illustrates the areas that can be covered by an average-build

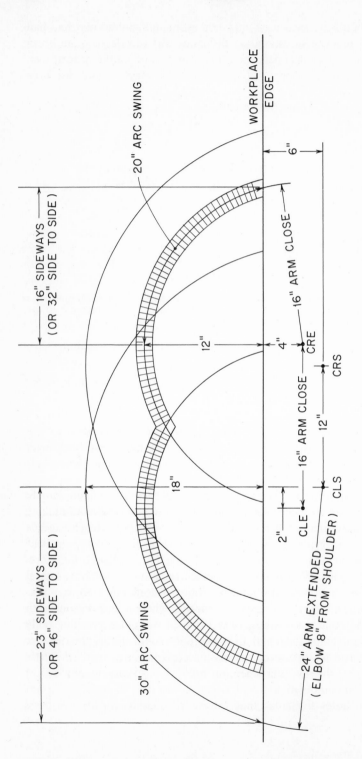

Fig. 9. Areas covered by *horizontal* Reaches and Moves without body assistance.

CRS = CENTER OF RIGHT SHOULDER
CRE = CENTER OF RIGHT ELBOW
(WHEN ARM CLOSE TO BODY)

CLS = CENTER OF LEFT SHOULDER
CLE = CENTER OF LEFT ELBOW
(WHEN ARM CLOSE TO BODY)

operator with arms extended and also for the condition where the elbow is close to the body. As shown in the figure, the distances covered are:

Arm Extended	Elbow to Body
18" Forward	12" Forward
23" Sideways	16" Sideways
30" Arc Swing	20" Arc Swing

The shaded areas near the inner arc boundaries represent the optimum location of materials, parts, and tools for the most efficient use of a worker's hands with minimum fatigue. To promote motion economy in tasks, *standard workplace* layouts should be based on this factor. Another noteworthy point is that, as a matter of regular policy, the operator should not be required to work for extended periods either beyond the outer limits shown or within the triangular area directly in front of his body. This figure thus gives valuable clues to guide the motion analyst when he prescribes the *workplace layout* to which any assigned working method is directly connected.

If the workplace requires the operator to Reach beyond the areas indicated, this is a general clue that it should be closely studied to see if arrangements could not be made to bring the material and the work area closer to the operator. Then assisting body movements which require more energy are not needed.

Body Assistance

The MTM data found on the data card is all based on motions made without the aid of body assistance. Therefore, if the body moves and thereby shortens the effective distance that the hand or arm must travel in making a Reach, or for that matter a Move, this assistance must be subtracted from the total distance traveled in order to determine the proper distance to use on the MTM data card. This net distance would also be shown in the symbol. You will recall, for example, that it has previously been stated that the average person is not able to Reach more than 24 inches radially from the body in the horizontal direction without utilizing a body movement to assist the arm and wrist movements.

The first case of body assistance is a simple one where the shoulder or torso moves simultaneously with the arm and in the same direction as the hand is traveling. To calculate the effective length of the arm motion, it is merely necessary to subtract from the total distance traveled by the hand the distance that the shoulder moved.

Figure 10 illustrates pictorially the situation just described. The allowed distance, and therefore the distance shown in MTM symbolism, is equal

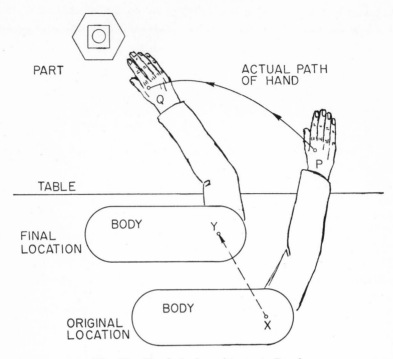

Fig. 10.   Simple body assistance to Reach.

to the total distance moved by the index knuckle from P to Q *minus* the distance that the shoulder moved, from X to Y.   This rule automatically adjusts the time allowed for the motion to a value which MTM research has shown to be justified for the kind of situation in question.   An alternate method of measurement of perhaps greater accuracy and ease would be to place the body in final position, while holding the hand and arm in the original location relative to the body and then measure the hand travel to get the allowable distance directly without extra measurement and calculation.

All MTM Reach and Move data is based on the distance moved without the help of body assistance.

When measuring shoulder movement, it is suggested that a point be selected about six inches from the spine, which is about the tip of the shoulder for most people.

A more complicated situation exists when body assistance is given the arm motion by means of a turning action due to pivot of the body about the spinal axis.   This is known as radial assistance, but actually consists of a combined assistance partly due to lateral assistance of the type described above and partly due to the pure radial assistance effect.   The amount of lateral assistance can be ascertained by noting the shoulder movement as already described. The amount of radial assistance can best be found by the theory of concentric circles as shown in Fig 11.

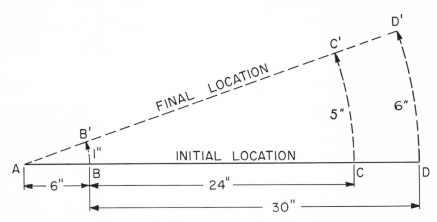

Fig. 11. Radial body assistance to arm motion.

The normal length of the *fully extended* arm being about 30 inches, a forward travel of 1 inch by the *shoulder* with the spine as a pivot will cause the *hand* to travel 6 inches. To get the allowable distance of Reach, then, would require deduction of 6 inches from the total Reach distance; however, 1 inch of the deduction is lateral assistance and the remaining 5 inches is due to radial assistance. The length ratios on the diagram should make this clear. Note that 5 inches of radial assistance was caused by 1 inch of shoulder movement under these conditions.

In case the arm is only *partly extended,* which would normally mean a length of 24 inches from the *shoulder* to the hand, a forward travel of 1 inch by the shoulder with the spine as a pivot will cause the *hand* to travel 5 inches. Therefore, 5 inches must be deducted from the total Reach distance to get the allowable Reach distance without combined body assistance. Note again that, although 1 inch of this distance is lateral assistance and the other 4 inches is radial assistance, the net effect is to gain 4 inches of radial assistance from 1 inch of shoulder travel.

To summarize the above information, at least insofar as the *radial assistance* itself is concerned, the following formula can be stated:

Allowed distance = total distance hand moved $- X \times$ distance shoulder moved

where $X = 5$ if the arm is fully extended or 4 if the arm is bent in the normal working position.

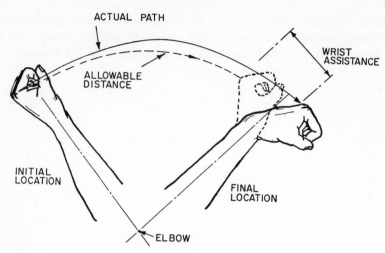

Fig. 12. Wrist assistance to arm motion.

Another case of body assistance occurs when the wrist assists the arm motion as illustrated in Fig. 12. The object was actually moved a distance equal to the distance moved by the arm plus the distance moved by the wrist. However, the wrist motion is not to be allowed because it was done simultaneously with the arm motion, which was, of course, the limiting factor and took up the total amount of time required.

Allowed distance = total distance moved by the index knuckle — distance attributable to wrist motion.

This last situation is mostly encountered in motions such as hammering.

When finger movements are used with arm movements similar to the above wrist assistance, the method for determining allowed distance is:

Allowed distance = total distance moved by the index knuckle — distance attributable to finger movement.

One of the best and most commonly used ways of determining the amount of any kind of body assistance is to make the arm and body movements separately, so that the amount of each can be measured. To do this, first move the body to its final position while holding the arm stiff in its original position, then move the arm along to its final position and note the effective arm movement. This technique works especially well for radial assistance. In using this method one is not required to use the formula for calculating allowed distance, because the measurement is directly the allowed distance.

It is well to remember in applying MTM that the average worker will usually tend to use body assistance in his motions, and only rarely will it be found that the worker uses body action which increases the chargeable distance—what could be termed body resistance. In some rare cases, body resistance is legitimate to the job. When this situation is encountered, it is obvious that the body resistance to the movement should be added to the effective length of the motion, rather than being deducted as is the case with body assistance.

Type II and III Reaches

Practical formulas for computing a TMU value for cases and types of reach *not shown directly on the data card* are as follows:

FORMULA NUMBER	CASE AND TYPE OF REACH	SYMBOLS FOR THE MOTION*	FORMULA FOR TMU VALUE*
(1)	Case A, Type III	mR (Dist.) Am = A Std. − 2 (A Std. − Am)	
(2)	Case B, Type III	mR (Dist.) Bm = B Std. − 2 (B Std. − Bm)	
(3)	Case C, Type II	mR (Dist.) C = C Std. − (B Std. − Bm)	
(4)	Case D, Type II	mR (Dist.) D = D Std. − (B Std. − Bm)	
(5)	Case E, Type II	mR (Dist.) E *or*	
		R (Dist.) Em = E Std. − (B Std. − Bm)	
(6)	Case E, Type III	mR (Dist.) Em = E Std. − 2 (B Std. − Bm)	

* "Std." represents the TMU value for a Type I Motion of the same case and distance as listed directly on the data card. An "m" in either the symbol or the formula designates the "m" value involved when acceleration and/or deceleration is absent from the motion, while Bm refers to the Hand in Motion B column time value from the data card. Am represents the time value from the Hand in Motion A column of the data card.

As an example of the use of these formulas, consider a reach symbolized by mR12Am. Using Formula (1) and the data in Table 2,

$$\text{TMU value} = 9.6 - 2 (9.6 - 8.1) = 9.6 - 2 (1.5) = 6.6 \text{ TMU}$$

The basis for these formulas becomes self evident with a little study of the Type of Motion section. They are merely algebraic expressions for the rules cited there. In essence, they show how the values in Table 2 are used to remove the time value of an "m" (see Table 1) in order to account for the absence of either an acceleration and/or deceleration period during the motion. The symbols themselves show the number of "m" values to be considered.

Odd Distance Reaches Over 10 Inches

The data card distances are listed at each inch up to the 10-inch value. Beyond this point, only the even number distances to 30 inches are shown. It can be shown from a plot of time versus distance that the curves permit use of straight-line interpolation to obtain inbetween values to sufficient accuracy. By the time the 10-inch value has been achieved, the curve becomes very close to a straight line for the remaining distances.

To find the time values for reaches of odd distance between 10 and 30 inches, therefore, merely add to the next lower "even inch" time half the difference between that time and the time for the next higher "even inch." For example, to find the time for R19C the procedure is as follows:

$$R20C = 19.8 \text{ TMU}$$
$$\underline{R18C = 18.4 \text{ TMU}}$$
$$\text{Diff.} = 1.4 \text{ TMU}$$

So that R19C = 18.4 + 0.5 (1.4) = 18.4 + 0.7 or *19.1* TMU

Similar procedure would be followed for odd distances exceeding 30 inches.

Reaches Over 30 Inches

This situation is encountered, for both reaches and moves, even though it was previously stated that reaches over 24 inches radially from the body do not normally occur without body assistance in the *horizontal* plane. If the operator is reaching straight out in front of the workplace in a horizontal dimension he normally cannot exceed a distance of 24 inches if body assistance is eliminated. However, if a sweeping motion is made from the right side of the work area to the left side with the arm extended, the total allowable distance traveled can be well over 30 inches. Reaches exceeding 30 inches can also occur when the motion is vertical.

To calculate TMU values for reaches over 30 inches, use the following formula:

$$R x'' \text{ (Case of Reach)} = R30 \text{ (Case of Reach)} + (x'' - 30'') \times \text{(factor for case of reach shown in Table 3 below)}$$

where: R = Symbol for reach;
  x = Distance reached, inches

Examples: *A.* TMU for an R42B:
  R42B = 25.8 + 12(.7) = *34.2* TMU

  B. TMU for an R39A:
  R39A = 17.5 + 9(.4) = *21.1* TMU

Table 3. TMU Values for Reach Increments Over 30 Inches

Case of Reach	A	B,C,D	E	Am	Bm
Additional TMU per inch of Reach over 30 inches	0.4	0.7	0.6	0.4	0.75

The above formula is based on the theory that the MTM data curves for distances over 30 inches have become straight lines. The factors in the table were therefore determined for each case of reach by subtracting the TMU value for 28 inches for each case of reach from the TMU value for 30 inches and dividing this by 2 to get the effective time value for 1 inch of movement. It is therefore not necessary to memorize the formula since the factors can always be redetermined in a very simple manner from the data card. It is only necessary to remember that the slope of the curve has become a straight line and the TMU value for 1 inch of movement is determined as outlined. Therefore, to calculate any time above 30 inches, once the factor is found, it is necessary merely to set down the TMU value for a 30-inch movement for the case of reach involved and add to it an amount equal to the TMU value for 1 inch additional reach multiplied by the number of inches over 30 inches that has been traveled.

How to Identify and Analyze MTM Motions

In making MTM studies, it is suggested that the *kind* of basic motion be first identified—such as reach, move, etc., and that the proper symbol, such as R, M, etc., be written on the analysis form. No attempt should be made to analyze the complete symbol for each motion in turn; attention should be focused on one thing at a time as discussed here.

The next thing for the observer to determine is the *classification and type* of each reach, move, grasp, etc. For example, when reach is observed, it is, of course, necessary to determine which of the five *cases* of reach are involved and this part of the symbol is next written down. The *type of motion* is indicated next. The other MTM factors for move, grasp, position, turn, etc., are handled in a similar manner.

The final step is to fill in the *distance* involved. In doing this, one must be careful to set down the correct allowed distance, taking into account the effect of body assistance, wrist assistance, finger assistance, etc. Similar practical rules will be given for each MTM element.

The last thing to put down is the TMU values. This can be done in the office, as it is a clerical routine. TMU time values are to be shown to the nearest tenth.

For the benefit of those not having previous experience with MTM, it might be mentioned that the problem of simultaneous motions, how to analyze these motions, etc., will be given as part of the material in later chapters and the reader should not concern himself with such questions at this point. They will be discussed only when all of the MTM elements have been explained in sufficient detail to make such consideration worthwhile.

SUMMARY

Reach (symbol R) is the basic hand or finger motion employed when the *predominant purpose* is to move the hand or fingers to a destination.

Table 4. Factors Causing Reach Time Variation and Symbols Employed

Causes of Reach Time Variation	Symbol
I. Length of Motion—The Distance	Arabic Numeral (or f)
The hand's path length measured in inches	
II. Destination—The Case	Case Letter
Case A—Reach to an object in a fixed location, in the other hand, or on which the other hand rests. (If a sharp change in direction occurs, the time for a Case B Reach is used.)	A or ACD
Case B—Reach to a single object whose location may vary slightly from cycle to cycle	B
Case C—Reach to an object jumbled with other objects in a group so that search and select occur	C
Case D—Reach to a very small object or where an accurate grasp is required	D
Case E—Reach to an indefinite location to get the hand in position for body balance, the next motion, or out of the way	E
III. Continuity of Motion—The Type	
Type I —Hand *is not* moving at either the beginning or end of the reach	None
Type II —Hand *is* moving at either the beginning or end of the reach	m
Type III—Hand *is moving at both* the beginning and end of the reach	m—m
IV. Examples of MTM Symbolism	
R6A R16ACD R10Bm mR8C mR4Bm RfE	

QUESTIONS

1. Write the MTM symbol and TMU time value required to reach, while in a standing position, from your right-hand trouser pocket to a pencil clipped in your shirt pocket.
2. Show the MTM symbol for reaching from your right-hand coat pocket, while in a sitting position, to brush a fly off the center of your forehead.
3. Write the MTM symbol for reaching into a totepan for a rivet. The totepan is normally full of rivets. Let the distance reached be 12 inches.

4. Write the MTM symbol for picking up a single common straight pin on the table directly in front of you. Assume your hand to be at rest in a normal position in front of you and that the distance reached is 8 inches.

5. Assume that you have a 12-inch deep, 10-inch square box sitting in front of you. Assume that you are sitting 8 inches from the edge of a table of normal height and that your hand is resting in front of you in an at-ease position. There is a pencil at the bottom of the box that you wish to obtain. Write the MTM reach symbols for the situation just described.

6. With the above-mentioned (see Question 5) pencil in your hand, reach to grasp a sheet of paper located directly to the right and 20 inches from the side of the box. Assume the hand starts its motion at the bottom of the box. The pencil is "palmed" during the movement but make no indication for this motion. Write the MTM symbol for this situation. Time value should also be shown.

7. Assume that you are sitting 4 inches from a table. A pile of common pins is located 8 inches from the table edge directly in front of you. Write the MTM symbol and time value for reaching from your right-hand coat pocket to pick up one pin from the pile.

8. Assume a bowl of mixed fruit at the center of a 3½ foot square breakfast table containing apples, oranges, pears, and several bunches of grapes. Suppose that you are going to reach to the bowl of fruit to obtain a grape. Write the MTM symbol and time value for the reach involved.

9. Assume that you are starting to drive an 8-penny nail while standing in front of a 30-inch high work bench. The nail already has been started into a 2 x 4 lying two feet in and parallel to the edge of the work bench. Raise the hammer so that the head touches your shoulder. The hammer is then brought down to strike the nail. Write the MTM symbol for this situation and state specifically how you arrived at the distance shown.

10. Assume that you are sitting in front of a rather long table, on the long side, and that your hand is 24 inches out from the right side of your body and on the edge of the table. You are now to reach to a pencil found at the left-hand edge of the table 24 inches out from the left-hand side of your body. Write the MTM symbol and time value for the reach involved. State specifically how you arrived at your answer for distance.

11. Assume that you are again sitting at a table and that you have in your left hand a common box of unused crayons containing 24 different colors. Your left hand, holding this box, is resting just at the edge of the table and is lined up with the left-hand side of your body. Your right hand is 12 inches to the right side of your body and at the edge of the table. Reach for a blue crayon in the box held in your left hand. Write the MTM symbol and time value for the situation just described.

12. Assume that you have been operating an arbor press on a certain operation for the past thirty days. Write the MTM symbol and time value for reaching from the bed of the press to the operating lever of the arbor press. Use whatever distance you feel is reasonable for this situation.

CHAPTER 8

Move

Definition[1]

MOVE[2] is the basic hand or finger motion employed when the predominant purpose is to transport an object to a destination.

*1. Move is performed only by the fingers or hand. Pushing an object with the foot would **not** be classified as a move.*

2. The hand must exert control over the object during the motion. In tossing an object aside, for example, the move motion ends when the fingers or hand releases the object.

3. The fingers or hand may be pushing the object or sliding it; it is not necessary to carry the object.

4. Using the fingers or hand as a tool is classified as a move. The fingers or the hand itself would be considered as a tool being carried by the hand.

As was true for reach motions, the deciding factor in classifying a motion as a move is its predominant purpose. An example of this distinction from the needle trades was given in the Reach chapter. In that case, reaches were made while a pair of scissors were palmed, their presence in the hand being ignored if the predominant purpose was to locate the hand in a given area—this being a reach motion. Now suppose that, after pinning some pieces of cloth together, the operator unpalms the scissors and brings them to the edge of the cloth to begin cutting. This latter motion is definitely a move of the scissors to bring them to cutting position, and the motion would be so classified. Generally, carrying such hand tools as pliers,

---

[1] From "MTM Basic Specifications" (Footnote 1, Chapter 7).

[2] The reader will recognize this motion as basically equivalent to the Therblig called Transport Loaded. Along with Reach, Therblig Transport Empty, it is the only other manual motion in which large distances of movement can be involved. All other MTM motions are of relatively small displacement, and this fact is a definite key to motion recognition.

tweezers, tongs, screwdrivers, etc. to a destination for the purpose of picking up or working on a part would properly be classified as a move.

The predominant purpose of the motion is the deciding factor in classifying it as either a reach or a move. Another mode of expression should make this matter crystal clear. If the hand is empty, the motion will obviously be a reach, except in the special case where the hand is used as a tool as described below. If the hand holds an object which must be located in a different place, the motion is definitely a move. Finally, if the hand holds an object as an incidental fact to the reason for the motion, a reach will be performed. Basically, then, the decision as to predominant purpose hinges on the reason for moving the hand—was it to relocate the hand, or was it to relocate the object? Answering this question in any given case will leave no doubt as to the kind of transport motion involved.

The use of the hand as a tool will be classified as a move, not a reach. In other words, when the hand performs useful work on the workpiece, the intent of the Move definition is fulfilled. The case of Move involved will naturally depend on the conditions of operation observed. Examples of using the hand as a tool are pounding with the fist to seat an object in a packing carton or using the fingers to crease a piece of paper.

KINDS OF MOVES

At present, the MTM Association recognizes three different cases of move, as identified by the following letters of the alphabet: A, B, and C. It is important to mention at the beginning that these are not equivalent categories to those given for reach motions. Such assumption would lead to errors in recognition, classification, and combination of move motions. Rather than attempting to match the cases in his mind, the reader should rely on the definitions for each case of move independently of reach cases which happen to be identified by the same letter of the alphabet.

Case "A" Move

Case A Move may be defined as follows:

Move an object to the other hand or against a stop.

The same time value was found to be appropriate for both parts of this definition. It is believed that this is due to the degree of automaticity imparted to the motion by either the "kinesthetic sense" of the operator or the presence of an object which will automatically cause motion to cease. At any rate, the degree of muscular control required by a Case A Move is at a minimum for move motions.

An instance of the first type of Case A Move occurs when a bridge player moves the shuffled deck from tapping it on the table toward the other hand to begin dealing the cards. The dealing hand, in this example, often performs a Reach, Case A toward the deck during the same time interval. This could, therefore, be one example of the fastest types of reach and move being performed simultaneously.

The point to notice about this part of the definition is that, because the destination of the object is the other hand, little doubt exists in the operator's mind as to the final location due to its being within the limits of proximity to the body where kinesthetic sense will function accurately. In this respect, the "fixed location" portion of the definition for Case A Reach is fulfilled; and remarks made about automaticity of motion under that discussion apply with equal force here.

There is an inference in the last paragraph that mental certainty of the object's location at all times during the move will promote the likelihood that a Case A Move is occurring. This justifies classifying another frequently observed move as a Case A—when the motion path of an object being moved is mechanically constrained or controlled.

Typical occurrences are lowering a drill spindle with the feed lever, operating the gear shift lever of an automobile, and sliding a coat hanger along a rack bar to obtain clearance for hanging additional clothing. In each of these events, there is almost no hesitancy in the motion, since the moving object is guided mechanically along a path of travel while the hand essentially supplies only the motive power. Measurement of the line or circular distance of knuckle movement in such cases greatly simplifies distance determination as well, the hand imparting almost negligible arc travel. All lateral motion of the object will depend on the mechanical constraint, the only deterring factor to excessive move speed being the exertion of a minimum degree of control to prevent damage to or by the object moved. In most (but not all) cases of mechanically constrained or controlled moves the MTM analyst will, therefore, specify a Case A Move. The main exception to this is when the object must be approximately or precisely located somewhere along the direction of travel at the end of the motion.

The second part of the definition, move an object against a stop, is typified by many common examples such as moving a book end against a group of books. The motion needed to close an open desk drawer that offers only minor resistance to sliding shut fulfills both parts of the definition for a Case A Move. Opening the same drawer fully could also exemplify a Case A Move if the travel was limited by another set of stops. Partial opening could be justified as a Case A Move on the basis of mechanical constraint by the slide rails, as discussed above.

The Case A Move is the fastest move up to a distance of 14 inches, at which the Case B Move becomes faster. This behavior probably is due to a change in the degree of muscular control required for the Case A Move as the travel distance increases. Some effort is then needed to avoid building up so much momentum (which depends on the weight and speed of the object) that the impact against the stop will endanger the part, the stop, or the operator. The resulting damage, injury, or loss of grip to any of these would not be worth a small time reduction in performing the motion. Apparently, this tendency is no problem at distances short enough to prohibit the attainment of excess velocity.

Moving an object against a double stop such as is shown in Fig. 1 is an additional action which sometimes occurs. A very skilled operator

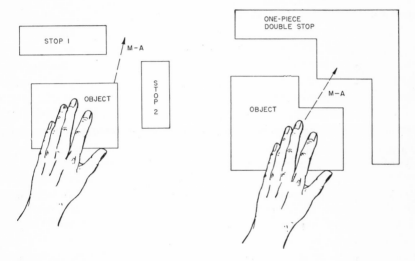

Fig. 1.   Moving an object against a double stop—single Case A Move.

will essentially bring the object against both stops in a single A move. Film analysis during MTM research indicated, however, that the average worker will first bring the object with a Case A Move against one stop, and this will be followed by a very short Case A Move of the object against the second stop. This is illustrated in Fig. 2 where the motion lengths have been exaggerated for pictorial purposes. The second move would actually be only two inches or less in length.

The angle between the stops or their configuration will affect the motion analysis in an interesting way. As the included angle between two straight stops becomes less than ninety degrees (within reasonable limits), the possibility of sliding the piece down into the proper location with a minimum amount of extra motion becomes greater. As the included angle goes above ninety degrees, however, the tendency to make two separate motions to seat the object in the stops is increased. Refer to Fig. 3 for clarification.

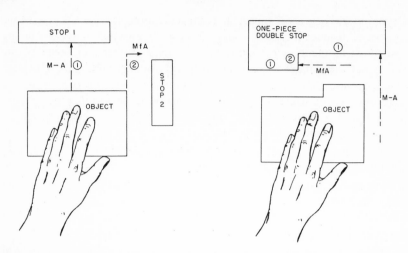

Fig. 2. Moving an object against a double stop—double Case A Move. An average worker will first bring object with Case A Move against one stop followed by very short Case A Move against second stop.

The MTM analyst must determine at the time of observation whether a given configuration will require one or two moves by the average operator to place the object against both stops. All will be A moves, however.

The preceding discussion on double stops affords an opportunity to present some more basic and general points of MTM theory. When the

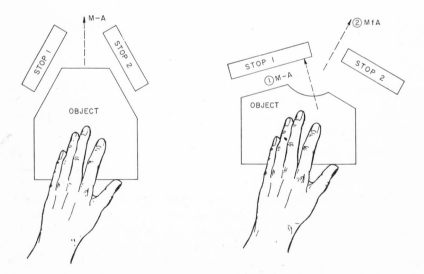

Fig. 3. Effect of angle between stops on number of Case A Moves needed. The tendency to make two separate motions to seat the object in the stops is increased as the included angle goes above 90 degrees.

reader attempts to actually observe the second short move against the double stop, he often becomes dubious about the above analysis. There is a perfectly logical reason for such confusion as to whether the second move actually takes place. This reason is that the motion time is less than the time for him to actually "see" a motion occur. In fact, an Eye Focus time of 7.3 TMU (refer to Eye Time chapter) is the minimum motion time that can actually be observed by the naked eye, and any motion taking less than this time must be recognizable by some other means. This would be with the aid of one of the MTM "rules of thumb," such as was given above for double stops.

The justification for many of the working rules of MTM is the fact just noted. Such rules are not wishful thinking or crude approximations. They result from the fact that the researcher is viewing films and/or analyzing other recorded data, much of it in great detail, to establish MTM times and motion rules. He is thereby armed with far more information than an analyst working on the factory floor or in an office without such aids. In practical terms, based on the Eye Focus time value, the research man can see the motions in anywhere from four to sixteen times as much detail, considering possible film speeds, as the MTM analyst can observe in the same motion sequence. The obvious import is that the MTM analyst must accept the "rules of thumb" in good faith with the research until such time as further research indicates a need for revision in the rules.

His attention should be on correct usage of the rules rather than on venturing to discover flaws and errors in them. If an apparent mistake in rules is believed to exist, the proper procedure is to send a request for further research to the MTM Association, since this is one of their most important and vital functions.

In practice, then, the MTM analyst must consider all of the factors and working rules involved prior to his decision as to what constitutes the correct identification for the motions in a given situation.

Case "B" Move

This case of move may be defined as follows:

Move an object to an approximate or indefinite location.

Moves of this kind are frequent in industrial operations and are relatively easy to identify in practice. Examples are:

1. Laying aside a paint mask
2. Moving a pair of wiring pliers to a clear area on the assembly bench prior to dropping them
3. Moving a pencil to another place on a desk to make room for work papers.

As was true for a Case B Reach, approximate location implies that location of the object within an inch or two of a certain point is sufficient. Obviously, which point in a given area might make little difference so long as the object's location was satisfactory at the end of the motion.

The second portion of the definition refers to an indefinite location. This covers such instances where at any convenient point in the path of travel of the object, optional within sensible limits of measurement, the object is tossed aside by letting go of it. Since the point at which the toss aside move ends will vary from piece to piece, a definite measurement cannot be made. However, a sensible average distance for the normal length may be estimated even though it is an indefinite quantity.

Clarity on the Case B Move is best served by a little historical elaboration. As would seem quite logical, the inventors of MTM presumed the existence of a definite similarity in the cases of reach and move and hence the need for similar case classifications. Reference to their book shows:

Move Case B—Move object to approximate location[3]
Move Case D—Toss object aside[3]
Move Case E—Move object to indefinite location.[3]

Interestingly enough, the time values listed for the B and E Cases were identical, while Case D times equalled those for in-motion Case B.

The subsequent research and examination of the records showed that these similarities were, in fact, true identities. In other words, there is not of necessity any one-to-one connection between the motions of the hands during reaching and moving, and this fact obviates the need for the original manner of classification of move. The old Case E Move category was therefore added to the present definition for Move Case B, and *tossing movements* (old Case D) *are properly identified as an M—Bm.* The latter type of motion is a Type II as discussed below. Symbols D and E are therefore no longer used to designate Move cases.

A distinguishing feature of the Case B Move is that a low degree of control exists, and no special care or caution is needed to accomplish the move. It might be termed in everyday language as an "ordinary" move.

Case "C" Move

The Case C Move is defined in this manner:

Move an object to an exact location.

---

[3] By permission from *Methods-Time Measurement* by Maynard, Stegemerten, and Schwab. Copyright, 1948. McGraw-Hill Book Company, Inc.

Examples of such moves are transporting a screw to a threaded hole or bringing the point of a screwdriver to the slotted head of a screw.

The term exact location usually implies that the hand will transport the object within half an inch or so of the destination point. Because of this closer distance limitation, it is evident that Case C Moves require appreciable control of the object, which causes greater time consumption. Case C moves are the slowest moves at all distances, although the differences are not as great as one might expect. Besides being due to higher mental and muscular control requirements, this is even more directly caused by the general requirement for the eyes to provide a high degree of visual control during the performance of Class C moves. The operator must either be looking at the destination point, or there must be some way in which equivalent information can reach his mental centers via kinesthetic sense. He must certainly know where to stop the motion in order to exert the proper degree of muscular restraint during the movement.

The analysis of assembly motions permits another example of the practical type of decision required of an MTM analyst. Since the reader does not know about the MTM motion called Position at this point, it should be mentioned that it basically consists of all assembly motions which follow movement of the parts to within the final limits for a Case C Move given above.

Now, looking at the question of assembly, suppose an object held in one hand must be assembled closely to another object in the other hand. This could occur in several ways. A highly skilled worker might assemble them under highly repetitive conditions with a Case A Move, since he is capable of developing a high level of automaticity where the hands end up close together. Even an average assembler with sufficient practice could perform certain such assembly using only a C move. The normal occurrence, however, would be a Case C Move followed by a Position. Keeping these alternatives in mind, the MTM analyst must resolve each occurrence to the proper motion categories, since time differences are noticeable in the three working methods.

Case C Moves will not necessarily be followed by Position motions. It should be clear, however, that when objects must be Positioned, the prior performance of a Case C Move is essential to bring them within half an inch of each other. This leads to the important MTM rule that *Positions are always preceded by Case C Moves.* Only rare exceptions have been found to this rule.

General

The three cases of Move recognized in the MTM procedure should now be clear. As was done for the reach categories, a memory device, or mnemonic, to assist the MTM analyst in identification is given by the following word associations:

Case A Move—Automatic
Case B Move—Basic or Broad
Case C Move—Control or Careful

TYPE OF MOTION

Most of the comments made in the Reach chapter concerning the nature and theory of Types I, II, and III motions apply equally well to the motion defined as move.

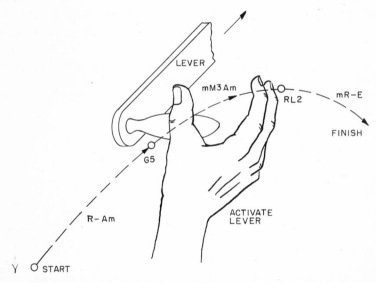

Fig. 4. Striking a machine feed lever with a cupped hand. Here a Case A, Type III Move is used as part of a sequence to activate an automatic feed lever of a machine.

Case A Moves of Types I, II, and III motions are all possible. One example of this would be a Case A, Type III Move used as part of a sequence to activate an automatic feed lever of a machine using a cupped hand as in Fig. 4. Such a sequence would consist of a Reach-in-motion-at-the-end, a Contact Grasp (explained in a later chapter), the Case A Type III Move, a Contact Release, and, finally, a Reach-in-motion-at-the-start. Examples of Type II Moves may be seen in Figs. 5 and 6 in the chapter on Reach.

All three motion types can also occur with Case B Moves. For instance, the now obsolete Case D Move was found to be a Case B Type II Move. It is the move involved in tossing aside an object, symbolized in MTM as shown:

Toss object aside	M12Bm	⎞	10.0 TMU
Let go of object	~~RL1~~	⎟	—
Hand to clear	mR4E	⎠	4.7 TMU
	Total		14.7 TMU

The dash (—) in the TMU column for RL1 shows the time is limited out; the meaning of this term will be given later in this text.

Disposing of objects in this manner obviously saves time, provided no injury to the part occurs from such handling.

The nature of the destination and control involved would naturally eliminate the possibility of Case C Moves in motion at the end. This leaves Type I and Type II in-motion-at-start as the only categories for C Moves.

As was true for Reaches, the MTM data card provides a means of determining the effect of acceleration and deceleration on Move motions. It was found that the effects of all cases of Move were essentially the same as for Case B Moves. The data card listing for hand-in-motion, Bm, shows the result of eliminating only one period of either acceleration or deceleration from the Type I Motion and therefore gives the times for Case B, Type II Moves.

A set of formulas is given later in this chapter for all other Type II and Type III Move motions. They all depend on subtraction to obtain the time value of one "m" or its equivalent and it is instructive to note the variation of these "m" values throughout the data-card distance range in Table 1. As in the case of Reach, the assumption is made again that, when developing times for Type II and Type III Moves exceeding 30 inches distance, the "m" value listed in Table 1 for 30 inches will govern beyond that distance.

Table I. Value of "m" in TMU for all cases of Move versus Distance in Inches

Inches	1	2	3	4	5	6	7	8	9	10	12	14	16	18	20	22	24	26	28	30
TMU	0.6	1.7	2.1	2.6	3.0	3.2	3.2	3.4	3.6	3.6	3.4	3.2	3.0	2.8	2.6	2.4	2.2	2.0	1.9	1.6

The values of "m" as shown in Table 1 can be copied on the data card and are then always available when needed.

It will be noticed that the effect of one period of acceleration or deceleration gradually increases to a maximum of 3.6 TMU and then decreases back to 1.6 TMU. It is believed that this effect is caused by the relatively lower degree of motion confinement in longer distances, the use of heavier and stronger muscles for longer moves, and the characteristics of velocity and acceleration which change to some degree at distances longer than about one foot.

Whether the suppositions just noted are valid or not, the "m" values given represent validated results of careful analysis of motion picture films. Recall the earlier explanation of the significance of this fact near the end of the discussion covering Case A Move above. Reporting values based on adequate research is not the same thing as validating reasons why the values vary as they do. In other words, the reasons behind the variation of validated data are highly desirable and should be determined; but this requires more complex and exhaustive research than that necessitated by determination of the values alone. This latter type of research as yet has not been done regarding the variation of "m" values; perhaps it might be at a future date.

CHANGE IN DIRECTION

Variation in moving time does occur due to change in direction, but the magnitude of this effect is so small as to justify neglect of it. Velocity compensations in the motion effectively cancel out the slight time increase caused by the small additional control in the moves.

EFFECT OF WEIGHT OR RESISTANCE

That an object's weight or the resistance it offers to motion will affect the time required to move it is a recognized fact. The originators of the MTM technique tentatively evaluated the extent of this factor's influence on moving time, and the result was a set of data utilizing percentage increases in time values as the weight being moved increased. These factors were used until March of 1955, when the MTM Association made official a new set of data by which the effect of weight on the movement of objects could be found.

The new factors are based on MTM research which may be found in detail in MTM Research Report No. 108.[4] The latest data for the evaluation of time effects of weight may be seen in Table 4.

The research was basic and exhaustive concerning the effect of weight on move time and provides answers to almost any question which could be

[4] R.R. 108 (See Ch. 5).

raised concerning it. Two main factors were determined to be major influences on the time needed for weighted moves. One factor which is usually, but not always, present was identified as the *Static Component*. The other factor, which is always present to increase the time for a move with weight, is known as the *Dynamic Component*. Both of these factors, and all other major considerations involved with moving weighted objects, will be summarized in the material following next.

Factors in Weight Control

1. TYPE OF MOVEMENT

An object may be moved in two general ways, depending on conditions surrounding the motion. It may be transported from one location to another *spatially*. This means that the only control and restraint of the object is by the hand(s) and that the object travels through space with no attachment to or guidance from any other agency. The other means of movement depends upon or is influenced by the contact or attachment of the object with other objects. For lack of a better term, this is denoted as *sliding movement*. In this case, part of the control comes from the hand(s) and the remainder from the support or guidance of all contacting or attached objects along the path of motion.

When an object has sufficient weight or resistance to movement to influence the time of movement, it then becomes important to identify which type of movement—spatial or sliding—is being evaluated. In the case of spatial moves, the full weight of the object must be overcome and controlled by the worker. For sliding moves, however, the effects of friction must be considered in addition when determining the actual amount of force and control required of the operator In the case of horizontal non-spatial (sliding) moves the operator must merely overcome the sliding friction. When the move is on a raised incline, there is a combination or resultant force (between the sliding frictional force and that of gravity acting upon the object being moved) which must be overcome. Stated in another manner, for all non-spatial moves of an object, the manual control or effort must over-balance the restraining force offered to performance of the motion, besides overcoming the weight, itself.

2. STATIC COMPONENT

The prior relationship between the object to be moved and the hand will directly influence the extent of manual control which must be gained and the amount of time involved in the total moving time Two conditions are possible.

(1) Either the hand already had enough control to start the movement, as when the object has been held spatially during earlier motions in a cycle; or

(2) the hand has not yet assumed sufficient control to permit the move to start, even though the fingers are already closed on the object.

For the latter case, the preceding grasping motion has been completed before move time begins. Reference to Chapter 12 on the MTM element Grasp will show that motion to be completed, by definition, as soon as the fingers have closed on the object to be moved. However, the Grasp times do not include the time to overcome other than minimal weight. As a practical approach, therefore, all the extra time due to controlling the weight of the object has been included in the Move weight factors. This avoids complicating the analysis for Grasp with weight factors in addition to those required for analyzing the Move of the object.

To move an object that has been grasped, the worker must first achieve *full* control of the weight of the object. This effort to gain control or "make ready" for moving is the *Static Component* of a weighted move. The time required to perform this portion of the Move depends primarily on the weight lifted or resistive force to be overcome. The MTM procedure provides a set of TMU time values that are constant for any given amount of weight or force application involved in a given move motion.

The data card table is based on a TMU time constant of $0.475 + 0.345 \times$ weight (in pounds). The value given by this formula may be used directly for very precise work. The constant time accounting for the static component of a given weight must be added to the total Move time in all cases *except when the object was under full control of the hand prior to the start of the move.*

3. DYNAMIC COMPONENT

The movement of an object having negligible weight requires the expenditure of a certain amount of time and energy which basically depend on the degree of control and the distance through which the object is moved. These factors are accounted for by the case of Move and the net distance traveled. However, during the movement of a weighted object, a number of *additional* variables increase the time needed and tend to induce greater fatigue. These will be discussed below. Their effect upon performance time is covered in MTM practice by the use of a multiplying factor which depends on the effective net weight of the object being moved. This multiplier accounts for the time increase that is attributable to the *Dynamic Component* of a weighted move. In other words, the Move of a weighted object, besides requiring the basic motion time and the time required for the static component where it is applicable, also involves or requires more time for the "travel" portion of motion.

It is easy to understand the dynamic component when one remembers that work measurement procedures basically evaluate the amount of work an operator performs. In physics, work is defined as the product of force or weight and the distance of action: Work = Force × Distance. For a given distance, then, the energy needed to do the work of moving a weight will increase as the amount of weight increases.

Moving a greater weight, in addition to requiring more energy will require more *time* to make the move. This fact emerged from the MTM research on weighted moves which showed that the average individual is capable of a certain power or rate of energy expenditure. Physics defines power as a given amount of work done in a given amount of time:

$$\text{Power} = \frac{\text{Work}}{\text{Time}} = \frac{\text{Force} \times \text{Distance}}{\text{Time}}.$$

Since the power of a worker is limited, he will logically be governed by a certain time limit to perform a given amount of work (the work to move a weighted object). Therefore, the time consumed by the dynamic component of movement will vary with the weight. The net result of this is a tendency for workers to move larger weights through shorter distances (less arc travel—more straight line travel) than they would for smaller weights.

The basic MTM Move data accounts for the Move "travel" time except for the effect of weight, which is logically and easily compensated for by an appropriate multiplier. The exact increase, usable for precise work, is 1.1 per cent per pound over the basic time.

There are two things which the analyst must be cautioned against regarding the movement of heavy objects. The first is that, when visualizing moves for MTM analysis, the engineer must be careful to specify reasonable distances which the normal operator can be expected to move the weight. During observation analysis, this is not a problem because the actual distance involved is directly measured. The second point is that mechanical handling with hoists, cranes, conveyors, and other material handling aids is indicated and used in most modern plants when the power output of the worker to move a given weight might be exceeded or where the power required will induce undue fatigue.

A suggestive per hand figure for the upper limit of weight to be handled is 35 pounds for women and 50 pounds for men. This will vary greatly with the class of worker, nature of the job, state of health, and similar considerations. In many states, legal limits are specified by law (usually in terms of total weight of objects *to be lifted*) and the reader should check the applicable laws in his locality to avoid making errors in work content specification.

4. DYNAMIC COMPONENT VARIABLES

By the nature of the film analysis used, the effect of the following variables on ordinary unweighted moves was fully included in the basic data times. However, when appreciable weights are being moved, *additional* time is consumed over the basic values because the variables here discussed assume greater effect on the velocity and acceleration characteristics of the movements. Several of the variables have a negligible effect, while others significantly influence the time to move a weighted object.

A. Manner of Hand Usage

There exists a number of ways in which the movement of a weight by the hands can occur. When an operator is right-handed, his right hand is termed the preferred hand; the opposite is true for a left-handed worker. It was found in the research that the use of preferred or non-preferred hands by a given operator made no great difference in the time to move a weight. Handedness thus appears to be more directly related to habit than to the time to perform work.

When transporting a weight either spatially or by sliding, the worker can use either one or both hands. The basic time values and the new weight factors were developed directly for the use of one hand. During the study, however, investigation was made into what effect was produced by the use of both hands to move a weighted object. This effect depends on the manner in which the two hands hold the object.

When both hands are actively supporting the weight, as for instance when they are both underneath a boxlike object, half of the weight will be supported by each hand. The *effective net weight* (*ENW*) for each hand in this case is one-half of the gross weight of the object for spatial moves, or one-half of the net friction force to be overcome in the case of sliding moves.

It also sometimes happens that one hand fully supports the weight of the object or overcomes frictional resistance, while the other hand merely aids in guiding the object. For example, a box may be held during a move with the right hand beneath it and the left hand contacting the left side of the box to steady it. In this case, the effective net weight for the right hand is the gross weight of the object, while the left hand essentially exerts zero effort to overcome the weight of the box.

The procedure is the same for either manner of two-handed moves. The *effective net weight* (*ENW*) is shown with the symbol for each hand motion in accordance with the actual situation for the hand in question. When time is assigned in accord with the rules governing "limiting" given in a later chapter, the hand carrying the same or greater ENW, whichever is applicable, will govern the time assigned. In essence then, when both hands are dividing the weight, the time assigned will amount to the same value as would be assigned in the case of one hand carrying a weight half as large as the weight actually being moved. The same procedure holds for cases of two-handed sliding except that friction must also be included in the calculation as discussed below.

B. Angular Direction of Movement

The research showed that the angular direction of the move path with relation to the vertical plane of the body as a reference does have more effect when weights are moved than is true for negligible weights. However, the time increase is not significant enough to require accounting for it in practical applications.

No apparent time differences appeared for up and down motions (vertical path) or left to right movement and vice versa. This lack of effect was not dependent on the weight of the object moved.

Radial directions of motion in the horizontal planes, in or out from the body cause small time differences. Motion toward the body seems to take slightly less than movement of weights away from the body; but, as mentioned above, this need not be considered in setting practical standards.

When the direction of motion is intermediate to the vertical and horizontal, the motion path will be at some angle between zero to ninety degrees from the horizontal. There is again a small move time increase for weights at the larger angles, but practically this can be neglected. Further research into the methods value of direction of motion may, however, be worthwhile.

C. Effect of Gravity

The time difference to move a weight straight up or straight down is extremely small. This was not the anticipated answer for the research. The data showed that the only difference is in the velocity and acceleration characteristics of the move. The velocity varies at different stages of the same path length, but the same end point for total time taken is achieved for either up or down movement. Also the maximum velocity attained is equal for both directions although the velocity peaks are at different length points in the path of travel. In any event, though, the length of path permitted by the arms is relatively so short that neither velocity nor acceleration affect the total time significantly.

D. Sex of Operator

The ability of male or female workers to handle weights in respect to the time required differs chiefly when larger weights are being moved. The proportional difference was found to be relatively constant regardless of the weight moved or the distance of movement, although the numerical difference increased with added weight.

For methods value, it is instructive to know that female operators are slightly more dextrous with weights of five pounds or under, the reverse is true for weights of over five pounds. The prevalent practice of using female operators for light hand assembly is thus verified, while the use of male workers for assembly of heavier parts is also suggested. For very large weights, a female will require from 10 to 18 per cent more move time than a male worker.

Sex differences are not therefore important from the time standpoint so long as the male workers are properly assigned to heavy jobs and legal or sensible limits as to weight are respected in specifying job content for either sex. The weight factors as given are directly applicable to male operators. For either sex, fairness to the operator demands any reasonable revision in the methods of handling, such as mechanical devices, with heavier weights.

E. Effect of Friction

The static and dynamic factors were developed directly for spatial moves and are to be applied in accordance with the ENW for the move in question. When sliding moves occur having friction or equivalent resistive effects, the same factors will apply provided the true ENW (which will ordinarily be less than for a spatial move of the same weight object) is determined by the laws of friction.

The object's weight will be the primary cause, for example, of frictional resistance to sliding a large packing case along a concrete floor. The differentiating point about such cases of friction or similar weight-induced resistances to moves from the spatial type is the fact that part of the weight is borne by the supporting or guiding surface along which the object is moved. The hands must exert only enough extra control to overcome the friction force component in the direction of motion, and this is almost always smaller in terms of ENW than for spatial movements. However, one may occasionally encounter a case where the worker must overcome the friction forces caused by a mechanically constrained system. Also, in some cases he must also overcome, as mentioned earlier in this chapter, some or all of the weight of the object, the amount being dependent upon the angle to the horizontal of the movement involved. In the latter case the weight component and friction forces must be added to find the ENW. In all cases involving friction, the easiest way to determine the ENW may often be to use a spring scale and observe the amount of pull required to move the object.

Obviously, the engineer applying MTM can utilize his knowledge of Applied Mechanics effectively in determining the net value of the resistance in such occurrences. When measurements are difficult or impossible to make for the data needed to apply this knowledge to a given problem, the sound engineering judgment of the MTM analyst should enable a reasonable estimate of the friction effect. Note also that when adhesives are present, special motion analysis should be made, since this would not exemplify the ordinary concept of sliding friction.

To determine the ENW per hand when friction is present, the ENW as found for a spatial condition must be multiplied by a factor, always less than one, known as the coefficient of friction. For all practical purposes, a good average figure for all conditions is 0.4, in other words the ENW for sliding will be 40 per cent of the ENW for spatial moves of the same object weight. Actually, the coefficient of friction varies with the composition of the surfaces, the nature of surface finish, the velocity of motion, and there is even a difference between static and dynamic coefficients.

Research has shown that, for the complexity and range of velocities encountered in manual motions, the effective change in coefficient of friction is very small. As to the surface composition and nature of finish, as well as state of lubrication, it may be desirable to account for the change in the coefficient in some instances. For this purpose, the commonly accepted values of friction coefficients given in Table 2 should prove adequate.

Table 2. Coefficients of Friction (Average Values)

Surface	Friction Coefficient	Average Value
Wood on Wood	0.3 to 0.5	0.4
Wood on Metal	0.2 to 0.6	0.4
Metal on Metal	0.3	0.3

It can be seen from this table that use of 0.4 as an average value is a relatively safe procedure.

Effective Net Weight

When all of the variables discussed above are summarized, a practical procedure for the evaluation of the extra time involved in moving weights above the basic time value will obviously depend on the ENW for the case in question. The new weight data provides a constant factor for the *Static Component* and a variable factor for the *Dynamic Component,* but both of these factors are based on the ENW of the move being assigned a time value. The procedure in any particular case is as follows:

1. Decide the case of Move and the net distance involved for the hand(s)
2. Determine the ENW, per rules given below
3. Write the complete motion symbol, as described in the section on THE SHORTHAND OF MOVE below, for each hand (either one or both hands may be involved)
4. Find the TMU value for the basic motion of each hand from the data card
5. Find the dynamic factor to be applied to the basic time value for the ENW of each hand from the data card. For precise work, the exact value of 1.1 per cent increase per pound may be used instead
6. Multiply the basic time for each hand by the dynamic factor
7. Read the constant factor to be added to the time for each hand for the static component, *if* the static component is needed. It is needed if the grasp was just completed. It is not needed if the object was already under firm control by the hand in question. For precise work, the exact value of $[0.475 + (0.345) \times (\text{weight in pounds})]$ TMU may be used
8. Add the constant value to the time for each hand found in Step 6
9. When both hands are involved, allow the time for the hand taking the greater amount of time as found in Step 8.

Although it takes a number of words to describe this process of finding the time for weighted moves, the calculation is very *easy* and *quick* after a little practice. For analysts who prefer charts, the authors have prepared

Table 3. Rules for Determining Effective Net Weight (ENW)

Spatial Moves	ENW	Sliding Moves	ENW
One Hand	W	One Hand	$W \times Fc$
Two Hands:		Two Hands:	
One Active Only	W	One Active Only	$W \times Fc$
Both Active	$\frac{1}{2}$ W	Both Active	$\frac{1}{2}$ $W \times Fc$

W = Gross weight of object in pounds.   Fc = Coefficient of friction.   Average value of 0.4 may be used with acceptable results in most cases.

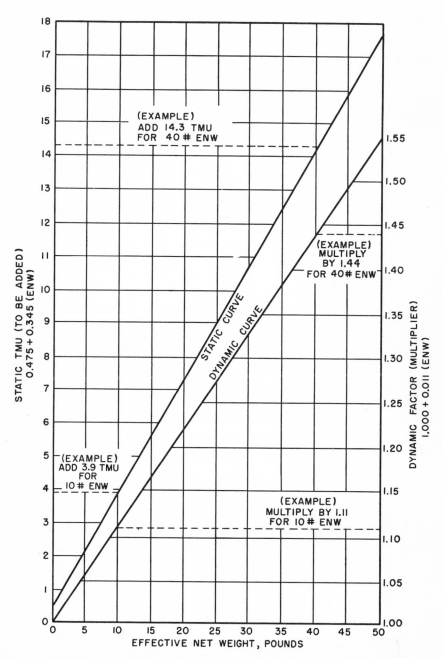

Fig. 5. Plot of exact weight-allowance time for Moves.

the one given as Fig. 5. This chart includes examples which make its usage obvious. The rules for determining the Effective Net Weight (ENW) are given in Table 3. The reasons behind these rules have been fully explained in the section on variables in movement of weights. A little practice will make this computation almost automatic.

THE SHORTHAND OF MOVE

To enable the analyst to record the various Move motions in a minimum amount of time, the conventional symbols outlined in the following paragraphs are used. These are similar to the shorthand for Reach motions.

Move

Each time the work element Move is encountered, the analyst will record the capital letter M denoting move on his study chart.

Distance of Move

The distance in inches that the operator moves the object is written after the letter M. Rounding off to the nearest whole inch is the practice except for distances less than 1 inch. Fractional dimensions (refer to Reach chapter) will be indicated by either the known fraction or a small case f.

Examples: M12 denotes a Move of 12 inches.

M⅝ shows a ⅝-inch Move.

Mf indicates a short Move under ¾ inch, precise distance not known.

Case of Move

The case of Move is identified by the letters A, B, and C appearing after the distance specification.

Example: M12A denotes a Move of 12 inches to the other hand or against a stop.

Type of Motion

This variable is symbolized exactly as was done for Reach.

Weight Factor

Following the convention for the case of Move, there is written the necessary numerals for the effective net weight (ENW) corresponding to the weight factor used from the data card.

Examples: M12B25 shows that a 25-pound object was moved 12 inches to an indefinite location.

M12Bm5 shows that a 5-pound object was moved 12 inches and then dropped or tossed aside as the hand opened. (This kind of motion is often encountered when an operator drops an object in a tote pan and continues on to reach for another object or when he tosses aside an object.)

Notice that the measured or estimated weight or resistance to the nearest pound is written in the symbol to show what weight factor was used to determine the Move time. Refer to the "up to and including" specification mentioned in the paragraph following Table 4.

If the MTM analyst wishes to make a record of how an exact measured weight or resistance was determined for the particular Move motion, he should do this in the word description column of the work study form. When a weight was accurately determined during observation, the method used does deserve mention on the study form. In fact one MTM convention (accepted rule) uses this idea to distinguish between two differing possibilities. The two would otherwise be indeterminate by the usual method of recording motions on the study form. Assume that, on the same line of an analysis, the left-hand column shows an M12B5 and the right-hand column an M12B15. If no other MTM symbol appears, this means that simultaneously the left hand moved a 5-pound object and the right hand moved a 15-pound object. If actually a 20-pound object was moved using both hands, with the left and right hands supporting 5 and 15 pounds respectively, the convention requires writing of the symbol "20/2" in both description columns. This shows that one object was handled by both hands together, with each hand supporting the amount of ENW shown in the symbol recorded for that hand.

When the weight moved is so minor as to not require mentioning, no numerals after the case letter need be shown. To indicate token resistance for any special reason, the symbol may show a "2" for weights not exceeding that amount; since the weight factor would then be 1.00, the time would be the same as for the base move motion.

Example: M16B2 illustrates the presence of more than minor resistance, but not enough to affect the move time.

DATA CARD INFORMATION

The MTM analyst obtains his data for the work element Move from the MTM data card, and as is reproduced fully in Table 4. As was true for Reach data, certain time values obtained from extrapolation of curves rather than direct observation appear on Table 4 and the official data card in light-faced type. These are Move Case B in motion at 3 inches and under, Case C Moves for 26 inches and greater, and in motion B Moves at 26 inches or more distance. Remarks on this subject in the Reach chapter are equally valid here. The research report on *Short Reaches and Moves*[5] suggested several modifications of the data in question.

The data card information, combined with the information previously given, plus practical working rules which follow in this chapter will enable the MTM analyst to establish time values for the various kinds of moves met in ordinary work situations.

It is often the practice for MTM analysts to weigh or estimate objects to the nearest five pounds. This fact influenced the way in which the data card factors for weight allowance shown in Table 4 were tabulated.

Table 4. Time Data for Move (MTM Data Card Table II—Move—M)

Distance Moved Inches	Time TMU				Wt. Allowance			CASE AND DESCRIPTION
	A	B	C	Hand in Motion B	Wt. (lb.) Up to	Factor	Constant TMU	
¾ or less	2.0	2.0	2.0	1.7	2.5	1.00	0	
1	2.5	2.9	3.4	2.3				
2	3.6	4.6	5.2	2.9	7.5	1.06	2.2	A Move object to other hand or against stop.
3	4.9	5.7	6.7	3.6				
4	6.1	6.9	8.0	4.3	12.5	1.11	3.9	
5	7.3	8.0	9.2	5.0				
6	8.1	8.9	10.3	5.7	17.5	1.17	5.6	
7	8.9	9.7	11.1	6.5				
8	9.7	10.6	11.8	7.2				
9	10.5	11.5	12.7	7.9	22.5	1.22	7.4	B Move object to approximate or indefinite location.
10	11.3	12.2	13.5	8.6				
12	12.9	13.4	15.2	10.0	27.5	1.28	9.1	
14	14.4	14.6	16.9	11.4				
16	16.0	15.8	18.7	12.8	32.5	1.33	10.8	
18	17.6	17.0	20.4	14.2				
20	19.2	18.2	22.1	15.6	37.5	1.39	12.5	
22	20.8	19.4	23.8	17.0				
24	22.4	20.6	25.5	18.4				C Move object to exact location.
26	24.0	21.8	27.3	19.8	42.5	1.44	14.3	
28	25.5	23.1	29.0	21.2				
30	27.1	24.3	30.7	22.7	47.5	1.50	16.0	

The first column of the Weight Allowance section of Table 4 is headed "Wt. (lb.) Up to." The values above 2.5 pounds in this column are the end points of five-pound weight intervals. The factors given in the two adjacent columns apply to all weights in the respective five-pound interval up to and including the weight value alongside the factors. The factor of 1.11 and 3.9, for example, apply to any ENW above 7.5 pounds up to and including 12.5 pounds.

[5] R.R. 106 (See Ch. 5).

The values of the factors listed are actually correct only for the middle of the weight intervals shown, which would be at the five-pound breakpoints. Thus, for example, the factor 1.11, which applies for weights in the interval from 7.5 pounds up to and including 12.5 pounds, is, strictly speaking, correct only for an ENW of 10 pounds and is only approximately correct for all other ENW's in the interval. When more precise answers are warranted by study conditions, the exact formulas given in the weight factor discussion should be applied. The data card values are, however, adequate for the usual motion analysis and were therefore presented in the form shown to eliminate the need for interpolation when weights slightly more or less than the midpoints in the five-pound intervals are encountered.

Because body motions or both hands are usually present when very large weights are lifted, there is seldom need to extrapolate the data card weight factors for loads in excess of 47½ pounds. In most such cases, the use of mechanical handling equipment or adequate exploration of body motion application is strongly indicated. However, when on occasion pure Moves for loads in excess of 47½ pounds must be evaluated, the static and dynamic weight factors can be evaluated from the following extrapolation formulas which are based on *the exact formulas previously given:*

$$\textit{Static:} \; 15.5 + 2.2 \left(\frac{\text{ENW} - 45}{5} \right)$$

This extrapolation formula says that for an ENW greater than 45 pounds the number of TMU is equal to 15.5 TMU for the first 45 pounds plus 2.2 TMU for each 5 pounds of ENW in excess of 45 pounds.

$$\textit{Dynamic:} \; 1.495 + 0.055 \left(\frac{\text{ENW} - 45}{5} \right)$$

This extrapolation formula says that the dynamic factor for an ENW greater than 45 pounds is equal to 1.495 for the first 45 pounds plus 0.055 for each 5 pounds of ENW in excess of 45 pounds.

As an example of the use of these formulas, the weight factors for an 80-pound ENW would be:

$$\textit{Static:} \; 15.5 + 2.2 \left(\frac{80 - 45}{5} \right) = 15.5 + 15.4 = 30.9 \text{ TMU for 80 pounds}$$

$$\textit{Dynamic:} \; 1.495 + 0.055 \left(\frac{80 - 45}{5} \right) = 1.495 + 0.385 = 1.88 \text{ for 80 pounds}$$

PRACTICAL WORKING RULES

Most of the information contained under this heading in the Reach chapter will apply equally well to the motion defined as Move. The main exception would be the practical formulas used to compute TMU values below. Therefore, only reference listing will be made here unless additional factors affect the particular topic listed.

Measurement of Distance

This is the same as for Reach motions. Note especially that Fig. 9 of the Reach chapter applies specifically to Moves without body assistance.

Body Assistance

One extra factor not listed in the Reach discussion merits mention here. Since large weights will be moved with either body assistance or extra body motions, rather than with the hands and arms alone, the MTM engineer should carefully notice during analysis of such Moves just what the true facts are. Being alert to this idea will help him to classify his motions correctly.

Types II and III Moves

Practical formulas for figuring types and cases of Move not shown directly on the data card are as follows (where the symbolism is the same as in the Reach chapter for similar formulas):

Formula Number	Case and Type of Move	Symbols for the Motion	Formula for TMU Value
(1)	Case A, Type II	m M (Dist.) A or M (Dist.) A m	$=$ A Std. $-$ (B Std. $-$ Bm)
(2)	Case A, Type III	m M (Dist.) A m	$=$ A Std. $-$ 2 (B Std. $-$ Bm)
(3)	Case B, Type III	m M (Dist.) B m	$=$ B Std. $-$ 2 (B Std. $-$ Bm)
(4)	Case C, Type II	m M (Dist.) C	$=$ C Std. $-$ (B Std. $-$ Bm)

The basis for these formulas becomes self-evident with a little study. The point to remember is that the acceleration or deceleration time for a given length of Move is a constant, regardless of the case of Move.

Odd Distance Moves Over 10 Inches

This is the same as for Reach motions.

Moves Over 30 Inches

This is the same as for Reach motions except for the extension TMU values. These are given in Table 5.

Table 5. TMU Values for Move Increments Over 30 Inches

Case of Move	A	B	C	Bm
Additional TMU per inch	0.8	0.6	0.85	0.75

How to Identify and Analyze Move Motions

The general analysis procedure for Move motions is the same as was described in the Reach chapter. However, several additional items are presented here which broaden the reader's analysis techniques.

Occasionally an analyst observes moves which do not fit exactly any of the standard MTM definitions. Examples of such moves are those found in spray painting, welding, metal filing, buffing, hand rubbing, polishing, etc. In practically every such case, an object being used to produce useful work is in the operator's hand. However, the control of the move is not strictly manual due to process factors. There seems to be some room for analyst judgment here. If most of the control is by the operator, some analysts accept a slight loss of accuracy and assign MTM moves to the task. Others "tinker" with the situation to make up the time deficit from a normal MTM move by assigning, say, a Case C Move instead of Case A or B or by adding synthetic weight factors. While both of these practices often yield a workable answer, they are a *misuse of the MTM procedure*. The proper analysis is to recognize them as process time and use a stop watch or other timing instrument to more correctly and accurately determine the required time.

However, as previously mentioned, MTM Moves are correct for the usage of many hand tools. This does not imply that the application is simple in all cases, as is illustrated by considering hammering motions. Raising the hammer to get ready for striking definitely is a Case B Move. If the hammer weighs more than 2.5 pounds, the raising motion always would involve the dynamic weight factor; and the first time it was picked up and raised would also require the static weight factor. To this point, the analysis has been routine with respect to MTM motions.

Analysis of the striking motion, however, presents some challenge to the determination of hammering movements. To establish the first fact, the striking motion definitely is operator controlled rather than process controlled. But does it conform to the usual behavior reflected by the MTM Move motions with respect to acceleration and deceleration? At the start of the striking motion, the acceleration does build up in the normal manner. However, the stroke does not achieve a relatively stable velocity and then gradually decelerate (for a period of time regarded equal to the acceleration period) to the end point as does a normal spatial MTM move. Indeed, the whole purpose of the striking motion is to increase the momentum of the hammer head to assure that the required impact force is generated. This means that the aim is to continue speeding up throughout the stroke. Only at the point of impact does any deceleration appear, and then it is extremely abrupt. Therefore, the striking motion must be similar to a Type II Move in motion at the end; but it probably requires less time than does the normal MTM Type II Move. Thus, either the striking motion should be timed for accuracy or else the analyst can specify an MTM time with the knowledge that it may be too "loose." If the hammering is a relatively small part of the total work cycle, the latter approximation may well be reasonable. To carry this illustration forward, let it be assumed that such is the case.

With this assumption, the striking motion can be analyzed as follows. The dynamic weight factor will apply for all hammers over 2.5 pounds in weight. Also, wrist assistance will tend to shorten the net move distance, as well as to impart some of the required momentum. An easy way to measure the wrist assistance is to first move the wrist to its final orientation and then determine the length of the remaining striking path at the index knuckle without the complication of wrist assistance. As to case of move, the destination accuracy required will decide this. Case A will apply for rough pounding blows, Case B for routine hammering, and Case C for accurate aiming of the hammer head. The net analysis therefore could be M—Am, M—Bm, or M—Cm together with the appropriate net distance and ENW. Note that the M—Cm is not an exact motion description, because Type II Case C Moves are not possible; this is merely a way to show deduction of the deceleration time for this analysis. Actually, the M—Am and M—Bm also would not denote in-motion at the end either. This is an approximation of the real event—an "equivalent" motion—for purposes of assigning a reasonable time value by eliminating the deceleration time in these two cases as well.

To complete the hammering analysis, consider next the return stroke after striking has occurred. Usually this will be an M—B with any required ENW for the dynamic weight factor. However, in certain types of hammering, the struck object imparts a definite and significant bounce to the hammer head. To shorten this analysis, the reader should recognize that this would justify an "equivalent" motion of mM—B, a Type II in-motion at the start. Of course the ENW and wrist assistance would again enter into the symbol and time assigned.

With this discussion of process time and the "equivalent" motions as illustrated by the hammering analysis, the reader should be able to apply the Move data with greater awareness of both its utility and limitations. Also, this knowledge will aid in understanding practical usage of all other MTM motion data.

SUMMARY

Move (symbol M) is the basic hand or finger motion employed when the *predominant purpose* is to transport an object to a destination.

Table 6. Factors Causing Move Time Variation and Symbols Employed

Causes of Move Time Variation	Symbol
I. Length of Motion—The Distance	Arabic Numeral
The hand's path length measured in inches	(or f)
II. Destination—The Case	Case Letter
Case A—Move an object to the other hand or against a stop	A
Case B—Move an object to an approximate or indefinite location	B
Case C—Move an object to an exact location	C
III. Continuity of Motion—The Type	
Type I—Hand *is not* in motion at either the beginning or end of the Move	None
Type II—Hand *is* in motion at either the beginning or end of the Move	m
Type III—Hand *is in motion at both* the beginning and end of the Move	m—m
IV. Weight or Resistance	
The effective weight of the object lifted or its counterforce resistance to motion expressed in pounds. See text discussion	Arabic Numerals
V. Examples of MTM Symbolism	
M10A M6Bm M14B15 mM20C MfA	

QUESTIONS

1. What MTM symbol and TMU time value would correctly depict the motion of bringing a cigarette to a smoker's mouth from a pack held in his left hand?
2. A man who is standing 18 inches from the center of a door brings a key from near his right-hand trouser pocket to the keyhole of the door, which

is located on the right-hand portion of the door about level with his belt line. Write the MTM symbol and time value he employs for this.

3. Suppose a mechanic kneeling near a tire lying flat on the cement floor in front of him has just picked up a rubber-headed mallet near his right knee. He wishes to strike the tire rim a sharp blow to drive it into place. What sequence of MTM motions will he perform to raise the mallet into working position, strike the tire rim, and bring the mallet into position for another blow on the rim? Hint—The elasticity of the rubber head of the mallet will cause it to rebound from the tire rim when the blow is struck.

4. An operator has just finished using her right hand to place two small screws into a paper envelope held directly in front of her by the left hand. Her left hand will next convey the envelope about 12 inches to the left by a circular path, drop the filled container in a tote box, and continue the circular path toward an empty envelope from a supply in a second tote box about 16 inches further. This series of motions will proceed in a continuous circular sweep. By what MTM symbols and time values should the observing analyst account for the actions of her left hand?

5. You are sitting about 4 inches from the edge of a table and have just picked up a pencil which had been laid parallel and 2 inches from the table edge earlier. You used your right hand, and the pencil was directly in front of the normal location of the right hand relative to the body. You will now place the pencil on the table as far back as possible, using a motion path perpendicular to the edge of the table, without leaving the seat of your chair. Write the complete MTM symbol and TMU value for this motion, and state specifically how you made your decision. Also indicate the final distance of the pencil from the table edge at the completion of the motion.

6. Place two pencil dots approximately 6 inches apart on a sheet of 8½ x 11 paper. Hold a foot ruler about 10 inches away from the two dots, almost parallel to the dots. Now tell what MTM symbols and time values will properly describe any *Moves* you will make to bring the ruler edge into alignment with the dots. Although the MTM element called *Position* might also be involved in placing the ruler correctly, you are asked to ignore this for purposes of this problem.

7. After having completed placing the ruler as mentioned in the last question, you then have set the point of your pencil on the left dot. Now move the pencil along the ruler edge to the other dot. What is the MTM shorthand symbol and applicable TMU value for the latter motion you performed?

8. Using your fingers only, crease in the lengthwise direction a piece of folded paper 12 inches long that is being held in the air by your other hand. Following this, perform a similar creasing operation while holding the paper on a table top, using light pressure against the table surface by the fingers. Analyze the symbols and time values with MTM for both creasing operations.

CHAPTER 9

Turn

Definition[1]

TURN[2] is the basic motion employed to rotate the hand about the long axis of the forearm.

1. The hand may be empty or holding an object.

2. Turn cannot be made while holding the wrist firm. Turn involves the two bones in the forearm and a pivoting motion at the elbow.

While pure Turns as defined above do sometimes occur in industrial operations, they occur more frequently in combination with Reaches and Moves. This fact has led to statements by some sources that Turn is a special way of performing a Reach or Move. Such is not the case. While it is true that Moves and Reaches may include performance of the basic motion Turn, this does not preclude the ability of the worker to accomplish pure Turns alone.

Clarity on the distinction just made may be afforded by resorting to the reader's knowledge of mechanics and physiology. When the hand reaches or moves, with no shoulder or body assistance being employed, the manual members (hand, wrist, forearm, and upper arm) all exert their muscular influence on the motion with essentially *hinging* actions of each

---

[1] From "MTM Basic Specifications" (Footnote 1, Chapter 7).

[2] The motion defined here is not a Therblig, but was first identified and isolated as to time during the Methods-Time Measurement research. That it is a distinctly different motion from Reach or Move as to performance, time, and measurement will be evident from this chapter. This discovery afforded ready explanation of many previously dubious motion occurrences, and the results derived from its use in a practical way has justified separate consideration.

or several skeletal joint(s) guiding the performance. When, however, the manual members must accomplish a Turn, the required rotating effect of the hand must be produced by additional muscles not used during Reach or Move. The bone joints must now be subjected to *torsional* actions by the employment of less efficient muscles, and this clearly indicates a distinct performance time from that described above. Logic thus amply supports the isolation of this Turn motion from other manual actions.

Turn as just described may occur as a separate motion or in combination with others. When it occurs by itself as a pure Turn, the forearm axis (axis of rotation) is not displaced laterally. When in combination

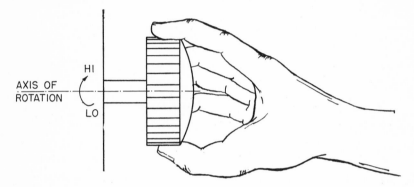

Fig. 1. Example of pure Turn. A pure Turn illustrated by the rotation of a control knob about its fixed axis. That the axis of rotation does not change location is evident.

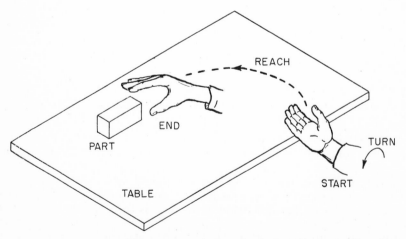

Fig. 2. Example of Reach-Turn. With the palm initially facing upward, a Reach for an object is made while the palm revolves to face downward. The axis of rotation for the turning has obviously shifted almost as great a distance as was reached.

with Reach or Move, lateral displacement of the forearm axis does occur. Examples of Pure Turn, Reach-Turn, and Move-Turn are shown in Figs. 1, 2, and 3.

A pure Turn motion practically always involves the use of only one hand. This is because the long axis of the forearm must be nearly perpendicular to the plane of rotation to permit the Turn to occur. This is

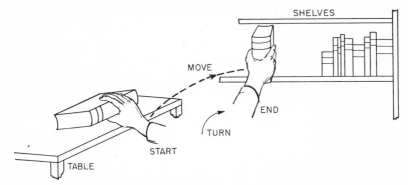

Fig. 3. Example of Move-Turn. Suppose a book was lying flat on a table just prior to being grasped by the operator. Should it next be moved to a library shelf nearby in such a manner that it will be inserted upright, a right-angle Turn must have taken place in the distance of movement. During this Move-Turn, of course, the axis of rotation again shifted almost as much as the Move distance.

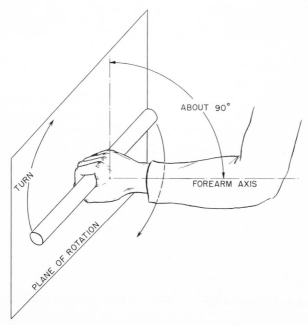

Fig. 4. Relation of forearm and plane of rotation in Turn.

an important recognition fact to remember, and is pictured in Fig. 4. There are occasions, however, when simultaneous Turn motions will be made by both manual members. These may be simultaneous independent Turns or a coincident Turn where both hands are on the object being turned. Taking a shower bath provides a simple example of a simo Turn situation. The hot and the cold water handles are often turned using both hands simultaneously.

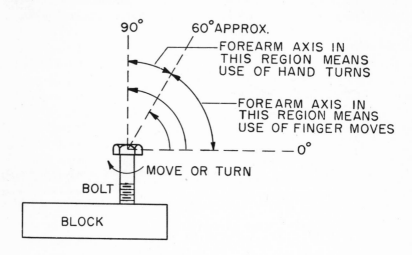

Fig. 5.   Location of forearm as it affects Turn or Move.

The MTM analyst must be careful to avoid confusion sometimes caused by the ordinary expression of "Turn the object." This instruction will not of necessity imply the use of a Turn motion as defined in MTM since objects can also be turned with Move motions of the fingers or hand, and by means of a special motion called Crank (See Chapter 10).

The criterion is the location of the forearm long axis. Study Fig. 5 which shows a loose bolt that is to be turned into a threaded block. As long as the arm axis is at an angle of from zero to approximately sixty degrees to the surface of the block, the fingers and hand will perform a series of Move, Release, Reach, Grasp, Move, etc. But when the axis of the arm is located between about sixty to ninety degrees with the surface of the block, the fingers and hand will execute a series of Turn, Release, Reach, Grasp, Turn, etc. Thus, the motion analysis requires clear distinction if proper classification is to be achieved.

In the MTM element known as Position (see Chapter 14) objects must often be turned slightly to provide orientation prior to insertion. This kind of Turn need not be indicated as a separate motion during analysis, because its presence and time value has been integrated into the Position motions, which also involve other basic MTM motions.

TURN VARIABLES

Two major variables, *Degrees of Turn* and *Resistance to Turn,* have been evaluated for Turn motions.   These are discussed in detail in the following material.   A possible third variable is also discussed briefly.

Degrees of Turn

The further the action of the forearm muscles causes the wrist and hand to be rotated, the longer will be the time required.   The most rational manner in which to express the amount of Turn performed is in terms of the number of angular degrees involved.   Experimentation by the reader will show, however, that the rotation cannot exceed 180 degrees due to the physical structure of the forearm.   The two bones of which the forearm is composed limit the rotation to this maximum amount.

As a practical matter, there is also a lower angular limit for Turn (about 15 degrees) below which it becomes difficult for the analyst to distinguish the Turn motion from ordinary minor twisting of the wrist present in all normal Reaches and Moves.   It would, in fact, be correct to state that small amounts of Turn are present in almost every Reach and Move motion of the hand.   To attempt to isolate and measure such Turns, however, would be impractical.

Resistance to Turn

The rotation of the *empty* hand will obviously not require any effort or work above that normally associated with such muscular movements.

When a Turn is applied to an object having appreciable weight or offering resistance to rotation, however, the net result is to increase the time required to produce the rotation desired.

For a given amount of rotation, existing experimental data indicates that the time for Turn due to resistance generally increases with the weight of the object as a smooth curve.   The amount of data available did not permit the originators of MTM to develop a complete weight curve, so therefore they classified objects being turned into three weight categories:

Small   — 0 to 2 pounds, inclusive
Medium — Over 2 to 10 pounds, inclusive
Large   — Over 10 to 35 pounds, inclusive

From a practical viewpoint, no substantial loss in the accuracy of time values has resulted from using this simplified classification procedure.

When weights larger than 35 pounds must be rotated, motions other than Turn will be involved. This fact explains why the upper limit of the classifications was set at 35 pounds. Until additional research is made (a need for which was indicated by the originators of MTM) these classification ranges should suffice. Successful use has validated this conclusion.

The first type of situation in which the weight of the object can prolong the Turn time occurs when the object is turned while essentially free of attachment in space, that is, the entire weight is supported by the unaided hand of the operator. The weight will retard the Turn motion according to the magnitude of the weight; light objects will slow the Turn but little, while heavy objects will create a noticeable reduction in the speed of Turn. This behavior parallels that of weight in Move motions because the worker's muscles must overcome the pull of gravity in much the same way to maintain control of the object.

Not only does the weight of an object influence the time of Turn, but the distribution of the mass of the object also has an effect. This can be verified simply by picking up a steel bar, say 1 inch in diameter and 12 inches long, holding it horizontally with one hand, and turning it back and forth about its long axis. If the same bar is next grasped at the center of its length, and twisted back and forth about an axis at right angles to the axis of the bar (with the forearm aligned to the perpendicular axis), it will be found that considerably more effort and time is required to make, say, ten turns back and forth than in the first case. The explanation is simple: The moment of inertia of the object about the given axis of rotation is greater when the bar is held in the second position; hence, greater turning effort is required in accelerating and decelerating the bar during the Turn motion.

Under certain conditions, resistance effects may actually exceed the weight of an unattached object. Study of the laws of levers in physics will show that minimum operator effort in turning will prevail when the object is being held at a point close to its center of gravity. When the object is held at a point sufficiently displaced from its center of gravity and with its axis of rotation perpendicular to the force of gravity, the unbalanced condition could easily cause an increase in the control effort required of the arm muscles and, therefore, an increase in Turn time. This unbalance factor will require evaluation during future research since no data now exists on it.

For the present, the actual weight of the object is used in determining which of the three weight categories previously defined apply to evaluate the Turn resistance of free objects as just discussed.

A second type of Turn resistance occurs when the object being rotated is attached to or part of another object, or when mechanical constraint is present. In this case, the object and/or its attachments exerts a resisting torque in opposition to the turning effort of the hand and, if motion is to ensue, this resisting torque must be more than equalled by the product of the force applied by the hand and the distance from the point of holding to the axis of rotation. When the resisting torque is known, the hand force may be found from the following equation:

Resisting Torque (inch pounds) = Hand Force (pounds)
× Lever Arm (inches)

In using this equation, the lever arm is the measured distance from the axis of rotation to the point of application of the force as seen in Fig. 6. The force desired is that component perpendicular to the lever arm. It is this

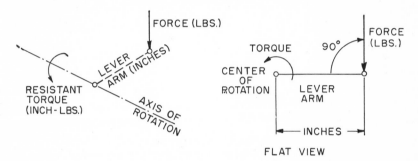

FLAT VIEW

Fig. 6. Measurement of resistant torque.

force that must be used as the weight factor in the three categories previously defined. The control effort the hand must exert to produce turning against a resisting torque is the same as it would exert to Turn a free object weighing the same as the force applied.

A torque wrench or torque balance may sometimes be used to obtain the value of the resisting torque directly without any need for applied mechanics calculations. In such cases the measured resisting torque and the length of the lever arm used by the operator's hand (measured from between the thumb and the most remote finger as actually gripped) are all that is needed to determine the desired hand force from the formula:

$$\text{Hand Force F in pounds} = \frac{\text{Measured Resistance Torque T in inch pounds}}{\text{Lever Arm L used by operator's hand, in inches}}$$

A direct method for obtaining the force or weight factor present when turning against a resisting torque is to use a spring scale applied to the object being turned at the point where the hand would hold it. The scale must, of course, be held perpendicular to the lever arm when the force reading is taken and only enough pull should be exerted to barely turn the object.

In the majority of cases none of the foregoing procedure will be necessary since the hand force applied by the operator to cause rotation can usually be estimated and classified as being in the small, medium, or large category with sufficient accuracy.

Three examples of torque application during pure Turns are:
Revolving a door knob when the lock mechanism is rusty.
Driving a wood screw into a piece of green or hard wood, with the arm almost perpendicular to the surface of the wood.
Setting a rheostat knob that is constrained by stiff detent springs.

Type of Motion

The third Turn variable is type of motion. Research has not yet shown whether Type II and Type III motions described in the chapter on Reach are possible during turns, but the inventors of MTM surmised the possibility in their textbook. They felt that, for isolated observations of what appeared to be Type II Turns, reduction of the table time value by 1.4 TMU would be a reasonable procedure. This may, therefore, be *used with caution* pending further research.

DATA CARD INFORMATION

The Time values for Turn given on the MTM Data Card are shown in Table 1.

Table I.   Time Values for Turn (MTM Data Card Table III—Turn—T)

Weight	Time TMU for Degrees Turned										
	30°	45°	60°	75°	90°	105°	120°	135°	150°	165°	180°
Small — 0 to 2 Pounds	2.8	3.5	4.1	4.8	5.4	6.1	6.8	7.4	8.1	8.7	9.4
Medium — 2.1 to 10 Pounds	4.4	5.5	6.5	7.5	8.5	9.6	10.6	11.6	12.7	13.7	14.8
Large — 10.1 to 35 Pounds	8.4	10.5	12.3	14.4	16.2	18.3	20.4	22.2	24.3	26.1	28.2

Turns with the empty hand are assigned times as given for the S (small) category.

Notice that time values are given for degrees of rotation in 15-degree increments. The 15-degree increments represent a practical division of the angular measure because of the difficulty of closer measure in most application cases. In view of this, it is logical to eliminate consideration of any turn 15 degrees or under; and the table therefore begins at 30 degrees Also, the time assigned from the data card should be that for the 15-degree interval nearest the measured angle, unless demands for increased accuracy prompt the MTM analyst to interpolate in the table. For example, a Turn measured at 62 degrees under normal accuracy requirements would be symbolized and given a time value for the 60-degree turn. For more stringent accuracy, the symbol and time for 62 degrees would be assigned.

The originators of MTM suggested that even the 15-degree increment may sometimes be too fine for identification of observed Turns. As an unofficial approach they suggested the use of the "45-degree step rule" which indicated that the analyst should only attempt to isolate angular values of 45, 90, 135, and 180 degrees in such cases.

Perhaps further research and better means of measurement will result in a change of such rules as are given above, but this type of practical approach combined with validated research and successful application has done much to advance MTM ahead of other predetermined time systems.

THE SHORTHAND OF TURN

This discussion presents the shorthand symbols, or writing conventions, for the MTM element defined as Turn.

Turn

The MTM analyst will show a T on his study sheet to indicate the occurrence or necessity of the work element called Turn.

Degrees of Turn

The amount of Turn expressed in degrees is noted on the study form following the letter T. This should normally show the relative amount of rotation to the nearest 15-degree interval in accordance with the data card limits. Thus, a turn of 36 degrees would be noted as 30. When greater accuracy is justified and desired, however, the symbol should show the true angular measure, in this case T36. (Refer to the previous section.)

In a manner similar to the handling of distances for Reach and Move motions, the amount of Turn will generally be determined and noted after all of the basic motions have been listed in sequence on the study sheet. That is, the analyst will first decide the kind of motions present or required and will then proceed to classify them.

Resistance Factor

This is denoted by the capital letters S, M, or L as needed (not needed for an empty hand) to show the relative size of the object being turned or the resistance it offers. Examples are:

T90L indicates a 90-degree Turn of an object weighing between 10.1 and 35 pounds; or it may also show that the force required to overcome the torque resistance of the object ranged in this equivalent weight category.

T150 would denote a 150-degree Turn of the empty hand, since this involves zero weight.

Type II Turns

It was indicated that Type II Turns might occur in some industrial operations. In such cases, it is suggested that the analyst use the conventional symbolization as given above, and then add a note opposite the symbol that it is a Type II Turn. Remember this is not official data, however.

The use of complete and correct symbolization will eliminate confusion as to whether the motion variables were properly considered.

COMBINED TURN MOTIONS

Under the definition for Turn, it was stated that pure Turns do not occur as frequently in industrial operations as do Turns in combination with Reach and Move. Clarification of this statement was delayed to now because consideration of the combined motions presumes prior familiarity with the pure Turns. The first step now is to achieve understanding of the specialized meaning of the term *Combined Motion* as used in MTM.

Up to this point, material on motions has discussed each MTM element without regard to the sequence in which it may appear during a task. Obviously, one way to perform the motions is to do them consecutively. Combining is another.

An example from everyday life illustrating consecutive and combined methods of performing a common task occurs when a man rides the bus to his place of employment and then reads his morning newspaper before the starting whistle blows. This exemplifies consecutive performance and would require addition of the time for each task to find the elapsed time. Both tasks might also be completed, obviously in less elapsed time, by the worker reading his newspaper on the bus while he is riding to work. In this way, he has *combined* both tasks to save himself time. This statement, extended to motion times rather than task times, should make readily apparent the meaning of *Combined Motion*.

A definition for Combined Motions is:

Combined motions are two or more non-consecutive elemental motions performed during the same time interval by the same body member.

The average industrial worker will naturally tend to combine Turns with Reaches and Moves as a matter of ease and convenience.

In respect to Turn motions, several questions (answered below) are raised by the definition of *Combined Motions:*

1. How is the time determined for combined Turns?

2. How are combined Turns symbolized?

3. What effect on the distance of Reach and Move is caused by their combination with a Turn?

A further question, covered in later chapters, concerns the kinds of motions which can be combined and the ways in which such combinations can occur with average operators. For the present, it is enough to realize that Turn can be combined with Reach and Move.

Limiting Time

When several motions are combined, the elapsed time allowed for the combination is the time to complete the motion requiring the greatest amount of time. A shorter way of expressing this is to say that the longest-time motion is "limiting" and the shorter-time motions are "limited." The allowed time is the "limiting time." The reason for this is obvious from the example just given.

To obtain the time for a Turn combined with Reach or Move, it is merely necessary to compare the Turn time with the Reach or Move time to see which is "limiting."

As an illustration, a T135 will "limit" an R3B because the Turn requires 7.4 TMU and the Reach takes only 5.3 TMU; a combined Turn containing these motions would thus be assigned the time value of 7.4 TMU, since the R3B is "limited out." In another instance, an M6B8 (11.6 TMU) will be "limiting" in a combined motion with a T75M Turn (7.5 TMU), which is the "limited" motion.

There are no special rules of thumb to find out which motion in a combined Turn is limiting. The analyst must examine the data card in each case. However, the likelihood of the Turn being limiting is greater with short Reaches or Moves; while for long Reaches or Moves, the Turn will generally be limited.

Combined Conventions

The symbolism for combined motions requires that the separate motions be written on two or more lines of the analysis form. The limited motions are shown by drawing a slanted line through them, as shown in the example at right. The bracket is used to denote the combination, as it helps show whether the limiting motion is the one written on the line above or below the limited motion. Note that a dash (—) in the TMU column signifies that the T135S time is not allowed.

Motion	TMU
R18B	17.2
G1A	2.0
M12B	13.4
~~T135S~~	—
G2	5.6
M6C	10.3
P2SSE	19.7
RL1	2.0
Total Allowed TMU	70.2

The method of writing both the consecutive and combined motions should be evident from the example, even though the reader may be unfamiliar with the motions other than Reach, Move, and Turn at this point. The manner of adding times for a task is also illustrated here, this being what is called a motion pattern. The time for the Turn, it being limited out, is not allowed in the total for the task.

Wrist Assistance in Combined Turns

A combined Turn will usually assist the Reach or Move; that is, it effectively shortens the allowable distance involved. In a few cases, a combined Turn can have the opposite effect—what may be called wrist resistance—

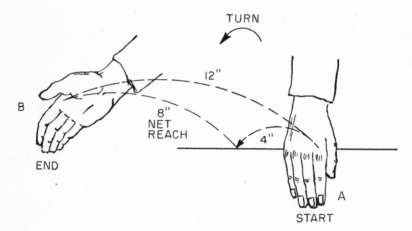

Fig. 7.   Wrist assistance in combined Turns.

it lengthens the effective Reach or Move distance. The idea of resistance would be the same as discussed in the Reach chapter—it increases the time needed to complete the motions.

An example of wrist assistance is shown in Fig. 7 along with the distances involved. In view A, the right hand starts palm down on a table and makes a 12-inch Reach to the right while the palm is turned upward with the thumb outward so that a combined 180-degree Turn has occurred. The Turn assisted the Reach by about 4 inches, about palm width for an average male operator. Thus, the knuckle-to-knuckle distance of 12 inches should be decreased to 8 inches to give the allowable distance of Reach for reference to the data card time value. Other cases of combined Turn assistance would be measured in a similar manner.

The best way to measure a Reach-Turn or a Move-Turn is to first make the Turn and then complete the Reach or Move. Then the degrees turned and the amount of assistance or resistance can easily be measured separately and distinguished from the total index knuckle travel.

PRACTICAL WORKING RULES

For all of the Turn variables isolated above, practical means of recognition and measurement of the quantities are necessary.

Angular Measurement

The long axis of the forearm was identified as the axis of rotation for the manual members during Turn motions. This axis intersects the hand through the middle finger. That intersection therefore serves best as the origin of the angle of Turn. Point A in Fig. 8 is this origin.

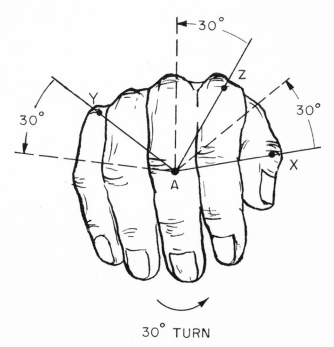

30° TURN

Fig. 8. Angular measurement points on the hand.

To observe and measure the angle turned, the analyst needs another point to watch. The line connecting this latter point and the origin will generate the angle of Turn as the hand revolves about the Turn axis. The further this second point is located from the origin, the easier will be the angular observation.

Another convenient point on the hand is often selected for this purpose. See Fig. 8 again. Point X, at the thumb knuckle, is the furthest from the middle finger and provides the best "measure point" on the hand. The knuckle of the little finger, at point Y, is next in desirability. Least desirable, because it is closest to the middle finger, is the knuckle of the index finger at point Z. None of these points travel more than a few inches during the Turn, which makes this means of measuring the angle difficult.

A better way to observe this variable is to extend the principle given above. Observe a point further away from the middle finger than the points on the hand just mentioned. This point may be located at some distance on the object being turned, somewhere on a prominent projection of the part, or on an object palmed for the purpose of providing an observation point. A rod or rod-like object such as a pencil palmed between the middle and index fingers provides the best means of finding the angle during a pure or combined Turn. This is especially true if the Turn is made with an empty hand that provides no object for selection of an observation point.

For MTM analysts with enough practice, the most practical way to obtain the Turn angle for normal accuracy is to estimate it to the nearest 15-degree increment shown on the data card. Notice that this suggestion differs from that given for distances in Reach and Move. For these distances, it is preferable to measure, although accurate estimation is permissible. For Turn angles, however, estimation is *usually* adequate.

Size Classification

Due to the relatively large differences in the weight categories on the data card for Turn, the MTM analyst can usually judge closely enough the small, medium, or large size classifications. For borderline cases, however, he may resort to a measuring device such as was discussed under resistance to Turn in this chapter.

A combined Reach-Turn would always be in the S time category because the empty hand carries zero weight. Combined Move-Turns may fall in any of the three size ranges, depending on the weight of the object or the resistance offered.

An interesting relation between the size or weight categories is the relative increase of performance times with increased weight. The data card values for Medium are 1.57 times the Small category, and those for Large are 3.00 times the Small value. In other words, the time required is increased 57 and 200 per cent in the respective cases.

SUMMARY

Turn (symbol T) is the basic motion employed to rotate the hand about the long axis of the forearm.

Table 2.   Factors Causing Turn Time Variations and Symbols Employed

Causes of Turn Time Variation	Symbol
I. Angle of Rotation	Angular Degrees
This is measured from the initial to the final location of the base line, using the plane of the palm as a reference plane. Maximum is 180 degrees	
II. Resistance to Turn	Capital Letter
Small — 0 to 2 pounds, inclusive Medium —Over 2 to 10 pounds, inclusive Large —Over 10 to 35 pounds, inclusive Empty hand—No resistance possible	· S M L None
III. Examples of MTM Symbolism	
T135S T90M T45L T128M	

QUESTIONS

1. An office worker has inserted the key in the lock of his desk drawer.   If he is *sitting* in front of the desk, what MTM motion will he use to unlock the drawer?   What MTM motion would he use if *standing* in front of the desk?
2. Give the complete symbol for the MTM motion employed to twist the key to open the lock of an ordinary door, under normal conditions.
3. With a Yankee screwdriver, you wish to tighten a vertical screw in a workpiece located about 10 inches back from the front edge, directly in front of you on the workbench at which you are sitting.   What kind of MTM motion will be involved?   What if the screw is horizontal with the head toward you?
4. Normally, what kind of MTM motion will be used in dialing a combination lock?   Give reasons for your answer.
5. Observe Fig. 9 picturing a radiator steam valve.   Its round handle is about 2 inches in diameter and located 24 inches or so above the floor level.   An operator, standing in front of the radiator, discovers that the packing is fairly tight when he adjusts the valve—assume he must apply a 5-pound force tangential to the valve handle to cause rotation and maintain it. Please write the motion symbol and TMU value he needs for a valve rotation of 67 degrees.
6. You will notice an ordinary straight chair weighing about 18 pounds is shown in Fig. 10.   Assume you have grasped the chair in the middle of the

top bar between the back uprights and lifted it a short way off the floor. What motion, symbol, and TMU value would you now use to rotate the chair 90 degrees while keeping the seat level? State specific reasons for the answer you analyzed.

7. An office worker sitting in front of a desk wishes to dump the contents of his ashtray into a wastebasket nearby. The ashtray sits about 6 inches to the right of his shoulder and about 15 inches back from the front edge of the

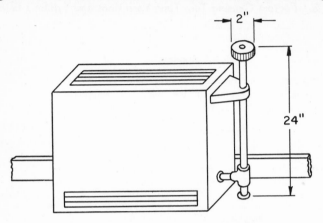

Fig. 9. Radiator valve for Problem 5.

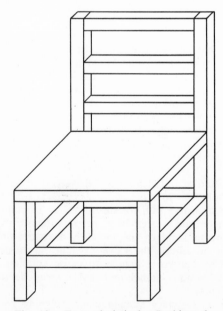

Fig. 10. Type of chair for Problem 6.

desk. He has grasped the ashtray and will now move it directly over the wastebasket, traversing a curved path 45 inches long. You are asked to write the following and give reasons for your answers:

a. The MTM motion pattern for the sequence of bringing the ashtray to the wastebasket, dumping it, and returning it to its place on the desk—to the same condition before the sequence started

b. The time values for each motion written

c. The total TMU task time for the MTM motion pattern

8. What are the motion conventions and allowed time to bring upright a water tumbler while locating it under a running water faucet? The tumbler had been standing upside down on a shelf 16 inches to the right from the faucet. Also tell the motion conventions and allowed time involved in bringing the right hand to the tumbler originally, if the hand came from 10 inches away to get the tumbler.

CHAPTER 10

Crank

Definition[1]

> *CRANK is the motion employed when the hand follows a circular path to rotate an object, with the forearm pivoting at the elbow and the upper arm essentially fixed.*

1. *Crank is defined in terms of manual action, not by object movement.*
2. *With small cranking diameters and light cranking loads, the wrist undergoes a whipping action while the forearm pivots only slightly.*
3. *With large cranking diameters and heavy cranking loads, the wrist stiffens to rigidity and the forearm pivoting generates a conical surface.*
4. *If the upper arm begins to move, cranking action has ceased and the object is being rotated by a move.*
5. *The axis of rotation of the object may be at any angle to the forearm pivot axis if the manual action meets the cranking criteria.*

Among the numerous examples of the motion are these:

1. Cranking a hand wheel to locate the carriage on the ways of a lathe
2. Starting a small gasoline motor by means of *cranking* a common crank
3. Rotating the stencil cylinder of a mimeograph machine to produce copies.

---

[1] Although Crank is generally recognized to be an MTM element, no definition for it was included in the "Basic MTM Specifications" (Footnote 1, Chapter 7). All Crank data are tentative and do not appear on the official MTM Data Card, since the preliminary research behind it has not yet been fully approved. Also, due to its relatively low frequency of occurrence, it is not high on the priority list for further research. Therefore, this definition is the authors' attempt to delineate its nature based on all available literature, including the training course manuals approved by the MTM Association.

At the outset, it is stressed that the motion Crank denotes a particular kind of muscle usage by the worker; it should not be confused with the employment of a common crank in a manner which may or may not coincide with the definition as stated. Crank may be used for many other purposes besides rotating a common crank, although a crank may be actuated with a Crank motion. The MTM motion identifies and assigns proper time values for actions performed by the *operator;* the motion of an *object* being observed is not necessarily described. In other words, Crank motions are recognized mainly by the defined muscular action rather than by the predominant purpose of the motion.

The muscular action in cranking involves the hand, wrist, and forearm in a compound series of motions. However, note that the definition of Crank specifies that the upper arm must remain relatively fixed in space during the motion. If the operator's elbow changes location during movement of a crank, a Move rather than a Crank is being performed. Of course, the muscles of the upper arm do act during Crank to increase the manual force applied, even though the upper arm is displaced very little during this action. The contribution of the other manual members during cranking may be understood by considering the extreme cases described by the second and third sub-definitions.

Light cranking, which means small cranking diameters and low cranking resistance, is illustrated in Fig. 1. The fingers and hand necessarily hold an object, because the purpose to "rotate an object" is given in the Crank

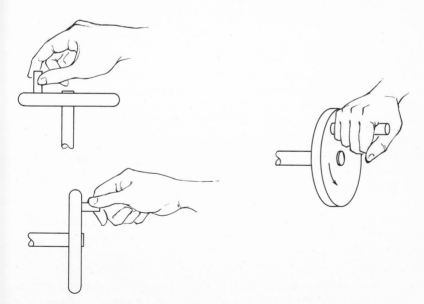

Fig. 1.   Examples of cranking with small diameters and light loads.

definition. Close scrutiny of light cranking reveals that the hand hinges about the wrist with a whipping action. The whipping action tends to give momentum to the object, since the hand hinges toward the direction of rotation. At the end of each revolution, the hand will have returned to the same angle it had at the start. During this hand and wrist motion, of course, the axis of the wrist is itself being displaced by the forearm action.

Heavy cranking, shown in Fig. 2, occurs when the cranking diameter is large and higher cranking loads are being rotated. The whipping action of

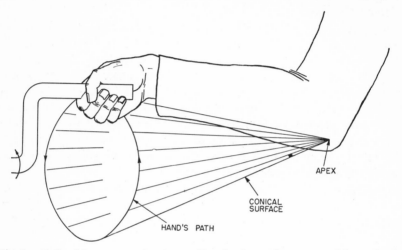

Fig. 2. Path of forearm motion in cranking for large diameters and heavy loads.

the wrist tends to disappear when the wrist becomes almost rigid during heavy cranking. Motive force is exerted on the object being cranked by the heavier muscles of the worker's arm. The forearm generates a conical surface in space as it pivots at the elbow with a rotary twisting. The apex of the cone at the elbow remains relatively fixed because of the high mobility of the ball and socket construction of this ideally equipped joint. Recognition of heavy cranking motions is greatly aided if the analyst has a clear concept of the conical forearm action.

Of prime importance in the identification and recognition of cranking is the relation between the *axis of cranking* and the *axis of rotation* of the object being cranked. The axis of cranking is the centerline of the pivoting action of the forearm during cranking. For the object being cranked, the axis of rotation is the line about which turning takes place. The manual action required for light cranking is frequently possible at almost any angle between these axes. However, the likelihood of such freedom of forearm location during heavy cranking is greatly reduced. Usually the axis of cranking must, as shown in Fig 3, be perpendicular, or nearly so, to the plane of rotation. The axis of cranking is an imaginary line passing through the elbow joint which would correspond to the axis of the conical surface shown. The plane of rotation is analogous to the base of the cone. In a true right cone, the base would be perpendicular to the cone axis; and this condition must be reasonably approached before heavy cranking is successful. That is, the axes of cranking and rotation usually coincide.

Since cranking causes an object to move with a turning action, it is interesting to compare the muscular actions it involves with those required

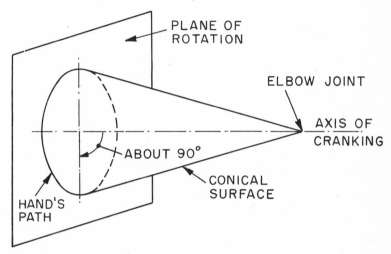

Fig. 3.   Relation of axis of cranking to the plane of rotation during heavy cranking.

by Move and Turn. There are fundamental differences which appreciably affect the time consumed.

Objects commonly called cranks can, under certain conditions, be motivated without employing cranking motions. If the elbow is displaced during the crank's operation, Move instead of Crank motions will have been used. A case of this is shown in Fig. 4 depicting a worker's arm turning a crank which lowers the cutting tool of a shaper to the work surface. Note that the criteria determining whether Move or Crank motions are performed is the movement of the upper arm.

On two counts, the forearm action during cranking differs from that found in Turn motions. First, the forearm does not *twist* about its own axis as is true in Turn, rather it maintains a fixed relation to its own axis all during cranking. Secondly, the forearm axis itself is relatively stationary during pure turning, while the requirement for the forearm axis to rotate during cranking was clearly shown above. Obviously, the differing muscular action during cranking—as compared to Move or Turn—will necessitate different time values.

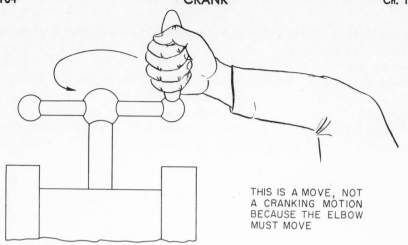

THIS IS A MOVE, NOT
A CRANKING MOTION
BECAUSE THE ELBOW
MUST MOVE

Fig. 4.   Lowering the cutting tool of a shaper to the work surface.

The Crank definition stipulated that the hand follows a circular path. Except for a slight discrepancy due to the whipping action of the hand at the wrist noted earlier, the path will ordinarily be nearly circular. However, the motion path need not be a pure circle to classify the motion as a Crank. It may be elliptical as when, for instance, an operator wraps twine around a relatively large rectangular package. A sensible limit to this idea is approached as the path becomes more nearly linear, say square or rectangular. The worker would then use a series of four Moves rather than a continuous cranking motion.

KINDS OF CRANK

Cranking motions may occur in two basic ways. The discussion that follows also includes one kind of motion resembling cranking that is an exception to cranking rules.

Continuous

The first basic way to crank an object is without pause or interruption. The time required obviously will be less than for intermittent cranking for a given path length of the hand. A further discussion of this is given in the Type of Motion section of this chapter.

A continuous cranking motion starts from rest, proceeds for the required revolutions, and only then stops completely. This is perhaps the most commonly encountered form of cranking. The operator's muscles develop a rhythm and force during the constant motion that results in appreciable momentum during the middle turns. Such cranking occurs when a fireman actuates a manual type warning siren long enough to caution the parties being notified. The momentum build-up mentioned above is obviously present in this example.

Intermittent

The second basic type of cranking includes noticeable pauses during its performance which cause it to require more time for a given number of revolutions of an object than continuous cranking. Accounting for the effect of alternating periods of acceleration and deceleration is made in the Type of Motion section.

In intermittent cranking, one single revolution from a start to a stop is completed before a succeeding turn is made. This means that each and every revolution will include an acceleration and a deceleration. The resultant pauses are the recognition cue for intermittency. Because the interval of continuous movement is shorter, the momentum given to the object cranked is less than for continuous cranking. Control requirements may also be present to affect the time requirements.

Encountering high resistance or inertia is a basic cause of intermittency in cranking motions and explains the slower movement.

Note that nothing about intermittent cranking, as defined, precludes either: (1) proceeding directly from the end of the completed revolution to another; or (2) extending the pause between revolutions for longer periods. High resistance cases often occur in the first way; the latter situation often arises when other operator motions or process time intervene. In any event, the time for an intermittent cranking motion is based on a single, complete revolution; so the extent of the pause is immaterial so long as the time is properly accounted for in developing the operator cycle time.

A common case of intermittent cranking is that of a milling machine operator raising the milling table with a calibrated crank to set the depth of cut for the next pass. The setting itself involves positioning to a line, discussed in a later chapter, but the intermittent cranking preceding the final setting is the result of several things: The milling table is heavy and there is friction on the vertical sliding ways; the need for care in setting the depth indicator on the rim dial requires control—overrunning of the mark would necessitate a reversal of cranking to remove the backlash in the mechanism before accurate setting is possible; and the type of control is of the same kind that prevents gathering of high momentum as mentioned earlier.

The symbols and time values for intermittent cranking obviously differ from those for continuous cranking, and will be explained later.

Exception

A special rule concerning cranking motions has resulted from research. It states that cranking motions involving less than half a revolution are to be treated as Moves. They are recorded as Moves and assigned time from the Move table.

Such motions occur, for example, during activation of indexing cranks, adjustment of machine feed wheels, and positioning to a line following the *Move,* which is pointed out in the Position chapter.

Another exception seen in machining operations is when the operator strikes a crank "on the fly" to move it less than half a revolution and then breaks contact with the crank in a continuous motion. This would definitely be treated as a Type III Move and not as cranking.

To further clarify the exception to cranking motions, it will later be shown in detail that any cranking motions of from one-half a revolution to a full revolution are treated as partial cranking motions.

CRANK VARIABLES

The variables associated with Cranking are the cranking diameter, the number of revolutions, the type of motion, and the resistance factor.

Cranking Diameter

Since it is logical that the time consumed increases with increasing diameters due to the longer path of hand travel, the cranking diameter is a major factor in determining the time for a given cranking motion.

Referring to the Reach and Move data, the reader will recall that most MTM times were based on the effective length of hand travel measured at the index finger knuckle. This point was chosen for convenient observation due to the essentially uniform correlation between the traversed distance and the knuckle travel. This condition is not present during cranking; the index knuckle, especially due to the whipping action described in the Definition section, follows a more complex path that is difficult to evaluate in a simple manner. Another measure point is needed.

It is simplest to measure the path diameter directly on the cranked object as shown in Fig. 5. The radius from the center of rotation to the point of grasp is normally measured on the machine part or object at the time of analysis. Twice this radius is the diameter of cranking. The point of grasp is the centerline of that part of the object held in the hand. It should be evident that the cranking diameter is much easier to obtain than would be the knuckle movement.

For cranking of objects other than a common crank, the rule just given applies if certain cautions are observed. The measured radius from the axis of rotation to the point of grasp should be perpendicular, or nearly so, to the axis of rotation. See Fig. 6 for clarification of this point. At the left there is shown string being wrapped around an object. It is obvious that the desired radius for any given revolution is the taut length of the string.   In the sketch at the right, however, measurement of the string's taut length would give a radius too large; the crank radius shown would be the correct one to use.

Wrapping string or other materials around an object normally results in a variable diameter for individual revolutions so that the diameter for all revolutions must be averaged.

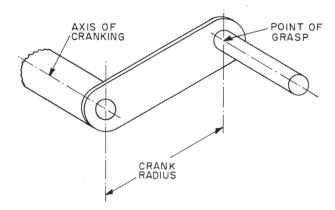

Fig. 5.   The diameter of cranking on a common crank is twice the radius from the axis of cranking to the point of grasp.

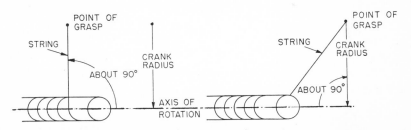

Fig. 6.   (Left) String being wrapped around an object.   The cranking radius for any given revolution is the taut length of the string.   (Right) Measurement of the string's taut length would give a radius too large; the crank radius shown would be the correct one to use.

The practicing MTM engineer will also encounter cases of cranking where one approach would be to measure or estimate the diameter of the curve described by the hand in space during the motion.   This is normally difficult to do and is, therefore, not recommended except as a last resort.

If an elliptical path is observed, a sensible method would be to obtain the average diameter.   This is equal to one-half of the sum of the shortest diameter and the longest diameter as shown in Fig. 7.

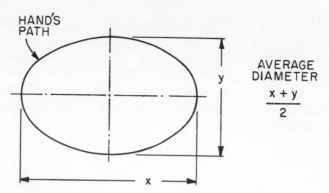

Fig. 7.   Average diameter of elliptical cranking path.

Number of Revolutions

The second cranking variable, the number of revolutions turned, must be counted or computed by the analyst at the time he writes his motion pattern.   It is quite clear that the cranking time is directly related to the number of revolutions involved.

Whether the revolutions are continuous or intermittent must, of course, be noted at the time of analysis.   That is, did five Cranks occur one at a time, or were five continuous Turns taken?   Other combinations are also possible.   For example, the first three turns might be intermittent, while the last two are continuous.   Close observation is certainly needed to be sure.

As explained earlier, anything less than half a revolution is treated as a move, but all partial revolutions beyond this minimum should be recorded. The partial turns may again either be directly measured or estimated as conditions warrant.   Three and one-half or four and one-quarter turns, for instance, would not be properly classified as four and five revolutions, respectively.   The fractional portion of a turn should be included and should be shown as fractional or decimal partial turns.   This is naturally more important for large cranking diameters than for small ones, because the partial turns then involve proportionately more time.

Type of Motion

The influence of the type of motion employed during cranking has been accounted for in the cranking time data.   In fact, intelligent use of the data requires clear understanding of the effect of this variable on cranking time.

Continuous cranking includes both Type II and Type III motions.   Thus, the first revolution is a Type II (in motion at the end), since no deceleration occurs at the end, while the start does involve an acceleration.   The middle turns are pure Type III, since there is no start or stop during these.

A Type II in motion at the start occurs for the last rotation because there is a deceleration but no acceleration in the motion.

When intermittent Cranks take place, however, each revolution is a Type I motion including a starting acceleration and a deceleration to stop. This explains why the time requirement exceeds that for continuous cranking.

Resistance Factor

The last variable affecting the time required for cranking is the amount of resistance offered by the object to the operator. This resistance is very similar to the kinds discussed in the Turn chapter. Most of the discussion there, especially that relating to torque evaluation, applies equally well here.

The effective resistance must be measured or estimated in pounds at the crank handle in a direction tangential to the path of motion at the grasping point. This may be done by spring scale, mathematical calculation, torque readings, or practical judgment depending on conditions. The weight factor data from the Move tables must then be applied to compute the resistance's effect on the time of cranking. Refer to the Turn chapter for more facts about this.

It is well to mention that high resistance is more likely to be present when intermittent cranks are performed. Since the time is longer for these also, it is likewise more important to evaluate the resistance factor than would be the case for continuous cranking.

CRANK DATA TABLE

A good and practical set of MTM time data does exist for the motion defined as Crank. However, application data given in Table 1 does not appear on the MTM Data Card for several reasons.

Basically, the MTM data appearing on the card has been placed there by the MTM Association for Standards and Research by the procedure described in the Reach chapter to indicate official approval; but this does not mean that data left in other status necessarily lacks the essential qualities of good standard times. In fact, tentative endorsement followed by application experience is a prior requirement for final approval. The cranking motion has been fully recognized as basic, and tentative approval has been given to the time data of Crank. For all practical purposes, it may be used as given below pending final action.

The cranking data was originally developed to meet the need of setting labor standards in the machining and metalworking industries where this motion occurs with greatest frequency. Because even this frequency is relatively low, and the data is seldom needed by other fields employing labor measurement, the MTM Association has no plans for further validating research at this time. So no prejudice to the cranking data is implied by its present status.

When cranking motions are encountered, the time data as given in Table 1 is at present valid for standards specifications.

Table I.   Crank Time Data—Light Resistance

Diameter of Cranking Inches	Leveled Time—TMU	
	Complete Revolution (K)	Intermediate Revolution (T)
1	13.7	8.5
2	14.9	9.7
3	15.8	10.6
4	16.6	11.4
5	17.3	12.1
6	17.9	12.7
7	18.4	13.2
8	18.8	13.6
9	19.2	14.0
10	19.6	14.4
12	20.2	15.0
14	20.7	15.5
16	21.2	16.0
18	21.6	16.4
20	21.9	16.7

Concrete examples of the use of this table will be given later; but at this point, several aspects of the table may profitably be noticed.

First, the data times as listed are for light resistance only. To obtain the time effect of other resistances, it will be necessary to refer to the Move Table on the data card for appropriate weight factors. These Move factors account for the increase in cranking time under load. They were not specifically validated for cranking during the moves-with-weight research; but, unofficially, extension of them to this situation is highly logical. Also no other factors would be otherwise available.

Remember that for any given weight factor there are a number of ways in which to measure or to calculate it. Review of this material in both the Move and Turn chapters is advisable at this point. Another important aspect of this problem is the application of the dynamic and static components of the weight factor data as explained in the chapter on Move. The static constant should be applied each and every time the cranking motion is begun from a stopped condition. The dynamic factor applies during all portions of the cranking motion in which the hand is actually moving the object being cranked.

Accordingly, the weight factors are applied in the following manner. For *continuous* cranking, the static factor is applied one time and the dynamic factor is applied once for each and every turn taken. For *intermittent* cranking, the static factor must be applied once for each and every revolution and the dynamic factor is also applied on the same basis. This application is fully clarified in the section on Practical Working Rules at the end of this chapter. Note, however, that weight during cranking is much more important from the time standpoint during intermittent cranking than it is for continuous cranking. This difference is due to the added number of times the static resistance must be overcome during the total cranking motion when intermittency brings the object being cranked to a stop.

Next look at the diameters given. These are measured as previously discussed. They range up to 10 inches by units and then by 2-inch increments up to 20-inches diameter. A plot of this data will yield a continuous curve that does not attain linearity. The rate of slope change, however, is such that interpolation for the odd distances over 10 inches would seem to yield proper results timewise. While cranking is essentially a one-hand motion as long as the cranking diameter is less than 20 inches, cases may arise when larger diameters are encountered. As was done for Reaches and Moves exceeding 30 inches, it would seem reasonable for Cranks exceeding 20 inches in diameter to make a straight-line interpolation. The error will be relatively small.

Finally, the two columns of time values differ by 5.2 TMU. This is because the K column lists the times for Type I revolutions, which include a start and stop time, while the T column lists the times for Type III revolutions involving neither acceleration nor deceleration. Hence, the 5.2 TMU represents the sum of one start and stop time, which is another way to say that the "m" value is 2.6 TMU all through the distance range for cranking.

The columns in Table 1 should be used in the following manner: For intermittent cranking, each turn's time is completely accounted for in column K, and the total time is, therefore, equal to the number of revolutions multiplied by the K column time. In the case of continuous cranking motions, the K column is used *once* (which will account for the start in the first revolution and the stop in the last turn) and all *remaining* revolutions will be multiplied by the T column time. By this procedure it is possible to list all cranking times in two rather than three columns and still account for the actual events of two Type II (first and last turns) revolutions with all others being Type III, if continuous cranking is done.

THE SHORTHAND OF CRANK

Crank motions are written using the following conventional symbols.

Crank

The presence of a cranking motion is recognized by the analyst when he records a capital C on his study sheet.

Cranking Diameter

Following the Symbol C for cranking will be a numeral for the inches of cranking diameter, determined as previously discussed. Decimals or fractions are to be rounded off to the nearest whole number.

> *Example:* C9 denotes that the operator turned a crank with a 9-inch effective diameter.

Resistance Factor

After the number denoting cranking diameter, the MTM engineer will record a dash (−) which is followed by the resistance factor in pounds as obtained either by measurement or estimation.

No resistance factor need be recorded for a weight factor of 2½ pounds or less. For all other cases of higher resistance, a number to the nearest pound value will be shown to indicate the resistance factor being used. This follows the same rules that were given in the chapter on Move motions.

> *Example:* C10–20 shows cranking, with 10-inch diameter, against a resistance of twenty pounds weight factor.

Revolutions

The numbers denoting the revolutions of the cranking will precede the letter C. The symbolism differs for continuous and intermittent cranking.

Continuous Cranking

This is symbolized simply by the number of turns taken. The numbers will be whole, decimal, or fractional depending on the actual count or visualized analysis.

> *Examples:* 4C9 shows four continuous turns of a low resistance, 9-inch crank diameter.
>
> 8.6C12–15 describes 8.6 turns with a 12-inch crank diameter and 15 pounds weight factor.
>
> 6¼C7–10 indicates six and one-fourths revolutions against ten pounds equivalent resistance or weight factor with a 7-inch cranking diameter.

Intermittent Cranking

The only difference for this kind of cranking is that the symbol must show that the revolutions are single instead of continuous. That is indicated by showing a 1 preceding the C, and separating this from the previous numbers by a hyphen. The previous numbers will be the amount of turns taken, and are written in the same manner discussed for continuous cranking.

Examples: 3–1C16 denotes 3 intermittent Cranks of a 16-inch diameter crank, small resistance being present.

5½–1C10–25 exemplifies that a 10-inch Crank diameter was turned 5½ single revolutions, possibly single because of the resistance factor of 25 pounds.

PRACTICAL WORKING RULES

Many of the practical working rules and hints given in previous chapters will apply to cranking motions. In general, this is true for the measurements of distances and resistance and the rule of rounding off time values to the nearest tenths of TMU values is also valid.

After having identified, analyzed, and symbolized a cranking motion, the MTM engineer needs to find the time value. This may be done with the Crank data table in two ways:

The first method uses the procedure given previously in the Crank Time Data section. It is the simplest computation method. Examples follow:

Example A: Cranking motion symbolized by 4C9–10
Column K time for first (and part of last) revolution   = 19.2 TMU
Remaining three turns are 3 × Column T or 3 (14.0) = 42.0

Sub-Total   = 61.2 TMU
From Move table in Chapter 8, 10 lb. factor gives
      1.11 (61.2) + 3.9 or 67.9 + 3.9   = 71.8 TMU

Example B: Cranking motion symbolized by 4–1C9–10
Column K for one complete single revolution   = 19.2 TMU
From Move table, 10 lb. factor gives
      1.11 (19.2) + 3.9 or 21.3 + 3.9   = 25.2 TMU
For intermittent turns, multiply by revolutions
      or 4 (25.2)   = 100.8 TMU

The effect of intermittency on time increase is readily seen from the examples. The second approved method that may be used to compute the cranking time employs an algebraic formula to account for the same variables. In the equations:

N = the number of revolutions
T = the time from column T of the crank table
K = the time from column K of the crank table
R = the dynamic weight factor (multiplier) from the Move tables
S = the static weight factor (additive constant) from Move data.

Continuous:
Cranking Time, leveled TMU = [(N) (T) + 5.2] (R) + S

Intermittent:
Cranking Time, leveled TMU = [(T + 5.2) (R) + S] (N)
                        or = [(K) (R) + S] (N)

Checking Example A above,
[(4) (14.0) + 5.2] (1.11) + 3.9 = (56.0 + 5.2) (1.11) + 3.9
                              = (61.2) (1.11) + 3.9
                              = 67.9 + 3.9 or
                                  71.8 TMU

Checking Example B above,
[(19.2) (1.11) + 3.9] (4) = (21.3 + 3.9) (4)
                         = (25.2) (4) or
                             100.8 TMU

That the first method is simpler and easier is apparent, results being the same.

Another aspect of cranking is encountered when experienced operators reduce their effort and fatigue by using a "spinning" motion to move cross slides, raise tables, etc. They take advantage of momentum to keep the mechanism moving for one or more revolutions. However, they sometimes keep a light hold on the crank handle or wheel rim while the spinning continues. Nevertheless, the spinning time is *process* controlled and must be determined by a stop watch or other timing device. The MTM cranking data does not cover this "spinning" motion.

SUMMARY

Crank (symbol C) is the motion employed when the hand follows a circular path to rotate an object, with the forearm pivoting at the elbow and the upper arm essentially fixed.

Table 2.   Factors Causing Crank Time Variation and Symbols Employed

Causes of Crank Time Variation	Symbol
I. Diameter of Cranking	Arabic Numeral
The effective diameter of the crank measured in inches.	
II. Resistance Factor	Arabic Numeral
The counterforce resistance to motion expressed in pounds. Under 2½ lb. not recorded, higher resistance noted to nearest pound. Then apply weight factors shown in the Move table.	
III. Number of Revolutions	Arabic Numerals
The observed or visualized amount of turning, provided one-half turn or more has occurred. Less than this minimum amount will be treated as Move motions.	
IV. Type of Motion	Hyphenated Revolutions
Continuous —Hand continues motion without slowing down until all revolutions are completed. Intermittent—Each revolution is completed with a start and stop until the total revolutions are all completed. Consists of repeated singles.	
V. Examples of MTM Symbolism	
5C8 7C12-18 6-1C5 4 1/2C10-10	

QUESTIONS

1. To start a gasoline engine requires three revolutions of a common crank with a *radius* arm of 8 inches when the resistance at the point of holding is judged to be about 20 pounds.   Analyze and state the kind of motions used, write the MTM symbol completely, and compute the TMU time value.

2. A clerk is required to wrap twine around an essentially rectangular package dimensioned as follows: 8 inches long, 6 inches wide, and 4 inches thick. Two complete wraps of the twine centrally spaced are specified for both the long and short dimensions of the package.   Write the MTM symbols and TMU time values for the cranking motions you believe he will perform. State your reasons for the cranking motions you identify.

3. Following a successful cast, a fisherman holds his casting rod in his left hand and smoothly reels in a 5-pound large-mouth bass with his right arm, wrist, and hand.   Please indicate the right-hand motions and give your reasons for your analysis.

4. A common mechanical duplicating machine, of the type found in many offices, is being operated by a clerk with his right hand on the crank.   One paper copy is produced for each revolution from the stencil, and about 3 pounds resistance is offered at the crank handle.   Write the MTM symbol

involved and specify the time needed to produce 22 printed sheets of paper.

5. Can a ball of shipping cord be unwound by utilizing a cranking motion? Please present specific reasons for your answer.

6. Was the motion used to ring the operator on an old-fashioned rural wall telephone a cranking motion?   Give the rule which explains your answer.

7. A factory worker is reeling electrical wire onto a wooden spool mounted in a cradle.   The spool and wire exert a 25-pound resistance at the point of grasp on the reeling crank which is 9 inches from the center of the spool. He can complete only 1 turn at a time, but must wind 20 turns on the spool.   Write the MTM symbol, and calculate the TMU requirement for this situation.

CHAPTER II

Apply Pressure

Definition[1]

APPLY PRESSURE is an application of muscular force to overcome object resistance, accompanied by little or no motion.

1. *Apply pressure is a hesitation or lack of motion.*
2. *The force required for apply pressure is greater than that required for a normal move or turn against resistance.*
3. *Apply pressure frequently is indicated by a setting of the muscles.*
4. *Apply pressure may be performed by any body member.*

The originators of MTM first called this element Final Tighten when they noted it during the final tightening of a screw by an operator who had first turned the screw down to its travel limit with a screwdriver. The considerable pressure exerted, characterized by a hesitation and passage of time, did not cause appreciable movement of the screw. Further evaluation showed its more general nature and application—resulting in the present name.

The application of restraining force known as holding often occurs while other body members perform other motions or while process time occurs. This should be shown by a descriptive note on the analysis. It should not be confused with Apply Pressure because the time consumed by the latter is a definite value that is easily exceeded by holding times.

Examples of the MTM element Apply Pressure illustrating purposes for which it may be used are:

1. *To achieve control, or "make ready" for subsequent motions.* After the hand has *contacted* a heavy object, for example, it cannot then be moved until control of the weight has been gained by the appli-

---

[1] From "MTM Basic Specifications" (Footnote 1, Chapter 7).

cation of some degree of pressure. This example should not be confused with the static component of a weighted Move which follows *grasping* of a heavy object. In this latter case, the Grasp achieves control of the object; but the static factor accounts for one part of the time required to achieve weight control during the subsequent Move.

2. *To restrain, or prevent, the motion of objects.* Apply Pressure will be used in such cases either when the period of restraint is shortly followed by another motion or when the restraint precedes the longer action known as holding. For instance, a mechanic will Apply Pressure to the top of a tire with one hand so that the wheel will not fall off the studs before he can start a holding nut with the other hand. In fact, he may use several Apply Pressures to get the wheel on the studs before holding begins as noted above.

3. *To overcome static friction, binding, or other resistance to motion.* This happens, for example, when a person loosens the lid of a filled mason jar to empty its contents. Usage of Apply Pressure in this manner is very frequent during the MTM motions called Position, in assembly actions, and Disengage, in cases of disassembly. Actually the Final Tighten observation which led to isolating Apply Pressure is another instance in this category. The force application in tightening assures that the last fraction of an inch of movement necessary to firm placement is accomplished.

While the definition indicates the use of muscular force to Apply Pressure, it does not restrict the action to any particular muscle group. When applying force to an object held in the hand, for instance, all of the manual members up to the shoulder joint have muscle groups aiding the action. Almost any body area can also apply force to objects under suitable conditions. The shoulder may push against a bulky shipping crate, the back can shove open a heavy door while the owner's arms are loaded with carried items, the hip might be used to steady a ladder, and many similar force applications by the body areas can be cited.

The absence of noticeable object displacement during Apply Pressure is also noted in the definition. The resistant forces, whether small or great, offered by objects to securing of control, prevention of motion, or surmounting of resistance as may be the purpose of the element require the expenditure of energy by the muscles, and obviously this requires time. Motion cannot ensue or be arrested until the muscular work has been expended.

The novice to MTM is sometimes disturbed because any significant object motion is specifically denied in the Apply Pressure definition. It is termed an element only, because its presence during human work must be recognized—indeed its time consumption may be large in comparison to elements known as motions. When the true nature of Apply Pressure becomes clear, however, the MTM analyst will readily recognize its existence and presence due to the obvious lapse of motion accompanying its performance.

That Apply Pressure is not a motion (where "motion" implies spatial displacement of the object), but is nevertheless an important MTM element, should now be clear. It occurs before or after motions, not during them. Weight or resistance factors account for force application during motions such as Move.

CASES OF APPLY PRESSURE

Two fully approved cases of Apply Pressure are next discussed.

Case I

Apply Pressure Case 1 can be defined as follows:

Apply Pressure Case 1 exists when the body member acting requires initial orientation or adjustment to avoid loss of grip, injury, or discomfort during force application on the object.

Other sources have used the terms "regrasp, preliminary setting, or the equivalent" to describe the action prior to force application. Still another term sometimes seen is "make ready." The basic idea is that the force is not fully applied until the operator has first made some minor body member adjustments.

Case 1 appears to be the most common in industrial examples. It frequently either precedes or follows a twisting action such as occurred during the screwdriver usage in the original research. Similar occurrences of Apply Pressure often appear before or after push or pull motions involving higher than normal resistances.

With the application of Apply Pressure involving the use of hands, the regrasp or gripping idea is readily understood. Obviously regrasping or gripping actions cannot occur for Case 1 Apply Pressure involving other body members. In the latter situation, the idea of equivalent pause noted previously accounts for the time consumed. The slightest movement or shifting of the body member prior to the force application is a clue that a Case 1 Apply Pressure is being observed. This action is used to orient, adjust, or attain a better location from which to apply the full force of the given body member.

Case 2

Definition of Apply Pressure Case 2 is as follows:

Apply Pressure Case 2 exists when the body member acting is already fully oriented or adjusted such that full force application to the object can be made immediately.

It can be seen that this involves the pure pressure only, since no "make ready" delays are needed prior to force application.

Sometimes skilled operators—during highly repetitive cycles—learn to place their hands on objects so that they can always use a Case 2 instead of the Case 1 Apply Pressure that an ordinary operator might require. Also, Case 2 occurs more frequently than Case 1 when the object has been held for quite some time prior to the Apply Pressure. Almost all pressure application with the feet is done with Case 2; this will often happen with operation of foot pedals, and a special body motion including it is one of the MTM basic motions.

DATA CARD INFORMATION

The time data for Apply Pressure appears at the bottom of Table III on the official MTM Data Card in the following form:

| APPLY PRESSURE CASE 1—16.2 TMU   APPLY PRESSURE CASE 2—10.6 TMU |

It can be seen that Case 1 and Case 2 differ by 5.6 TMU, which is the time equivalent for the MTM motion called Regrasp. This is the differentiation made in the material above.

THE SHORTHAND OF APPLY PRESSURE

The basic element Apply Pressure is identified by the two capital letters AP. The two cases are symbolized as follows:

$$\begin{array}{ll} \text{Apply Pressure Case 1} & \text{AP1} \\ \text{Apply Pressure Case 2} & \text{AP2} \end{array}$$

The arabic numeral readily identifies the case which has occurred.

OCCURRENCES WITH OTHER MOTIONS

The MTM element Apply Pressure has often appeared during research on other MTM motions either preceding or following in the motion sequences. It will be interesting and helpful to discuss this briefly here, although more complete information may be found in the chapters covering the other motions.

The MTM research on *Moves with Weight*[2] revealed some previously undefined data on force application. Before objects having other than

[2] R.R. 108 (See Ch. 5).

negligible weight can actually be moved, and after the fingers have completed closing on the object, control of the mass must be gained by the
application of varying amounts of pressure. The time required to apply
this pressure was evaluated to develop the static and dynamic weight factors.
The application of these factors therefore fully accounts for any concurrent
force applications during a Move. For this reason, no separate analysis of
Apply Pressure is needed when considering weight effects during object
movement. Similarly, the resistance effects during Turn already have been
included in the Turn time. Any included force application does not need
to be separately analyzed.

When the amount of force required to assemble objects having differing
degrees of fit is evaluated for the MTM motion called Position, one of the
major factors in the time required is the Apply Pressure used. The purpose
of the Apply Pressure in this case is mainly to overcome resistance to
motion. Again, this illustrates one of the concepts in the definition for
Apply Pressure.

Objects being disassembled frequently require the MTM motion known
as Disengage. The need to maintain control and overcome motion resistance again justify the use of Apply Pressure in this element.

How to account for the Apply Pressure element occurring with other
motions is fully clarified in the appropriate chapters. It must be said here
that, in general, the rules given for Apply Pressure in this chapter are
concerned with its occurrence as a distinct, separate MTM element in
work performance.

PRACTICAL WORKING RULES

Apply Pressure usually appears in situations requiring the handling of
heavier objects or where forces of relatively high magnitude must be employed. In such events, the analyst should look for hesitations which
reveal the usage of more than normal force. He can then correctly analyze
the Apply Pressures present during work sequences. Practical study of the
objects handled will generally give clues as to the proper case of Apply
Pressure being employed.

Apply Pressure is sometimes used to prevent injury to the body members,
avoid damage to the object handled due to dropping, and to provide other
protective or preventive action. To aid in recognition of such cases, the
MTM analyst can notice the physical characteristics of the objects handled.
Jagged edges or burrs which might break the skin, the presence of lubri-
cants on the surfaces which might cause accidents, objects whose nature
inherently cause awkward handling, and features of objects which necessitate enough controlling pressure to prevent slipping or other accidents all

flash signals to the good MTM analyst that Apply Pressures should be considered. The proper case to allow can be found by knowledge of the variables discussed in this chapter.

Since most of the Apply Pressures occurring in industrial work are Case 1, this fact can guide correct classification. Specific clues for recognizing the cases have already been given.

The last point worthy of emphasis is that Apply Pressure consumes relatively large amounts of time as compared to many other MTM motions. Care should be taken not to miss writing it into motion patterns. This is especially true if short, highly repetitive work cycles are being analyzed. Errors in time allowed for operations can be considerable if Apply Pressures are omitted during analysis.

SUPPLEMENTARY APPLY PRESSURE DATA

The preceding information comprises the entire Apply Pressure data fully approved by the International MTM Directorate at present. However, their rules permit member national associations to include on the official MTM Data Card Supplementary Data clearly labled as such. Under this provision the data card of the U.S.-Canada association now contains new Apply Pressure data based on additional research.[3] This data improves the understanding and usage of Appy Pressure in specific application areas.

The Laboratory Study

With the very first research report[4] of the MTM Association indicating a need for further study of Apply Pressure, and another report[5] containing some new data, the laboratory phase of the Apply Pressure project made a new start. This questioning of the basic nature of Apply Pressure fortunately has led to greater knowledge about the element. Also the new research has given firm experimental and statistical grounding to the element.

This study marked a departure from the former reliance of MTM research upon motion picture film analysis. Since previous projects considered spatial motions involving visible displacement of the body member, visual means of measurement were appropriate. However, motion is essentially excluded by the definition of Apply Pressure; therefore more sophisticated techniques were needed to measure body member force application rather

---

[3] R.R. 111 (See Ch. 5). Also "A Laboratory Study of Apply Pressure" by Barbara Ettinger Goodman, MTM Association for Standards and Research, Ann Arbor, Michigan, July 1959.

[4] R.R. 101 (See Ch. 5).

[5] R.R. 108 (See Ch. 5).

than member displacement. This need was met by using electrical strain
gages and other transducers which provided signals for graphical display on
a multi-channel time recorder. A discussion of this type of equipment is
presented in Chapter 22.

The laboratory investigation involved a representative variety of levers,
push buttons, and gripping devices. It considered various modes of force
application by the arm, hands, and fingers. The effects of body member
position and orientation also were evaluated. The resulting statistical data
were exhaustively analyzed by electronic computer equipment which produced both reliable statistical information and plotting data for curve fitting.

The basic behavior of Apply Pressure was found to include three components of a total cycle as depicted ideally in Fig. 1. This shows the

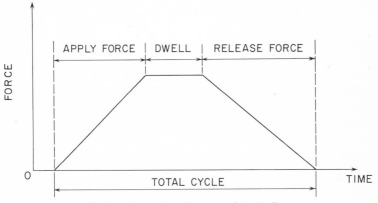

Fig. 1.   Idealized force-time diagram of Apply Pressure.

sequential application of force, some period of dwell, and the gradual removal of force from an object. Note that such a dwell period could be
minimal, while the necessary feedback between the operator and the task
occurs, or it can be more prolonged. It could even be extended into a
holding action so that the force reduction would occur at a much later time,
perhaps after another motion such as a Move or Turn had been performed.
Therefore this plot is sufficiently general to explain all modes of Apply
Pressure. However, a predetermined dwell time would of necessity be
restricted to the minimum value. Any longer time would involve process
time.

The total cycle of Apply Pressure therefore is defined in terms of time
components, rather than motions, as follows:

1. *Apply Force* is the period of time during which no movement occurs
   while an increasing, controlled muscular force is being applied to an
   object(s).

2. *Minimum Dwell* is the period during which a reaction occurs for the reversal of force, where the force is held relatively constant during the reaction interval.

3. *Release Force* is the period of time required for an operator to release muscular force.

With these official definitions and isolation of the significant variables in Apply Pressure resulting from the laboratory study, it was possible to structure a reliable industrial study. All of the time values for the Supplementary Apply Pressure data were obtained from the validated industrial study.

The Industrial Study

By using the newer measurement and analysis techniques developed in the laboratory study, the industrial research was very efficient and highly revealing. The three components were found to be valid, and additional qualifying data were generated.

Apply Force was found to involve a steady increase in force limited only by the operator's muscular capability. However, the required performance time levels off to a constant value of 4.0 TMU when 10 pounds or more force is being applied to the object. This is the maximum time value for Apply Force. Below this value, the exact equation which applies is:

Apply Force, TMU = 0.899 TMU + 0.335 TMU per pound of force

The Apply Force component ends when either the force being applied no longer increases or the force is large enough to cause motion of the object. In other words, Apply Force includes only the period while a *change in force* is occurring. Also note that the force application is *controlled*. If an object is struck with a ballistic motion, often used by experienced operators, the classification of such a blow or force application would not be an Apply Force as defined.

The *Dwell* component was found to occur at essentially a constant force level. The minimum time value required is 4.2 TMU. This time for the *Minimum Dwell* component always is used when the Apply Force is immediately followed by Release Force. In all other cases, the analyst must recognize the process time involved in a clamping or prolonged holding action. In other words, Minimum Dwell is the least time required for feedback between the operator and the task situation to occur so that the muscular force application can be relaxed.

Release Force was deliberately defined as a time component because it differs from the elemental motion Release described in Chapter 13. The Release (or Release Load) motion is a finger or hand element by which an object is physically separated from manual control. Release Force, however, merely shows that the pressure on the object is being removed.

Physical control of the object itself has not been lost at the end of Release Force. Note also that the opposite situation occurs at the beginning of Apply Pressure. In that case, Apply Force is not the means of gaining physical control of the object but merely the application of pressure to it. To obtain physical control of the object itself requires the use of the MTM element Grasp, which is described in Chapter 12. Another way to emphasize both distinctions is to point out that Grasp and Release are *motion* elements, whereas Apply Force and Release Force are only *time* elements. The time value of Release Force was found to be essentially a constant of 3.0 TMU.

Another result of the industrial study was clarification of the manner in which push buttons are actuated. After the button is contacted, Apply Force equivalent to its resistance or the counter-force of its return spring is used to begin motion. The ensuing travel of the button is an M–A to whatever distance is appropriate. At the end of the Move, the Dwell period begins. When Dwell is completed, a return Move occurs while the return spring balances the Dwell force. Then the Release Force begins and the pressure diminishes until contact with the button is broken. To summarize, actuating a push button requires an Apply Pressure *plus* two Case A Moves, which must be analyzed separately. Also, any process time involved in holding must be added.

Supplementary Apply Pressure Data Application[6]

For application purposes, four situations are possible with the supplementary Apply Pressure data:

1. *Only the Apply Force component occurs.* This covers the event where the Dwell is prolonged into a clamping or holding action. That is, the Apply Pressure is completed at a later point in the operation. For maximum clarity, this can be shown in an MTM pattern by using only the Apply Force symbol rather than the Symbol for a complete Apply Pressure.

2. *Only the Release Force component occurs.* This will naturally indicate the later completion of an Apply Pressure as described under the preceding situation. Again, maximum clarity is achieved by symbolizing the Release Force only rather than a complete Apply Pressure.

3. *A complete cycle of Apply Pressure occurs with no binding or other cause for Regrasp (see G2 motion in Chapter 12) or its equivalent.* Here, all three components will be present, with Dwell of a minimum

[6] "Application Training Supplement No. 9, Apply Pressure" by Franklin H. Bayha, James A. Foulke, and Walton M. Hancock, MTM Association for Standards and Research, Ann Arbor, Michigan, January 1965.

or greater value. Essentially, this case corresponds to the older AP2 as to descriptive content. In fact, the AP2 definition will cover this case with only a change in the elemental name.

4. *A complete cycle of Apply Pressure occurs with a preceding Regrasp motion or its equivalent.* This is called Apply Pressure, Bind. The Dwell will be minimum or greater. Because of its similarity to the older AP1, only an elemental name change will make the AP1 definition fit this situation.

The fact that the maximum Apply Force time is for 10 pounds force permits showing the complete cycle, symbolism, and maximum cycle time values with Minimum Dwell as in Figure 2. This diagram also obviously

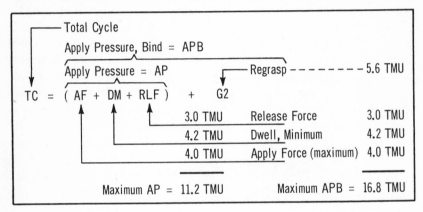

Fig. 2. Symbol diagram and cycle equation for Supplementary Apply Pressure data.

shows the symbol and time for the first two situations described above.

The MTM Data Card information for Supplementary Apply Pressure is given in Table 1. Note that in this table the exact equation for Apply Force has been simplified for ease of application; the error will be small.

Table I. Supplementary Time Data for Apply Pressure[MTM Data Card Table 2—Apply Pressure—AP (Supplementary Data)]

Apply Force (AF) =1.0+(0.3×lbs.). TMU for up to 10 lb. =4.0 TMU max. for 10 lb. and over	
Dwell, Minimum (DM) =4.2 TMU	Release Force (RLF) =3.0 TMU
AP = AF+Dwell+RLF	APB = AP+G2

A convenient form of the Supplementary Apply Pressure data for Minimum Dwell conditions is shown in Table 2. This table is a timesaver, but remember that Dwell may not be minimal and that Release Force also can occur as a separate element in an MTM pattern. However, the Apply Force time values for each pound are available from this table for application when it appears as a separately analyzed element in an MTM pattern.

Table 2. TMU for Total Cycle of Supplementary Apply Pressure with Minimum Dwell

Applied Force, pounds	1	2	3	4	5	6	7	8*	9	10 or more
AF only, TMU	1.3	1.6	1.9	2.2	2.5	2.8	3.1	3.4	3.7	4.0
AP, TMU	8.5	8.8	9.1	9.4	9.7	10.0	10.3	10.6	10.9	11.2
APB (G2 added), TMU	14.1	14.4	14.7	15.0	15.3	15.6	15.9	16.2	16.5	16.8

* Note that AP1 = 16.2 TMU and AP2 = 10.6 TMU are the values for Minimum Dwell (DM = 4.2 TMU) and AF = 8 pounds, approximately (the exact formula gives 7.5 pounds for AP2 = 10.6 TMU).

One additional application rule was *suggested* in the industrial study, although it was not officially included in the Supplementary Apply Pressure data. It concerns the Move time for depressing a push button. This is a mechanically constrained movement frequently limited by internal stops to distances as small as 1/16 to 1/4 inch. For this situation, the MfA time of 2.0 TMU as a minimum MTM time appears to be too large. The suggestion of reducing the push button Move time for short actuation travel to a one-direction value of 1.0 TMU may be used as a "rule of thumb" pending future investigation.

SUMMARY[7]

Table 3. Factors Causing Apply Pressure Time Variation and Symbols Employed

Causes of Apply Pressure Time Variation	Symbol
I. Purpose—The Case	Arabic Numeral
Case 1—Exists when the body member acting requires initial orientation or adjustment to avoid loss of grip, injury, or discomfort during force application on the object	1
Case 2—Exists when the body member acting is already fully oriented or adjusted such that full force application to the object can be made immediately.	2
II. Examples of MTM Symbolism	
AP1 AP2	

[7] This summary does not cover the supplementary data.

Apply Pressure (symbol AP) is an application of muscular force to overcome object resistance, accompanied by little or no motion.

QUESTIONS

1. Write the motion pattern and TMU time value used to fasten securely a common garden hose to a faucet when preparing to water the lawn. Start with the motions just after the hose coupling first touches the threads on the faucet, and end the pattern when the hand has let go of the hose.
2. Do you believe that an Apply Pressure will occur during the removal of a burned-out 60-watt incandescent lamp? If so, analyze the case when the bulb is unbroken and then the case where only a jagged base remains.
3. What kind of Apply Pressure occurs when you push heavily on the brake pedal of your automobile? Also, tell what happens from the time you touch your emergency brake lever until you have engaged it to the limit.
4. A man uses both hands to shift a 50-pound sack of potatoes about 12 inches to the right on a displayed stack at his right elbow. Assuming both hands will perform the same motions, write the right-hand motion pattern from the time he has already contacted the sack until when he just lets go of it. If you think he uses body actions, indicate this by writing "body" at the proper place in the pattern. State time values for all hand and arm motions.
5. Imagine that you have your hands on the rope just before the starting whistle blows for a tug of war to begin. Write the motion pattern with known time values covering the first foot of winning rope movement. As in the last question, show "body" when such motions are involved. However, this time specifically indicate whether the body motion recognized involves any case of Apply Pressure.
6. What MTM element might be used to activate the starting button of a large punch press, if the button has a stiff spring keeping it in the inactive position? Can you enumerate other examples where similar action might occur in the machining or riveting departments of a metalworking plant?

CHAPTER 12

Grasp

Definition[1]

GRASP[2] is the basic finger or hand element employed to secure control of an object.

1. *The hand or finger(s) must obtain sufficient control of the object to be able to perform the next basic motion.*
2. *The object may be a single object or a group of stacked or piled objects which can be handled as though they were a single object.*

The frequency with which Grasps occur is so great that examples are easy to enumerate. Besides the simplest type shown in Fig. 1, others are:

1. Obtaining hold of an MTM card to use it
2. Picking up one of a neat row of pencils to write an MTM analysis
3. Selecting a paper clip from a jumbled pile to fasten the analysis sheets together
4. Shifting the pencil to use an eraser on an error in the motions written
5. Transferring the completed analysis sheets to the other hand to lay them aside from the working area
6. Contacting the MTM card laying flat on the desk to pull it closer.

The performance of any of the manual motions discussed in earlier

---

[1] From "MTM Basic Specifications" (Footnote 1, Chapter 7).

[2] Grasp is not defined as a "motion" because it may involve one or several of the truly basic manual motions of Reach, Move, and Turn. Because *objects* are ordinarily the recipient of manual work, and control of them must first be attained to permit this work, it would be highly inconvenient if each instance of grasp required separate, detailed analysis of the motion components involved. The grouping of repetitive patterns of such components into a synthesized element such as Grasp is obviously much more practical. The Therblig Grasp is the identical element.

chapters might involve actions of any or all of the manual members up to and including the shoulder. With Grasp, however, the motions are confined almost exclusively to the fingers and hand, being generally shorter than an inch in length. Indeed, the fingers and hand are the only body members capable of grasping action. With all other members, contact is the only usual means of control.

Control of objects may also be secured by such tools as tongs, tweezers, and other mechanical devices. When this is the case, the motions used are Moves rather than Grasps. For example, closing tweezers on a very small part could require one or more M—A or M—C, depending on the precision with which the part must be gripped; the part would not be obtained with a Grasp. The Grasp definition involves the operator's fingers and hand themselves gripping the object before the MTM element Grasp is justified.

Another condition of the definition infers that Grasp is preceded and followed by other MTM motions. Since the usual purpose is to pick up or in another way to perform work on an object, a Grasp is usually preceded by a Reach and is normally followed by a Move, although other preceding and following motions are possible. This is important when recognition of Grasp is attempted because many Grasps occur during a time interval too short for the eye to actually see the action. There is no uncertainty as to Grasp being present, however, when the hand is empty one instant and appears the next instant holding an object. The purpose of Grasp is thus evident to the observer in that a controlled object must be in contact with or supported by the hand, and no other criteria is valid when deciding whether a Grasp has occurred.

GRASP VARIABLES

Grasp is a synthesized motion element. The analyst must understand this before he can clearly interpret the variables in grasping motions and the time they consume. Further help toward proper use of this MTM element is afforded by the Theory of Grasp covered in a later section of this chapter. Knowledge of both the variables and the theory will aid correct analysis of Grasp for the usual cases, as well as helping the analysis of unusual and unclassified Grasps.

Because all of the motions involved are one inch or less in length, distance variations are not considered in Grasp analysis. While the short motions of Grasping may well actually be Reaches and Moves, for which distance is a major variable, this does not mean that all the factors in the latter motions bear on the problem of identifying the type of Grasp performed. Some of the Reach and/or Move factors are pertinent, others do not apply. The established Grasping times have already taken account of the fractional (denoted f) distance involved.

Weight does not affect Grasp time because the application of pressure that control of weight involves will be made following completion of the Grasp. In other words, *control* in Grasping merely means that the fingers have closed on the object firmly enough to permit accomplishing any further motions that are to be performed. As explained in the Move chapter, the MTM procedure has placed the time to achieve the *additional* control required when grasping weighted objects exceeding 2½ pounds into the static component of the Move weight factors. The Grasp is completed as soon as the fingers have closed.

The observation time spent on motion study costs money. It would not be used economically if ordinary Grasp motions required analysis of the detailed finger movements at each occurrence. Easier, more accurate evaluation of Grasp follows when the categories and cases are defined in terms of the conditions surrounding the action rather than being defined solely on the basis of true motion content. The categories or cases of Grasp have therefore been grouped in terms of the object grasped in order to minimize the number of variables to be noted during observation and analysis of Grasp elements.

Selection Time

Selection time is caused by the necessity to choose which object to Grasp. It may be present in some types of Grasp and absent in other types. Discussion of a number of factors involved in selection will enable an MTM analyst to decide between cases and correctly account for any selection time present.

A worker uses muscular, visual, and mental control when he makes a choice. When the times required to exercise these types of control exceed that present in normal motions, the time difference is covered by selection time. The presence of such control may be noticed as a reduction in the motion speed, slight hesitation during a motion, or by minor extra motions that occur while selection is accomplished.

Part of the selection control is accomplished during the preceding Reach and the remainder will occur during the Grasp itself. Because of this, the type of Reach toward an object to be grasped depends directly on the nature or kind of Grasp to be made. The connection between any given kind of Grasp and the type of preceding Reach required will be discussed with each case of Grasp. Thus it will be seen that MTM does account for the interconnection and influence of one motion with another preceding or following.

Normal muscle control involves straightforward movement of the hand and fingers to the object being grasped with the speed usually associated with any given type of Reach. Selection time, however, may occur when the fingers must be positioned at the end of the travel before the Grasp can be made. This will slow the action.

The eyes normally are involved in almost all kinds of manual direction. When they must actually fix upon one certain object to be grasped from among many objects, however, more time will elapse. This is another kind of selection time.

A third kind of selection control, mental delay, is also present in some degree during all manual motions. The normal mental action included consists of only sufficient time to enable a rapid, simple yes or no decision. The mental delay included during selection, however, may exceed such simple decision time. When this occurs during a Grasp, the additional time must be included in the Grasp time.

Selection for grasping may include any or all of the forms of control noted and consideration need only be given to those cases where the time exceeds that normally found in motions where no selection occurs; unless the selection time is unusually prolonged, it has been included in the official data times reported for Grasp. This is because the data card times are derived from actual film studies which, obviously, included *all* the time needed to perform the particular type of Grasp in question.

When the object to be grasped lies clear of other objects, any selection time required will have been included in the preceding Reach. In other words, the fingers can readily perform any necessary motion to close on the object without hesitance. Thus single objects in isolated locations need no selection time.

Selection time is obviously needed when a single object must be grasped from a number of like or unlike objects nearby or jumbled with the object. Some of the time required will be covered in the preceding Reach, but successful grasping of the object will necessitate more finger control than for isolated objects. There is a special case of Grasp that covers this set of conditions, and all the time involved is included in the Grasp data time.

For unusual types of object selection in Grasp situations, correct times can be found by including in the motion pattern all the preceding extra MTM motions actually required by operating conditions. Selection time is no great problem so long as all of the motions or time elements actually required are correctly identified by the MTM analyst.

Nature of Object

It is evident that the time to grasp objects will vary with their size and shape. For instance, Grasping time will be less for some optimum object size than for objects either smaller or larger. Picking up a pencil will be easier than grasping either a straight pin or a common rolling pin. A readily accessible protrusion or extension of a part may simplify getting hold of it. When parts having regular geometrical forms such as cubes, balls, cylinders, and cones are handled, the mental processes are eased by much practice in grasping such shapes. When the configuration of a part will create unbalance in holding after being picked up, the worker will exercise more caution in selecting the point of grasp to assure a firmer hold.

All such variable factors were present in the film samples on which MTM times. are based, so the recognition of the proper case of Grasp based on object description will assure that the time allotted for grasping is adequate.

The effect of the nature of the object in determining Grasping time is covered in the MTM data both by case designation and size subclasses of cases. The size categories are not precise, nor are they to be literally interpreted. Rather, they are given to serve as guides to the relative volume or mass of objects which may be grasped in the data time given for the particular case of Grasp. The MTM analyst must use reasonable judgment in deciding the size class for the part he is analyzing. Sizes are denoted in either cubical limits or in diameter range for cylinders. Other geometrical shapes obviously are easily categorized with relation to these two basic configurations.

Object Surroundings

No one will dispute that a part lying clear of other objects will involve fewer finger motions to grasp than will a part restricted by its surroundings, or a part which must be handled in a special way. Many special kinds of restrictions imposed by object surroundings have been evaluated in the standardized cases of Grasp.

Objects contacting their surroundings on more than one surface can often be grasped with some relatively simple extra finger motions. An example of this is an MTM data card stored between two adjacent books between a pair of book ends on top of a desk (the books being close enough to barely admit the card) with one edge sticking out a bit. Sometimes a part, though hemmed in, has a protrusion which can be grasped "on the fly" or with minimum extra motion. Adjacent parts of dissimilar nature can also affect the ease with which an object can be grasped.

A need for special handling, as has been mentioned, can influence the finger motions in Grasp. Slick surfaces are harder to gain control of than usual textures. Roughness may present equivalent difficulty. Polished surfaces on a part to be grasped, or finishes sensitive to skin chemicals are other examples. Extra finger motions are needed to gain control of objects which can damage the fingers or which may be damaged by the fingers. The necessity to grip a part at a special point or within limiting areas further illustrates the special handling variable.

The procedure of evaluation given for Selection Time also holds for the variables introduced by surroundings. If the conditions fit those given for a standardized Grasp either closely or exactly, there is no problem.

When this is not so, correct motion analysis of *all* actions prior to the actual grasping will provide the proper answer to the case in question.

KINDS OF GRASP

Eleven varieties of Grasp have been standardized in the MTM procedure. There are five general types; the first and fourth types each have three cases and the third case of the first type has three subclasses for size variation. The major division is by Type of Grasp:

Type	MTM Name	Common Description
1	Pickup Grasp	Obtain or Get Hold
2	Regrasp	Shift Hold or Realign Fingers
3	Transfer Grasp	Pass Object or Shift to Other Hand
4	Select Grasp	Search and Select or Jumbled Grasp
5	Contact Grasp	Hook or Sliding Grasp

The types, cases, and subclasses will be discussed separately.

Type I, Case A

Definition: Grasp Case 1A is used to obtain control of a single object of any size in an isolated location when the simple act of closing the fingers will suffice to complete the action.

Examples of Grasp Case 1A are numerous, because it is the most commonly encountered type of Grasp. See Fig. 1. Other instances are obtaining a desk pen from its inkwell holder or getting hold of the feed lever on a lathe.

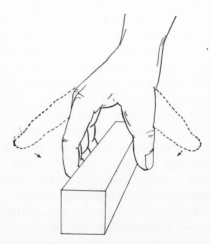

Fig. 1.   Case 1A Grasp.

The purpose of Case 1A Grasps is usually, but not necessarily, to pick up the object to move it. This is the ordinary meaning of *obtain*. At times, however, a Case 1A Grasp may be used merely to *get hold* of the object for any reason that dictates restraint or future semi-controlled movement of the object during work cycles. The example of the feed lever of the lathe illustrates this latter purpose. It is an easy case of Grasp to recognize.

The Reach required will depend on the basic variables in the situation. As the object is situated alone, no selection time beyond that involved in the preceding Reach will be used. The nature or size of the object is relatively immaterial for this case of Grasp and, since the object is by itself, surroundings are likewise not pertinent.

All these factors indicate either a Case A or Case B Reach to be adequate. If the other hand is on the object within 3 inches of the grasping point, a Case A Reach will be used. This is because kinesthetic sense, as discussed in the Reach chapter, is operative within 3-inch limits. In other cases, where mental certainty of the object's location exists due to automaticity developed by repetition of the operation, the preceding Reach will also be Case A. In most other instances, the worker will employ a Case B Reach.

Unless all of the conditions outlined hold true, the Grasp in question will not be a Case 1A. For example, when additional elements of danger, accuracy, or other difficulty are present, some other kind of Grasp will apply. This is because the only requisite of Case 1A Grasp—simple, rapid closing of the fingers—is not met when factors such as those just noted are present.

Type 1, Case B

Definition: Grasp Case 1B is used to obtain control of a single object of very small size in an isolated location or a thin object whose surface contacts closely a flat supporting surface when simple closing of the fingers is precluded by the need for accurate control or extra finger motions.

Two illustrations of Grasp Case 1B are given in Fig. 2, which shows the pickup of a celluloid ruler and a small pill. Other examples are: getting hold of the free end of the lead wire on a coil, obtaining a flat open end wrench lying on a bench top, picking up a piece of flat smooth steel from a table top, obtaining a $\frac{1}{16}$-inch diameter straight shank drill from a drill press table, and getting hold of the page of a book to flip it over.

The general purpose of Case 1B Grasps is the same as for Grasp Case 1A, the difference being that the nature of the objects and their surroundings are additional factors whose influences have been allowed for. Case 1B is an accurate Grasp for either reason. Research disclosed that both factors exert approximately equal influence on Grasp performance time.

As far as the isolated small object is concerned, no selection time is needed. The smallness of the object, however, imposes the need for accuracy in grasping. Either an accurate or controlled finger motion or two simple finger motions are involved. The term "very small" implies an object with a cross section of ⅛ x ⅛ inch or less, this being only a guide figure. The care needed to assure control is due to the relatively large size of the finger tip area whose receptors must sense the object and inform the brain that the object can be moved.

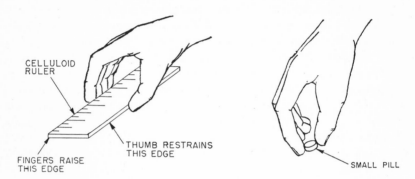

CELLULOID
RULER

THUMB RESTRAINS
THIS EDGE

FINGERS RAISE
THIS EDGE

SMALL PILL

Fig. 2.   Case 1B Grasp.

Selection time may be a minor factor in separating a thin object from a flat supporting surface or other, adjacent thin objects. The extra care and accuracy needed in grasping is mostly due, however, to its shape and position in relation to the supporting surface. This generally requires the use of two simple finger motions to separate the thin object from its support by extension of the flesh of the finger tips slightly under the edge of the object, with the thumb acting as a pivot point. This action is aided if the object is flexible like the page of a book. Generally, picking up a flat object from a flat supporting surface will necessitate lifting one edge of the object to permit completing the grasp.

One useful practice when many Case 1B Grasps must be performed is to lay a sponge rubber mat over the otherwise hard and rigid workplace surface. This may make it possible for the operator to use Case 1A Grasps to obtain the objects, which is both easier and less time consuming.

That a Case 1B Grasp will most often be preceded by a Case D Reach is logical from the definition and discussion of Case D Reach in the Reach chapter. This concept also indicates that objects presenting danger to the fingers or subject to damage will be grasped with a Case 1B Grasp, even though the same object could be obtained with a Case 1A Grasp when such factors are absent. A Case B Reach could logically be assigned as preceding this latter occurrence.

The MTM analyst should be cautious not to miss other MTM motions that may be required when Case 1B Grasp is encountered. It often happens that finger alignments, pressure application, or moving the fingers underneath the object occur in addition to the Case 1B Grasp itself. These would naturally require proper identification and extra time allowances.

Type I, Case C

Definition: Grasp Case 1C is used to obtain control of a single object approximating a cylindrical shape which contacts its surroundings with one longitudinal surface other than the one on which it rests.

The use of Grasp Case 1C in two kinds of situations is depicted in Fig. 3. Note that only one object is being obtained in both cases, although more than one object is present in the second example. Other instances seen in industry are getting hold of a straight shank drill, a welding rod, a pencil, or a stick of chalk from an orderly array of the same kind.

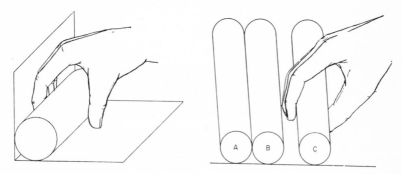

Fig. 3.   Case 1C Grasp.

While this Grasp is a Type 1 in general concept, involving the pickup of an object, its special nature has led to usage of the common name of "Interference" Grasp. Note that the objects included are rodlike in shape; and the cross section approaches cylindrical form, although cross sections of such other geometric shapes as hexagonal are not excluded, provided the length of the object is such as to satisfy the rodlike requirement. The idea is that a relatively long and slender object is being obtained from its position of rest on one long side and with a restriction to finger action on another long side.

The motion significance is that the fingers must first separate the object from its surroundings sufficiently to allow closure that will effect control. Actually, the sequence is as follows. The forefinger and/or middle fingers contact and roll the object toward the thumb, after which the leading finger or fingers shift around the object to effect closure, to complete the grasping action. The added time for this Grasp covers these extra finger motions. Note also that an object exceeding 1 inch in diameter will not require a Case 1C Grasp because its size relative to the size of the finger tips is large enough to permit easy closure with little difficulty. The two lines of contact will not prevent getting the fingers on an object as large as 1 inch, so no interference exists.

To justify classification of Case 1C Grasp as such, several conditions must be met. The shape and surroundings were noted above. The fact that only one object is being picked up is another. The object cannot be standing on end, but must be lying on its long side. Jumbled conditions deny usage of this Grasp because an orderly array is not then present. In short, the MTM analyst must recognize the special nature of this Grasp and avoid using it merely because the time seems applicable when the conditions are otherwise incorrect.

The Reach preceding a Case 1C Grasp will logically be Case A, B, or D by the definition of those classes in the Reach chapter. Cases C and E of Reach are excluded from consideration. Decision on which of the three possible Reaches is used will depend on the nature of the object, the surrounding conditions, and the operator's usual mode of performance. Each occurrence must be analyzed by the rules for determining the proper class of Reach. No restrictive rules can be given that will give unvarying answers for all instances of Case 1C Grasp.

Three subclasses of Grasp Case 1C are based on size variation of the nearly cylindrical cross sections involved:

1. Diameters exceeding ½ inch
2. Diameters of ¼ inch to ½ inch, inclusive
3. Diameters less than ¼ inch.

Remember that these dimensions are given as relative guides for decision. The only reason for the subclasses is to account for time variations among the actually observed instances of interference Grasps.

Type 2

Definition: Grasp Case 2, Regrasp, is used to shift the hold or realign the fingers on an object already under manual control to improve or increase control of the object or to relocate the object in the hand for later use in the work cycle.

The frequency of Regrasp in ordinary manual motions is extremely high. A typical example is the shifting of a pen or pencil in the writer's hand before, during, and after the action of writing. Other instances will readily occur to the reader.

Apparent inconsistencies in the original data were readily explained when Messrs. Maynard, Stegemerten, and Schwab isolated and identified this Grasp. This was the first time it had been recognized and thus represents a contribution by MTM to the basics of motion study. Attention to time and motion together revealed its presence when independent thinking on either failed to uncover Regrasp.

Essentially, Regrasp proceeds with a rapid series of very short finger motions involving a time lapse so short that control of the object is not lost. The grip is relaxed, the fingers are quickly shifted to new holding points, and the grip is reapplied to maintain control. Actually, the fingers slide along the object in a manner which relocates the object in the hand without allowing it to drop.

Regrasp occurs with multiple frequency without intervening motions taking place in a large number of actual motion sequences. The necessity for this is evident when a major repositioning of the object in the hand is considered.

Since prior control of the object exists as a condition of performance, Regrasp will not be preceded by a Reach. The preceding motion will be a Move or another type of Grasp. Regrasp often occurs between or during other motions, a common event being either during a Case C Move or between it and an accurate placement. It also appears with high frequency as a combined Move-Regrasp when the operator employs a Regrasp to improve his grip or for orienting during object transport. The rules for combined motion discussed in the Turn chapter will apply to such cases.

The recognition and classification of Regrasp present a minimum of difficulty for the MTM analyst. This makes one wonder why it was not isolated earlier, because its utility in motion study is obvious.

Type 3

Definition: Grasp Case 3, Transfer Grasp, is used to transfer an object from one hand to the other when the shift involves brief holding of the object by the fingers of both hands.

Occurrence of this Grasp should be low in industrial operations, because its elimination by proper placement of materials and workplace layout is a constant aim of engineers abiding by the laws of motion economy. However, since the complete elimination of Case 3 Grasps is difficult and sometimes impractical, it will at times properly belong in an MTM standard. An example of Transfer Grasp occurs when an eating fork is shifted from the left to the right hand after being used to hold meat to the plate for cutting.

The motions included in a Case 3 Grasp are a Type 1, Case A Grasp by one hand, a reaction time, and a release of the object by the hand first holding. The reaction time covers the pause during which mental or muscle assurance of the completion of Grasp by the receiving hand occurs. *This hesitation is the clue which distinguishes a Transfer Grasp.* If this pause is prolonged, the action is not a Case 3 Grasp—process time is involved.

When the reaction time is missing, motions other than those denoted under Case 3 Grasp have transpired. Highly skilled operators may pass an object without using reaction time by employing a Case 1A Grasp with one hand to pick the object out of the other hand, while the latter hand executes a contact release that involves no time allowance. A highly skilled worker may even toss the object between hands and not lose control. However, both of these situations should be analyzed for the actual motions used since assignment of a Transfer Grasp would be incorrect. Certainly, the tossing motion involves process time which should be determined by a stop watch instead of by assigning an MTM motion.

A Case A or Case B Reach, depending on the 3-inch rule for kinesthetic sense, by the receiving hand will normally precede a Case 3 Grasp. Or a Case D Reach will be involved when the object is very small, dangerous to the hand, or easily damaged. The other hand will be either holding or moving the object just prior to the Transfer Grasp, so no Reach is involved for it.

Transfer Grasp is very easy for the MTM analyst to perceive and classify. However, its presence in a productive situation usually is undesirable. The analyst should be alert to the possibility of eliminating it by methods improvement based on relocation of the parts in the operation. When such deletion is not possible or practical, however, he should allow the observed Transfer Grasp.

Type 4

Definition: Grasp Case 4, Select Grasp, is used to obtain control of a single object from a jumbled pile of objects when the act of search and select must precede closing of the fingers.

This grasp has become known as the "Totepan" Grasp because of typical examples like these:

1. Selecting one screw from a totepan full of screws
2. Picking out a nut from a pan full of screws, nuts, and washers.

Selection time, as previously discussed, is obviously a large factor in Case 4 Grasps. Because the fingers are definitely aiming for one particular piece, the same amount of selection will be needed whether the surrounding objects are similar or dissimilar. This time for aiming the fingers will always exceed the relatively rapid mental action additionally needed due to dissimilarity, as compared to selection of similar objects, so that no appreciable or discernible difference in time will inhere in the two events.

The definition requires that jumbling—lack of orderly array—be present to justify classification of a Case 4 Grasp. Parts neatly stacked, layered, or placed systematically will require less Grasp time or at least some other kind of Grasp.

On the other hand, a Case 4 Grasp implies that the object being aimed at can be easily separated from the others around it. Interlocking, tangling, or twisting together of parts presents a different problem. To obtain one from such parts will likely require Reaches, Moves, etc., other than those normally involved in a Case 4 Grasp. One part may possibly be grasped by Case 4 action, but subsequent additional Moves will probably be needed to separate it from the other parts or to otherwise surmount the adverse condition of the parts. Occurrences of Grasp for such situations require detailed motion analysis rather than cursory assignment of a Case 4 Grasp and its time value, even though the derived time value might equal the time for a Totepan Grasp.

The Reach preceding a Case 4 Grasp must, by definition and control involved, be a Case C Reach. No other class of Reach will logically connect the motions. Case D Reach might be thought proper when the possibility of danger or damage is present; but the time would not differ and the selection time idea in Reach Case C will overrule.

The relative size of object grasped justifies three subclasses of Case 4 Grasp:

1. Objects larger than $1'' \times 1'' \times 1''$
2. Objects from $\frac{1}{4}'' \times \frac{1}{4}'' \times \frac{1}{8}''$ to $1'' \times 1'' \times 1''$, incl.
3. Objects smaller than $\frac{1}{4}'' \times \frac{1}{4}'' \times \frac{1}{8}''$.

As a container of objects being grasped approaches the empty state, Case 4 Grasp would obviously no longer apply. However, the analyst should remember that MTM work patterns are always written for the normal or average situation encountered. If the container is usually full, he would specify a Case 4 Grasp. If it normally contains mostly isolated objects, he should fairly judge another kind of Grasp.

Type 5

Definition: Grasp Case 5, Contact Grasp, is used when enough control of a single object is gained merely by purposeful touch of the object surface by the finger(s) and/or hand. It is actually not a motion but rather a descriptive term.

Most commonly, this type of Grasp is called the Contact, Sliding, or Hook Grasp:

1. Contact because this is the aim of "purposeful touch";
2. Sliding because this is often the action on the object after the Grasp;
3. Hook because the hand and fingers often assume this shape in such Grasps.

Instances of Case 5 Grasp occur when a worker contacts the hinged cover of a box to swing it shut, lays his fingers on a part to slide it out of the way, or hooks his hand on the lip of a totepan to draw it toward him. Other typical examples are the *contacts* prior to pressing a typewriter or adding machine key, pressing an electrical contact button, pushing a door shut, etc.

Logical analysis makes it evident that Grasp Case 5 requires no time. One instant the manual members are reaching; immediately upon contact, they are either moving or constraining the object. The Contact Grasp, however, should be recorded in the MTM pattern to show that control of the object has been gained. In this way, the methods description is completed, even though no time is involved.

The use of Contact Grasp has no effect on the preceding Reach. The case of Reach used must be noted solely by examination of the part and analysis of the Reach by its own rules. It is obvious from this that the only type of Reach excluded is Case E; any other type might be required.

The absence of any perceptible pause between Reach and Move is a clue to the performance of a Case 5 Grasp. Pushing or pulling of objects is frequently the end result of a Contact Grasp and therefore a good clue to its occurrence. Another clue is when actions are taken on objects which remain on a surface or are mechanically constrained, such as a lathe feed lever. These situations usually involve Case 5 Grasps because the hand, after contacting, must supply only slight extra control—the object is basically controlled by the surface or mechanism.

Note that contact alone will not ordinarily permit the object to be lifted nor will an object's weight usually be controlled without MTM motions in addition to the Contact Grasp. If there is space to reach the hand under the object and lift it with a flattened palm, however, it is possible to do so with a Contact Grasp only.

Since Contact Grasp requires no perceptible performance time, the workplace and operating facilities should be designed to utilize this form of grasp whenever possible.

THE SHORTHAND OF GRASP

Grasp

The MTM engineer will show a capital letter G on his study to denote Grasp.

Type of Grasp

An arabic numeral shows the type of Grasp employed. Thus G1, G2, G3, G4, and G5 will show the complete gamut of types.

Case of Grasp

The case, as per previous discussion, is noted by a capital letter after the type number. The possibilities are: G1A, G1B, G1C, G4A, G4B, and G4C.

Size Subclass

A number will show the size subclass for a Type 1, Case C Grasp. The following listing thus completes all combinations of symbols: G1C1, G1C2, and G1C3.

DATA CARD INFORMATION

Table IV of the official MTM card lists the time values for Grasp. These are shown here in Table 1.

Examination of the MTM data card reveals that some of the time values are in light-face type, others in heavy-face type. The heavy figures were

Table I. Grasp Data (MTM Data Card Table IV—Grasp—G)

Case	Time TMU	DESCRIPTION
1A	2.0	**Pick Up Grasp**—Small, medium or large object by itself, easily grasped.
1B	3.5	Very small object or object lying close against a flat surface.
1C1	7.3	Interference with grasp on bottom and one side of nearly cylindrical object. Diameter larger than ½".
1C2	8.7	Interference with grasp on bottom and one side of nearly cylindrical object. Diameter ¼" to ½".
1C3	10.8	Interference with grasp on bottom and one side of nearly cylindrical object. Diameter less than ¼".
2	5.6	**Regrasp.**
3	5.6	**Transfer Grasp.**
4A	7.3	Object jumbled with other objects so search and select occur. Larger than 1" x 1" x 1".
4B	9.1	Object jumbled with other objects so search and select occur. ¼" x ¼" x ⅛" to 1" x 1" x 1".
4C	12.9	Object jumbled with other objects so search and select occur. Smaller than ¼" x ¼" x ⅛".
5	0	Contact, sliding or hook grasp.

obtained directly from actual research data. The light figures were either extrapolated from research data or synthesized by the Theory of Grasp described below. All of the values, however, have yielded good results in thousands of MTM analyses and may be used confidently for the present.

The MTM Association recognizes the need for further data and research on Grasp. Such research may either validate the light-faced values or provide new information to increase the worth of the MTM Grasp motion data. For example, the original MTM data card showed G1A to need 1.7 TMU performance time based on research done with a film speed taking that amount of time per frame. In evaluating short Reaches and Moves, with a film speed four times as fast, the newer and more accurate value of 2.0 TMU was found for G1A. After validation, this value is now official.

THEORY OF GRASP

It was mentioned at the outset that Grasp is by nature and definition a synthesized MTM element composed of very short basic finger and hand motions. Theoretically, all grasping is done by some combination of reaching or moving with the fingers, and the more complicated grasps may also require aligning of the fingers. An attempt to explain and isolate these more basic motions resulted in what is known as the Theory of Grasp. There are three purposes or uses for the Theory of Grasp:

1. To promote the ability of the MTM analyst to understand and visualize the standardized cases of Grasp now included on the data card.
2. To synthetically arrive at usable times for unusual kinds of Grasp not now included in the MTM data. This should be done in a cautious manner, however.
3. The data card gives time values for grasping only single objects, as reference to the definitions for each case of Grasp will show. In actual practice, multiple Grasps or Grasps of a handful of pieces are a frequent event. The Theory of Grasp enables the MTM engineer to evaluate such situations because it both increases his background data and shows the actual method of synthesis he may profitably follow.

The Theory of Grasp is presented in tabular array in Table 2. Both the basic motions and time values are given, along with comparison to research values and the data card for each kind of Grasp. The reader should study this information carefully. It is self-explanatory, except for the following specific comments.

The listing for motion significance at the bottom of Table 2 calls attention to the theoretical basic motion components used to synthesize each case of Grasp. It includes three kinds of fractional finger reaches, one fractional move of the object being grasped, and a case of Position (see Chapter 14) which covers aligning of the fingers to the object being grasped. Also note the listing of "Reaction time" in the synthesis for G3 Transfer Grasp. This phenomenon was mentioned in the discussion of this element as being the hesitation time which covers the pause involved. It is the reason why 5.6 TMU is required instead of the 4.0 TMU otherwise taken by the RfA and RfE components of G3. Because Release (RL2—see Chapter

Table 2. Theory of Grasp and Release

Case of Motion	Motion—Time Synthesis f = fractional inches or less than 1″	TMU Value		
		Theory	Experiment	Data Card
G1A	RfA + G5 = 2.0 + 0.0	2.0	1.972	2.0
G1B	RfA + G5 + MfB = 2.0 + 0.0 + 2.0	4.0	} 4.351	3.5
	RfD + G5 + MfB = 2.0 + 0.0 + 2.0	4.0		
G1C1	G5 + MfB + RL2 + RfA + G5 + MfB = 0.0 + 2.0 + 0.0 + 2.0 + 0.0 + 2.0	6.0	} 7.85	7.3
	G5 + MfB + G2 = 0.0 + 2.0 + (4.0 or 6.0)	6.0 or 8.0		
G1C2	RfD + G5 + MfB + RL2 + RfA + G5 + MfB = 2.0 + 0.0 + 2.0 + 0.0 + 2.0 + 0.0 + 2.0	8.0		8.7
G1C3	P1SE + G5 + MfB + RL2 + RfA + G5 + MfB = 5.6 + 0.0 + 2.0 + 0.0 + 2.0 + 0.0 + 2.0	11.6		10.8
G2	RL2 + RfA + G5 + RL2 + RfA + G5 + MfB = 0.0 + 2.0 + 0.0 + 0.0 + 2.0 + 0.0 + 2.0	6.0	} 5.899	5.6
	RL2 + RfA + G5 + MfB + RL2 + RfA + G5 = 0.0 + 2.0 + 0.0 + 2.0 + 0.0 + 2.0 + 0.0	6.0		
	MfB + RL2 + RfA + G5 + RL2 + RfA + G5 = 2.0 + 0.0 + 2.0 + 0.0 + 0.0 + 2.0 + 0.0	6.0		
	Occasionally RL2 + RfA + G5 + MfB = 0.0 + 2.0 + 0.0 + 2.0	4.0		
G3	RfA + G5 + Reaction time + RL2 + RfE = 2.0 + 0.0 + 1.6 + 0.0 + 2.0	5.6	5.257	5.6
G4A	P1SE + G1A = 5.6 + 2.0	7.6	} 9.204	7.3
G4B	P1SE + G1B = 5.6 + 4.0	9.6		9.1
G4C	P1SE + G1C2 = 5.6 + 8.0	13.6		12.9
	P1SE + G1A + G2 = 5.6 + 2.0 + (6.0 or 4.0)	13.6 or 11.6		
G5	Contact only—logically no time	0.0	0.0	0.0
RL1	RL2 + RfE = 0.0 + 2.0	2.0	2.041	2.0
RL2	Break contact only—logically no time	0.0	0.0	0.0

Motion Significance:

RfA	finger reach with automaticity
RfD	finger reach with care (smallness, accuracy)
RfE	finger reach to clear
MfB	grip *or* move of object to hold
P1SE	placement of fingers (including selection time)

13) motions are a part of the Theory of Grasp, the table also shows the Theory of Release.

It might be noted that there seems to be a lack of proper correlation among some theoretical, experimental, and data-card times. This should not disturb the reader, because the data-card times have yielded acceptable time standards in thousands of applications to date. Until data-card revisions are forthcoming, the analyst should rely on the present data and application rules.

PRACTICAL WORKING RULES

All of the major types of Grasp occurring with high frequency have been included on the MTM card in standardized form. That many other infrequent varieties of Grasp may well be possible is rather obvious, and for these a few practical hints will help the engineer to make reasonable analyses.

For the grasping of objects that are very large in relation to the hand or fingers, an analyst must decide what motions are most natural and likely. If the object is too large to permit the hand to close around it, then only G5 is possible and other MTM motions will be needed in addition. It is very likely that G1A is the logical choice for sizes between that extreme and the range of smaller sizes covered by the data card. For example, recall the 1-inch diameter limit for a G1C suggested in the discussion of that motion.

The presence of a readily accessible protrusion or extension on an object, whether jumbled or not, will tend to indicate use of a G1A. This is a case where the ordinary rules for grasping do not apply. However, the situation is not exactly the same as an ordinary G1A with a preceding A or B Reach. It is probable, when jumbling is present, that the Reach will be a Case C even though the Grasp is G1A. In other words, the controlled Reach will locate the fingers well enough to permit them to close easily on the prominent feature of the object without further selection time being needed during the Grasp itself.

The data on the MTM card applies directly to the use of bare hands. Then what motions should be written when gloves are worn? The answer will depend mostly on the texture, dryness, and fit of the gloves. In any event this must be judged in the light of whether the hand and fingers can act in a normal fashion. If they can, the regular MTM Grasps will apply. If not, other motion analysis or a stop watch should be employed.

Another assumption in developing the data card values was that the object being grasped was visible to the operator. Special rules have been developed and successfully applied in the field for blind Grasps; these cannot be completely sanctioned until validated by further research. One is that blind Grasps following a Case A Reach must be classified by the nature of the object grasped; they will tend to be some kind of G1 or a G5. Another rule used in the field says that blind Grasps preceded by B, C, or D Reaches appear, in researches to date, to require some case of G4. These rules will help the analyst until a final answer has been obtained.

Finally, every case of observed Grasp that does not reasonably fit the standard categories of MTM should not be given a standard designation. Neither should it be assigned the data card times unless they happen to be equivalent. When possible, the Theory of Grasp should be used to synthesize the true condition and the time assigned according to the motions determined necessary. When this approach is impractical or fails, the observer should rely on such other means of work measurement as time study rather than erroneously apply the MTM data.

SUMMARY

Grasp (symbol G) is the basic finger or hand element employed to secure control of an object.

Table 3. Factors Causing Grasp Time Variations and Symbols Employed

Causes of Grasp Time Variation			Symbol
I. Purpose—The Kind			
Type	*Case*	*Description*	
1	A	PICKUP—Small, medium, or large object by itself— easily grasped	1A
	B	PICKUP—Very small object or thin object lying close against a flat surface	1B
	C	PICKUP—Interference with grasp on the bottom and one side of a nearly cylindrical object	
		Subclass	
		1 Diameters above ½″	1C1
		2 Diameters from ¼″ to ½″	1C2
		3 Diameters below ¼″	1C3
2		REGRASP	2
3		TRANSFER GRASP	3
4		SELECT GRASP—Object jumbled with other objects so that search and select occur	
	A	Objects larger than 1″ x 1″ x 1″	4A
	B	Objects between ¼″ x ¼″ x ⅛″ and 1″ x 1″ x 1″	4B
	C	Objects smaller than ¼″ x ¼″ x ⅛″	4C
5		CONTACT GRASP	5
II. Examples of MTM Symbolism			
G1A G1C2 G4B G5			

QUESTIONS

1. As you are leaving your house, you wish to close the partially open front door. Ignoring foot or body motions, write an appropriate motions pattern with TMU values to describe your actions. State reasons for your selections.

2. What Grasp and time value will be needed to pick up a dinner knife from the table? Indicate the reason behind your answer.

3. Symbolize and assign a time value for the kind of Reach, Grasp, or other motions you believe will ordinarily be used to obtain one straight pin from a compartment full of them in your desk drawer. What symbols and time will apply to picking up one straight pin alone on a table top?

4. A man must move a piece of steel the size and shape of a common brick. What motions will be used to Reach, Grasp, etc., to move the brick? Symbolize and describe the motions involved and assign proper time values. Explain your choice of motions and indicate distances and weight assumed.

5. A bottle dropped on a concrete floor has shattered into various-sized pieces of glass. What kind of Reach and Grasp are required to get hold of the smaller pieces? Give the same answer for the larger pieces. How long will each Grasp take?

6. An amateur gardener has just driven his spade into the ground and will use his left hand to raise the spade full of dirt. What exact motions and times will he use to get hold of the spade handle?

7. What MTM motion will you enact to pass a small alarm clock from your right to your left hand? What sequence of motions and time is required to next grip the winding key with your right hand? Will the Grasp for succeeding winding twists differ in any way from that for the first twist? Will the winding consist of a series of turns or a series of other finger motions? Show detailed analysis and indicate your reasoning for answers to each question.

8. What kind of Reach and Grasp will a driver normally use to grip the post-mounted gearshift lever when he wishes to shift from third to reverse? Give all the motions and times up to the point when the reverse position is attained.

CHAPTER 13

Release

Definition[1]

RELEASE[2] *is the basic finger or hand motion employed to relinquish control of an object.*

1. Release is performed only by the fingers or the hand.

The purpose of Release is twofold. First, control of the object is no longer desired by the worker and it is thus, in common words, "let go." Second, Release frees the hand and fingers for use in other motions. The latter reason is a distinction which aids recognition of the necessity for Release in motion patterns where its occurrence might otherwise be missed. This is especially true when the motions are being visualized rather than observed directly.

Being one of the simplest possible MTM motions, Release consumes the minimum amount of motion time. Since the eyes cannot actually see the motion, recourse in its identification must be based on logic or the observable effect it produces on the object. This is similar to the situation discussed in Grasp; and in a sense Release is really the opposite of Grasp. When an object is seen to be controlled manually one instant and completely free of control the next instant, it is obvious that Release was performed. This is the recognition clue.

The performance of Release is restricted by the definition to direct action by the fingers or hand with no intervening devices between them and the object concerned. When various hand tools such as tweezers, hand clamps, and the like have been used to hold or control the object, it is then freed

[1] From "MTM Basic Specifications" (Footnote 1, Chapter 7).

[2] The well-known Therblig called Release Load is the identical motion as defined. For brevity in use, the term "Load" is usually omitted in MTM practice. Recognition of it is implied, however, in the second letter of the MTM symbol.

229

by Reaches or Moves which cause or allow the device to open. For example, letting go of a part held in the jaws of spring-loaded wiring pliers could involve only a Case B Move by the fingers, which hold the plier handles by contact pressure against the spring resistance. If the pliers are allowed to open fully, however, the Move would be a Case A to the maximum travel of the plier handles. If a pair of common pliers are being used, the motion analysis is more complicated because at least one of the plier handles must be "hooked" between the fingers to avoid dropping the pliers when the part is released. In this case, either the analysis above is possible or else the part could be released by performing an RfE with the thumb. It is also possible that a Move-Turn of the pliers prior to or combined with the opening motion would be needed to allow the part to fall free of the jaws of the pliers. If this is true, the actual releasing motion could be limited out in the analysis.

KINDS OF RELEASE

Because there are only two logical ways in which the fingers or hand can end control of objects, only two cases of release are needed.

Case I

Definition: Release Case 1 consists of opening the fingers as a separate, distinct motion.

Most MTM analysts refer to Case 1 Release as a "Normal" Release because it is a simple, easy, natural motion. Reaching of the fingers out of the way of the object is the only action involved. Research has definitely shown this to be a short Case E Reach, generally an inch or less in length. Refer to Fig. 1.

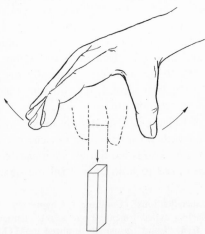

Fig. 1. Case 1 Release.

The value of isolating Release as an independent motion is in the descriptive worth of showing in motion sequences that an object is no longer controlled or restrained by the worker's hand. For purposes of merely accounting for the time taken by the motion, recording of an RfE would otherwise suffice. But recall that a good work measurement analysis shows *both* what the worker is doing and what happens to the workpieces. Writing a Release in the motion pattern achieves both aims, while an RfE would only show the operator's action.

The definition of Case 1 Release recognizes that the fingers may be opened while other MTM motions are performed. For example, in several of the kinds of Grasp there are internal events when the fingers open momentarily but the aim in that case is to *gain* control of the object. When, however, the same motion occurs in a separate and distinct manner with the aim of losing object control, the justification of Release as an independent motion category is readily evident.

The result of Case 1 Release on the object need not be identical for all occurrences. The object may be dropped, freed from restraining action, or merely left to rest on a supporting surface. The manual action is the same in each of these possibilities.

Case 2

Definition: Release Case 2 consists of breaking contact between the object(s) and the fingers or hand, when no discernible motion occurs.

The sole purpose of Contact Release, the common name for a Case 2 Release, is to provide an MTM element describing the fact that the object is no longer under manual control. Since no motion is involved, lack of this element in a motion pattern might cause the reader of it to wonder whether the object had been freed or was still under control.

Logically, since no motion occurs during a Release Case 2, this element will consume zero time. One instant the hand is in contact with an object, the next instant it is reaching away with no perceptible pause between. This element is thus the opposite of a G5, or Contact Grasp. The MTM analyst must discern the presence of Contact Release to account for operation method only. He can do this by being alert to relinquishing actions during work sequences.

THE SHORTHAND OF RELEASE

The conventional symbols for Release are as simple as the motion element.

Release

The basic element Release is shown by the two capital letters RL, which are an abbreviation of Release Load.

Case

An arabic numeral denotes the case of release performed thus:

RL1 shows performance of a Case 1 or Normal Release.

RL2 shows that a Case 2 Release was done, a Contact Release.

DATA CARD INFORMATION

Data for Release in Table 1 appears in Table VI of the MTM card.

Table I. Time Data for Release
(MTM Data Card Table VI—Release—RL)

Case	Time TMU	DESCRIPTION
1	2.0	Normal release performed by opening fingers as independent motion.
2	0	Contact Release.

THEORY OF RELEASE

The reader probably noted in the Grasp chapter, under the theory section, that the Theory of Release was combined with the Theory of Grasp for convenience. The only purpose served by a Theory of Release is to show that RL1 involves an RfE. The time for an RfE, and thus the time for RL1, was fully validated in the research on *Short Reaches and Moves.*[3] The films on which this data was based were taken at the high speed of 4,000 frames per minute (0.42 TMU per frame), therefore, the value for RL1 should need no further change.

PRACTICAL WORKING RULES

Recognition of the performance of Release during work cycles and correct decision as to the case observed is aided when the analyst's attention is focused on the type of control being relinquished. One key to this goal is the type of Grasp with which the object being released was originally obtained.

In most instances where an object was originally subjected to a pickup Grasp, it will normally be abandoned with an RL1. Another possibility

[3] R.R. 106 (See Ch. 5).

is when the use of a G5 to obtain is followed during the ensuing motion sequence by a G2 to gain further control or enclose the fingers around the object. This will almost always cause the Release to become an RL1.

The analysis is reversed for RL2. Normally an object obtained with a G5 will be abandoned by an RL2. Next assume the object was lifted by a pickup type of Grasp. If either a Regrasp (for example after the object is being guided along a surface) or an R—E of the fingers from the object occurs during the operating cycle, the use of RL2 to merely finalize loss of contact will logically be the correct Release classification.

An event where an R—E might be used *instead* of Release was discussed under that case of reach in the Reach chapter. This is where a handful of small parts are dropped by opening and spreading the fingers, which would require that the fingertip travel be measured to assign an R—E or a sequence of R—E motions.

When sticky substances are present on the surfaces of objects to be released, some delay time may occur during the Release. In such cases, the time of releasing must be found either by analyzing any other MTM motions involved, by means of a stop watch, or by film analysis. The MTM Release motions do not include any difficulty in letting go of the object.

Releases also occur at times in combined motions, as when objects are tossed aside or dropped "on the fly." The pattern at right fully shows what happens to the motions and time in such cases. The dash (—) in the TMU column for RL1 shows the time is limited out.

M12Bm	10.0 TMU
RL1	—
mR5E	4.6 TMU
Total Time	14.6 TMU

Release also occurs with great frequency during many such common motion sequences as the Reach, Grasp, Move or Turn, and Release as would be employed to turn a nut on a bolt. The MTM analyst should be alert for such short motion patterns involving Releases.

Because the performance of Release is so repetitive in motion patterns, the analyst must use caution so as not to miss it. The time for a single Release is usually not sufficient to invalidate the total time for a motion pattern of normal length; but, if a number of Releases are missed, especially in an operation of short duration, the cycle time can be affected adversely.

SUMMARY

Release (symbol RL) is the basic finger or hand motion employed to relinquish control of an object.

Table 2. Kinds of Release and Symbols Employed

Kinds of Release	Symbol
I. Purpose—The Case	Arabic Numeral
Case 1—Normal release performed by opening the fingers as an independent motion	1
Case 2—Contact release performed by merely lifting the fingers or hand off the object	2
II. Examples of MTM Symbolism	
RL1　　　RL2	

QUESTIONS

1. An auto driver has just shifted the gears of a conventional floor-mounted three-speed transmission into the high position. What kind of Release do you believe he will normally employ to terminate control of the shift lever?
2. What Release will a player in a dice game normally use to allow the dice to leave his hand when rolling for a score?
3. In lifting the fingers from a common wall toggle switch, such as is used to control the lights in most homes, which case of Release will be seen?
4. The operator of a special production machine has several kinds of buttons and switches to introduce variations in the machine cycle. He has push buttons which are contacted and quickly pushed before reaching to the next control. Other push buttons are held down against stiff spring resistance for 36-second intervals. The machine is started and stopped with a small toggle switch. Several rheostats are periodically adjusted with 90-degree rotations to control the tool speeds. There is also a lever to mechanically eject the finished part. In all five of these control devices, a series of motions including Releases occur. Write the motion pattern for each case from the time the operator's hand is 10 inches away from the control until he has reached back 12 inches (in motion) toward the next device. Show complete MTM symbols and give time values. Also compare the resulting activation times.

CHAPTER 14

Position

Definition[1]

POSITION[2] is the basic finger or hand element employed to align, orient, and engage one object with another to attain a specific relationship.
1. *An accurate and predetermined relationship between the objects must be attained.*
2. *The relationship may be a nesting or mating of the objects, or may be a visual locating of one object to another.*
3. *Normally, only objects can be positioned; occasionally, the finger or hand may be used as a tool and considered as an object in positioning.*
4. *Align is to line up the two parts so that they have a common axis.*
5. *Orient is to rotate the part about the common axis of engagement so that it can be mated with the other part.*
6. *Engage is to enter one part into the other part.*

The concept of Position was invented by the originators of MTM to overcome difficulty in the recognition, usage, and timing of the physical actions included when they tried to adhere to earlier micromotion categories. The Therbligs separated the align and orient motions as Pre-position and Position (not the same as the MTM variety); the blending of these into engagement resisted distinguishing of the end point, even on motion picture films. Likewise, the Assemble Therblig covering the en-

[1] From "MTM Basic Specifications" (Footnote 1, Chapter 7).

[2] As was true for Grasp, Position is a synthetic combination of the basic manual motions; it is, therefore, defined as an "element" to distinguish this fact. No Therblig matches this concept exactly, although combinations of Use, Pre-position, Position, and Assemble might connote the same action. The utility of Position (MTM variety) in expediting motion analysis will be appreciated by gaining an understanding of this chapter.

gaging action included such short distances as to make difficult the analysis and timing of minor depths of insertion. Visual and film analysis were notably easier when Position was defined as above to include up to 1 inch of insertion, the only necessity being the treatment of deeper engagements as separate elemental motions.

Since a major amount of industrial and business activity concerns assembly routines, examples of Position come readily to mind:

1. A machinist centers a punch to a cross mark on a template to punch mark it preparatory to drilling a guide hole
2. A test engineer slides the adjustment knob of a variable resistor to a close setting
3. A clerk installs an index tab into the metal slot of a file divider
4. A saleslady fits her coded key into the lock of a cash register
5. A factory hand locates a screw into a hole.

Note that in all of these instances, movement of the object being positioned to within 1 inch or so of the final location was completed just prior to the act described. Until the act of Position was completed, no further displacement of the object exceeding 1 inch would normally occur. It is possible that movements exceeding 1 inch after positioning could occur in Examples 3 and 5. Deeper insertion would be evidenced by a subsequent move of any distance greater than 1 inch following the defined positioning motion. Several important application rules are derived from the set of facts just stated; they will be discussed in detail later.

GENERAL DISCUSSION

Note that Position is a *manual* element, that is, it can be performed only by the fingers and/or hand-arm muscle combination. The reason other body members cannot perform Position is that it is a set of more basic motions involving moderate to extreme control beyond that normally expected of other body members. Accurate location of the foot, for example, cannot be made with a degree of precision comparable to that possible with manual members. The leg muscles can only rarely situate the foot closer than $\frac{1}{4}$ to $\frac{1}{2}$ inch of a certain location. With hand control of objects, however, it is possible to place objects within thousandths of an inch from a precise location.

For a Position to occur, more than one object must necessarily be involved. Obviously, one of the objects must be mobile, although it need not be completely free of restraint in space. The other object may be either stationary or mobile. The purpose of performing positioning motions is to bring the objects concerned into some definite physical relationship *relative to each other*. The nature of contact desired, final configuration, or spatial proximity necessary will dictate the kind and number of small motions required during positioning. These motions achieve one or more of the physical results known as *aligning, orienting,* or *engaging;* detailed consideration of these three factors will follow later. The motion analysis must account for the individual and combined effects of these three factors, as discussed under position variables below.

It is possible for more than two objects to be involved in a Position. For example, when a waitress inserts a fresh handful of toothpicks into an empty toothpick pot, the handful of toothpicks could be considered as a single piece of wood so long as they did not separate during handling. If the pot were already partially filled, causing separation of the handful, additional motions besides the standard Position would be needed.

It was indicated earlier that any major distance displacement of objects will require ordinary Reaches and Moves (exceeding 1 inch) by the hands of the operator. With the exception of Turn, Crank, and Apply Pressure, the remaining hand motions have been designated as synthetic combinations of these more basic motion elements. This idea was clarified in the Grasp chapter, particularly in explaining the Theory of Grasp. Such minor motions as Reaches and Moves 1 inch or less in length, together with whatever Turns and Apply Pressures might be needed, have been grouped for utility into the category known as Position. It would be impractical to make the detailed analysis of these short motions on each occasion during which their combined effect in positioning an object fitted a recognizable, recurring pattern. This pattern, having been grouped conveniently into measurable categories, can more justifiably be applied directly from predetermined data tables as a category in its own right.

As will be seen later, the official time data for Position was based directly on the Theory of Position which clearly identifies and groups the minor basic motions of which a given Position category is composed. In a sense, the use of such categories is an application by the motion analyst to his own work of several of the principles of motion economy by which he operates. In common time study language, Position represents a set of standard data. The development of such data will be explained later.

The reader must be cautioned that the analysis of Position departs somewhat from one MTM rule given earlier. It has been stated that the MTM analyst is concerned with the actions of the *operator,* not their effect on the workpiece. While this is still true for Position, correct analysis in this case requires that attention be directed to the objects as well. This is true because the factors by which a given occurrence of Position is classified into the data card categories have been based on physical relationships between the parts being positioned. The *fit, condition of symmetry,* and *ease of handling* are best determined by the analyst's examination of the parts relative to each other. However, attention to the operator's motions must remain the prime requisite, since such observance will disclose instances in which *required* motion sequences actually used do not coincide with standard Position sequences. Such discoveries may not occur unless the MTM engineer is alert to the worker's performance.

It has been stated several times that MTM is a practical procedure. The deviation from the regular MTM work procedure during Position analysis and the substitution of a second set of important guides—an analysis of the fit, symmetry, and ease of handling—is just another example of practicality. It is a sound approach to an accounting of the alignment, orientation, and engagement which the operator performs on the parts. Different configurations *require* varying motions that may be difficult to recognize readily, especially if no prior clues as to what may be expected exist. Prior study of the more easily measured and judged parameters of configuration in lieu of merely determining worker motions is obviously expedient and practical.

One predetermined time system—DMT—is founded and developed on this very concept used in establishing and applying MTM Position data—that performance time is related to the physical configuration of objects handled. The MTM approach has been completely open-minded and this attitude continues to permeate the research activity and continuing development of the MTM Association.

It should also be realized that size and similar attributes have not been eliminated nor ignored in other MTM data—they are suitably recognized when important.

Position is one of the most important single motion categories in the MTM system. It occurs with high frequency in many types of work, and, in addition, the time requirement is high when compared to many of the other MTM motions. Care in analysis and clear understanding of the concept of Position are therefore vital to the determination of correct times for motions and motion patterns. The accuracy of many otherwise correct MTM analyses can be reduced significantly by wrong identification and classification of the Position motions involved.

The original time data for Position was adequate for analysis of thousands of operations, and reflected the best set of answers that could be inferred from film taken at the original research speed. However, recent MTM research into Position and allied motions has provided Supplementary Position Data described later in this chapter. In line with MTM Association purposes stated in an earlier chapter, this research enlarged, refined, and clarified certain areas in both the motion and time data for Position. It is reassuring to note, however, as was true for earlier research of this nature on other motions, that no serious discrepancy in the original MTM data was found. Enlargement of the fund of knowledge, rather than replacement of older data, has resulted.

POSITION VARIABLES

The principal motions involved in Position are Align, Orient, and Engage. Each of these includes many variables that have been evaluated and covered by practical rules of the MTM procedure. For simplicity in the following elaboration, attention is restricted to two objects, although more than two can be involved in a given Position, as previously explained. One is called the engaging part, the other is termed the engaged part. It is assumed that the engaging part is the one held in the operator's hand, that is, the part being moved during the Position. The engaged part may be stationary, manipulated in the hand, or move in synchronization with the engaging part. The intent is to match the engaging part to the engaged; in most cases this also involves insertion.

In one variety of Position to be discussed later, no engagement occurs. This presents no difficulty, however, since it merely indicates the absence of one of the possible actions during Position. The concept of engaging and engaged parts will not suffer when applied to this type of Position, rather the engagement in this case may be thought of as one of the following: contact only, potential contact, or potential insertion. This type of Position is called Align Only. It may actually include both Align and Orient as discussed later, although usually the Align is the sole action. Align is the sole action.

Each of the three major actions will now be discussed separately.

Align

Definition: Align consists of all basic motions required to make coincident the insertion axes of the engaging and engaged parts during a Position.

The illustration of aligning in Fig. 1 makes use of three different axes. These axes are imaginary lines that facilitate description of aligning or other positioning motions. Examination of these axes and the motions needed to make two of them coincident will help in understanding the nature of alignment. In order to avoid confusion, it is necessary first to state explicitly what each axis represents.

The axis of the engaging part is the line along which the engaging part will later travel if it is inserted into the engaged part. The axis of the engaged part is the line or direction in which any successful insertion of another part must proceed relative to the configuration of the engaged part. Finally, the axis of insertion is the coincident line formed by the axes of the engaging and engaged parts during and after engagement. Note also in Fig. 1 that the general direction of the path by which the engaging part approaches the engaged part during the Move preceding the position may bear almost any arbitrary geometric relationship to these defined axes.

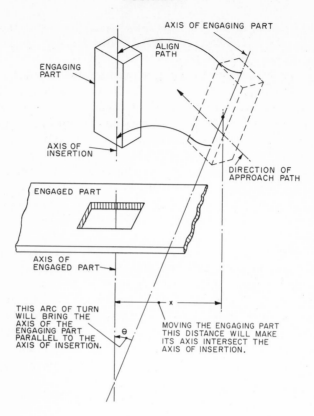

Fig. 1. Align in Position. The general Align motion shown consists of a Move of distance X and a Turn of angle θ during the same time interval.

Clarity on the nature of alignment is gained by examining the various possible spatial relations of the axis of the engaging part to the other axes at the completion of the part's approach, just prior to the Align motions of Position. Obviously, when it coincides with the axis of insertion (1) no Align is needed. If it intersects the axis of insertion at an angle, (2) a pure Turn of the engaging part will finish Align. If it is parallel to the axis of insertion, (3) only a short lateral Move is required to complete the Align. In most cases, none of these three simpler conditions applies. Therefore, the most general relationship of the axis of the engaging part to the other axes dictates the need for (4) *both* a short Move *and* a pure Turn of the engaging part relative to the engaged part to accomplish alignment.

Motionwise, the MTM procedure must account for the short Move and/or pure Turn as may be required for alignment. These motions are very short, indeed they cannot normally be detected with the naked eye. However, the film analysis showed that, considering the usual frequency of each of the four possibilities noted above, an average value of 5.6 TMU will suffice for the time needed to Align two objects. This has been included in the Theory of Position.

Another important fact regarding the Move preceding a Position emerges from this consideration of the spatial relationship of the parts and their axes in alignment. Referring back to the Move chapter, a Case B Move will locate an object within an inch or two of a given point, whereas a Case C Move will bring it to half an inch or so of the final location. In the beginning of this chapter, examples of Position were cited in which the engaging object was moved to within an inch or less of the engaged object prior to the act of Position. Since Position cannot be accomplished unless the object has first been moved to within half an inch to an inch of the engaged object, this fact leads to an important MTM rule deserving emphasis, namely: *All Moves immediately preceding Positions must be Case C Moves.* Only rare exceptions will be found to this rule. The MTM analyst must never forget this rule if correct analysis of the Moves preceding positioning motions is to be made.

It should also be noted that if a part can be adequately located with either a Case B or Case C Move, no Position is needed.

Orient

Definition: Orient consists of all basic motions required to geometrically match the cross-section of the engaging part (or its engaging projection) with that of the engaged part about the axis of insertion as evaluated or gaged by their projections on the plane of initial engagement.

It is called to the reader's attention that the hole can be in either the engaged or engaging part. The Position data is equally applicable to either situation.

Reference to Fig. 2 will reveal that orienting accounts only for the additional motions needed for matching after alignment but prior to insertion. Actually, much of the total orientation of the engaging part may be partially accomplished during both alignment and the Move preceding a normal Position.

The axis of insertion provides a convenient reference line for evaluating the geometric relationship between the shapes of the parts. In addition to this line, the plane on which the projected cross-sections of the engaging part and the engaged part are to be evaluated must be selected. While an infinite number of planes perpendicular to the axis of insertion would show the projected cross-sections, one particular transverse plane is most convenient for gaging the geometric relations. This is the plane of initial engagement, which is defined as the plane perpendicular to the axis of insertion at which any lateral motions of the engaging and engaged parts would cause point or line contact between the parts. If, as is shown in

Fig. 2, the cross-sections of the parts are projected on the plane of initial engagement, it is then possible to compare their geometric relationship with ease. Of course, this is usually a mental process on the part of the MTM analyst, although it may often be judged correctly by manipulation of the parts being positioned.

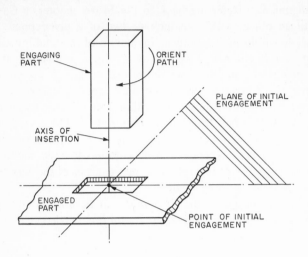

CROSS SECTIONS
(ON PLANE OF INITIAL ENGAGEMENT)

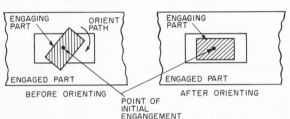

Fig. 2.   Orient in Position.

The stated purpose of orienting is to match the cross-sections of the parts. With the means of observing or visualizing the cross-sections given above, comparison of the square, rectangular, circular, triangular, or other shape of the engaging and engaged cross-sections will readily reveal the amount of rotation about the axis of insertion which the operator must perform to permit insertion.

In terms of motions, orienting is accomplished with finger turns or equivalent manual actions of the worker which provide the same rotation. The number of such turns or their angular magnitude will vary with the relative cross-sections of the parts. In the Theory of Position, three general classes have been categorized, although it is recognized that the possibilities are infinite. Practical considerations, however, would indicate the sufficiency of limiting categories to a few easily determined classes, the details of which are later discussed.

Engage

Definition: Engage consists of all motions required to effect up to 1 inch of insertion of the engaging part into the engaged part following completion of aligning and orienting.

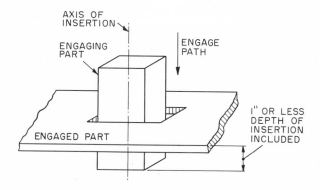

Fig. 3.   Engage in Position.

The act of engagement shown in Fig. 3 is the easiest Position component to understand, although it involves more motions and more judgment to evaluate correctly. Basically, the motions of Move (1 inch or less), Apply Pressure to overcome any resistance to insertion, and Regrasps to maintain control of the objects are all potentially present during engagement.

Referring again to the examples at the start of this chapter, it will be noted that Position time does not include any Move greater than 1 inch. Another MTM rule for Position results from this manner of limiting the scope of Position motions: *All insertion beyond 1 inch from the plane of initial engagement must be analyzed and assigned additional time.* The analysis of this additional insertion usually shows that it is some case of Move; time assignment should follow the regular rules for that motion. When other motions are appropriate, the additional time will be determined by the rules for such motions.

The next factor in engagement, overcoming resistance to insertion, relates to the amount of force the operator must apply to effect insertion. Apply Pressure, or actions equivalent to it, has been isolated in MTM as the motion which accounts for this force. In order to judge the amount of force, or the number and case of Apply Pressures needed to meet the many possible conditions of insertion resistance, classes of fit of the engaging part relative to the engaged part have been categorized in the Theory of Position. Again, while many fit relationships are possible, practicality suggests a limited number of classes.

Finally, control of the objects must be maintained if successful insertion is to be accomplished. The MTM motion, or its equivalent, needed to improve or maintain hold on the objects is Regrasp. The Theory of Position has accounted for the number of Regrasps needed in two ways. Part of them (what can usually be expected) have been covered during the Engage time assigned to various classes of fit; an additional Regrasp is then assigned if the object is of more than usual difficulty from the handling standpoint. Note that an AP1, consisting of the equivalent of an AP2 and a G2, also includes part of the Regrasps that might be included in the engage values for the theory. The total number of G2 needed during a given Position is also a matter of frequency and observation of a large number of Positions on motion picture films, so the MTM analyst again relies on research results rather than attempting to evaluate this for himself.

Effect of Weight

The present MTM data for Position does not make direct accounting for the weight of the objects being handled. Obviously, the weight will have some effect on the time to Position an object. The MTM procedure has up to now, however, been based on the idea that the presence of significant weight would make necessary observably different motions in order to Position a significantly weighted object. Logical deduction would indicate, however, that any possible effect would not involve the static weight component isolated in the research on weighted Moves. This is because the object weight obviously is under close control at all times during a successful Position. If control is lost, new positioning motions will be needed, and not a revision of the normal Position in question.

That the dynamic component of weight might affect Position time is more reasonable, although the numerical percentages might not be the same as for spatial Moves. As discussion of the preceding variables has shown, the Position times are an admixture of the MTM motions of Move, Turn, Regrasp, and Apply Pressure. At all times during the action, the full weight of the object being located is in the hand. Weight with Moves has been fully explained, and the use of three categories to account for weight in Turn is also known to the reader. How weight affects regrasping is less well-defined, but the G2 for difficulty in handling is an example of MTM thinking, since weight increases handling difficulty. And Apply Pressure, with its explanation in terms of force, evidently varies in magnitude to some extent by the weight handled. Therefore, unless weight effects are very significant, their influence in normal Positions is already indirectly included in the Theory of Position upon which the present time values are based.

KINDS OF POSITION

The present data includes eighteen different kinds of Position. Each kind is a combination of three classes of fit, three cases of symmetry, and two handling categories. The manner in which the fit, symmetry, and handling account for the Position variables of Align, Orient, and Engage will be the next topic. They are the factors in Position which are judged directly in practical application of MTM time values to positioning motions.

Class of Fit

Definition: The fit of engaging and engaged parts is a measure of the clearance between them and/or the pressure required for insertion.

The fit between parts that can be assembled by manual action will vary from practically no clearance to very generous spaces of the order normally associated with Moves only; it is rather obvious that the time for insertion will vary accordingly. Actually, there is a continuous relation between fit allowance and performance time. As practicality dictates, however, the MTM procedure has assigned arbitrary limits to restrict to three the number of classes of fit which must be distinguished.

Since the class of fit is directly related to Engage time, Engage as a Position variable is evaluated by determining the class of fit. The point of initial engagement is the only point from which measurements of fit can be made correctly. This point in a Position action occurs when the engaging part first contacts the plane of initial engagement as defined earlier. In other words, engagement has begun when any lateral motion of the parts will cause line or point contact between them. It is incorrect to judge the class of fit at any other plane transverse to the axis of insertion. The fit may be judged by either the amount of *total* lateral clearance or the force of insertion needed, provided the point of initial engagement is used to determine these.

The total lateral clearance for a $\frac{1}{4}$-inch rod being positioned into a $\frac{5}{16}$-inch hole, for example, would be $\frac{1}{16}$ inch. Finding the clearance is more difficult with irregular or odd shaped parts, but the same principle is used as for common geometric cross-sections. When the clearance cannot easily be judged, recourse to the pressure required to engage must be employed.

A commonly used means for determining the amount of pressure required for insertion is known as the gravity test. In this test the engaging part is held so that the axis of insertion is vertical and the part is close to the engaged one, following which it is released and the resulting effect observed. If the parts engage readily, no pressure will be needed to Position them. If a slight nudge or push of the fingers is needed to complete insertion, light pressure will accomplish the engagement. If the parts will not engage unless the tester must grip them and apply appreciable force, heavy pressure is indicated during performance of a Position with the parts.

These engaging pressures and the clearances associated with them have been assigned class-of-fit designations as follows:

Class of Fit	Clearance	Pressure
1. Loose	Appreciable, but not in excess of ½ inch total	None
2. Close	Visible, parts are snug but will slide with only slight resistance or friction	Slight
3. Exact	None visible, very slight tolerance, but parts can still be engaged manually	Heavy

A rule of thumb states that when the fit is so loose as to raise a question whether a Position is proper, Class 1 is involved; when difficulty in insertion is evident, Class 3 is indicated; all other conditions are Class 2. Class 2 fit occurs with highest frequency, Class 1 next, and Class 3 is rare in industrial operations, since mechanical devices are normally used when heavy pressure is needed to engage parts. Admittedly, judgment is involved in any case—but this judgment is objective and does not subjectively evaluate the operator. Practice will enable the MTM analyst to correctly judge the class of fit.

Case of Symmetry

Definition: The case of symmetry describes the geometric properties of the engaging and engaged parts as they affect the amount of orientation required prior to insertion.

Just as the class of fit gages the engagement of parts, the case of symmetry accounts for the Orient motions needed by examining the relationship between the cross-sections of the parts. The cases have been set up in terms of the number of ways in which the relative configurations of the parts will permit insertion to occur. Symmetry, at least for the simpler shapes, is thus made easy to determine; difficulty in assigning the case of symmetry will be met only when borderline shapes are present or when the analyst attempts to assign the case without remembering that alignment is theoretically assumed to be completed before orienting begins.

The basis on which symmetry is judged is the amount of orientation needed during the Position motions themselves; any pre-orienting of the object during the Move preceding Position is discounted. Many operators either pick up parts so that little or no orientation is needed, or they employ Turns and/or Regrasps during the preceding Move to reduce the orienting motions. In fact, it is the aim of good motion analysts in reducing Position time during assembly to so design the workplace and material delivery as to reduce or eliminate the need for orienting of parts during Positions. This would permit the legitimate assignment of a lower case of symmetry. Recall, however, that the MTM standard is set for an average operator working with a given set of conditions. High levels of skill and/or effort will also disclose observed Positions that are of lower case than would be true of average performances, but allowing these would not set a standard for the average operator.

If the amount of legitimately allowed pre-orienting is correctly analyzed prior to classification of the Position, there should be little difficulty in determining the case of symmetry involved.

The three cases of symmetry used in MTM can be described as follows:

Case of Symmetry	Description
Symmetrical	The parts can be engaged in an infinite number of ways about the axis of insertion
Semi-Symmetrical	The parts can be engaged in two or several ways about the axis of insertion
Non-Symmetrical	The parts can be engaged in only one way about the axis of insertion

Figure 4 shows obvious instances of all three cases of symmetry. A *suggestive* limit to the meaning of "several" in the semi-symmetrical category is up to ten ways. However, the number cannot be infinite.

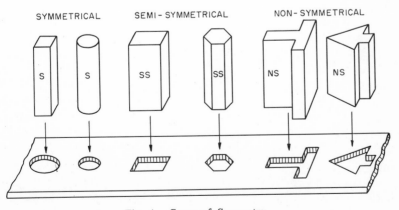

Fig. 4. Cases of Symmetry.

Note that the geometry of both parts must be considered in deciding symmetry. For example, it is incorrect to state that positioning of a hexagonal shaft is non-symmetrical. This would be true only if the hexagon were not of equal sides and the hole was of like shape. If the hole and shaft were both regular equal-sided hexagons, the insertion would be semi-symmetrical. If the hole was circular and of sufficient diameter to permit insertion of the hexagon shaft, regardless of the regularity of the hexagon sides, the Position would be symmetrical. So for the one hexagon shape, if no further data are known, the case of symmetry could not be decided; the shape and size of the hole must also be known.

When an object being positioned is mechanically constrained, an exception to classification by shapes may be taken. The use of guides, swivels, or fixed arms may enable an operator to perform symmetrical or semi-symmetrical Positions even though the parts configurations would otherwise indicate non-symmetrical insertion. No fixed rule for such cases can be given; each must be examined for the orientation required of the worker.

Ease of Handling

Definition: An engaging part is considered easy to handle if no change of grip during Position is necessary, desirable, or made for convenience.

Justification for this factor in Position has already been explained in the discussion of Engage. What must be added is reasons to which handling difficulty justifying the extra Regrasp can be attributed. With this data, visualized analysis becomes possible; observations would reveal directly the extra G2 for handling difficulty.

The decision as to whether the part is Easy to Handle or Difficult to Handle must be based on considerations of the rigidity of the part, its size relative to its weight, and the manner of grip the worker has upon it. These factors determine how well the part can be controlled during Position. It is also evident that, since control requirements are greater when the fit is close, the difficulty of handling will tend to increase with close tolerance Positions. No definitive rules have been set in MTM for these factors, but a few examples are suggestive.

A rigid part is stiff and can be easily controlled unless it is held at some distance, depending on the fit, away from the point of engagement. Flexible items such as string, thread, stranded wire, and some types of springs are hard to handle unless held very closely, even when the fit is generous. Maynard, Stegemerten, and Schwab suggest that a $\frac{1}{16}$-inch diameter rod would be difficult to insert into a closely fitting hole unless the point of grasp were within $\frac{1}{2}$ inch of the point of engagement. On the other hand, they state that it would be easy to handle a 3-inch diameter rod of light plastic while positioning it into a loose fit though the holding point was 4 to 5 inches from the initial insertion.

SHORTHAND OF POSITION

Position

Recording of a capital P will show that Position has occurred in the study.

Class of Fit

The class of fit is indicated by the arabic numerals 1, 2, or 3 following the symbol for Position.

Example: P1 shows the presence of a Position with a loose fit.

P3 shows the presence of a Position having an exact fit.

Case of Symmetry

Capital letters following the symbol for class of fit identify which of the three cases of symmetry is involved in a Position. The letters are S for symmetrical, SS for semi-symmetrical, and NS for non-symmetrical.

Example: P1NS describes a loose-fit Position with a non-symmetrical relationship between the engaging and engaged parts.

P2SS shows the insertion of a close fitting part into a hole that it could enter in two or more, but not an infinite number of ways. This is the semi-symmetrical situation.

Ease of Handling

The capital letters E and D, respectively, symbolize easy and difficult cases of parts handling during Position.

Example: P1SE fully symbolizes the symmetrical positioning of an easy-to-handle part into a loose fit with the engaged part.

P2NSD are the symbols needed to indicate the close-fitting insertion of a difficult-to-handle part into one with which its configuration permits only one manner of orientation for positioning.

It is noteworthy, especially with Position symbols, that motions can be written with much greater facility and ease in coded fashion than would be possible if word descriptions of sufficient completeness were necessary.

THEORY OF POSITION

Up to this point, the *variables* in Position have been discussed to show what manual actions are involved and the *factors* by which these variables are evaluated, timewise, were explained. The Theory of Position inter-relates the variables and factors in such a way as to obtain the present time data shown on the MTM card. As indicated earlier, the Theory was developed to explain observed experimental data. The combination of theory and experiment resulted in such practical data that it became the MTM standard. Further experimental checks have tended to confirm these time values, and usage has confirmed that they produce adequate answers.

The Theory of Position serves two useful purposes: (1) It helps the analyst to understand precisely the motions being evaluated in Positions; and (2) it enables him to examine and develop standards for unusual types of positioning which do not fit the standard categories so clearly defined. In this respect, it is much like the Theory of Grasp previously discussed. Full development of the Theory in self-explanatory form is given in Fig. 5.

Align is always the minimum motion present during Position; and, to-gether with one inch of Move for insertion, it explains the total time effect in P1SE. Orientation is accounted in terms of the degree of Turn needed for the three cases of symmetry—none for symmetrical, 45 degrees for semi-symmetrical, and 75 degrees for non-symmetrical. These angular values were determined from a series of averaged observations. The rea-son they are not greater, as might be suspected, is the normal occurrence of pre-orienting in most cases during the Move preceding Position. En-gagement, in terms of class of fit, is explained by the amount of force or pressure indicated by varying amounts of AP2 and G2 employed by the worker. The one-inch Move time for engagement is combined with align in the P1SE time value. Finally, difficulty in handling causes the usage of an extra G2 as previously explained. More detailed accounting of the data backing up the Theory can be found in the text by Maynard, Stegemer-ten, and Schwab. The preceding should, however, satisfy the average reader.

DATA CARD INFORMATION

The data card issued initially by the originators used the experimental values, but all data cards issued by the MTM Association have used the theoretical values. Note that the synthetic (theoretical) values are gen-erally on the safe side. This was done to give benefit to the average operator for which the MTM technique is intended. Data in Table V of the official MTM data card is shown in Table 1. Note that it is arranged so that it reads directly from the shorthand symbols for a given Position.

KEY TO MOTION VARIABLES IN POSITION

Variable		Factor Evaluated	Motions Assigned by Theory		Time, TMU
Symbol	Meaning				
C	Constant	Align + Insertion	Constant for all classes (up to 1″ of depth included)		5.6
T	Orient (Case of Symmetry)	S	T0 (Symmetrical)		0.0
		SS	T45 (Semi-Symmetrical)		3.5
		NS	T75 (Non-Symmetrical)		4.8
F	Engage (Class of Fit)	1	None		0.0
		2	AP2		10.6
		3	$\overbrace{AP2 + AP2 + \overbrace{G2 + AP2}^{AP1}}$ 10.6 + 10.6 + 16.2		37.4
H	Handling (Ease of)	E	None (Easy to Handle)		0.0
		D	G2 (Difficult to Handle)		5.6

MOTION–TIME SYNTHESIS OF THE DIFFERENT KINDS OF POSITION

Factors			Variables		Total Time, TMU		
Class of Fit	Case of Symmetry	Ease of Handling	Motions (Refer to Key)	Time, TMU	Theory	Exp.	Data Card
1 (Loose)	S	E	C	5.6	5.6	5.6	5.6
		D	C + H	5.6 + 5.6	11.2	9.0	11.2
	SS	E	C + T	5.6 + 3.5	9.1	6.6	9.1
		D	C + T + H	5.6 + 3.5 + 5.6	14.7	13.7	14.7
	NS	E	C + T	5.6 + 4.8	10.4	?	10.4
		D	C + T + H	5.6 + 4.8 + 5.6	16.0	16.3	16.0
2 (Close)	S	E	C + F	5.6 + 10.6	16.2	?	16.2
		D	C + F + H	5.6 + 10.6 + 5.6	21.8	19.6	21.8
	SS	E	C + T + F	5.6 + 3.5 + 10.6	19.7	14.1	19.7
		D	C + T + F + H	5.6 + 3.5 + 10.6 + 5.6	25.3	25.5	25.3
	NS	E	C + T + F	5.6 + 4.8 + 10.6	21.0	21.9	21.0
		D	C + T + F + H	5.6 + 4.8 + 10.6 + 5.6	26.6	27.2	26.6
3 (Exact)	S	E	C + F	5.6 + 37.4	43.0	39.4	43.0
		D	C + F + H	5.6 + 37.4 + 5.6	48.6	?	48.6
	SS	E	C + T + F	5.6 + 3.5 + 37.4	46.5	43.9	46.5
		D	C + T + F + H	5.6 + 3.5 + 37.4 + 5.6	52.1	?	52.1
	NS	E	C + T + F	5.6 + 4.8 + 37.4	47.8	53.1	47.8
		D	C + T + F + H	5.6 + 4.8 + 37.4 + 5.6	53.4	?	53.4

Fig. 5. Theory of Position.

Table I. Data for Position
(MTM Data Card Table V—Position*—P)

CLASS OF FIT		Symmetry	Easy To Handle	Difficult To Handle
1—Loose	No pressure required	S	5.6	11.2
		SS	9.1	14.7
		NS	10.4	16.0
2—Close	Light pressure required	S	16.2	21.8
		SS	19.7	25.3
		NS	21.0	26.6
3—Exact	Heavy pressure required	S	43.0	48.6
		SS	46.5	52.1
		NS	47.8	53.4

* Distance moved to engage—1" or less.

PRACTICAL WORKING RULES

A number of special types of events connected with Position motions deserve further explanation to aid the MTM engineer in making correct analyses.

Positioning to a Line or Point

Reference was made earlier to a type of Position known (misleadingly) as "Align Only." Actually, this type of action usually includes both align and orient motions, but the *engagement* is restricted to contact of the object with the line or point in question. The engaging part may be said to be engaged as soon as it is properly located or has contacted the line or point desired, this being usually on a stationary object.

Examples of this type of action are:
1. Locating a pencil point to the intersection of several lines on paper (Align only)
2. Locating a centerpunch to a scribed line, point, or intersection (Align plus minor orienting)
3. Immersing an object into a liquid to some certain depth or to a line on the surface of the part (Probable Position to immerse plus double Align or Align including orienting to final limit)
4. Aligning a ruler to a point, points, or line for measurement or for drawing of a line on an object (This is explained below)

Since the alignment involved can be approximate, close, or exact, a special rule of thumb has been developed to standardize the practice for such actions.

A. For alignments over ½″   M–B only
B. For alignments within ½″ to ¼″   M–C only

C. For alignments between ¼″ to 1/16″   M–C + P1SE or P1SD
D. For alignments within 1/16″ or less   M–C + P2SE or P2SD

Notice that all such alignments are considered to be symmetrical. The fit can vary and the object may be easy or difficult to handle.

Judgment is required in the use of this rule of thumb. For instance, the rough location within ¼″ of a ruler to a point would be adequately covered with a P1SE. For more exact location, this could change to a P2SE. These analyses would hold even for several points so long as they are not separated more than 3 or 4 inches. For separation greater than 4 inches, however, it is logical that more than one Position or alignment and possibly some orienting is involved. At least two Positions would be needed for points as much as a foot apart, and for greater distances the operator might even use three. He would locate the ruler to, say, the left point first, then to the right point, then correct the minor shifting on the left point that usually occurs. Each of these Positions should be considered separately in allowing time for the sequence.

Positioning the Hand

In some operations, the hand and/or fingers must be located in some definite orientation or dimensional relation to the workpiece prior to actions which follow. Another MTM rule of thumb states that positioning of the hand and/or fingers is always a symmetrical case of orienting. This is exemplified when, after an R–B or R–A to a pre-positioned part in a delivery chute which always brings the part into the same orientation, the hand and fingers must be rotated or otherwise located for pickup of the part. Be careful, however, not to assign a Position when a simple Reach or Reach-Turn will suffice for the case in question. Another instance of finger location transpires when a typist inserts her fingers into the inner hole of a wax dictation cylinder for handling it so as not to disturb the cut recording on the outer surface. Typists often do this when handling cylinders, which they then grip by spreading their fingers against the inside diameter of the cylinder.

Moves and Positions

The analyst must be careful not to call all insertions Positions. Many insertions, and approximate locations as well, can adequately be made with only Case B or Case C Moves. The fit tolerances mentioned under kinds of Position above and also in the chapter on Move should govern such analysis.

Another question often arising concerns the analysis of Moves following the initial engagement distance of 1 inch covered by Position. The depth of insertion obviously will cover the length of Move in this case. As to the case of Move, however, this will depend on the conditions in the operation. The fact that initial insertion has a guiding effect may indicate the use of M–A. M–B might be justified, particularly if the additional insertion is quite lengthy. The amount of control to an approximate stopping point may make an M–C correct. It is even possible that a further Position will occur at the end of the additional insertion, in which event an M–C followed by a Position would be the proper analysis. Some cases might also require separate and additional applications of pressure. No definite rules, other than the guiding rules previously given, can be set down for this type of operation.

Placing one part into another does not always mean that a Position has occurred. An assembly might be disposed to a tote pan with a toss, as shown in the Move chapter. Ordinary stacking of the assembly in the tote pan could require M–C. Precise nesting of the assembly in the tote pan, however, would likely necessitate the use of a Position. Another example where placing a part does not require a Position is that of dropping an object with a conical point into a hole at the end of a Move of the object to the hole. Correct application of the rules concerning point of initial engagement and fit should make this case obvious.

Multiple Positioning

Note also that when the engaging part is held in a tool, the Position and preceding Move do not differ in analysis from a hand-held case— the tool is essentially an extension of the hand. However, it may increase the classification of the Position since the combination might comprise a more difficult-to-handle part.

Many parts require two or more Positions to fully engage them in the hole. For example, a steel shaft with a Woodruff key located more than 1 inch from the end of the shaft might be inserted into the hole of a drive pulley. The end of the shaft would be symmetrically positioned first, and then a non-symmetrical location of the key to the keyway would be needed to complete insertion.

The important thing to remember is that multiple Positions must be analyzed in the same order in which they occur. If the parts truly cannot be located with a single Position, the second Position might be influenced greatly by the fact that the first Position limits the amount of additional location needed. A part that must be engaged on both ends might have the Position on the second end reduced in both class of fit and case of symmetry by the constraining effect of the positioned first end.

In all such cases, attention to the order of Positions and reliance on the rules given for aligning, orienting and engaging parts should suffice to make proper analysis. The operator should also be observed to see the type of motions he uses in such cases.

SUPPLEMENTARY POSITION DATA

The present Position data is accurate and reproducible as far as it goes. Recall that this data was established on the concept of accounting for specific combinations of Align, Orient, and Engage. Based on the physical characteristics of the engaging and engaged parts, the analyst merely identifies the combination observed and/or visualized and then applies the time values for that combination as derived from the Theory of Position. This procedure has yielded thousands of satisfactory analyses of motion and time with a relatively direct and simple usage of the existing data. However, the analyst frequently must distinguish between positioning movements which require a finer subdivision of motions and times. This is especially true for tasks which involve a large number of positioning elements, as often is found in light hand assembly.

Accordingly, the MTM Association sponsored basic research[3] into Position which culminated in 1965 when the Supplementary Position Data was added to the U.S.-Canada MTM Data Card. This research involved a complete inquiry into the basic nature, true motions and variables, and interaction of the variables in positioning movements. It also developed comprehensive new definitions and more objective measures of these variables, thereby greatly increasing the understanding of this basic MTM element. Three Application Training Supplements[4] resulted from an eight-year period of application research and validation which preceded the data card change. This change is fully explained by Application Training Supplement No. 8. This information, plus necessary data from R.R. 109 and R.R. 110, is presented in the remainder of this section.

During the discussion of the Supplementary Position Data, understanding will be enhanced by referring to Table 2, which summarizes the wealth of detailed statistical information from the research regarding the components and internal variables of Position.

The supplementary data is based directly on validated laboratory and industrial data with no need for supporting theory other than that included in the research reports. It directly evaluates the methods basis and time requirements of all *Total Position* components demonstrated to exist. This is accomplished by better definition of the components and more exhaustive

---

[3] R.R. 109 and R.R. 110 (See Ch. 5).

[4] Published by the MTM Association for Standards and Research, Ann Arbor, Michigan:
    a. "Application Training Supplement No. 6—Position", October 1960.
    b. "Application Training Supplement No. 7—Position and Apply Pressure" by Franklin H. Bayha and James A. Foulke, June 1964.
    c. "Application Training Supplement No. 8—Position" by Franklin H. Bayha, James A. Foulke, and Walton M. Hancock, January 1965.

Table 2. Variables in Supplementary Position Data

Motion Equation: P = (M + O) + (A + E1) + E2
Time Equation: P = M + O + (A + E1) + E2

Type of Position	COMPONENT and Symbol	PURPOSE of Component	Qualification Notes	Effect of INTERNAL VARIABLES on Component Time		
				CLASS OF FIT based only upon radial clearance	CASE OF SYMMETRY relative only to geometric cross-sections	DEPTH OF INSERTION from plane of initial engagement
TOTAL POSITION	MOVE (M)	Transport object to vicinity of destination	Control is high, normally Case C. Direct effect from both external variables of travel distance and object weight	No effect	No effect if pre-orient completed prior to Total Position / Time greater as included orientation is increased. Its total effect is included in the time data for Position Proper	No effect
	ORIENT (O)	Rotational adjustment of object about the axis of insertion	Not present if object completely pre-oriented prior to Total Position	No effect	Direct effect for all degrees of maximum possible orientation	No effect
	ALIGN (A)	Linear adjustment of object axis to axis of insertion	Normally limits out Primary Engage (except for P21S and P21SS)	Direct effect is the main cause of time variation. Align time highly sensitive to decreased clearance.	Direct effect is minor except for 90 to 180 degrees of maximum possible orientation	No effect
PROPER POSITION	PRIMARY ENGAGE (E1)	Transport object to surface of destination	Always present, but normally limited out by Align component	No effect	No effect	No effect
	SECONDARY ENGAGE (E2)	Transport object into destination or on its surface	Always the last motion, if present	Direct effect due to highly controlled movement	No effect	Direct effect due to highly constrained movement.

analysis of the variables within each component. An important aspect of the research was the verification of the additivity of these components, subject only to methods constraints and the limiting time principle.

Positioning Components

Application Training Supplement No. 8 redefines the components of positioning motions. To facilitate the discussion to follow, the revised definitions are quoted together here:[5]

"Definition 1. *Position Movements* are those motions necessary to transport an object to a predetermined destination and to seat it in or on this destination in a precise manner.

Definition 2. *Total Position* includes the hand and arm motions which occur from the moment an object is grasped until it is released after being positioned.

Definition 3. *Position Proper (Position)* includes the motions align, Symbol P orient, primary engage, and secondary engage which may be required in addition to the basic transporting Move motion.

Definition 4. *Move Component* is the transporting motion which brings Symbol M the positional object to the vicinity of the positioning destination.

Definition 5. *Primary Engage Component* is the motion in Position Proper Symbol E1 which brings the object to the destination surface.

Definition 6. *Secondary Engage Component* is the motion in Position Symbol E2 Proper which seats the object in the destination; it must be the last component motion of a given positioning.

Definition 7. *Align Component* is the linear adjustment of the object or Symbol A tilting motion required to make the axis of the object coincident with the axis of the positioning destination.

Definition 8. *Orient Component* is the rotational adjustment of the object Symbol O or turning motion required to geometrically match the cross-sectional shapes of the object and the positioning destination."

Because of interaction effects, the Supplementary Position Data considers integrally all the motions between the completion of the Grasp and the start of the Release of the engaging object. These motions basically include all the Position motions of the older data plus the preceding Move, which requires some additional interaction time above the time it would require when not followed by a Position. Also, the engagement motions have

---

[5] Identifying symbols have been added.

been subdivided into Primary Engage, up to the plane of initial engagement, and Secondary Engage, which describes the penetration of the engaged part by the engaging part. Therefore, the validated components listed above are completely expressed by the Position Motion Equation:

$$P = (M + O) + (A + E1) + E2$$

The parentheses in this equation indicate the correct usage of the Limiting Principle. In the *motion* sense, the shared terms *may* limit each other, whereas the E2 term must occur independently. Stated another way, the terms sharing parentheses can be performed concurrently. However, there is nothing in this equation which prohibits a Position Proper during which all of the motion terms are performed independently—as though the parentheses were missing—and in any order, provided that the M occurs first and the E2 occurs last. Also, in an actual Position Proper, any given term may be missing, except that E1 must always be present for a Position to occur. These distinctions are important in understanding the Supplementary Position Data.

Finally, for the new motion synthesis, a dual classification of the components may clarify the actions included. As to purpose, the components are either *transporting* motions or *adjusting* motions. The transporting motions may be considered to sequentially move the engaging object to the final destination. They include the M, E1, and E2 components, which must occur in that order. The Move brings the object to within an inch or so of the destination surface. The more highly controlled Primary Engage completes the travel to the destination surface. Then the Secondary Engage after contact of the objects involves the final insertion of the engaging part into the target or the destination cavity. The adjusting motions accomplish the geometrical matching of the parts. They are the A and O components. Align is a linear shift of the object axis, or a tilting motion, or both (see Fig. 1) to cause coincidence of the object axis with the axis of insertion. Orient is a rotation of the engaging part about the axis of insertion to attain the requirements of symmetry between the engaging and engaged objects. With this description, the full significance of the Total Position components in the motion sense should now be clear.

However, the Position Time Equation may be expressed as follows:

$$P = M + O + (A + E1) + E2$$

Note first that the parentheses around the M and O are missing. This signifies the means of accounting for the Total Position time effect of Orient. Actually, part of the orientation time can occur during the Move component and the remainder during Position Proper. The latter must be accounted for within Position Proper anyway. However, the Orient time during Move will not be totally limited out by the Move time; instead it has the effect of increasing the Move time above the value normally assigned to Case C Move. To solve this problem, the new data reflects the difference between the total Move and Orient time and the normal Case C Move time as the Orient time assigned within Position Proper. With this simpler approach, the normal Move time data need not be changed to apply the Position data, since the interaction time effects within Total Position are included in the time for Position Proper. However, if an object is or has been completely pre-oriented before the Move motion begins, no Orient component will be needed during the Position action. Next observe that the Align and Primary Engage components are subject to being limited by each other. As a matter of fact, the E1 time normally is limited out by the A time except for the loosest fit cases with symmetrical and semi-symmetrical rotations. As was true for the Position Motion Equation, any time component except the E1 time can be missing during a given Position. The Supplementary Data on the MTM Data Card have been determined for the most prevalent time combinations of Position Proper components. When an analyst wishes to separately evaluate the various component times, the data are available as presented later.

Internal Variables of Position

With the components of Position thus clarified, attention is directed to the internal variables. These are again defined together for maximum clarity, directly from Application Training Supplement No. 8 as follows:

"Definition 1. *Fit* or *Clearance* is the minimum distance (inches or centi-meters[6]) between the positional object and the positioning destination when the object is centrally located at the plane of initial secondary engagement, which is the surface of the destination.

Definition 2. *Depth of Insertion* for Secondary Engagement is the travel distance (inches or centimeters[6]) from the plane of initial engagement to the end of insertion, with a maximum value of 1¾ inches; travel beyond this 1¾ inch limit should be carefully analyzed and the proper motion so noted.

Definition 3. *Symmetry* cases are a measure of the orientation required by the positional object expressed as the maximum possible orientation necessary to permit final insertion into the positioning destination. The Cases of Symmetry are judged directly by the geometric properties of the cross-sections of the object and the destination, when projected on a plane perpendicular to the axis of insertion."

---

[6] Centimeters applies only to metric system data cards.

Since it is the internal variables which actually are measured or decided when determining the applicable time for a Position, these variables merit careful discussion. Their interrelationships with each of the components of Position are important to correct usage of the Supplementary Position Data. Again, refer to Table 2 for clarity.

As defined, the fit or clearance is a different measure than was used for the older Position data. Instead of using total lateral clearance to suggest the required force of insertion, or instead of using a drop test to decide the amount of pressure required, the analyst has objective dimensional criteria in the new data. The clearance is expressed as *radial clearance,* which is one-half of the total lateral clearance. Alternately, it is the permissible distance of the engaging object axis from the axis of insertion which will permit completion of the Secondary Engagement. For example, a 1.0-inch cylindrical shaft has 0.25-inch radial clearance when it is inserted into a 1.5-inch round hole. This distance, measured at the plane of initial engagement, is the sole fit criterion for the new data.

As before, three Class of Fit categories have been assigned to cover the continuum of radial clearance in discrete steps:

Class 21   0.150 to 0.350 inclusive, inch radial clearance
Class 22   0.025 to 0.149 inclusive, inch radial clearance
Class 23   0.005 to 0.024 inclusive, inch radial clearance

Note the use of two-digit class numbers to avoid conflict with motion patterns based on the earlier data. Also, radial clearance less than 0.005 inch probably involves motions in addition to Position for complete insertion; and these must be separately analyzed for the additional motions and time actually required. Of further interest would be a rough comparison of these new classes with the older classes, although definitive statements regarding this cannot be made due to the difference in basis for each set of data. Approximately, then, P21 corresponds to P1, P22 and P23 represent a splitting of the P2 class, and the P3 which covers almost interference fits is not covered by the new data. Actually, P3 is rare in practice anyway; P22 and P23 are most frequent.

Regarding the effects of radial clearance on the five Position components, the following statements apply. Move, Primary Engage, and Orient are not affected. Radial clearance is the principal cause of Align time variation, and the sensitivity is high. The direct effect of radial clearance on Secondary Engage stems from the necessity for higher movement control as the fit decreases.

The explanation of Depth of Insertion is much easier than for the other internal variables. As compared to the earlier Position data, two main changes are seen. The maximum penetration included as a part of Position has been increased from 1.0 to 1¾ inches; deeper insertions must be separately analyzed for the motions actually required. Secondly, rather then one depth category, a continuum of penetration distances is recognized by four discrete categories. The category symbols actually key to the nearest ¼-inch increment of insertion as follows:

Depth of Insertion, inches	Research Range, inches	Symbol
0	0 (0 to ⅛ inclusive in application)	0
½	over ⅛ to ¾ inclusive	2
1	over ¾ to 1¼ inclusive	4
1½	over 1¼ to 1¾ inclusive	6

Note that the absence of insertion, which is measured from the plane of initial engagement, is uniquely recognized as a zero depth Secondary Engagement to a target. Actually, even finer divisions than those given above, with accompanying time data, can result from utilizing the regression equations in the research reports. The only Position component affected by Depth of Insertion is the Secondary Engage. The studies show that the direct effect of increasing constraint with deeper penetration results in larger per inch performance times at every distance than would be applicable for unconstrained spatial arm and hand movements of the same distance.

Case of Symmetry is the most complicated internal variable of Position in its effects and time interactions. However, the three cases of S, SS, and NS are identical to the older Position data. The contribution of the research is a precise, minute definition of both the motion and time variation caused by the Orient component of Position. Only Primary Engage and Secondary Engage are unaffected by Symmetry conditions.

The key to understanding Symmetry is the *maximum possible orientation* of the engaging object with respect to the engaged object. This is a purely geometrical concept amenable to mathematical analysis with no need for experimental proof in the laboratory or shop. Such an analysis is fully detailed in R.R. 109, in which it is demonstrated that the required degrees of maximum possible orientation for geometric matching of the parts is not a continuous variable. Rather, the discrete steps are easily defined, integral angular rotations which can be computed from the relative shapes of the parts. However, a simplification results from the fact that the performance time variation is rather limited over the full range of angles. This permits the following measurement criteria for only three Cases of Symmetry:

Case of Symmetry	Symbol	Maximum Possible Orientation, degrees	Description of Insertion Possibilities
Symmetrical	S	0	*Any* orientation
Semi-Symmetrical	SS	Between 0 and 90	*Two* or *several* orientations
Non-Symmetrical	NS	180	*Only one* orientation

As noted earlier, objects pre-oriented before the start of the Move component require no orientation, and therefore their positioning involves only the S Case of Symmetry. The geometric properties of the parts are the only determinant of the required maximum possible orientation. As this increases, the Move component time also increases, but the time increment is included in Position Proper instead of being accounted for with the Move. The Orient component, being affected only by the maximum possible orientation, requires more time for increased amounts of rotation. However, the time is almost constant between the 90- and 180-degree points because this range covers a discrete step in orientation possibility. On the other hand, Align component behavior is practically opposite. Align time increase is almost negligible in the 0 to 90 degree range, but shows a sizeable shift in the 90 to 180 degree range. The combined effects of maximum possible orientation are to increase Total Position time as the required angular rotation increases. The same statement is true for Position Proper. However, since Position Proper includes all orientation time not limited out by the normal Move time component, the total time increase due to additional angular rotation actually appears entirely within the Position Proper time.

Supplementary Position Time Data

As indicated earlier, each Position Proper component has been separately evaluated for its time variation. The previous discussion of Position components and internal variables, as summarized in Table 2, provides a sound basis for clarity on this time data. Following the component time data, their combination into the MTM Data Card information will be given.

Primary Engage (E1), the minimal motion in a Position, requires a constant performance time of 3.4 TMU. This is unaffected by the internal variables. Except for the P21S and P21SS cases, it is limited out by the Align time. Essentially, the Primary Engage is a special motion to the destination surface with above average control.

Secondary Engage (E2), always the last component of a Position when it is performed, is affected by the internal variables of Class of Fit and Depth of Insertion. Using the symbols presented earlier, Table 3 includes the complete time data for Secondary Engage.

Table 3. Supplementary Secondary Engage Time Data, TMU

Class of Fit	Depth of Insertion Symbol			
	0	2	4	6
21	0	3.2	4.3	5.4
22	0	4.7	5.8	7.0
23	0	6.8	9.2	11.5

Orient (O) component time changes only with the Case of Symmetry, and is unaffected by the internal variables of Class of Fit and Depth of

Insertion.   The three performance times are: S = 0.0 TMU; SS = 6.9 TMU; and NS = 10.7 TMU.

Align (A) normally limits out the Primary Engage time except for P21S and P21SS categories of Position.   While unaffected by Depth of Insertion, the Align time varies with the internal variables of Class of Fit and Case of Symmetry.   Table 4 gives the performance times in TMU, based on the previously defined symbols.

Table 4.   Supplementary Align Time Data, TMU

Class of Fit	Case of Symmetry		
	S	SS	NS
21	3.0	3.0	4.8
22	7.2	8.0	9.5
23	9.5	10.4	12.2

Position Proper (P) time data results from combining the component times in accordance with the research results and the application rules presented in the next section.   Table 5 presents the completed data table for Supplementary Position.

Table 5.   Supplementary Time Data for Position
[MTM Data Card Table I—Position—P (Supplementary Data)]

Class of Fit and Clearance	Case of† Symmetry	Align Only	Depth of Insertion (per ¼″)			
			0	2	4	6
21 .150″ −.350″	S	3.0	3.4	6.6	7.7	8.8
	SS	3.0	10.3	13.5	14.6	15.7
	NS	4.8	15.5	18.7	19.8	20.9
22 .025″ −.149″	S	7.2	7.2	11.9	13.0	14.2
	SS	8.0	14.9	19.6	20.7	21.9
	NS	9.5	20.2	24.9	26.0	27.2
23* .005″ −.024″	S	9.5	9.5	16.3	18.7	21.0
	SS	10.4	17.3	24.1	26.5	28.8
	NS	12.2	22.9	29.7	32.1	34.4

*BINDING—Add observed number of Apply Pressure
DIFFICULT HANDLING—Add observed number of G2.

†Determine symmetry by geometric properties, except use S case when object is oriented **prior to** preceding Move.

Supplementary Position Data Application

The application procedure for the Supplementary Position Data may be described in four steps:

(1) In accordance with the Position Motion Equation and the Position Time Equation, analyze the observed or visualized Position for its components and their relative order of occurrence.   This includes consideration of the restrictions described below.

(2) Analyze the internal and external variables affecting the Position under consideration. This includes motion frequency determination.

(3) Symbolize both the Position Proper and the required external motions.

(4) Assign appropriate Position times and times for the required external motions.

These steps are elaborated below to assure correct interpretation of the restrictions and exceptions for the Position Proper data on the MTM Data Card. This is necessary because the combination of the component data into the Supplementary Position table resulted from extended application research that determined the appropriate form of the data in the light of these restrictions and exceptions.

When performing the first application step, attention to measurement restrictions is included. These are based on the laboratory and industrial research samples. The new data should not be applied against these restrictions without cautious analysis of the effects. The *laboratory* sample employed positional objects with six different cross-sectional shapes. The engaging objects were five-inch long steel shafts with essentially equal weights of 2.5 pounds. They were positioned into six sets of three hardwood blocks four inches square by two inches deep weighing about three ounces each. In the *industrial* sample, the objects included only rigid materials not deformed by either the motions or the act of insertion, although their weights varied. Types of operations studied were drilling, tapping, burring, forming, and assembly. The effects of contouring—radiusing or chamfering either the positional objects or the destination entry—were not investigated. Neither were dual-handed or simultaneous methods of positioning evaluated. Therefore, the applicability of the new data may be restricted unless careful analysis is applied to objects; (1) flexible or deformable, (2) over 2.5 pounds in weight, (3) with contouring that aids insertion, and (4) which are positioned with both hands together or simultaneously. Conversely, if the new data are found by careful analysis to cover particular cases exceeding these restrictions, it should be a responsibility of the analyst to annotate such analysis.

The second application stop involves several considerations. The internal variables are analyzed according to the preceding text sections. An exception is the situation formerly called Align Only. The new data replace the former rules-of-thumb for positioning to a line, point, or points. Such cases still are symmetrical and to be judged on clearance by the desired accuracy relative to the target. However, the actual method can be reflected with the new data. If the object is moved spatially an inch or less to the target, a Position with zero Secondary Engage has been performed. If the object is slid along the destination surface an inch or less to the target, the Align Only column of the data card will apply. Examples of these will be given with the discussion of the third and fourth steps below. The exceptions for Depth of Insertion and Case of Symmetry are covered by the external variables.

External variables are those motion and time occurrences not covered within Total Position. However, the principal ones are noted on the Supplementary Position Data table. Binding upon insertion requires Apply Pressure motions to be separately analyzed, whereas its effects were formerly included within the Theory of Position. A similar situation holds for Difficult Handling. While the Theory of Position assigned a single G2 to cover this variable, the new data requires separate allowance of the actual number of G2 observed or visualized. Pre-orienting of the engaging object before Total Position (sometimes called Pre-Position as with the Therbligs) requires any motions for that purpose to be separately analyzed as well as a recognition that the Position Proper will involve only symmetrical performance. Finally, when the 1¾-inch limitation on Secondary Engage is exceeded, the resulting external variable must be recognized and separately analyzed. In this event, any continued Move motion may or may not be constrained and thus requires analysis. However, other motions or even process time may be appropriate for extended insertion and should be carefully examined for separate allowance.

One remaining question pertaining to the second application step concerns the analysis for simo Positions. That is, which simo rules govern the new Class of Fit categories? Here definitive research is needed to provide a conclusive procedure. However, the current practice is to use the P1 simo data for P21, and the P2 simo data for P22 and P23, when deciding simultaneity for applying the Limiting Principle.

For the third step of application, the Position Proper may be symbolized in four parts according to the following display:

Position	Class of Fit	Case of Symmetry	Depth of Insertion (per ¼″)
			A (Align Only)
			0
	21	S	1
P	22	SS	2
	23	NS	3
			4
			5
			6

Examples: P21S0, P23NS4, P22SS2, and P21SA.

Note that the Depth of Insertion may be recorded to the next highest ¼-inch symbol even though the time assignment is restricted to the next highest symbol of 2, 4, or 6 on the data card. Also note that Align Only has its own symbolism to clearly differentiate it from a Position with zero Secondary Engage, which requires a different time value. The required symbolism for the external variables follows that given in other chapters. This holds for AP in binding, G2 for difficult handling, Move or other motions involved in extended insertion, etc.

The fourth application step is best explained by several examples of completed positioning analysis:

a. Positioning a difficult-to-handle object with no		3.4	P21S0
Secondary Engage:		5.6	G2
	Total	9.0	TMU
b. Positioning an object which binds two times on		32.1	P23NS4
the average during insertion:		33.6 2	APB
	Total	65.7	TMU
c. Positioning a ten-pound object to a total depth		21.9	P22SS6
of 3½ inches:		5.8	M2C10
	Total	27.7	TMU
d. Sliding an object less than one inch to Align		3.0	P21SA
Only (compare this to the P21S0 above):	Total	3.0	TMU

On infrequent occasions, an analyst may wish to know a positioning component time when he has only the MTM Data Card available. The Supplementary Position Data table can then be used as follows:

1. *Align* component times are listed directly in the Align Only column of the data card.
2. *Orient* component times can be found by subtracting between the P22SS0 and P22NS0 values and the corresponding Align Only times; this procedure yields 6.9 TMU for SS and 10.7 TMU for NS orienting.
3. *Primary Engage* component time is a constant which corresponds to the time for P21S0, or 3.4 TMU.
4. *Secondary Engage* component times for any desired Class of Fit and Depth of Insertion may be found by taking the difference between the zero column and any other column on the same line of the data card. For example, the insertion time for P22S4 is: 20.7 − 14.9 = 5.8 TMU. In the same manner, all of the other insertion times can be determined.

SUMMARY[7]

Position (symbol P) is the basic finger or hand element employed to align, orient, and engage one object with another to attain a specific relationship.

[7] This summary does not cover the supplementary data.

Table 6.   Factors Causing Position Time Variation and Symbols Employed

Causes of Position Time Variation		Symbol
I. Class of Fit		
Class 1—Loose, no pressure required to engage		1
Class 2—Close, light pressure required to engage		2
Class 3—Exact, heavy pressure required to engage		3
II. Case of Symmetry		
Symmetrical	The parts can be engaged in an infinite number of ways about the axis of insertion	S
Semi-Symmetrical	The parts can be engaged in two or several ways about the axis of insertion	SS
Non-Symmetrical	The parts can be engaged in only one way about the axis of insertion	NS
III. Ease of Handling		
Easy to Handle	Initial grasp is adequate	E
Difficult to Handle	Grasp adjustment possibly needed	D
IV. Examples of MTM Symbolism		
P2SE P1NSD P3SSD P2SSE		

QUESTIONS

1. A billiard player performs motions on, among other things, his cue stick, the cue ball, the chalking block, the ball rack, and the scoring beads. Positions may be included in the following actions; identify and classify each one, stating reasons for your choices of values.
    A. Placing the last ball into the rack at the start of a game
    B. Addressing the cue ball with the cue stick before shooting to bust
    C. Chalking the tip of his cue stick, a cavity having been worn in the chalk
    D. Tallying his game score with the tip of his cue stick
    E. Locating the ball rack on the table center to rack the balls
    F. Placing his cue ball on the table preparatory to his bust shot.

2. The variables in Position are (A) Align, (B) Orient, and (C) Engage. The factors by which they are evaluated are (1) Class of Fit, (2) Case of Symmetry, and (3) Ease of Handling. Briefly explain how the variables and factors are related in terms of actions involved and means of measurement. Which variable(s) must always be present to justify identification of a motion as a Position? How are any motions of the objects in excess of 1 inch length analyzed? At what clearance, in inches, does the Class of Fit indicate that a motion of insertion is not a Position? How and where is this clearance measured?

3. Assuming the fingers are grasping the knob, what motions will be needed

to set the hands of a mantel clock? Would this differ any from setting the alarm hand on an alarm clock? In what way would setting the minute hand of a wristwatch be unlike either of the other two cases?

4. The insertion of keys into locks almost always involves Positions. Classify those you believe will occur with the following types of locks: ordinary door lock, padlock, Yale lock, cash register lock, watchman's clock, lock on a vending machine, and office file lock. Knowledge of these locks and the type of keys used is obviously needed; this illustrates why the objects being Positioned, as well as the operator's actions, must be observed to arrive at proper analysis of positions.

5. A gear, 1 inch thick and 4 inches in diameter, must be fitted on to a shaft having a spline 6 inches long on one end and then slid to the end of the spline so that a drive pin may be engaged snugly into a hole through the side of the gear. The gear and shaft have been previously brought into close proximity by the necessary Moves. Analyze all the MTM elements, including symbols and time values, which will transpire before the worker will release the completely fitted gear.

6. As an example of the time synthesis in the Theory of Position, list and explain briefly all the MTM motions and times included in a P2NSD. Would the actual order of motions made by a worker necessarily need to follow your motion sequence to justify assigning this Position? What clues would you examine when attempting to classify an actual Position in this way?

7. A vending machine is equipped with a mechanical changer so that nickel purchases may be made also with dimes and quarters. There is only one coin slot. Analyze, symbolize, and assign times to the insertion of all three coins into the coin slot. To completely accomplish the insertion of the coins, what additional MTM element(s) might follow the end of the Positions? *Hint:* Most changers are made with a spring entrance to the coin chute.

8. The same kind of Position could be used to insert an electric plug into a wall receptacle, a cord plug into an electric iron, and a toaster cord into the receptacle on the toaster. Identify and symbolize this Position if the parts were new, used moderately, and very worn from usage. Assume all of the plugs are of such shape and size as to be easy to handle.

CHAPTER 15

Disengage

Definition[1]

DISENGAGE[2] is the basic hand or finger element employed to separate one object from another object where there is a sudden ending of resistance.

   *1. Friction or recoil must be present. Merely **lifting** one object from the surface of another would **not** be a disengage.*

   2. There must be a noticeable break in the movement of the hand.

The frequency of Disengage in most industrial work is relatively low for two principal reasons. First, most industry is concerned with building —assembling objects rather than dismantling them—which makes the frequency of Position, for example, higher in expectancy. Secondly, when objects are disassembled or otherwise taken apart, the condition of the parts or the motions used may not require the Disengage element defined —even though assembly of the same parts required a Position. Often, more common motions of less complexity will suffice for the disassembly of objects, as is more fully explained later. Typical examples of Disengage are:

   1. Removing the handle of a socket wrench set from a socket
   2. Pulling a plug gage out of a snugly fitting hole in a part being inspected
   3. Uncapping a fountain pen having a friction-fit cap
   4. Pulling a radio tube from its socket

---

[1] From "MTM Basic Specifications" (Footnote 1, Chapter 7).

[2] Disengage is another convenient grouping of the more basic motion elements into a more practical, easily utilized category of motions. In Therblig terms, it comprises one type of Disassemble action; but the Therblig Disassemble could encompass more of the basic MTM motions than is the case for Disengage, which consists only of very short motions plus one longer special type of Move that is called recoil.

5. Lifting a riveted assembly out of a nesting anvil after the ram of the machine has squeezed a staked component into the contour of the nest.

Position is concerned with the assembly of objects by align, orient, and engage motions. In direct contrast, Disengage concerns taking apart objects previously joined, such that the sudden elimination of resistance between the parts will cause recoil of the finger, hand, and arm muscles used. The requirement for some recoil evidencing resistance to the breaking of contact is basic to fulfilling the definition of Disengage. This recoil is the main distinguishing feature of the type of object separation defined as Disengage. Provided no recoil occurred, one could therefore disassemble objects previously joined by a Position without employing Disengage. For example, only a Grasp would suffice to break contact between a ruler and the surface on which it was previously positioned to two points. Obviously, no resistance to separation of it (other than the minor effect of gravity) from the points or the surface would be present in this example. Recoil action would be conspicuously absent.

Note that only the hand and fingers are capable of gripping and controlling objects in the manner required for the occurrence of Disengage. The action concerned can be performed only by the fingers, hand, and arm working in a concerted fashion at the task of object removal. Disengage can occur, however, when a tool is used to apply the force because tools held in the hand are essentially extensions of the manual members that permit greater leverage, grip, or control than is possible with the bare hands. Disengages with such tools as pliers, tongs, tweezers, etc. used essentially to *pull* apart objects are quite commonly seen. The recoil of a worker's hand in such cases will signal a Disengage just as surely as if the tool were not present. Note also that the same tools used to *pry* objects apart will not involve a Disengage action by the worker, even though a recoil might result; the Grasps, Moves, and Apply Pressures used to pry are not the same in method or combination as those covered in a standard Disengage.

Broadly speaking, Disengage consists of two major actions. One set of motions is first used to break the contact resistance which keeps the objects together, followed by the recoil movement when the object being gripped is suddenly freed from the other object. The first set of motions usually consists of Turns (very small), Regrasps, Apply Pressures, and short Moves (1 inch or less) involving the part being removed. The recoil, as discussed in detail later, is presently understood to be *equivalent* to a Type II Case B Move. Recoil is an involuntary movement, that is, one not under complete control of the operator. The moment complete control has been resumed, Disengage is ended and either motion ceases or a subsequent Move of the disengaged object ensues.

This summary of the basic nature of Disengage serves to introduce the fact that at one time the Disengage data was questioned as to its adequacy to fully describe and allow time for the set of motions referred to above. The very first research report of the MTM Association offered possible alternates to the means of handling Disengage described in this chapter. A *Preliminary Research Report on Disengage*[3] indicated a desire to make further, more complete studies of the present Disengage data or any alternate which might evolve during such studies. Knowing this will help the reader to understand certain parts of the detailed discussion in this chapter.

There is no question about the Disengage description which refers to the "sudden ending of resistance" that causes the recoil. What was questioned is: (1) Of what detailed motions do these actions consist? (2) Is the present system of Disengage categories adequate to cover most occurrences and differentiate between them? (3) Has the set of rules presently governing application of the data yielded sufficiently correct results? In other words, the present data was deemed by the originators to suffice for the defined actions included in Disengage; but further clarification and study may be necessary before the MTM Association will be completely satisfied with a set of Disengage data. The time values now on the data card were actual observations validated for the categories presently recognized, but possibly other categories may be needed.

In stressing the need for additional data on Disengage the authors do not intend to cast doubt on the validity of the present data. It is merely in the interest of being thorough that the following facts are mentioned: (1) Disengage does not occur too frequently in the average motion pattern; (2) The present data, although based on a minimum of original research, has given adequate results; (3) Exploratory, but inconclusive, research done since the original determination suggests the need for further study to better understand the nature of Disengage; and (4) Because of its relatively infrequent occurrence, it is very low on the priority list for further investigation. The present data can be used with full confidence that it will continue to provide satisfactory results pending additional developments.

DISENGAGE VARIABLES

A number of variables are present in Disengage. Figure 1 depicts the breaking of contact, the recoil motion, and the move of the object away after the recoil ends. As will be seen shortly, it is not possible to accurately describe the exact nature of the recoil path, since it is the resultant of two forces—the combined momentum of the object and the involved body

[3] R.R. 101 (See Ch. 5).

members plus the reflex action of the operator's muscles in trying to regain complete control of the freed object. Thus, the path is not completely under the conscious control of the worker. Note that Disengage ceases when the recoil ends, the recoil being the only large displacement of the object; very little object relocation results during the earlier task of breaking contact.

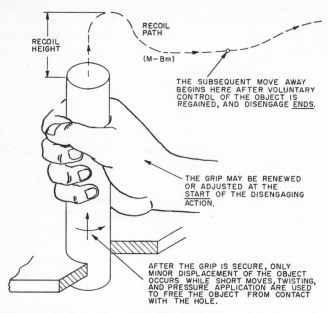

RECOIL PATH

RECOIL HEIGHT

(M — Bm)

THE SUBSEQUENT MOVE AWAY BEGINS HERE AFTER VOLUNTARY CONTROL OF THE OBJECT IS REGAINED, AND DISENGAGE ENDS.

THE GRIP MAY BE RENEWED OR ADJUSTED AT THE START OF THE DISENGAGING ACTION.

AFTER THE GRIP IS SECURE, ONLY MINOR DISPLACEMENT OF THE OBJECT OCCURS WHILE SHORT MOVES, TWISTING, AND PRESSURE APPLICATION ARE USED TO FREE THE OBJECT FROM CONTACT WITH THE HOLE.

Fig. 1. Nature of Disengage. Since recoil is an involuntary motion, the recoil path is rather indefinite and unpredictable but of the general nature here shown.

Unless recoil occurs, Disengage, as presently defined, has not been performed. It is not always visually perceptible with loose to medium fits, but can always be detected by resistance to separation if actual Disengaging of the parts is employed for analysis purposes.

Tightness of Engagement

Since separation of the objects is the first action during Disengage, the intimacy of contact between them will affect the initial motions required and the total Disengage time. The degree of contact may vary from what may be termed integral, as seen in certain cutting actions, to the ordinary sliding fits found in most Disengages.

Integral contact implies that one portion of the same object is cut or broken away from it with actions that cause recoil of the appropriate manual members to occur. This happens, for instance, when a knife is used to cut twine or string. Several sawing motions, usually analyzed as

Case B Moves—possibly with a resistance factor—of short distance, are first employed to sever strands of the cord or string. Following this, a break of contact between the pieces of cord is evidenced by the recoil which signals a Disengage of the cut piece from the remainder of the cord.

When Disengages occur between physically discrete objects, the mechanical fit is a measure of the degree of contact. This may vary from the tightness which would require assembly with a Class 3 Position, an exact fit, to a sliding fit that will cause little or no recoil upon separation. Obviously, from this condition, there is really a continuum of cases during Disengage that would justify a range of performance times in rather finely divided steps. As a practical matter, however, the number of steps must be limited in such a way that the MTM analyst can readily categorize any given occurrence of Disengage in relation to easily recognized differences in the time required. The relative time value for a Disengage to the other motions in a pattern or sequence in which it occurs will also have a bearing on the size of divisions needed for desirable accuracy of the total pattern time. Present MTM data, with three major steps, possibly needs revision into a greater number of categories.

It is now believed that the breaking of contact is actually accomplished by varying combinations of Regrasps, Turns (very small), short Moves, and Apply Pressures. It has been fairly well established that the number of each of these motions is not *directly* related to the amount of initial resistance to Disengage, although the difficulty of separation will dictate their usage in varying degree. At present, the data is qualitative in nature, not quantitative.

Just as application of force inward is needed to Engage objects during Position motions, the employment of Apply Pressure outward would logically be needed to Disengage them. The brief hesitations which identify Apply Pressure are very prevalent during Disengage, particularly where the Disengage does not result in successful separation of the objects. This is not illogical when it is realized that the application of greater force may well have resulted in separation of the same objects. Also, remembering that AP1 is defined as AP2 plus G2, the presence of Regrasps during Disengage is acknowledged as probably due to shifting the grip for applying greater force when the initial effort fails to break contact between the objects.

The reader has probably noticed when he has disengaged objects himself that a twisting action is frequently employed. This is often performed as the initial action, with a concurrent Apply Pressure. Apparently, a twist will often loosen objects or at least reduce the friction component in the direction of travel during separation. Essentially, the Turn motion used in this manner overcomes inertia or contact at the boundaries of the parts and is most effective when a slight amount of taper exists between the parts.

Also note that the relative location of the hand and arm to the object being Disengaged will determine whether the twist is actually a Turn or only a short Move with heavy force applied. If the Turn is 30° or more or the Move is appreciable, however, separate time should be allowed for them.

Another interesting phenomenon observed during Disengage research was the occurrence of flying starts that seemed to reduce the Disengage time. In flying starts, the hand hits the object being separated with sufficient force to provide momentum of travel that loosens the part enough to permit a quick Grasp and lifting of the object out of its cavity in a continuous motion. The use of this technique appeared in the research films to be associated with highly skilled operators. It was questionable whether average operators could perform the Disengages in the same manner. The conclusion was that the use of flying starts is really a skill factor and should not be considered in establishing Disengage times for normal workers. In addition, Research Report No. 101 pointed out that if the object becomes dislodged purely from the impact of the operator's hand, the absence of recoil would indicate that no Disengage motions are actually involved.

Path of Recoil

MTM Research Report 101 has an excellent analysis and detailed plots of recoil during Disengage. Perhaps its most important contribution to the Disengage data, however, is that it establishes the validity of approximating the time for recoil as an M–Bm. It is worthwhile to discuss the major ideas presented, to clarify recoil action during Disengage.

The idea of recoil, the second major action during Disengage, was described earlier as the muscle action caused by the sudden release or freeing of the object being gripped from the other object. This inherently implies that a measurable displacement of the freed object must occur— indeed recoil is the one essential characteristic to which the definition of Disengage is most firmly connected. If it is absent, even though objects are in some manner separated, Disengage was not the motion used.

The most vexing problem, timewise, in developing valid data for Disengage is due to the fact that the measurable displacement noted above occurs while the operator does not consciously control the object. Recoil is an *involuntary* movement which occurs following the breaking of resistance between engaged objects. It has been stated that the recoil time can be *approximated* by a Type II Case B Move of appropriate distance. The time measurement problem consists of (1) determining the exact shape of the recoil path, and (2) obtaining a distance measurement practical for use by the MTM analyst who does not have films to view in detail.

Employing plots of vertical distance versus horizontal distance, Research Report 101 shows seven different types of recoil paths that can occur.

Only the essential differences will be discussed here to highlight the problem of determining the shape of the recoil path. Refer to Fig. 2 as this is discussed. Remember that *as soon as conscious control is regained, the recoil—hence the Disengage—has ended* and the next motion, if any, begins. The small circle shows this on the diagrams, and small arrows show the direction of pull at the start of the recoil.

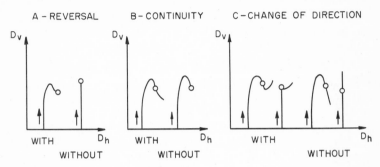

Fig. 2.   Path of recoil. D_v is the height of recoil, D_h is the lateral recoil travel.

A. *Reversal* of path during recoil.   A recoil may be straight or curved, depending somewhat on the magnitude of the forces of the Disengage.   Reversal causes compensating changes in the velocity of recoil which tend to equalize the time for equal heights of the two cases shown.   With reversal, a slight hesitance during which the regaining of control is realized following recoil balances the higher velocity associated with the forces that cause reversal; whereas there is extra uncontrolled acceleration of the object when reversal is absent.   Analysis in Research Report 101 of the velocity-time plots, where the area under the curve is proportional to the distance traveled, shows both cases to be adequately approximated by a Case B, Type II Move.

B. *Continuity* of motion following recoil.   After control is consciously regained, the operator may further move the object or stop its travel.   If a Move follows, it is probably a Type II in motion at the start.   If the object is stopped, a deceleration time occurs. These actions also cause differences in the velocity-time plots, but the results seem to average out for the two cases so that an M–Bm again suffices.

C. *Change of Direction* in connection with a subsequent Move.   The path of this Move may continue tangent to the end of the recoil or veer off to a new direction.   The velocity-time compensations associated with the regular analysis of Type of Motion in Reaches and Moves would apply in this case so that any time differences

associated with a Move following Disengage would not be a part
of the problem of Disengage time.

D. *Dampening* of the recoil.   It is possible for a recoil to be less
uncontrolled if special effort is exerted to dampen it.   This will
alter the behavior seen with regular Disengages.   Special rules of
thumb have been developed for Disengages where restrictions are
present as a result of analysis of dampened recoils.   The restrictions and rules are discussed later.

Having seen the kind of difficulties connected with the shape of the
recoil path, it is easier to understand the problem of distance measurement
for recoil.   While the length of recoil path is proportional to the initial
resistance overcome during Disengage, it is not directly determined by the
force of separation.   The nature of grip on the object and the relative

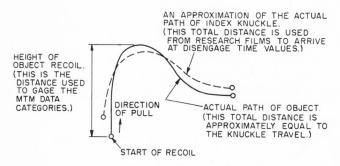

Fig. 3.   Measurement of recoil length.

body position of the operator also affect the path length.   For example,
a longer recoil will occur when the object is at arm's length than would
be true if the arm was close to the body of the worker.

Measurement of the distance of recoil may be clarified with the aid of
Fig. 3.   Remember that, in the analysis of films to assign MTM times,
the reference point for distance measurements is the index knuckle.   The
manual time will depend on the *total* index knuckle travel during displacement motions.   This travel path does not coincide with the recoil path of
the object, although the distance difference is small.   To attempt accurate
measurement of either of these paths would be difficult in practical MTM
usage, if not impossible, especially since the recoil path may vary for
successive Disengages of the same kind of objects.

Since the actual path length is difficult to measure, a practical compromise was used to set up the MTM categories for Disengage.   The observed
recoil *height*—obviously an approximation under even the best conditions—
is taken to be a gage of the total path, and thus becomes one of the factors
in establishing the time for the basic action.   This makes for ease of meas-

urement with relatively small resultant error, in most cases, although in some cases the error could be large. Depending on the engineer to observe the operator and estimate the extent of recoil is perhaps a minor inconsistency in determining the time allowance and does increase the difficulty of writing an accurate MTM standard through visualization.

Nature of Grip

The kind and tightness of grip can affect Disengage time. For example, a tighter grip will increase the amount of force it is possible to exert and could thus increase the length of recoil. Also, when the hand does not grip an object in a manner permitting the application of force readily, Disengage will be delayed until the fingers and/or hand are adjusted properly. Such.corrective action may range from a minor finger movement to a full G2 Regrasp; the type of Regrasp labeled "occasional" in the Theory of Grasp occurs frequently during Disengage.

In addition to the type of grip improvement just noted, Regrasps due solely to the difficulty of handling the part can occur at the start of Disengage; this type of Regrasp was discussed at some length in the Position chapter. When present during observed Disengages, this type of Regrasp is revealed by finger shifts or hesitations at the start of Disengage. The same Easy and Difficult classes of handling as were assigned for Positions are used in the MTM data for Disengage to account for the nature of grip, and they are judged in a similar manner.

Restrictions

Disengage time will also vary when restrictions are placed on the conditions under which the worker performs a Disengage. Basically, restrictions have the effect of limiting the amount of pull and/or the recoil path (shape and distance) the operator can allow to occur. The nature of the grip could also be altered.

Proximity of nearby objects, can restrict the Disengage by either preventing travel in certain directions or beyond certain distances. Either the objects in proximity or the object being removed may endanger the worker's hand due to fragility, burrs, or sharp cutting edges. The objects could likewise damage each other upon contact resulting from an uncontrolled recoil. Disengaging a metal object from a tight clamp used to hold it partially submerged in a caustic chemical plating solution, for instance, would be an operation requiring a worker to prevent a recoil path that would splash, drip, or throw the caustic on himself or his fellow workers. Also, removing a gear keyed to a shaft mounted inside a rough cast housing would present a Disengage problem, especially if the projections on the inner surface of the housing were sharp.

Another type of Disengage restriction exists when care to prevent damage of the object or injury to the worker is needed during the action prior to recoil. Pulling a broken lamp from a bayonet type socket would require caution to protect the fingers and hand from cuts. Less force would be applied to Disengage a highly polished shaft than a rough one merely to avoid marring the finish. In both of these examples, the break contact action during Disengage would be altered, even though the recoil might be unrestricted.

Binding, or resistance to separation other than that associated with the fit or friction, may place restriction on Disengage from the standpoint that extra motions not normally needed are required to break the bind. These might be the renewal of grip, reapplication of force, or both, in such manner as to permit the Disengage to continue. Binding may be caused by cocking of the part in the hole, compression of the part against the hole sides due to the pulling, or snagging of projections of the part. A familiar example is a lock key snagging in the tumblers of the lock. Corrective motions in such cases permit the Disengage to proceed.

Restrictive variables during Disengage are generally handled by rules of thumb. Another approach is to determine statistically the frequency of occurrence, as explained in a later chapter, and then use a percentage modification of the normal basic time for the motion.

KINDS OF DISENGAGE

As was true for other MTM motions, categories for Disengage were assigned to aid classification of the variables present in a way that permits application of pre-determined times which reflect the average occurrence for that situation or set of motions. This aim was perhaps not as well met for Disengage as for other motions, in that the large number of variables just discussed are categorized into relatively few classes that might fail to permit adequate time differentiation. In addition, the observer is expected to evaluate an object-muscle reaction identified as recoil that at best is only a reasonable approximation.

The present data lists six classes or kinds of Disengage. Further research might well reveal new data justifying additional classes of fit, accounting separately for the break contact and recoil portions of the action, and more explicitly expressed restrictions. It is helpful to note that class of fit and ease of handling, which comprise the two lumped variable categories of Disengage, are expressed in terms similar to some of the classes found in Position. These bear no direct relation, however, but are similar only on the basis of being defined limits. The classes are arbitrary breakpoints even though Disengage times actually vary on a continuum that may be more finely approximated in future data editions.

Class of Fit

The three classes of fit for Disengage each account for the break contact and recoil actions present in terms of either the effort required or the height of recoil. This is similar to the class of fit for Position which categorized the engagement in terms of amount of clearance present or amount of engaging force applied. Such classes do not purport to describe adequately the complete Disengage action, but are a practical substitute based on ease of use in lieu of careful accounting for the Disengage variables on a separate item basis. The force and recoil height are more easily judged than are the detailed separating motions and the total path length of the recoil.

Class 1—Loose Fit

Definition: A Class 1 Disengage requires only *slight effort* to break contact and results in separation with *minimal recoil* that blends smoothly into the subsequent Move.

Although some resistance or constraining effect must be present—or else only a normal Move would be needed to disassemble—it is not easy to see the recoil that distinguishes a Class 1 Fit. *Minimal infers that it will be no more than approximately one inch.* Likewise, little or no pause would be discernible to an observer when control of the disengaged object was regained. To verify his doubts as to whether a Disengage actually occurred, the analyst should perform the motion himself; in this event he can feel the resistance and sense the recoil directly. For example, it is common to find that parts which were Positioned with a Class 1 Fit will seldom require more than a Class 1 Fit to Disengage. If no resistance or recoil is experienced, however, the motion observed should correctly be assigned a regular Move category and time.

Class 2—Close Fit

Definition: A Class 2 Disengage requires *noticeable effort* to break contact and is followed by *moderate recoil* denoting separation.

The height of *recoil suggested for a Class 2 Disengage is up to approximately 5 inches.* The contact can be broken with very little pressure application. This kind of Disengage occurs with the highest frequency of all classes. Reversal of recoil is often associated with this class, as well as some pause or deceleration as control is regained.

Class 3—Tight Fit

Definition: A Class 3 Disengage requires *considerable effort* to break contact, and is readily evidenced by the hand *recoiling markedly.*

The use of Apply Pressure is obviously necessary, for considerable effort must be exerted to effect the separation. The *recoil is unmistakable, being over 5 inches high* and sometimes suggesting a violent muscular reaction to the pull exerted to break contact. The analyst will have no difficulty classifying this kind of Disengage without trying the motions himself.

That the classes of fit, as just described, do not adequately cover all the Disengage variables they are intended to cover may be a valid criticism. That more research study is needed on the element is frankly admitted; possibly future research will result in an approach more similar to that used for Position. The advantages of explanation and differentiation found in Position would then prevail for Disengage, perhaps permitting a Theory of Disengage that would directly yield useful time values.

Ease of Handling

In essence, Disengages are classified as to the nature of the part being removed in terms of whether additional grasping motions beyond the initial Grasp are needed to permit continuance of the separating motions. Odd shapes, flexibility, unusual surface texture, and the like might be properties of the part necessitating adjustment of the Grasp. It was also indicated that additional grasping is often needed due to proximity restrictions. It is relatively easy for the analyst to decide, however, which of the two handling categories is appropriate.

Easy to Handle

Definition: Parts which can be grasped securely and disengaged without changing the original Grasp are easy to handle.

Difficult to Handle

Definition: Objects which cannot be readily grasped securely enough to permit their disengagement without correction of the Grasp are difficult to handle.

THE SHORTHAND OF DISENGAGE

Only six combinations of coded symbols are used to cover the kinds of Disengage.

Disengage

The capital letter D is written to symbolize the occurrence of a Disengage.

Class of Fit

The classes of fit encountered in Disengage are denoted by Arabic numerals 1, 2, or 3 following the letter D to correspond to the defined categories of fit.

Example: D2 shows a Disengage, Class 2 Fit, where noticeable effort and moderate recoil are involved.

Ease of Handling

The use of either the capital letter E or D following the numerical designation of the class of fit will identify the ease or difficulty of handling during a Disengage.

Examples: D1D is the convention for the disengagement of a difficult-to-handle part with a Class 1 Fit, which shows little effort or recoil.

D3E indicates that an easy-to-handle object was forcibly disengaged with considerable effort and marked recoil, a Class 3 Fit.

DATA CARD INFORMATION

The MTM Data Card information shown in Table 1 is self-explanatory.

Table I.   Disengage Time
(MTM Data Card Table VII—Disengage—D)

CLASS OF FIT	Easy to Handle	Difficult to Handle
1—**Loose**—Very slight effort, blends with subsequent move.	4.0	5.7
2—**Close** — Normal effort, slight recoil.	7.5	11.8
3—**Tight** — Considerable effort, hand recoils markedly.	22.9	34.7

THEORY OF DISENGAGE

The time values appearing on the MTM data card for Disengage were all taken from research films. A theory was later synthesized to attempt to explain the motions involved during Disengage in terms of the times observed. This theory in its present form is summarized in Table 2. It may be changed by further research on Disengage. At present, such research is low on the priority list due to the infrequent occurrence of this motion.

In contrast to the Theory of Position which is considered so adequate that the data card times for that element were developed directly from the theory, the present Theory of Disengage is primarily a rationalization of the observed data. This rationalization is evident from the motion significance notes at the bottom of Table 2. While it is an aid to understanding what happens motionwise during Disengage, the use of this theory for synthesis of non-standard time values should be limited. One of the few features about it rather well validated at present is the approximation of the recoil movement by a Type II, Case B Move.

Table 2. Theory of Disengage

Case of Motion	Motion-Time Synthesis f = fractional inches or less than 1"	Time Value, TMU		
		Theory	Experiment	Data Card
D1E	M3.5Bm = 3.95	3.95	4.0	4.0
D2E	M8.5Bm = 7.55	7.55	7.5	7.5
D3E	AP2 + M15.5Bm = 10.6 + 12.45	23.05	22.9	22.9
D1D	MfB + M3.5Bm = 2.0 + 3.95	5.95	5.7	5.7
D2D	MfB + RL2 + RfA + G5 + M8.5Bm =2.0 + 0 + 2.0 + 0 + 7.55	11.55	11.8	11.8
	RfA + G5 + MfB + RL2 + RfA + G5 + M8.5Bm = 2.0 + 0 + 2.0 + 0 + 2.0 + 0 + 7.55	13.55		
D3D	AP2 + AP2 + M15.5Bm = 10.6 + 10.6 + 12.45	33.65	34.7	34.7
	G2 + AP2 + G2 + M15.5Bm = 5.6 + 10.6 + 5.6 + 12.45	34.25		

Motion Significance:

RfA	finger reach with automaticity
MfB	minor twisting movement of object while still engaged
G2	regrasp of the object (or its equivalent) prior to the exertion of force or pressure
AP2	application of force or pressure to insure grip and/or apply pull to object to break engagement contact
M–Bm	synthetic equivalent of recoil motion with length of recoil path shown. In actual practice, the motion cases are judged as to recoil distance breakpoints by height of recoil as follows:

Motion Case	Height of Recoil	Recoil Path Length
D 1	Up to 1"	3.5"
D 2	Over 1" to 5"	8.5"
D 3	5" and over	15.5"

PRACTICAL WORKING RULES

It is important to stress that resistance to separation must be present for a Disengage to occur. The recoil is the main clue in considering whether the removal of one object from another should be classified as a Disengage. A Disengage does not *necessarily* occur when disassembling objects merely because they were engaged with a Position, although Disengage *usually* takes place when friction and/or close spatial tolerance are involved in their separation.

The class of fit for a Disengage does not necessarily indicate the same tolerance or clearance as the class of fit for Position having the same numerical case. Also a part that was difficult to handle during Position might be easily handled while subsequently being Disengaged. The threading of a needle would likely entail a Class 3 Position, and the thread is difficult to handle; however, the thread could be removed from the needle with a Class 1 Disengage and no difficulty in holding the thread firmly—the actions of the hands and fingers are quite dissimilar in the two cases. It is even more likely that the thread would be removed with a simple Case B Move, rather than requiring a Disengage, since recoil is not usual for this task.

There are several rules of thumb that facilitate practical application of the MTM data for Disengage. These are based primarily on the behavior of the motions observed in film studies of the element and relate to care in handling and the occurrence of binding. These will be recognized as the other two Disengage restrictions previously mentioned but not covered directly in the standard Disengage categories.

Care in Handling

If damage to the part or injury to the worker is likely during Disengage unless caution and care are exercised, the slowing of the motion is usually recognized by making the following adjustment in the motion analysis and time allowance:

1. If the class of fit normally would be Class 1, the need for care is accounted for by assigning a Class 2 Fit to the Disengage.
2. If the class of fit normally would be Class 2, a Class 3 Fit will be allowed to cover the need for care in Disengaging.
3. Where care is required on what normally would be a Class 3 Disengage, the Disengage should be analyzed for possible elimination from the work. If this cannot be done, the extra MTM motions actually observed to be necessary to avoid injury or damage should be allowed in addition to the normal Disengage time.

In effect, this rule of thumb raises the class of fit to the next higher when care in handling is an additional factor in an otherwise normal Disengage.

Binding

When binding action results in an unsuccessful attempt to Disengage, the Disengage motion ceases and new, additional motions are made to overcome the binding. These extra motions should be allowed in addition to the Disengage motion that would normally be appropriate if the binding had not happened. Binding is not likely to occur with a Class 1 Disengage, but for the other two classes the following rules of thumb apply:

1. For binding in conjunction with a Class 2 Disengage, a Regrasp (G2 of 5.6 TMU) should be allowed each time binding occurs. This presumes that the binding can be broken by obtaining a new grip on the part.

2. For binding during a Class 3 Disengage, an Apply Pressure (AP1 of 16.2 TMU) should be allowed each time binding occurs. The assumption here is that, besides obtaining a new grip, the operator will need to re-apply the force normally used to break contact in a Class 3 Fit.

It is important to note when applying the Disengage data that the object being removed *has been assumed to be gripped once before the Disengage begins.* Obviously, any other MTM motions such as Reaches and Grasps performed prior to the beginning of Disengage must be analyzed in the usual manner in addition to analysis of the Disengage action. To remove a long bolt from a closely fitting hole, for example, would require that the operator apply a wrench to the bolt to loosen it, lay aside the wrench, Reach to the head of the bolt, Grasp the head of the bolt, unscrew the threads with a series of Turns and Reaches or Moves and Reaches, and only then—for removal from the hole—will the Disengage action begin. Even this latter motion will not be a Disengage unless it results in recoil of the operator's hand. Binding could occur if the axes of the bolt and hole became misaligned during removal of the bolt and would require revision of the class of Disengage assigned. If another object were in close proximity to the bolt, the Disengage could be considered as difficult-to-handle even though the bolt itself is not hard to grip firmly. Finally, any reason for the exercise of care would justify additional G2 or AP1 motions in the motion pattern if the Disengage were other than a Class 1.

SUMMARY

Disengage (symbol D) is the basic hand or finger element employed to separate one object from another object where there is a sudden ending of resistance.

Table 3. Factors Causing Disengage Time Variation and
Symbols Employed

Causes of Disengage Time Variation	Symbol
I. Class of Fit	Arabic Numeral

CLASS 1—Loose
    Slight effort with minimal recoil (no more than one inch) that blends smoothly into the subsequent move
CLASS 2—Close
    Noticeable effort followed by moderate recoil (up to approximately 5 inches)
CLASS 3—Tight
    Considerable effort with the hand recoiling markedly (over 5 inches)
	1
	
	2
	
	3

II. Ease of Handling	Capital Letter

EASY to handle
    The original, secure grasp needs no changing to permit the Disengage
DIFFICULT to handle
    The original grasp requires correction before Disengage can successfully occur
	E
	
	D

III. Examples of MTM Symbolism	
D1E D2D D3E	

QUESTIONS

1. A machine repairman must remove a snug-fitting cotter key to disassemble certain mechanism components from a drive shaft. After straightening the body of the key, he grips the loop with a pair of vise-grip pliers. Tell exactly what MTM motion will follow and the time it will take in seconds. If he attempts successfully to remove the cotter without completely straightening the body of it, will a different answer be appropriate?
2. For the following situations, classify the kind of Disengage normally expected and assign TMU values to each:
   a. Pulling a new floor lamp plug from the wall outlet of a new house.
   b. Unplugging an old table lamp from a wall outlet in an old apartment.
   c. Removing a key from a lock that just had new tumblers installed.
   d. Lifting an Allen wrench from the socket of an Allen head set screw.
   e. Uncapping a quart bottle of ginger ale fresh from the cooler with a common bottlecap opener held in the hand.
   f. Disassembling the handle and reel holder section from the rod of a fishing pole with cork-lined joints.
   g. Jerking the carbons from a set of "snap-out" business forms.
   h. Unsheathing a hunting knife from a tight-fitting scabbard.
   i. Removing a common wood toothpick from a holder that the waitress has just filled compactly.

3. A homeowner wishes to pull a cylindrical line fuse from his main switch box after overloading his power saw to a stall. Being safety-minded, he employs a fiber wrench made for this purpose. The fuse box is at head height on the wall 20 inches directly in front of him, with the puller lying on top. Write the MTM pattern and assign times from the instant he is standing with his arms at his side until he has laid aside the fuse and puller on a table 24 inches to the right at hip level.

4. What kind of MTM motions will likely be involved in removing a rubber handle bar grip from a bicycle? The left hand is holding the handle bars firmly.

5. A mother is gripping in both hands a stick of peppermint candy that is ¼ inch in diameter and 8 inches long. What MTM motion will she use to break the candy in two for her two small children? Describe the same motion if she divided it after the smaller child had first had one end of the stick in his mouth. Remember peppermint candy is brittle.

6. Would obtaining a desk pen from an inkwell involve a Disengage? If so, classify the motion. If not, classify the Disengage required if the pen has not been used for so long that the ink has corroded the point. The left hand is used to hold down the inkwell.

7. While changing the wiring of a master circuit board, an operator of a business machine must remove jumper wires from their plugs without causing disconnection of complicated jumper patterns nearby. What MTM motion will he use in disconnecting the jumpers?

CHAPTER 16

Eye Motions and
Allied Topics

In connection with the discussion of the Methods-Time Measurement definition in Chapter 4 the major body subdivisions were considered in relation to the motions used in the MTM system. These included: (1) the manual members; (2) the sense organs of the head, notably the eyes; and (3) the heavier limbs associated with MTM body motions. The motion chapters to this point have elaborated in great detail regarding the motions of which the manual members are capable and the MTM means of measuring them. Motions of the body will be treated in the next chapter. In this chapter the reader will find information concerning the motions of which the eyes are capable, how these intermingle with other motions, and the MTM treatment of several other topics that include major usage of the eyes. Thus, this transitional chapter provides another link in the complete study of the human body considered as a muscle machine. At the end of this study, following the next chapter, the text will show how all of the data considered can be used to reflect a worker's smoothly coordinated actions during actual productive sequences.

The eyes are used almost constantly as the body performs its work; eye usage is obviously a vital part of human performance—work study must necessarily include analysis of this function. Ample proof of this is evident from observing blind workers; they use different motions than employees with sight and must rely on non-visual senses for the information needed to achieve their tasks. On the other hand, it is equally evident that the eyes do not usually control the total time required for a task—particularly when factory work, as opposed to office clerical work, is being analyzed for motion and time content.

To achieve intelligent understanding of eye motions, it is necessary to consider the circumstances under which eye time is the limiting factor during the performance of work.

MTM data already given includes reference to the fact that the use of the eyes while performing other motions has been recognized as one of the control factors that tend to prolong the performance times of those motions. For example, the main reason a Case C Reach takes longer than any other Reach is because during the Reach the operator is searching and selecting one object from a jumbled pile and he will next employ a G4 to achieve control of the chosen object. These motions involve the use of the eyes in a very direct manner. Obviously, the motion picture films from which the total time for these motions was obtained included the time for visual control, so that the time needed for eye action in this example is included in the Reach and the Grasp times reported on the MTM data card. It is thus unnecessary to allow additional eye time for such cases as these two motions, or others like them, when the required eye time has already been included with the over-all motion during which it occurred. Attention to this fact is essential for the MTM novice or ill-trained practitioner who tends to allow excessive eye time in setting MTM standards.

Contrarily, the eyes are used in certain work sequences in a manner that precludes performance of other motions until the eyes have finished their tasks. In such instances separate eye time must be allowed. Typical operations that either cause or tend to cause the operator to cease other motions while the eyes accomplish their distinct and separately required work appear often during inspection routines, the reading of instructions and other printed matter, and the visual perception of data from instruments and measuring devices. It is in such cases that the MTM analyst must recognize and allow time for eye motions.

Although it does not determine the total time required, eye time comprises an important element in the task of printing and writing. It can easily be proved that printing and writing involve the use of the eyes as a prime control factor if the reader will attempt to write or print with ease and legibility with closed eyes. While the coordinated use of the manual members controls the allowed time for printing and writing, and not eye time, treatment of these topics so closely allied to eye time is included in this chapter as a matter of convenience since the MTM data on printing and writing is a combination of manual motions that does not readily lend itself to discussion in either earlier chapters or as a separate topic.

The following rule summarizes the preceding discussion:

Eye time is allowed only when it occurs during a complete lapse of other operator motions or limits out other simultaneous operator motions, with the specific provision that the eye motions in question are necessary for the worker to complete his task or before the next manual motion can be performed.

There are many places in this chapter where this rule could appropriately be restated but, with the emphasis just given it, this should not be necessary.

To provide a unified concept of eye time, this chapter begins with basic data on eye motions and rules governing their time requirements; sections on inspection and reading are next in order; and the subject is concluded with a discussion of printing and writing.

EYE MOTIONS

The original MTM text by Maynard, Stegemerten, and Schwab did not include any specific discussion or data on eye motions but did note a time value for visual inspection that appeared in the original research and later proved to be the MTM value for Eye Focus. Isolation of Eye Travel and Eye Focus as distinct MTM elements, and determination of the time required for eye travel, was accomplished later by research sponsored by the originators. It is instructive to note that the originators had diligently accounted for all of the most frequent MTM motions before they released their data; the relative infrequency of instances in which eye time controls the working time in the more usual manual tasks partially explains why eye time data did not appear in their text.

Eye travel and eye focus, the only two actions of which the eyes are capable in work performance, were investigated by the originators soon after the formation of the MTM Association. The resultant data on eye time which was added to the basic MTM data is next discussed.

Eye Focus

DEFINITION:[1] *EYE FOCUS is the basic visual and mental element of looking at an object long enough to determine a readily distinguishable characteristic.*

1. *Eye focus is a hesitation while the eyes are examining some detail and transferring a mental picture to the brain.*
2. *The line of vision does not shift during the eye focus.*
3. *Eye focus is a limiting motion only when the eyes must identify the readily distinguishable characteristic before the next manual motion can be started.*
4. *Eye focus is not the normal control over the reaches, moves, positions, grasps, and other motions; eye control affects the time for these motions and this time is included as an integral part of the motion.*

The eye muscles accomplish a focus by altering the contour of the lens of the eye and thereby changing its focal length. Several important conditions

---

[1] From "MTM Basic Specifications" (Footnote 1, Chapter 7).

are essential for the eye to achieve clear perception of an image. Since they are all included in the above definition, adequate analysis of eye focus requires taking account of them.

Note that the definition covers a specialized manner of "looking" at an object, not the ordinary usage of the eyes in viewing objects without sharp distinction of details.

First, the eyes cannot focus *as defined* while they are in motion; the eyeballs must be stationary long enough to permit the necessary adjustment of the lens. After aiming of the eyes at the particular image or object characteristic being examined, they must be stopped long enough for completion of the focus before the target can actually be seen. The eyes can *maintain* their focus on an object (moving object), however, so long as the focal length required does not change significantly.

To see details of objects in motion, the eye adjusts to its initial focus and then holds it ("locks on") while the head is moved in synchronization with ("tracks") the motion of the object. This can succeed only if the object's velocity is low enough so that the eyes will not lose their point of aim while the initial focus is being made; at higher speeds, the eyes only isolate a blur because the initial focus cannot be made successfully before the target area passes from view. Also, focus cannot be achieved initially or maintained if the object distance from the eyes varies greatly while focusing action is occurring. Therefore, the eyes cannot achieve initial focus on an object in motion until the *relative* motion and distance between the eyes and the object becomes essentially fixed.

Secondly, the eyes cannot "see everything at once." They must search and aim at specific target areas. To get the total image of a large object, the eye must scan the object with a series of individual focuses. Additional factors are the amount of illumination present and the distance of the object surface in respect to the focal capability of the eyes.

The object area included by one focus will vary somewhat with the individual and especially with the degree or ease with which the characteristic(s) being sought can be differentiated from other surrounding characteristics on the object being examined. Obviously, the "area of normal vision" must be defined with respect to persons involved. The research data was developed with persons having the accepted norm of 20/20 visual acuity. The time values, therefore, properly apply only to persons with this degree of vision or to those with correction to this norm by eye glasses.

During MTM research, using persons with 20/20 vision, the average area covered per Eye Focus was found to be that within a 4-inch diameter circle at a distance of 16 inches from the eyes. This was then defined as the "area of normal vision" and is diagrammed in Fig. 1. As previously mentioned this area can be affected by the size of the characteristics or features of the object being examined. The area defined as normal is average for situations ordinarily encountered. The area of normal vision, incidentally, is an important factor in the MTM system for judging whether certain motion combinations are possible for the normal operator; this is discussed in Chapter 18.

The last part of the Eye Focus definition refers to the necessity that the focus be maintained on the target "long enough to distinguish it." As soon as the image is clearly perceived, the Eye Focus is completed. That is, the purpose of the focus has been accomplished as soon as the mind quickly notes the nature or characteristic of the image seen. Note that Eye Focus, therefore, inherently includes a minimal amount of mental decision time. This is important in analysis of inspection operations. The mental time included is adequate to permit simple "yes or no" decisions regarding the nature of the image perceived. Eye Focus time does not, however, include time for complex judgments or extensive reasoning. A single Eye Focus is complete as soon as the minimal mental action required has occurred. Beyond that, either additional focuses are required to clarify the impression received or else thinking time not covered by any MTM motion begins, this being a prime example of "process time" requiring stop watch study.

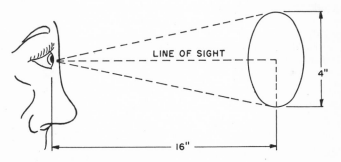

Fig. 1. Area of normal vision.

The preceding information should help the reader to realize that the definition for Eye Focus is a precise one that fully accounts for the eye action involved. A simple but typical instance involving analysis of Eye Focus occurs when an operator is required to check the legibility and uniformity of the impression he has just made on the identification tag of a product with a rubber stamp. He knows what to expect, being familiar with the stamp and quality requirements; the mental decision is quick and easy. If a defect appears in the stamping, however, the image will not be normal and the fact that an error is present will be recognized immediately. He may next focus again to classify any obvious defect prior to rejecting the tag and/or segregating it into a pile to be restamped. He may even require thinking time to isolate the cause of the defect so he can take corrective action in stamping further tags.

Eye Focus is symbolized in MTM by the capital letters EF. The time for a normal operator is a constant value of 7.3 TMU. This is about ¼ second or 0.00438 minutes. This value was confirmed by independent sources cited in MTM Research Report No. 102[2]; an average value of 7.35 TMU for EF in reading was obtained by a number of psychologists. Because the eye (or more particularly its lens) takes that long to accommodate a clear image, it is noteworthy (as mentioned in a previous chapter) that *no motion whose complete performance takes less time than an EF can actually be seen and identified by the naked eye.* The effects of the motion on objects can, of course, be seen and also the observer of a situation including the motion knows logically that it must have occurred if certain following conditions are observed. Remember that "see" as used here refers to the clear perception, identification, and mental recognition required by the MTM definition of EF; what has been said may not hold for casual glimpsing, ordinary visual sensing of movement, or other conditions of eye usage which do not involve manual motion identification of the type required by MTM.

Eye Travel

DEFINITION:[3] *EYE TRAVEL is the basic eye motion employed to shift the axis of vision from one location to another.*

1. Eye travel is a limiting motion only when the eyes must shift their axis of vision before the next manual motions can be started.

Just as the eyes must pause to allow Eye Focus to occur, they must be in motion during Eye Travel; these are the only useful actions of the eyes in work performance. Adding the necessary variable Eye Travel time to the correct number of Eye Focuses multiplied by their constant time value will yield any work cycle time *under sole influence of the eyes.* As is true for other MTM motions, correct use of the times depends on clear understanding of the precise nature of the motions in question.

The aiming of the eyes to actually "see" an object, or a given characteristic of the object, is analogous in many respects to the aiming of a gun at a target. Indeed, the point at which the eyes are directed is designated as the target in many accepted treatises on the subject of vision. The nature of the viewing area and what happens after the eyes are aimed at the target has already been fully explained under Eye Focus above.

---

[2] R.R. 102 (See Ch. 5).

[3] From "MTM Basic Specifications" (Footnote 1, Chapter 7).

What needs clarification here is the meaning of "axis of vision" in terms of motions and their measurement.

In discussing vision, reference is commonly made to what is known as the line of sight, this being an imaginary line from the eye directly to the target. This useful concept is adequate to explain the action of each eye individually, since the eye can readily focus and perceive the image when the line of sight has been established. It does not serve as well when considering the combined action of both eyes[4] because of the additional element of depth perception. For the operator to ascertain depth (or distance) of the target from himself, his eyes must converge on the target. When this occurs, there is a line of sight from each eye to the target, and these lines intersect at the target as seen in Fig. 2. The "axis of vision,"

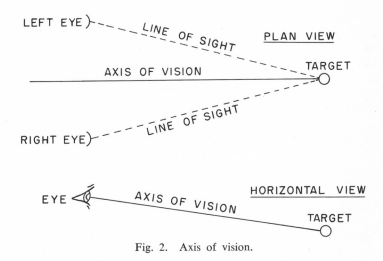

Fig. 2. Axis of vision.

the displacement of which is what is measured for Eye Travel, then consists of an imaginary line equidistant between the eyes and passing through the intersection of the lines of sight.

Eye Travel occurs only when the axis of vision moves in space. When the eyes are not moving, they can only focus; but to perceive more than a single point image, the eyes must execute a series, succession, or pattern of travels and focuses dependent on the nature of the total area which a succession of targets will encompass. The axis of vision may be displaced by (1) the eye muscles positioning the eyes, (2) the eyes being stationary in their sockets while the head is rotated, or (3) a combination of head rotation and eye movement. The latter case is most frequent when long distances between the areas of vision as defined under Eye

---

[4] This is also known as "binocular" vision.

Focus are involved. The first case occurs quite often, however, when close distances between target points and careful discernment of the images is a requirement of sight.

Because head assistance invariably occurs with Eye Travel beyond certain distance limits, the MTM procedure has placed a maximum time value of 20 TMU on Eye Travel. Regardless of the theoretical answer produced by either of the two formulas to be given shortly, *no single Eye Travel will be assigned more than 20 TMU.* The MTM eye time procedure must thus permit a way to find the time for eye travel between values limited out by other motions and the maximum value of 20 TMU.

MTM research has shown the exact Eye Travel time to be 0.285 TMU per degree of angular sweep between the initial and final points on the target. Note that the maximum travel time of 20 TMU thus imposes a mathematical limit of about 70 degrees (exactly 70 degrees, 10 minutes, 30 seconds) of angular sweep without head assistance as shown in Fig. 3.

Fig. 3.   Exact Eye Travel time.

For actual applications, estimating the degrees of sweep would be an awkward method of evaluating eye travel. The inventors of MTM therefore developed an approximation formula and a table for use by application engineers. The formula, which appears in Table VIII on the official data card, is given in Table 1. The tabular data is given in Table 2.

The table, although based on the exact Eye Travel formula, is entered by the T and D values used in the approximation formula given in Fig. 4 and Table 1. It should be kept in mind that, while the times given hold true for industrial operations, a different situation holds and appropriate data are given later for reading times.

Table I.   Eye Travel and Eye Focus Times

(MTM Data Card—Table VIII—Eye Travel Time and Eye Focus—ET and EF)

> **Eye Travel Time** $= 15.2 \times \dfrac{T}{D}$ TMU, with a maximum value of 20 TMU.
>
> where T = the distance between points from and to which the eye travels.
>   D = the perpendicular distance from the eye to the line of travel T.
>
> **Eye Focus Time** $= 7.3$ TMU.

Table 2. Eye Travel Time—TMU

Formula: ET = 0.285 × degrees

This table gives ET time in terms of T = inches travel between target points and D = perpendicular inches between eyes and line of travel between points.
The maximum allowed ET time of 20.0 TMU is used to the right of the heavy line.

D	1	10	11	12	13	14	15	16	17	18	19	20	22	24	26	28	30
10	1.52	15.2	16.4	17.7	18.8	20.0											
11	1.40	14.0	15.2	16.3	17.4	18.5	19.5										
12	1.29	12.9	14.0	15.2	16.2	17.2	18.2	19.2									
13	1.20	12.0	13.1	14.1	15.2	16.2	17.1	18.0	18.9	19.8							
14	1.12	11.2	12.2	13.2	14.2	15.2	16.1	17.0	17.8	18.6	19.5						
15	1.05	10.5	11.5	12.4	13.4	14.3	15.2	16.0	16.8	17.7	18.4	19.2					
16	.99	9.9	10.8	11.7	12.6	13.5	14.3	15.2	16.0	16.7	17.5	18.3	19.7				
17	.93	9.3	10.2	11.1	11.9	12.8	13.6	14.4	15.2	15.9	16.6	17.4	18.8				
18	.88	8.8	9.7	10.5	11.3	12.1	12.9	13.7	14.4	15.2	15.9	16.6	17.9	19.2			
19	.84	8.4	9.2	10.0	10.8	11.6	12.3	13.0	13.7	14.4	15.2	15.8	17.2	18.4	19.6		
20	.80	8.0	8.8	9.5	10.3	11.0	11.7	12.4	13.1	13.8	14.5	15.2	16.5	17.7	18.9	20.0	
21	.76	7.6	8.4	9.1	9.8	10.5	11.2	11.9	12.6	13.2	13.9	14.5	15.8	17.0	18.1	19.2	
22	.73	7.3	8.0	8.7	9.4	10.1	10.7	11.4	12.0	12.7	13.3	14.0	15.2	16.3	17.4	18.5	19.6
23	.70	7.0	7.7	8.4	9.0	9.7	10.3	10.9	11.6	12.2	12.8	13.4	14.6	15.7	16.8	17.9	18.9
24	.67	6.7	7.4	8.0	8.6	9.3	9.9	10.5	11.1	11.8	12.3	12.9	14.0	15.2	16.2	17.2	18.3
25	.64	6.4	7.1	7.7	8.3	8.9	9.5	10.1	10.7	11.3	11.9	12.4	13.5	14.6	15.7	16.7	17.7
26	.62	6.2	6.8	7.4	8.0	8.6	9.2	9.8	10.3	10.9	11.4	12.0	13.1	14.1	15.2	16.1	17.1
27	.60	6.0	6.6	7.2	7.7	8.3	8.8	9.4	10.0	10.5	11.0	11.6	12.6	13.7	14.7	15.7	16.6
28	.58	5.8	6.3	6.9	7.5	8.0	8.5	9.1	9.6	10.2	10.7	11.2	12.2	13.2	14.2	15.2	16.1
29	.56	5.6	6.1	6.7	7.2	7.8	8.3	8.8	9.3	9.8	10.3	10.8	11.8	12.8	13.8	14.7	15.6
30	.54	5.4	5.9	6.4	7.0	7.5	8.0	8.5	9.0	9.5	10.0	10.5	11.5	12.4	13.4	14.3	15.2

Note: The second column gives times for $T = 1$. To compute values when T is between 1 and 10 inches, multiply by T.

Geometry and trigonometry were employed to obtain the approximate formula used for calculating Eye Travel time. How this was done is shown in Fig. 4. The arc distance S was assumed approximately equal to the chordal distance T and the resulting formula, based on the exact formula, was then corrected for the average per cent error to obtain the constant of 15.2. The time values yielded by the formula ET = 15.2 × T/D will show

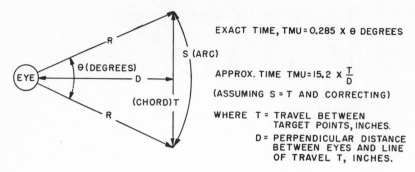

EXACT TIME, TMU = 0.285 X θ DEGREES

APPROX. TIME TMU = 15.2 x $\frac{T}{D}$

(ASSUMING S = T AND CORRECTING)

WHERE T = TRAVEL BETWEEN TARGET POINTS, INCHES.

D = PERPENDICULAR DISTANCE BETWEEN EYES AND LINE OF TRAVEL T, INCHES.

Fig. 4. Approximate Eye Travel time.

less than 1 TMU error in the usual ranges of the T/D ratio. For example, if $\theta = 50$ degrees and $D = 10$ inches, then $T = 2D \tan \theta/2 = 2 \times 10 \times 0.466 = 9.32$ inches. The approximate Eye Travel time is thus

$$15.2 \left(\frac{9.32}{10}\right) = 14.166 \text{ TMU}$$

which is in error by only 0.084 TMU (since the exact Eye Travel time is $0.285 \times 50 = 14.250 \text{ TMU}$).

The easiest measurements to make or estimate in practice are the distance of travel between focus points (denoted by the symbol T) and the perpendicular distance from the eyes to the line of travel (denoted by the symbol D). In fact, the Eye Travel symbol convention consists of ET for Eye Travel, followed by a fraction that shows the ratio between T and D which is needed in the use of the approximation formula. For example:

ET $^{10}\!/_{16}$ shows Eye Travel between points 10 inches apart at a distance of 16 inches from the eyes. The time allowed would be $15.2 \times {}^{10}\!/_{16} = 9.5$ TMU.

The authors have provided an additional aid for finding ET time by charting the approximation formula. This is given in Fig. 5. As was true for the weight factors in Move, the analyst has a choice of using a formula, a table, or a chart to apply time data to Eye Travel.

Application of Eye Motions

If the analyst watches a worker's eyes, the focuses and travels can be seen as distinct pauses and sweeps during performance of eye motions. When visualizing the motions, however, he must rely on knowledge of the eye motion data and then examine the method he would use himself. In any case, it is important to remember that *eye time is not allowed unless it is limiting.*

ET is seldom limiting over other MTM motions when T is less than 10 inches, nor is ET or EF allowed unless there is a recognizable pause

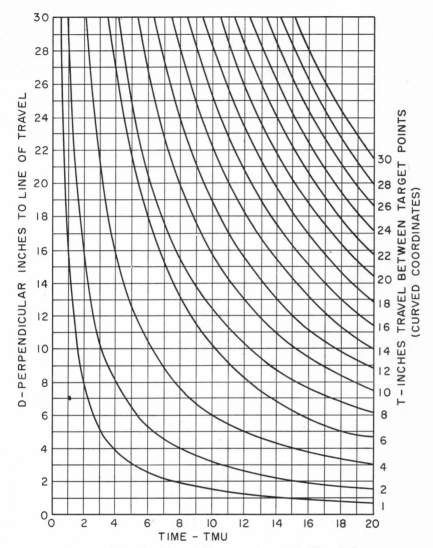

Fig. 5.   Chart for determining approximate Eye Travel time.

(To use chart, enter with *T* at the right, trace proper curve to its intersection with *D* at the left, and read vertically downward to the TMU time scale.)

between other MTM motions, provided the eye motions are necessary to complete the task or before the next motion can be performed. A note may be entered in the motion pattern anyway to show that the necessity for actions by the eyes was recognized and analyzed for the method record. The tendency of the MTM neophyte to allow excessive eye times can be overcome to some extent by reiterating that normal MTM motions do contain, to some degree, eye time and mental choice; the eye time discussed in this chapter is only that additionally demanded by observed methods.

It is not necessary that ET occurs or is allowed for each and every EF that is assigned. Oftentimes, the ET is accomplished during other motions, and is therefore limited out. In this case, the EF following might be the only eye time permissible; this is more likely to be true if the simple mental decision time included in EF must be expended before later manual motions can properly ensue. One or more EF are often assigned when visual checking is needed while other motions cease; these often do not involve ET. In addition, the eyes may have been already directed at the target because of the need for visual control in accompanying manual motions (e.g. a Case C Move) preceding, in which event they can easily focus as required without any ET preceding the focus.

Such occurrences are fairly frequent before and after critical Positions, when motions involving care to prevent damage or injury are made, and in the reading of measuring instruments. For instance, from two to four EF would reasonably be allowed when reading a 1–inch micrometer to the nearest thousandth; one for the tenths of an inch, another for the nearest 0.025-inch mark, and one or two to decide which vernier mark is nearest to the index line. The same reasoning could apply to reading a vernier scale to thousandths. The eyes would not shift sufficiently in these cases to necessitate allowing ET.

On the other hand, aligning a ruler very accurately to several points (in addition to any Positions included) might involve an EF at the first end, an ET to the other end, a short Move and a Position, a second EF, an ET back to the first end, and a final EF to assure that the align has been completed correctly. In this example, the alignment of the second end of the ruler cannot be properly made until the eyes are brought to that end, so that the need for ET is clearly indicated.

Remember that MTM sets time values for average operators. This naturally assumes normal vision or vision corrected to normal by proper eye glasses. This point should not bother the analyst in visualizing, but he might have difficulty in reconciling some stop watch times to the indicated MTM eye motion times if he did not make his observations on an operator with normal vision.

While other MTM motions are usually best observed from alongside or behind the worker, it is usually easier to see eye motions by standing in front of the worker. At times, particularly when the operator's head is bent over the work, it might even be necessary to stoop to observe the eye actions for accurate analysis. This type of observation requires tact and finesse because employees who do not mind having their hands observed are often more self-conscious with a work analyst peering intently into their faces and eyes.

INSPECTION

One of the more obvious places in which the foregoing data on eye motions is especially important and applicable is in inspection operations. While no official MTM rules or detailed data exist for this type of work, a number of application rules and suggested procedures have been sanctioned by the MTM Association pending future research. To aid the reader who may wish to apply eye time data to inspection, as has been done successfully by many practicing engineers in a wide variety of industries, the presently available material on the subject is included here.

The MTM eye time data is valid for inspection work that involves only relatively simple judgments or reasoning similar to that included in making rapid "yes" or "no" decisions. This was explained under Eye Focus. To any focus motions deemed necessary under the rules previously given and any additional rules given below must, of course, be added the necessary Eye Travel time between the pauses which signal focuses. Observation of an inspector will readily reveal the complex series of "shifts" and "pauses" in eye action during an inspection operation. Such direct viewing of the working inspector is much more reliable for determining the inspection time by MTM than is the visualization method, since frequencies and kinds of both eye and body member motions during examination of parts are of paramount importance in achieving correct time standards for inspection.

It is commonly thought by many persons dealing with industrial inspection that eye time and mental decision time comprise the major portion of inspection routines. Many MTM applications engineers have found, however, that this is not usually so. Pure inspection work as practiced in industry often averages from 85 to 90 per cent manual and body elements as limiting motions, with the eye and mental time accounting for the balance. The latter do occur constantly as the parts are examined; but, as this is also true of all other MTM motions, the real problem in inspection standards is only when eye and mental elements must be completed during a cessation of other necessary motions or when they limit out other motions in respect to the elapsed time for the work cycle. The eye time can be handled with MTM; the mental time—if not covered—can only be adequately evaluated by stop watch study or dependence on previously accumulated time formulas. Thus, to write inspection patterns, all of the necessary manual and body motions must be considered as well as eye and mental time. Failure to do this has been the principal reason why some efforts to time inspection with pre-determined standards did not succeed—a major error was committed.

Since Eye Travel time between focuses during visual inspection is relatively easy to measure and account for after the correct number of Eye

Focuses has been determined, the latter becomes the central problem in the use of eye time data for such work. The variation in the types of inspection, kinds of objects to be examined, nature and size of defects, and operator differences obviously creates a wide difference in the total Eye Focus requirement of such operations. No rules or procedures could, therefore, possibly substitute for the skill of a good analyst in arriving at valid times.

A knowledge of the true nature of the inspection process is a great aid in analysis. Basically, inspectors must (1) recognize a defect and (2) dwell on it long enough to "classify the defect." The word "defect" implies that an object is being compared to an established standard or mental concept of another object which possesses no flaws, or at least does not have the flaws which are of concern at the inspection station. It is absolutely necessary to have a standard of comparison that has been defined by instructions to the inspector and that he in turn has translated this into a mental image or concept; that many industrial inspection operations fail in this respect has been attested frequently by responsible parties. However, this requirement is necessary for satisfactory and successful inspection and many aids to this communication process exist. These include data tables, photographs of standards of comparison, standard samples, procedures, and oral instructions (least reliable) by the persons setting the original quality requirements. No system of timing could possibly be valid unless the inspector's concept of the acceptable part was correct and only the more simple decisions are required. A system like MTM requires that such conditions exist. The use of such inspection instruments as gages, magnifying lenses, profilometers, etc., are of additional help in setting up an inspection station amenable to successful establishment of time standards.

The inspector must exercise sufficient "vision" to allow sighting of the defect and then apply further EF as required to classify, if necessary, what variation from the norm exists. Each of these looks requires at least one Eye Focus.

The practical significance of the foregoing is as follows. Inspectors do not normally search out every possible defect in each part, but instead they scan the part or inspection instruments by shifting the eyes from point to point. This sequence will occur without additional pauses until a defect by which the part deviates from the mental image of the acceptable part appears or the indicators show the part out of acceptable tolerance. The number of Eye Focuses for the scanning action will depend mainly on the area which can be covered per Eye Focus, as discussed next. The presence of defects which prompt closer scrutiny will then require additional Eye Focuses. The time standards problem can be solved, therefore, by determining the number of Eye Focuses required for both scanning and defect classification and adding to this the Eye Travel time between focuses.

The area covered per Eye Focus apparently is a function of the ease with which the potential defects can be seen. For such flaws as deep, open cracks in a large casting, one EF could easily cover 2 square feet. Conversely, the checking of minute scratches on a dull surface might dictate only 2 or 3 square inches per EF. An MTM investigation reported at the first MTM conference *suggested* that an operator can normally check an area 16 times the size of the expected defect per EF needed. The limits of the area of normal vision provide another means by which to gage the area covered by each EF. The work analyst must determine, with these two guides, how many Eye Focuses are needed to cover the total area of the part and the average distance between the points of focus.

The number of additional EF's required for defect classification can be best judged by the frequency with which the various attributes or characteristics that define the defect appear. The normal frequency of occurrence for a given type of defect must, therefore, be known for proper analysis leading to a time standard. Size, shape, and color might be three inspection criteria, for instance; the MTM engineer must decide or know how often defects in each of these categories will be found in the part being inspected. Inspection and quality control records will greatly aid the analyst in this; but it is more common that he must determine the frequency himself from observation.

Figure 6 provides a hypothetical illustration of one manner in which an inspection operation can be analyzed by MTM for the EF and ET involved. In this case, specific points are checked for specific kinds of defects that may be expected to occur with frequencies as discussed in the

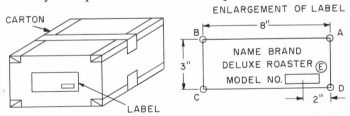

Fig. 6. Example of inspection allowance for eye motions *(see also page 302).*

example. For many other practical situations, the allowable EF and ET may be found to depend more directly on area, with the type and frequency of defect unknown. Such inspection proceeds on the basis that any defect whatever is caught and classified by the inspector as it arises from full coverage of the concerned area. While analysis of the latter situation is more involved, the same principles involved in the example and the rules given earlier will apply.

Inspection Requirements for Fig. 6.

Cartons pass the inspector seated at a roller conveyor so that his eyes are about 20 inches from the side bearing the label. He must check adhesion to the carton at all four corners of the label. He must also examine a model number stamp for inclusion and legibility. Rejects are defined as the amount of error allowed. All cartons with rejects are shunted to a side branch conveyor.

MTM Analysis for Fig. 6.

	EF Req'd.
Eye Focus:	
Scanning—Allow one EF for each pattern point as shown by the letters on the sketch above	5.000
Defects—One extra EF for each loose corner found to see if it is a reject. Maximum 7% per carton from inspection records	.070
One EF for absence of model stamp. Average missing has been 1 for each 200 cartons sealed since revision of the packing method	.005
One EF for poor legibility of stamp. Occurs on 10% of packs at the most	.100
Total EF allowed per carton	5.175 = 37.8 TMU

Eye Travel:

Eyes to Carton, ET $\frac{30}{20}$		20.0 TMU (Max.)
Label Corners, 2 ET $\frac{8}{20}$ + ET $\frac{3}{20}$		
= 2 (6.4) + 2.4	=	15.2 TMU
Model Stamp, ET $\frac{2}{20}$	=	1.6 TMU
Total ET allowed per carton	=	36.8 TMU

Total TMU inspection time allowed per carton   74.6 TMU

This amounts to 0.04476 minutes average per carton.

READING TIME

Another specialized use of the eyes during work sequences sometimes occurs with sufficient frequency to justify specific MTM information on the matter. This is the nature of eye usage in reading and the time required for reading. Operators must read instructions, check material tickets, read labels on the product and on packages containing materials or the product. Inspectors must check quality specifications, read information from blueprints, and examine data written by operators or test personnel. Clerks and timekeepers obviously spend much time reading various forms and other printed matter. Other examples where a work analyst might wish to include reading time in a pattern containing other manual, body, and eye motions could be cited abundantly.

The second research report issued after formation of the MTM Association was an analysis of *Reading Operations.*[5] While the results there reported are especially applicable to the reading of printed non-technical prose at normal speeds, the data is a guide to what the expected reading

[5] R.R. 102 (See Ch. 5).

time for other types of writing and printing (including handwriting and hand printing) and at other speeds might be. More important, the research did accumulate in a single source a number of interesting facts and isolated the more vital variables concerning reading and its nature. It consisted essentially of employing the extant data on reading by a number of psychologists together with a motion-conscious effort to relate known facts to physiological eye action.

The time for reading varies greatly in actuality, due principally to the fact that the methods employed, in terms of eye motion, can be greatly divergent. Three main variables affect the process of reading. They are:

(1) Complexity of the material read. Reading speed commonly ranges from 500 words per minute for easy prose to 150 words per minute or less for highly technical or scientific expositions. For the general run of reading, however, 330 words per minute is the accepted norm by many authorities.

(2) Length of line printed. There exists an optimum line length which facilitates the eye motions to minimize the reading time; longer and shorter lines require more reading time. The accepted optimum line length seems to be 3.2 inches, or slightly less than the width of two standard newsprint columns.

(3) The style and size of type in the printing. Examination of a printer's font will reveal the large range of styles available in any given size of type; and the combinations are further magnified when the range of sizes is also included. As to size, 10 to 12 point type is apparently easiest to read, but no agreement exists on the easiest style. Style seems to be a matter of taste and habit, suggesting that the reader will read easiest the style of type he is accustomed to seeing most.

How does the eye behave during reading? Basically, of course, it can only focus on a word or section while not moving, and then perform travel to the new focus point. For inspection operations, the eyes were said to "shift" and "pause" in a series of jumps that cover the area being scrutinized. The MTM system has adopted special terms used by psychologists for the Eye Travel and Eye Focus; they are *saccades* for the "shifts" and *fixations* for the "pauses." The reason is that a number of special eye motion variables are found in reading that differ somewhat from normal eye usage, as discussed below. The problem in establishing reading time is to determine the number of saccades and fixations required to read a given number of words. With this known, the number of words can be counted or estimated and the corresponding time computed.

Very simply, the number of words per fixation averages 1.56 over a wide range of researches and types of reading. This means that division of the number of words by 1.56 will yield the number of Eye Focuses required for the passage by an average operator reading with average speed under normal conditions. The more complicated analysis of saccades is next discussed.

The purpose of all saccades (or saccadic movements) is the same as for Eye Travel—to permit the next focus. Three varieties have been isolated that describe the task performed by the travel in relation to the total task of reading the material at hand. The three types of saccades are:

(1) Interfixation. This kind of saccade includes the Eye Travel between fixations in the same line. Since it is possible to have one or more fixations per word, for example three in a long three-syllable word, the saccadic distance can vary greatly. It is always very short, however, in relation to the distances associated with other usages of Eye Travel; which is one reason the term saccade is used for reading rather than simply Eye Travel. A further interesting fact is that any given individual cannot consciously vary his saccadic speed, although normal Eye Travel is subject to a good degree of conscious control; variation of saccadic speed between people is very noticeable, however. Only by remedial reading exercises and practice at increasing reading speed can a person significantly change his normal rate of saccadic movement.

(2) Return sweep. As the eye finishes reading the end of one line, it must rapidly sweep back to the beginning of the next line to continue the reading pattern—this is the performance of return sweep saccades. The length of these travels will approximate the length of line being read. The distance also includes the line spacing of the printing.

(3) Regressive. Oftentimes, due to lack of concentration or unfamiliarity with the material, a reader wishes to reread some portion of the material he has already covered. As his eyes travel back, they perform a regression or regressive saccade. Some regression is necessary in reading highly technical or complex matter. Also, for instance, when a word is hyphenated to carry another syllable to the next line, the meaning might be obscured without a regression. The distance chargeable to this saccade would be highly unpredictable in advance, except for the more patently necessary regressions.

Another variable which affects all saccades is the distance from the eye to the printed material. For persons with normal 20/20 vision, most doctors and oculists recommend that the reading be held from 12 to 16 inches from the eyes, with the proviso that the amount of lighting might affect this distance. If industrial operators must read as a normal part of their cycle, it is thus important that illumination be adequate.

MTM Research Report 102 showed one way to find the total time for the saccades required in reading a certain passage. It involves laborious computation to account exactly for the degrees of Eye Travel for the saccades and then applies the Eye Travel time of 0.285 TMU per degree. A less cumbersome method was evolved based on the fact that, for a wide range of reading material, the saccade time will average about 8 per cent of the fixation time. Since the fixation time depends directly on the number of words read, a practical formula for average reading time would be:

$$\text{TMU reading time} = \text{Fixation time} + \text{Saccade time}$$

$$= 1.08 \times \text{Fixation time}$$

The fixation time, being the time for an EF multiplied by the number of fixations per word, can be expressed as follows:

$$\text{TMU Fixation time} = \frac{7.3(N)}{1.56}$$

where N = the number of words read.

The MTM formula for reading average material results from substitution of the latter expression into the earlier one:

$$\text{TMU reading time} = \frac{1.08\,(7.3)\,(N)}{1.56}$$

$$= 5.05\,N$$

Other ways of stating the same result are: 5.05 TMU per word, 0.003 minutes per word, or 0.182 seconds per word. A check of these constants will show that the formula corresponds to the accepted average reading rate of 330 words per minute. The reading time data can be applied in several ways. Figure 7 shows the method of determining the time required, with the regressive saccades being obvious from the numbers that appear out of normal forward reading order above the words. In actual normal usage, however, the analyst merely counts the total *words* in the passage, with allowances for more than one "fix" for extremely long words, and then applies the simplified reading formula given above. Alternately, he may only estimate the total words instead of counting them. The most widely used method, however, unless the passage is short enough to count the words easily, is to count the words in several lines, count the number of lines in several pages, and then multiply to obtain the approximate total number of words. This figure is then used in the simplified reading formula to compute the allowed time.

In every line of the passage below, each word is given a sequential number to identify a suggested order in which the eyes might see the material—some regressive saccades are thereby illustrated. It is suggested that the reader first check himself against the average time of 17.8 seconds to see that the TMU rate computed will be close for most readers.

Reading Passage	Regressive Fixations	No. of Words
2 1 3 4 5 6 7 8 9 10 11 "While it is true that a good work analyst must be	1	11
2 1 3 4 5 6 7 8 9 10 a good observer, keen to note and succinctly clas-	1	10
2 1 3 4 5 6 7 8 9 sify minute motion details, it does not follow that	1	9
1 2 3 4 5 6 7 8 all work analysts possess this necessary trait. By	0	8
1 2 3 4 5 6 7 8 9 the same token, some work analysts fail to qualify	0	9
1 2 3 4 5 6 7 8 9 for commendation of their work purely because they	0	9
1 2 3 4 5 6 7 employ slipshod analysis, circumventing good prac-	0	7
2 1 3 4 5 6 7 8 9 10 tices of work study, in the mistaken belief that a	1	10
1 2 3 4 5 6 7 8 rapid and "practical" answer will endear them in	0	8
1 2 3 4 5 6 7 8 9 10 11 the eyes of those who depend on their work for data	0	11
1 2 3 4 5 6 permitting management decisions which prove correct."	0	6
Totals	4	98

TMU reading time = 5.05 × 98 = 494.9 TMU

Fig. 7. Example of exact reading analysis.

WRITING AND PRINTING

Because the eyes are in constant use during printing and writing, even though the motions controlling the time for the operation are all hand and finger motions, this subject has been included in this chapter. Another reason is that the mental activity connected with such operations is not too dissimilar to the type of "yes" and "no" decision noted for Eye Focus. Usually, a person setting down his thoughts or data is well aware of what he wishes to do; the control required is therefore principally limited by muscular, rather than mental requirements.

Examples in which a worker might need to write or print are not difficult to list. Typical are noting production data on time tickets, signing for tools, requisitioning items needed for his work, noting facts about his job as required by process instructions, recording data and informative details on paper work accompanying the task, initialing production tags, and making minor arithmetical computations for his own needs. Only when such activity is essential and necessary to the task at hand should the work analyst allow time for it in the motion pattern. Oftentimes, companies prefer to cover such activity with a miscellaneous allowance against a base standard from which writing operations are omitted; this data would not then be needed.

Consider printing and writing as a total operation. The writing implement—pen, pencil, electric etch-writer, chalk, or crayon—is a tool adequately held and controlled by the worker, and is subjected to a series of motions by the hand which can be described and timed by MTM elemental motions. The time required for obtaining the implement prior to use and laying it aside when finished can be determined by the usual Reach, Grasp, Move, etc. data as found in ordinary MTM analysis. It is only the act of writing or printing itself that is described in this section. Several factors concerning the use of writing implements should be clarified before considering the MTM method of handling these topics. Of prime importance is the fact that methods deviations between operators can be extreme. Few people write or print exactly like anyone else. It is, therefore, impossible to pre-determine accurately for all persons exactly what time they will use to write certain words or the precise motions they will employ. While this is true mainly in regard to frequency with which they apply the two basic motions of which printing and writing are composed—moves and positions—it is still true that the motions themselves have been isolated and can be accounted for timewise where they occur in the analysis.

Skill and effort, especially as they affect legibility of the script, are important variables in writing and printing. A person's writing skill cannot be consciously varied in a short span of time, but he can vary his effort at will. Poor writing methods that usually accompany poor skill result in waste of time and lack of legibility; the reverse is also true. Because of these factors, any MTM standard on writing and printing must be properly understood as being strictly an average estimate for the situation, not a precise determination for any given individual who may write.

The MTM motions presently assigned (this is application practice, not research data) for the use of writing implements to produce either letters or numerals (specific examples of which will be given later) are as follows:

(1) POSITION. An easy-to-handle, symmetrical Position with the class of fit appropriate to the type of script produced (P–SE) is allowed:

(a) Each time the implement touches the paper or makes a dot, as when a period is placed at the end of a sentence, the writer dots an "i", or a "t" is crossed. For touching the paper, the implement must first be given a short M–C in accord with the regular MTM rule for Moves preceding Positions; this Move will be allowed, for example, each time the implement begins a new word after having been lifted from the paper at the completion of the preceding word.

(b) Each time an *abrupt* change in the direction of writing or printing occurs. By abrupt, the analysis implies that a change of direction appreciable enough to cause a cessation and resumption of motion has occurred. It reflects the presence of deceleration and acceleration in the writing motion. In general, the direction change must exceed 90 degrees for a Position to be valid, unless a sharp corner can be clearly seen in the writing.

(c) Each time the ending must be clearly defined or limited. This accounts for the action in accurate lettering where the implement is brought to a definite stopping point before lifting from the paper. Blueprint drafting, for example, requires sharp lettering. Ordinary writing and printing do not require this kind of Position, since the implement is merely lifted from the surface in motion at an approximate location, without a definite deceleration.

(2) Move. All connecting Moves in writing will logically be M–C because basically the implement progresses from Position to Position on the surface. The distance will be the average of many lengths of motion that appear in a given size and style of writing. It is from fractional—symbolized MfC—to no more than 1-inch long for ordinary-sized writing and printing. Writing large words, as for example with chalk on a blackboard, might indicate an average Move length of 2 inches or more. The time standard will be incorrect if the shorter distances are used. Moves are allowed for:

(a) Each time the implement approaches the surface. Beginning to write (after the initial M–B to bring the implement to the general area on the paper), starting of the next word, and just prior to Positions as in (1) (a) all justify counting a new Move.

(b) Each time the direction of motion changes enough to require control exceeding that for which no velocity change occurs. This will, in general, be true when the path departs more than

45 to 90 degrees from its original course. Whether the direction change is sharp or blended does not alter the need for control; this merely affects the finished appearance of the penmanship.

(c) EXCEPTION. No Move is allowed for the lifting of the implement away from the end of a writing action. This is due to the fact that the Move always allowed for starting to write as in (2) (a) above will tend to average out as the implement is brought to the next word or letter. If the Move in question is the one after the writing is finished, it will actually become a part of the Move normally used (much longer) to lay aside the writing implement, and no additional time is needed.

In terms of application, this data will be described in relation to four usual kinds of writing. Examples of each can be seen in Fig. 8A and 8B. Each example is displayed in normal size and the larger specimen shows the MTM method of analyzing the Moves and Positions involved. Solid arrows show the Moves on the paper and dotted arrows show the Moves off the paper. Small circles show the positions, plain for P1SE and blackened

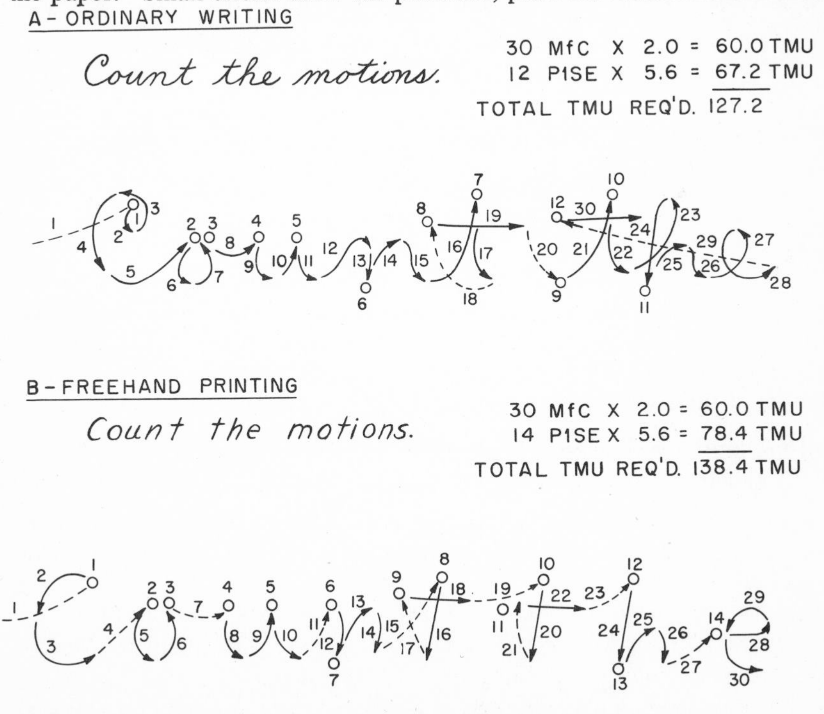

A - ORDINARY WRITING

Count the motions.

30 MfC X 2.0 = 60.0 TMU
12 P1SE X 5.6 = 67.2 TMU
TOTAL TMU REQ'D. 127.2

B - FREEHAND PRINTING

Count the motions.

30 MfC X 2.0 = 60.0 TMU
14 P1SE X 5.6 = 78.4 TMU
TOTAL TMU REQ'D. 138.4 TMU

Fig. 8A. Examples of writing and printing.

C-CAREFUL LETTERING

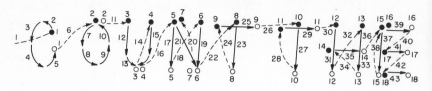

43 MfC X 2.0 = 86.0 TMU
18 P1SE X 5.6 = 100.8 TMU
18 P2SE X 16.2 = 291.6
TOTAL TMU REQ'D. 478.4

D-TYPICAL SPECIAL MARKS AND SYMBOLS

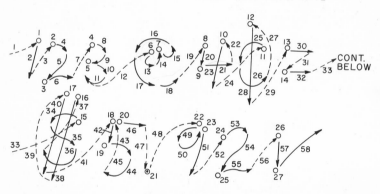

58 MfC X 2.0 = 116.0 TMU
27 P1SE X 5.6 = 151.2 TMU
TOTAL TMU REQ'D. 267.2

CONT.
BELOW

Fig. 8B.   Examples of writing and printing (*cont.*)

for P2SE.   The Moves and Positions are numbered to show the sequence of motion and also the motion frequency needed to compute the MTM time value as at the right.

(1) ORDINARY WRITING. Use MfC = 2.0 TMU and P1SE = 5.6 TMU. Count the actually observed or apparent Moves and Positions in accord with the rules given above. It will be found that this kind of writing consists of relatively few Positions and a large number of Moves.

(2) FREEHAND PRINTING. Use MfC = 2.0 TMU and P1SE = 5.6 TMU. This kind of lettering is not precise. It differs from ordinary writing only because each letter is separated from all others, which increases the number of positions necessary and takes longer. Words are not continuous pencil lines as found in writing.

(3) CAREFUL (DRAFTING) LETTERING. Use MfC = 2.0 TMU unless the letters are large enough to justify longer moves, such as found in most poster size printing. In many cases, the Position time can be covered by assigning a P2SE = 16.2 TMU at the start of each letter or separate pencil line and a P1SE = 5.6 TMU at the end of each letter or pencil line. These are "rules of thumb" sometimes used. It is obvious that positions will normally equal or exceed the moves for this kind of printing, with the attendant time allowance matching the greater time requirement. It is obvious that the use of lettering guides or devices will require other MTM analysis than that given here.

(4) SPECIAL MARKS AND SYMBOLS.. When check marks, division signs, and other special marks and symbols appear in the script, the analyst must decide which kind of Positions and what length of moves are appropriate. No special rule can be given, except that the Moves and Positions tend to match those found in the context where the symbols and marks occur.

In MTM patterns, the usual way to record data on writing and printing is to show the symbol for Moves and Positions in the left- or right-hand columns and the number counted in the frequency column of the analysis form. Sometimes, an analyst may wish to sequentially list each motion separately for certain reasons, but this is wasteful of analysis forms and requires more analysis time.

A little practical judgment is also required. For example, the average name on a timecard might be written, say, with twenty moves and eight positions. Some names could be much less and others vastly more. With judgment, the analyst might decide to write the frequency for the longest name of the persons who will usually perform that operation, since all other people obviously will have enough time permitted for their signatures. The same would be true with regard to the number of words normally needed to perform such operations as manually marking a shipping carton with a destination. An MTM analyst who must record writing analyses will thus find frequency of occurrence, both of the content and of the individual Moves and Positions, the major problem in his efforts.

QUESTIONS

1. Industrial Engineering has been asked by the Personnel Department to study the security recognition problem at the guard house during the start of the day shift. They wish, if possible, to restation one or two guards in the limited parking lot to handle parking problems, and must know how many of the four guards (one in each lane) are actually needed to man the security check. Although he initially feels this to be a time study situation,

the analyst assigned decides to see whether MTM can give the answer. On the average, the recognition check proceeds as follows: the guard waits as the entering employee approaches two paces (30.0 TMU—see next chapter), looks from about 24 inches away at the worker's face, shifts his eyes (usually about 16 inches) to where the badge is held or worn, checks both whether the badge is present and also for the security color code, nods his head while the worker advances one step, and readies for the next person while the one just checked walks another step.

a. Including and identifying the process time covered by the worker's paces, write a pattern of the guard's motions and convert the time total to minutes per check.

The analyst next notes that about one minute is lost each time an employee must be handled for missing or wrong badges, and that the guard's records indicate about 2 per cent frequency for this loss. He also counts 800 employees arriving during each 30-minute period, essentially continuously.

b. How many of the guards can be restationed to the parking lot and still permit adequate security checks to be maintained? The unused lanes would be closed and the remaining guards would make all security checks.

2. To check the performance of a typewriter, the repairman sits in normal position and types the following copy (exactly as shown here):

abcde	fghij	klmno	pqrst	uvwxyz
ABCDE	FGHIJ	KLMNO	PQRST	UVWXYZ
12345	67890	L"#$%	_&'( )	

He then scans the copy to check it, using one EF per group. If the copy appears normal, he merely cleans the machine. If he finds imperfections, he looks again to see exactly what is wrong; after completing the check, he proceeds to make necessary repairs prior to cleaning. He estimates from experience that imperfections appear 5 per cent of the time. Based on this data, compute the average time he needs to check the copy typed in select TMU. Don't forget the ET needed to scan the copy!

3. Seat yourself in front of a standard office desk (30" × 60") in a position that you would normally assume when writing on a pad of paper placed in front of you. Assume an artificial inspection task of looking at the four corners of your desk from the seated position to determine whether any imperfections are present in those locations. Assume one defect out of each one hundred desk corners is possible. Establish the inspection time for this task and write the eye motion pattern required.

4. Using all available MTM methods, establish the time required to read the second paragraph in this chapter. Compare the answers you get by the various methods of checking the reading time. Taking precautions not to unfairly affect the time by extraneous factors, check your actual reading time with any timing device handy. Compare this time to the MTM times.

5. On a sheet of ruled paper, sign your name in the usual way. Then print your name freehand on the next line as you would on a report to be typed. Apply the MTM data on printing and writing to determine the time for each task, neglecting the motions to obtain implement, bring to paper, and aside implement. How do the total times to write and print your name compare?

CHAPTER 17

Body, Leg, and Foot Motions

Body, leg, and foot motions are by nature the most noticeable and easily recognized human motions because their relatively high time requirement assures ample opportunity for their recognition. Similarities in these motions, plus the fact that the reader is by now conversant with MTM concepts, permit them to be discussed together in this chapter.

Body, leg, and foot motions may, in general, be defined as all usual motions which the operator might perform that are not included in the definitions for the basic manual (finger, hand, arm) and eye motions in earlier chapters. Since these latter motions have been presented previously in detail, the data in this chapter will complete consideration of the motions of the "human machine."

GENERAL CONCEPTS

Body, leg, and foot motions in work cycles are used to: (1) locate the hands and arms to permit their proper functioning in performing work elements; (2) orient the hands and arms with respect to the materials and/or the workplace layout involved in a work process; and (3) perform directly required elements of the work.

Since body motions ordinarily require a different kind of control and accuracy of movement as compared to manual motions, they are often termed *gross* motions and are, normally, affected by fewer variable factors. For example, most foot and leg motions are made in conjunction with mechanical guides so that any control needed to operate the equipment is small.

Body, leg, and foot motions will usually account for only a small proportion of a time cycle because they are often limited out by other simultaneous motions. Recall again that the time to perform any MTM motion is allowed only when it is a necessary part of the work cycle that controls the performance of the work being accomplished. However, since the times for body, leg, and foot motions tend to be large in magnitude, the observer must not overlook or neglect to properly analyze them in a motion sequence—especially when they are not limited out and/or if the frequency of the body motions is unusually high or if many different types of body motions appear in the same sequence. In other words, errors in time allowance can readily occur if the body, leg, and foot motions have been missed in analysis.

The data card time values for these motions were obtained by a combination of film analysis and conventional timestudy techniques. Although future research and refinements may require a change in values, they have provided satisfactory and reliable results in thousands of applications.

In order to justify classification of human actions by MTM motion designations and, accordingly, to allow assignment of the appropriate time values, it is essential that the actions truly correspond to the defined motion classifications. The MTM engineer must be especially careful not to confuse *body motions* with the many forms of *body assistance* previously discussed. When distinct body motions occur, there are specific MTM rules to aid classification. In the case of body assists to manual motions, the time for the body movement is limited out by the time for the concurrent manual motions; and this is not *of necessity* true for body motions as defined below, although it *might* be true. Also, the principal effect of body assistance on the classification of the accompanying manual motion is to decrease the chargeable path length of the manual motion, while a body motion usually is performed for other reasons than to produce a similar effect on any simultaneous manual motion.

Proper placement of the correct symbols for body, leg, and foot motions on the study form is a distinct aid in helping avoid errors in the calculation of pattern times. Just as left- and right-handed motions are noted in their respective columns when writing symbols for manual actions, the same scheme is used for the lower limbs. Actions with the left leg and/or left foot are noted in the left-symbol column, while the right leg and foot motions are listed in the right column on the form. Because the trunk lacks the attribute of handedness, however, it is the practice (as was true for eye motions) to always *show general body motions in the right-hand column.* With this convention, the analyst will be less likely to make errors in regard to combined and/or simultaneous motions that could result in incorrect times for individual motions.

BODY MOTIONS

The predominant purpose of body motions is to move the trunk or torso in certain ways or to locate it in a specified manner so as to facilitate subsequent action of the limbs; any attendant actions of the limbs are incidental to this predominant purpose. Often body motions are executed to preserve body balance during use of the limbs for other specific purposes.

Because the bulkiest, heaviest parts of the body are involved, these motions take place with less precision, speed, and control than those of the upper limbs. They are gross motions with large time values which are subject to very little variation.

In the discussion which follows, body motions are grouped into categories which depend on the kind of trunk displacement or relocation achieved. This should help clarify the reader's thinking in regard to classification and/or analysis of the body motions as contrasted to situations discussed in earlier chapters where only body assistance was involved. This grouping will further aid an analyst in deciding, during visualization, which body motions will be needed to attain certain desired results in a motion sense, thus avoiding confusion and saving analysis time in assigning the correct body motion to a pattern. The logical possibilities of trunk displacement are as follows:

1. Vertical displacement to and from the sitting position. This body action is described under Sit and Stand.
2. Lateral displacement of the trunk to either side with accompanying leg and foot action. The MTM motion accounting for such body movement is Sidestep.
3. Pivotal or rotational displacement with the aid of the legs and feet. Action of this sort is categorized as Turn Body.
4. Vertical displacement without movement of the feet, but with accompanying forward or backward action. Such motion occurs when Bend, Stoop, Arise from Bend, and Arise from Stoop are performed.
5. Vertical displacement including foot movement and concurrent forward and backward location of the trunk. This is what happens when the kneeling motions are made: Kneel on One Knee, Kneel on Both Knees, Arise from Kneel on One Knee, and Arise from Kneel on Both Knees.
6. Lateral displacement forward and backward with accompanying leg and foot action. The MTM motion accounting for this movement is Walking and is discussed as a sub-topic under leg and foot motions for reasons later described.

The various actions just indicated are discussed below in detail, together with the definitions, isolation, and discussion of the variables, and the delineation of measurements connected with each kind of body motion. They comprise a rather complete coverage of the motions by which the location of the trunk or torso of the operator can be affected.

Sit and Stand

DEFINITION:[1] *SIT is the motion of lowering the body from an erect standing position directly in front of the seat and transferring the weight of the body to the seat.*

1. *At the completion of sit, the weight of the body is supported by the seat.*
2. *Sit does not include such motions as stepping in front of the chair or shifting the position of the chair.*

DEFINITION:[2] *STAND is the motion of transferring the weight of the body from the seat and raising the body to an erect standing position directly in front of the seat.*

1. *Stand does not include such motions as shifting the position of the chair or stepping to the side of the chair.*

MTM Symbols: Sit   SIT   Time Values: 34.7 TMU

                Stand   STD   43.4 TMU

Neither SIT nor STD includes moving or locating the chair or seat; any motions required for this purpose must be analyzed separately. Also, any motions needed for the operator to place himself in front of the seat prior to SIT or remove himself from near the seat after STD must be considered independently of SIT and STD. Note further that during performance of either SIT or STD the feet will remain fixed on the floor. With all these qualifications, it should be obvious that SIT and STD motions include only vertical displacement of the trunk or torso to and from a resting position on the seat.

SIT begins when the body descent starts and ends when the lean back has been completed. While it is difficult to perform any precise motions during the descent time of SIT, it is possible to reach to and grasp large objects such as a chair arm. More precise motions can be performed during the lean back portion of SIT. However, the SIT time will usually limit out the major portion of this latter type of action, so that the analyst needs to allow time for other motions only from the point at which the lean back is completed.

MTM research has resulted in several tentative conclusions regarding the true motion variables in SIT as outlined in an MTM Bulletin dated February, 1953. The Lean Back portion apparently requires 10.3 TMU. The Descend time depends on the arc distance traversed by the hip joint. An arc distance of 15 inches or less consumes the minimum time of 20.2 TMU, while each extra inch of travel will increase the time by 1.5 TMU; the average hip traversal during the study was 18 inches for the complete

---

[1] From "MTM Basic Specifications" (Footnote 1, Chapter 7).
[2] *Ibid.*

Descend action. Using this data, the average time for SIT should include 20.2 + (18–15) (1.5) = 24.7 TMU for Descend, which added to the Lean Back time of 10.3 TMU gives an average time for SIT of 35.0 TMU. This value compares well with the data card time of 34.7 TMU.

STD begins with the start of the lean forward to place the weight on the feet, continues as the weight is shifted from the seat to the feet, and is completed as soon as the rising action has brought the body to an erect stance in front of the seat. As was true for SIT, it seems to be difficult to perform any overlapping manual motions during the portion of STD in which the main relocation of the trunk takes place; this occurs during the arising part of the STD motion. Simultaneous manual motions can be made during the initial stages of STD, however, while the Lean Forward and Shift Weight are proceeding. In other words, overlapping motions can be made during the start of STD or during the finish of SIT motions.

Referring again to the tentative research results, STD variables were evaluated as follows. The Lean Forward time averages 10.3 TMU. Shift Weight, which approximates an AP2 in nature, was found to require about 11.0 TMU. The arc distance of hip joint travel again appears during the Arise portion of STD, with an average of 20 inches being the measuring point for time evaluation. However, the Arise time varies depending on whether the operator completes the STD as a Type I motion or a Type II in-motion-at-the-end. This latter case can occur when walking follows the STD and the worker does not pause before the first step. For the Type I Arise, distances of 15 inches or less take the minimum time of 25.9' TMU, with 1.0 TMU per inch being required for extra distance. For the Type II Arise, the time for 15 inches or less travel is 20.8 TMU; for 20 inches it is 23.1 TMU; and for 25 inches it is 25.6 TMU.

Using the data just given, the data card time for STD can be checked as follows. The average Type I STD requires 10.3 TMU for Lean Forward, 11.0 TMU for Shift Weight, and 25.9 + (20–15)(1.0) = 30.9 TMU for Arise; this gives a total of 52.2 TMU for a Type I STD. The average 20 inch Type II STD takes 10.3 TMU for Lean Forward, 11.0 TMU for Shift Weight, and 23.1 TMU for Arise; the total in this case is 44.4 TMU. Therefore, the data card time of 43.4 TMU that was found to be average in the original MTM research checks out as being closer to the "in motion" time found from the additional research.

In applying the MTM information to analysis of SIT or STD, the engineer can either apply the data card times or make a more detailed analysis based on the times developed in the later research. Which course is justified depends on the relative frequency of these motions in the pattern being developed, and also on the purpose of the time standard resulting. If SIT and STD occur rarely and the job is not too repetitive under daywork conditions, the data card time will suffice. However, if they are very frequent in a highly repetitive condition under incentive payment limitations, it would be wise to make the more detailed analysis. Remember that even the average person is very proficient at either SIT or STD, so overlapping motions should normally be anticipated.

From the methods standpoint, it is desirable to minimize the need for SIT and STD time. This might involve requiring the operator to maintain one or the other condition during his work. Other production factors, such as personnel policies, reduction of boredom and fatigue, and psychological satisfaction of the employee have traditionally dictated that where possible the choice be left to the worker himself—and provision is generally made for him to either SIT or STD at his work and to change as it suits him. Usually a change in position under such circumstances is ignored, however each situation needs to be analyzed before deciding what is proper.

Sidestep

DEFINITION:[3] *SIDESTEP is a lateral motion of the body, without rotation, performed by one or two steps.*

1. The body moves directly to the side without any noticeable raising or lowering or rotation.

While there are two basic kinds of Sidestep, the fact that two directions—right or left from the operator's original body location—are possible makes a total of four combinations of Sidestep possible. The discussion of the variables below will be based on a *right* Sidestep, but it is obvious that changing of certain words would make the analysis cover left Sidesteps; this will shorten the presentation.

Analysis of Sidestep during MTM research has shown that it is seldom limiting unless the trunk has been displaced more than 12 inches to the right or left. Shorter Sidesteps occur rather frequently while the manual members perform Reaches or Moves, in which case the latter motions will *usually* be limiting. Sidesteps under 12 inches thus provide another form of body assistance, in effect, which reduces the allowable Reach or Move distance by the distance of the Sidestep. For example, an R—B to an object 20 inches to the right of the operator which is assisted by a 7-inch Sidestep will be noted as an R13B and allowed 13.7 TMU. However, if a Sidestep of less than 12 inches is necessary for *body displacement,* and no Reach or Move occurs simultaneously, the correct Sidestep distance should be noted; but the assigned time will be that for a 12-inch Sidestep, which is the minimum Sidestep time value for all distances up to and including 12 inches.

Sidestep, Case 1 (to the right) proceeds as follows:

1. The entire body weight is shifted onto the left leg and foot.
2. The right leg and foot are raised from the floor.

---

[3] From "MTM Basic Specifications" (Footnote 1, Chapter 7).

3. The right leg and foot are moved toward the right.
4. The right foot is placed on the floor.
5. About one-half of the body weight is shifted onto the right leg and foot for body balance.

Note that the left foot and leg remain in place, and that they carry all the weight of the body, while a right Case 1 Sidestep occurs. Since the feet after a Case 1 Sidestep will be more than the normal distance apart, the body of the operator may not be in the most comfortable working position. For this reason, Sidestep Case 1 may be considered as a temporary expedient to facilitate the operator's work.

Having completed the right Sidestep, Case 1 (note that the body weight will then be approximately equally distributed between the feet), the operator must use another Case 1 Sidestep to relocate either leg. However, actual operations often involve the performance of a Case 1 Sidestep in which the weight shift is continued to the point where the leading foot essentially assumes all of the weight. For this occurrence it is believed that the time of performance is practically identical, since the readjustment of weight between the feet does not occur. In this situation, it is possible to bring the lagging foot alongside the leading foot at a later time by using another Case 1 sidestep which may or may not be limited out.

Sidestep, Case 2 (to the right) proceeds as follows:

1. The entire body weight is shifted onto the left leg and foot.
2. The right leg and foot are raised from the floor.
3. The right leg and foot are moved toward the right.
4. The right foot is placed on the floor.
5. The entire body weight is shifted onto the right leg and foot.
6. The left leg and foot are raised from the floor.
7. The left leg and foot are moved toward the right leg and foot.
8. The left foot is placed on the floor near the right foot.
9. About one-half of the body weight is shifted onto the left leg and foot for body balance.

During a Sidestep, Case 2 the right and left lower limbs each obviously support the full body weight in turn. Note further that after completion of a Case 2 Sidestep, the final standing position achieved can be maintained for any length of time; return motions need not of necessity appear later in the motion pattern. If and when a return to the original location is needed after a Sidestep, Case 2 was employed, a full Sidestep, Case 2 in the opposite direction can be used. It would also be possible to make a Sidestep, Case 1 in the return direction temporarily and later on use another to return the right leg and foot to the starting point.

From the discussion just presented, it should be obvious that the two cases of Sidestep differ in the body action involved, the time required, and the ways the operator can return to his original starting position. Also note that when complete control of body balance is desirable after a lateral displacement, the analyst should, in fairness to the worker, allow the Case 2 Sidestep in his motion pattern.

One additional relationship between the cases exists: Case 1 Sidestep must be followed by Sidestep, Case 1 before another Sidestep in the same direction can occur. The MTM data card uses the term leading leg for the first leg moved and the term lagging leg for the movement of the other leg. To move in the return direction from a Case 1 Sidestep, the first step can be only another Case 1 Sidestep. After a Case 2 Sidestep is completed, another Sidestep of either case can be made in either direction. Therefore, only one step at a time can be taken with a Case 1 Sidestep, whereas any number of sidewise steps can be made successively as long as only Case 2 Sidestep is employed.

Nothing has been said yet as to how the distance of Sidestep is measured. The method of measuring should, of course, correspond to that used in the MTM research on which the data card times are based if the time allowance is to be valid. The data card times are based on considering the lateral distance moved as the *displacement of the trunk,* not the distance moved by the legs and/or feet. Hence, present MTM application rules state that the sidewise movement should be measured at the centerline of the trunk—the belt buckle or the base of the spine would be convenient measure points, as they correctly reflect centerline displacement. It would also be possible, of course, to measure from any other point on the trunk.

It has been recognized that manual motions can be combined with Sidesteps. Any such concurrent motions will be symbolized, limited out (where proper), and assigned times in the same manner as was discussed for other combined motions in the Turn Chapter. Since the legs and feet are involved in Sidesteps, the symbol should be written in the left- or right-hand column on the study form as appropriate. Sidesteps to the right are shown in the right-hand column, those to the left in the left-hand column. If concurrent manual motions with either of the hands occur, they will likewise be shown in the proper column along with the Sidestep. Therefore, these concurrent motions can be either combined or simultaneous motions as discussed in the Motion Combinations chapter and the conventions on writing of symbols would be followed accordingly.

Sidesteps are symbolized as follows:
    1st —Numeral(s) for the paces taken (if more than one)
    2nd—Capital letters SS for Sidestep
    3rd—Numerals for the inches of travel distance (centerline)
    4th —C1 or C2 to denote the case of Sidestep performed

Examples of the complete symbols are:
SS16C1 which shows a Case 1 Sidestep involving 16 inches trunk travel
SS20C2 illustrating a 20 inch Sidestep, including both legs acting
2SS18C2 symbolizing two Sidesteps, Case 2, each covering 18 inches of sidewise motion

As explained previously, it is seldom necessary to allow time for a Sidestep less than 12 inches long, but assign the 12-inch time when shorter Sidesteps must be allowed. At 12 inches the performance times for the two cases are:

SS12C1 — 17.0 TMU   and   SS12C2 — 34.1 TMU

For each extra inch of travel over 12 inches, the additional time allowance will be:

SS–C1 — 0.6 TMU per inch   and   SS–C2 — 1.1 TMU per inch

Computation of the times for the three illustrative examples given will demonstrate the use of this data:

$$SS16C1 = 17.0 + (16 - 12)\ (.6) = 17.0 + 4\ (.6)$$
$$= 17.0 + 2.4 = 19.4\ \text{TMU}$$

$$SS20C2 = 34.1 + (20 - 12)\ (1.1) = 34.1 + 8\ (1.1)$$
$$= 34.1 + 8.8 = 42.9\ \text{TMU}$$

$$2SS18C2 = (2)\ (34.1) + (2)\ (6)\ (1.1) = 68.2 + 13.2$$
$$= 81.4\ \text{TMU}$$

Turn Body

DEFINITION:[4] *TURN BODY is a rotational movement of the body performed by one or two steps.*
1. In performing the turn body, the steps are made with the feet turning in the same direction as the body.

There are two basic cases of Turn Body, as was true for Sidestep, with the additional possibility of either clockwise or counter-clockwise rotation. Only *clockwise* Turn Body need be used in this discussion and only a change in directional wording is necessary for describing counter-clockwise Turn Body.

Simplification of the Turn Body discussion results from knowing at the start that MTM research showed it to be seldom limiting when the body was turned less than 45 degrees. Lower degree Turn Body action often seen during concurrent limiting manual action can also be regarded as equivalent in effect to the type of body assistance earlier detailed as radial

4 From "MTM Basic Specifications" (Footnote 1, Chapter 7).

assistance; the rules for that kind of assistance should suffice to enable the MTM analyst to assign the correct net distance for Reach or Move aided by any Turn Body less than 45 degrees.

The reader should not confuse Turn Body, however, with rotation of the shoulders to provide radial assistance, since the latter action occurs with the feet kept stationary To say that Turn Body under 45 degrees often has the net effect of radial assistance does not imply that the body actions are identical.

The true variables in Turn Body are the degree of rotation and the state of body balance resulting. The balance will depend on whether one or both feet are moved as the Turn Body is performed, which is accounted for by the Case of the motion.

Turn Body, Case 1 (clockwise in direction) proceeds as follows:

1. The entire body weight is shifted onto the left leg and foot.
2. The right leg and foot are raised from the floor.
3. The right leg and foot are moved angularly clockwise.
4. The right foot is placed on the floor.
5. About one-half of the body weight is shifted onto the right leg and foot for body balance.

The left leg and foot remain in place at all times during a clockwise Case 1 Turn Body. Since after completion of Turn Body, Case 1 the working position will not be comfortable for long periods of time, the motion tends to be a temporary means of facilitating the worker's task. To bring the feet together again will normally require another Case 1 Turn Body; the rules will determine whether it is limited or limiting. Another possibility following Case 1 Turn Body is to start walking with the lagging foot taking the first pace.

Turn Body, Case 2 (clockwise in direction) proceeds as follows:

1. The entire body weight is shifted onto the left leg and foot.
2. The right leg and foot are raised from the floor.
3. The right leg and foot are moved angularly clockwise.
4. The right foot is placed on the floor.
5. The entire body weight is shifted onto the right leg and foot.
6. The left leg and foot are raised from the floor.
7. The left leg and foot are moved angularly clockwise toward the right leg and foot.
8. The left foot is placed on the floor near the right foot.
9. About one-half of the body weight is shifted onto the left leg and foot for body balance.

The right and left lower limbs thus alternately fully support the body weight, and the degree of body balance at completion of the Case 2 Turn

Body is normal—permitting even the most difficult manual motions. A full Case 2 Turn Body in the opposite direction will restore the original location of the worker. Likewise, either two Turn Body, Case 1 in the return direction, or only one followed by a subsequent motion in the same direction, will achieve the original body position. The differences in Case 1 and 2 should now be apparent. Fairness to the operator will also dictate assignment of a Case 2 Turn Body when complete control of body balance must exist after the rotation is finished.

The performance of either case of body turn implies that the degree of rotation will be between 45 and 90 degrees. There will be few occasions for a worker to Turn Body more than 180 degrees, since this amount of rotation could be achieved by a Turn Body of smaller angle in the opposite direction. To cover the range from 90 degrees to 180 degrees, several MTM rules—which are merely logical extensions of the actions for the two cases above—delineate how to assign the motions and decide limiting action. When the turn is over 90 degrees, the first Turn Body will be a complete Case 2. If the remaining rotation desired does not exceed 45 degrees, the idea earlier discussed of manual motions limiting further action will hold. When the remaining angle exceeds 45 degrees, however, an additional Turn Body of either case will be performed; the case will depend on the desired state of body balance. This covers the range of motion possibility for Turn Body.

Distance has no bearing on the measurement—the body pivots about the spine and is not essentially displaced by the rotation. By reference to this point it is relatively easy to analyze whether a Turn Body or some other motion occurred. The analyst needs merely to estimate whether the 45 degree breakpoints discussed have been swept and for case determination to observe whether one foot or both feet were used. The spine is the correct pivot point about which to gage the number of degrees, although the difference between the initial and final locations of the leading foot also provides an indication.

The comments on concurrent manual motions—either combined or simultaneous—made under Sidestep apply equally well to Turn Body. This is also true for the conventions regarding the columns in which the symbols belong and whether the manual action can be considered as combined or simultaneous.

Turn Body symbols consist simply of:

    1st—TB in capital for Turn Body
    2nd—C1 or C2 for the case, depending on the rotation and leg action.

The only possible examples, with their time constants are:

    TBC1   18.6 TMU   *and*   TBC2   37.2 TMU

Bend, Stoop, and Arise

DEFINITION:[5] *BEND is the motion of lowering the body in a forward arc, from a standing position, so that the hands can reach to or below the level of the knees.*

1. *Bend is performed with little or no rotation of the body or flexing of the knees.*
2. *Bend is controlled by the back muscles and leg muscles.*

DEFINITION:[6] *STOOP is the motion of lowering the body in a forward arc, from a standing position, so that the hands can reach to the floor.*

1. *Stoop is performed by bowing forward at the hips and at the same time lowering the entire body by bending at the knees.*
2. *Stoop lowers the hands further than bend through a simultaneous "bend" and knee bend.*

DEFINITION:[7] *ARISE FROM BEND is the motion of returning the body from a bend to an erect standing position.*

DEFINITION:[8] *ARISE FROM STOOP is the motion of returning the body from stoop to an erect standing position.*

MTM Symbols:	Bend	B	Time Values:	29.0 TMU
	Stoop	S		29.0 TMU
	Arise from Bend	AB		31.9 TMU
	Arise from Stoop	AS		31.9 TMU

These four motions are characterized by vertical displacement of the trunk with the feet remaining fixed on the floor at all times during the motions. The usual purpose of these body motions is to locate the manual members or the head in a more useful position, using conscious control of the back and leg muscles for balance of the body during and after lowering or before and during rising.

The principal difference between these motions and body assistance to Reach or Move is that, for the assistance referred to, only the upper trunk to about the waist level is involved. Assistance motion is not consciously done, although the performer can notice it if he is paying particular attention. The body motions discussed in this section must, however, be consciously controlled because some of the larger body muscles are used and just maintaining balance is enough to require attention.

Bend begins as the shoulders start their descent forward, normally proceeds while the arms swing naturally forward and down, and is technically completed as soon as the hands could or do pass the knee level. While it is difficult for preceding motions to blend into a Bend, the hands can

[5] From "MTM Basic Specifications" (Footnote 1, Chapter 7).
[6] *Ibid.*
[7] *Ibid.*
[8] *Ibid.*

smoothly continue a Reach or Move at the end of Bend—in fact, they can be considered as reaching or moving all during the Bend. All the hand motion prior to the time the trunk stops moving, however, would be limited out by the bending action which controls the time. For these reasons, it is common to see Type II Reaches and Moves follow Bend, with the hands being in motion at the beginning of the separately shown Reach or Move. Note that the slight amount of bending action present during body assist to Reach or Move differs mainly in the amount of trunk displacement and the degree of conscious control as compared to Bend.

Stoop can be conceived as a Bend with a simultaneous leg action that brings the trunk and hands lower. The leg action is completely limited out, which explains why the time values are equal for both motions. During Stoop, the thigh muscles share the work load with the back muscles to a greater degree than is true for Bend. The worker would naturally, therefore, find Stoop more fatiguing even though it would require no greater time. This is a good example of why fatigue allowances are used.

Arise from Bend or Stoop starts as soon as the ascent is initiated and is finished as soon as the body has been brought to a fully erect standing position. In opposition to what was true for the downward motion, preceding motions can blend into Arise; while following motions tend to begin only after the Arise is completed. The time to Arise is about 10 per cent greater than descent because the body balance is achieved in a different manner and the pull of gravity must be overcome. Since the straightening of the legs required by Arise from Stoop is concurrent with the body action, the time is equal to that for Arise from Bend.

Handedness has no connection to these body motions, so the MTM symbols are always indicated in the right-hand column of the study form. Consistency in this convention will help avoid analysis errors and the assigning of incorrect times.

Kneel and Arise

DEFINITION:[9] *KNEEL ON ONE KNEE is the motion of lowering the body from erect standing position by shifting one foot forward or backward and lowering one knee to the floor.*

1. *At the completion of kneel on one knee, the weight of the body is supported on one knee and one foot with the other foot helping to maintain balance.*

DEFINITION:[10] *KNEEL ON BOTH KNEES is the motion of lowering the body from erect standing position by shifting one foot forward or backward, lowering one knee to the floor, and placing the other knee adjacent to it.*

[9] From "MTM Basic Specifications" (Footnote 1, Chapter 7).
[10] *Ibid.*

1. At the completion of kneel on both knees, the body is supported by both knees with the feet helping to maintain balance.

DEFINITION:[11] *ARISE FROM KNEEL ON ONE KNEE is the motion of returning the body from kneel on one knee to an erect standing position.*

DEFINITION:[12] *ARISE FROM KNEEL ON BOTH KNEES is the motion of returning the body from kneel on both knees to an erect standing position.*

MTM Symbols:

Kneel on One Knee	KOK	Time Values:	29.0 TMU
Kneel on Both Knees	KBK		69.4 TMU
Arise from Kneel on One Knee	AKOK		31.9 TMU
Arise from Kneel on Both Knees	AKBK		76.7 TMU

The general purpose of these motions is the same as that stated for Bend and Stoop. The principal difference, motionwise, is the concurrent leg and foot action which provides a final body position that is firmly balanced and may be maintained for a greater length of time. Note that the final body position for Bend or Stoop, while balanced, is much less steady and cannot be held for long periods. Maintaining Bend and Stoop is also more fatiguing than is true for kneeling. On the other hand, no reason would exist for kneeling motions unless the work requirements justified allowing the operator to expend more time than he would for Bend or Stoop. As for all other MTM motions, intelligence, judgment, and understanding by the analyst will be needed; it would be prohibitive of clarity and practicality for any pre-determined time system if every minute choice were rigidly bound into a plethora of rules and exceptions.

KOK is performed with the following progression: the weight is shifted off the leg and foot to be lowered; the trunk and knee descend simultaneously while the supporting leg bends at the knee and its calf and thigh muscles carry the load; the lowered knee is placed near the stationary foot on the floor; most of the weight is shifted to the knee; and body balance is regained with the other leg and foot exerting a stabilizing force on the body through a horizontal thigh. Most people also tend to rest their elbow near the knee on the level thigh as a further assurance of adequate balance. All of this muscular action is obviously not simple, as most body members are involved in some manner; this makes difficult the performance of other purposeful motions during KOK without great skill or much practice. The KOK, when achieved, is almost always the limiting motion.

KBK may actually be performed with two distinct sequences. Completion of a KOK followed by a separate leg action to place the other knee on the floor; shifting of an equal load to this knee; and regaining of body

---

[11] From "MTM Basic Specifications" (Footnote 1, Chapter 7).
[12] *Ibid.*

balance comprises one method. The alternate method includes a downward trunk movement without shifting the position of the feet; lowering the trunk until almost sitting on the heels of both feet; swinging the trunk forward to bring both knees to the floor; and regaining of body balance. Because the motions are less blended and balance must be shifted and reassumed an additional time, it is evident why KBK requires more time than KOK. The muscular control requirements are also greater.

With an understanding of the KOK and KBK motions just outlined, the reader can readily extend the remarks concerning Arise under Bend and Stoop to cover the motions known as AKOK and AKBK. The body motion which consumes the greatest single motion time is AKBK.

To record the MTM symbols and other motion conventions, the appropriate right- or left-hand column (based on the knee lowered) should be used for KOK and AKOK; to show KBK and AKBK, however, only the right-hand column can properly be used.

LEG AND FOOT MOTIONS

In the performance of various body motions previously discussed, actions of the legs and feet were included with the total motion. Such usage of the lower limbs as was cited in those cases was incidental to the predominant purpose of effecting displacement of the trunk in a given manner. The legs and feet are, however, often used in an independent manner that does not essentially involve the body trunk; the predominant purpose of employing the lower limbs in this manner is to perform effective labor or to locate the legs or feet as an essential part of the work cycle. Such separate action of the lower limbs is analyzed as leg and foot motion, with attendant motion analysis and time values as discussed in this section.

As a matter of convenience, walking is also discussed in this section. It is the remaining type of major body displacement—forward and backward—not discussed under body motions earlier. The walking data fills in this gap concerning actions directly involving the trunk or torso of a worker during productive labor. The basic reason for deferring it until now is the nature of the motions by which walking is accomplished. The *purpose* of walking is trunk displacement; but the *mechanics* by which it is accomplished depend almost entirely on the action of the lower limbs.

Remember that Leg and Foot Motions, as defined here, do not include any purposeful motion of the trunk in any direction—the lower limbs are used for other purposes under this motion category. Walking, however, includes displacement of the body forward and backward as an accompanying effect to displacement of the lower limbs in those directions. In other words, when the legs and feet displace the body in other than the forward and backward directions, some other category of body motion rather than walking is being performed.

Leg Motion

DEFINITION:[13] *LEG MOTION is the movement of the leg in any direction with the knee or the hip as the pivot, where the predominant purpose is to move the foot rather than the body.*

1. *Leg motion may be made while either sitting or standing.*
2. *Leg motion made while standing usually has the hip as the major pivoting point.*
3. *Leg motion made while sitting usually has the knee as the major pivoting point.*

Leg Motion as defined above—to locate the leg and/or foot rather than facilitate body action—is frequently performed in order to allow the leg or the foot to accomplish a task directly. The foot can be used, following Leg Motion to get it into position, to: operate pedals, shove objects along the floor, brush objects aside (if not too heavy), and do similar tasks. The leg can also perform useful labor after a Leg Motion has placed it in contact with an object to be activated by having it: make a further Leg Motion to operate the knee lever of an electric sewing machine or rotary ironer; operate the water valve of a surgical washbasin by a pressure application (AP) and another short Leg Motion; shove open swinging doors; or to perform holding or restraining action on objects that would move into the worker's way without the leg action. In general, it is good methods practice to employ the legs and feet as much as possible when they free the manual members for more productive tasks or even make some job sequences with the hands possible at all.

A standing operator can pivot the leg in any desired direction—forward, backward, or sideways—and usually does so about the hip joint. The leg can also be swiveled about the knee while standing. When sitting, however, most leg action results from pivoting about the knee. For example, Leg Motions can be used to roll a chair with casters while sitting; this probably will require some AP's. Large movements of the leg while sitting, as when crossing one's legs, will ordinarily display pivoting about the hip as well.

In any of the cases cited, the measuring point for Leg Motion is the ankle or instep of the leg moved. This distance is either scaled or estimated to the nearest inch. It has been found that a constant minimum time of 7.1 TMU will be required for all Leg Motions up to and including 6 inches distance. Each extra 1 inch of travel will require 1.2 TMU additional time.

The MTM symbol for Leg Motion consists of the capital letters LM

[13] From "MTM Basic Specifications" (Footnote 1, Chapter 7).

(the initials of the motion name) followed by a numeral that shows the travel distance. Some analysts always record a 6 for all distances equal to or below 6 inches, although this is not an official MTM rule—they use it to remind themselves of the minimum time.

An example of the symbol and time calculation is: LM14 designating a Leg Motion of 14 inches that requires 7.1 + (14–6) (1.2) or 7.1 + 9.6 = 16.7 TMU to perform. The symbol should be shown in the left- or right-hand column of the methods analysis form as appropriate for the leg acting.

LM is easy to recognize and measure, but care must be taken to check whether it is limited out by concurrent manual and/or eye motions. Many of the LM performed will be part of a combined motion with the work of the hand; the usual rules for combined motions will govern the time allowance for such situations.

Minor LM are sometimes made that have no bearing on the allowed time; such cases are often not even written into the motion pattern. They are essentially balance or reflex actions that are not consciously made as required by the LM definition. In using the LM data, therefore, an analyst may often include or omit it in the pattern on the basis of whether it is an essential action to task achievement.

Foot Motion

DEFINITION:[14] *FOOT MOTION is the movement of the ball of the foot up or down with the heel or the instep serving as a fulcrum.*

1. Motion of the toes of the foot generally is 2" to 4".

2. Foot motion, with pressure, includes a hesitation for the application of force directly by the foot or a transfer of body weight in conjunction with the foot motion.

MTM Symbols:

Foot Motion	FM	Time Values:	8.5 TMU
Foot Motion with Heavy Pressure by the leg muscles	FMP		19.1 TMU

FM or FMP usually occurs in activating pedals, levers, and switches. They are more easily executed when the operator is seated. Whether seated or standing however, the operator will be fatigued by excessive repetition of FMP. Its use to relieve the hands of possible tasks should, therefore, be judicious. The symbols for Foot Motions obviously should be shown in the left- or right-hand column of the analysis form to show which foot is acting.

The direction of foot motion may be either vertically up or down or it can occur sideways. Note that the added motion and time when pressure is used is an AP2 taking 10.6 TMU.

[14] From "MTM Basic Specifications" (Footnote 1, Chapter 7).

The distance of movement, in any case not involving LM as well, will be small—from 2 to 4 inches long; it is therefore only a minor variable and does not require measurement and notation on the MTM analysis. The two time constants given are based on the maximum condition of motion and therefore no analysis of the motion except for recognition of its occurrence is required.

Walking

DEFINITION:[15] *WALKING is a forward or backward movement of the body performed by alternate steps.*
　1. Walking does not include stepping to the side or turning around.

According to this definition, the act of walking is essentially an alternate series of LM by each leg and foot for the purpose of conveying the trunk to a new location.　The direction of travel is restricted, however, to forward and backward only; any lateral or rotational movement of the trunk will be done with either SS or TB as previously discussed.　While walking seems to be a simple act (probably because almost everyone is highly experienced and skilled at it) the relatively large number of variables associated with it in industrial situations will be included in this section.　Remember while considering this data, however, that the MTM motion and time values basically apply to purposeful walking during work sequences—it would be improper to use it to compute the time for a leisurely stroll.　The MTM walking data may not compare too well to walking rates generally accepted for other purposes.

Besides the data given in the MTM procedure, variously published rates that have been well established for purposeful walking (or marching) are given and these tend to corroborate the results reported from rather extensive MTM research based mainly on time study.

1. AMERICAN ARMY.　The parade standard of 128 paces per minute with a 30 inch stride can be converted to *3.62* miles per hour, effort being noticeable.
2. BRITISH ARMY.　An hour's march is defined to include the coverage of 3.00 miles in 50 minutes followed by 10 minutes rest to overcome fatigue prior to continuation of the march.　The steady marching rate would be based on the actual time to cover the specified distance, or 3.00/50 = 0.06 miles per minute.　The hourly rate would then by (60) (.06) = *3.60* miles per hour.　The effort, again, would be at an average or higher level.
3. A rather exhaustive investigation by United States Steel Corporation resulted in a standard of *3.57* miles per hour.
4. Walking standards from other sources range from *3.00* to *4.05* miles

[15] From "MTM Basic Specifications" (Footnote 1, Chapter 7).

per hour. The conditions specified were not all equal, however.

5. MTM RESEARCH. As described in the MTM text by the originators, time study under controlled conditions with no loads being carried showed an average velocity of *3.57* miles per hour with a 34-inch pace. This will correspond to rates of *5.3 TMU per foot* or *15.0 TMU per pace* for no load walking over an unobstructed path; this is the MTM walking data.

In addition to the data just given, other tentative time values for carrying loads and accounting for the hindrance offered by obstructions are part of the MTM data.

Maynard, Stegemerten, and Schwab discuss in their text the effect of walking variables and provide graphs and tables to show this variation. Since the MTM analyst ordinarily should choose an average operator for observation, however, this data is informative rather than essential in nature.

It is instructive, on the other hand, to record here some of the variables and how they influence the time for walking. Men tend to walk faster than women—particularly when carrying loads. Younger and older walkers apparently walk slower than those between 17 and 24 years. Physical condition and health will affect walking ability, since they will be reflected in both the pace and effort. Heavy shoes, or high heels, will also slow down the walker. A smooth, hard, level surface will result in better velocity than will be true with a less desirable foothold; this is further discussed under obstructed walking below. Objects that interfere with a clear path result in extra steps or more caution to avoid stumbling and thus slow the walking rate. Effort will affect not only the time per pace, but also the length of pace employed. Low effort reduces the length of stride and increases walking time per foot; high effort lowers the per foot walking time because of an increased stride.

A *tentative* time value of 17.0 TMU per pace has been used with success for obstructed walking. Obstructions may be defined as physical objects in or near the usual pathway or as surface conditions differing from those in the original research just noted above. Walking on sand, loose dirt, oily or slippery floors, ice and snow, railroad ties and similar impeding objects are all instances of obstructed walking that will slow the rate. Besides reducing the pace or causing increased caution, obstructions result in an increased length of path to get around objects in the way. For such cases, the 17.0 TMU value may be used cautiously.

The MTM walking standard is stated in connection with a definite length of pace. Short striding walkers tend to exert greater effort, so that their per pace walking rate tends to equal that of long striders in spite of a shorter pace. Operators with other than average build normally use a pace length appreciably different than the average and therefore require a different number of paces to cover equal distances as compared to average operators. Also, operators using other than average effort tend to alter their pace length and therefore the number of paces required to travel a given distance. Note in all of these cases that the MTM time per pace is essentially constant, for a given walking condition. The number of paces used, however, depends on the pace length. Backward walking seems to require the same time per pace but the pace length is reduced from what it would be for forward steps. Similarly, heavier loads seem to reduce the pace length with little change in the per pace rate.

All of the preceding data and discussion can be combined into a practical table (see Table 1.) which applies to walking by average operators. While this table includes several tentative time values, it also includes the official MTM Data Card information as indicated.

Table I. Walking Data for Average Operators

WALKING CONDITION		UNOBSTRUCTED		OBSTRUCTED	
LOAD, pounds	PACE, inches	TMU per Pace	TMU per Foot	TMU per Pace	TMU per Foot
0– 5 incl.	34	15.0*	5.3*	17.0	6.0
Over 5–35 incl.	30	15.0	6.0	17.0	6.8
Over 35–50 incl.	24	15.0	7.5	17.0	8.5
Over 50	24	17.0	8.5	17.0	8.5

* Official MTM Data Card information.

Walking up and down stairs presents another analysis problem. Essentially, the 15.0 TMU per pace value is applied and the number of paces must be found. In addition, such walking should be examined for the use of extra leg motions and even, at times, the use of AP by the feet. A stairway consists of vertical pieces called risers and horizontal members called treads or steps; when these are of average dimensional proportions, one pace per tread is the usual requirement. If a long flight is climbed frequently during a work sequence, however, an extra fatigue allowance will be in order. Risers over 12 inches high, or extra deep treads, or whether the treads are enclosed rather than open present further need for practical analysis that probably will be best resolved by using time study.

The conventional MTM symbols should always be shown in the right-hand column of the analysis form. They are as follows:

1st. A capital W for walk
2nd. A numeral for either the paces taken or the distance in feet traveled
3rd. The capital letters for paces—P—or for feet—FT, as appropriate
4th. A capital O when obstructed conditions are present

Examples, including the time values are:

1. W5P (Walk 5 paces)   75.0 TMU
2. W20FT (Walk 20 feet)   106.0 TMU
3. W5PO (Walk 5 obstructed paces)   85.0 TMU

The MTM engineer must choose between analyzing walking by the per pace or per foot methods, since times are available for both systems. Factors influencing the choice are indicated in the following:

1. PER PACE. The time value per pace is essentially constant for given walking conditions. It applies even for the somewhat shortened paces at the start and finish of walking. A pace should be counted each time a foot strikes the floor. It is easier to record paces, rather than measure the path, when single paces or short distances are walked. With the originators' data, it is possible to adjust the allowed number of paces from these actually done by an observed off-average operator or one who does not walk with average effort. For most walking conditions, workers tend to use the average pace. The analyst can pace the distance himself if necessary. When writing a visualized analysis, however, the per pace method is harder to use than the per foot method.

2. PER FOOT. When analyzing motions based on lay-outs, it is easier to determine the number of feet covered than the number of paces. It is also easier to specify distance to walk than the paces to take. The per foot walking rate is, however, not really constant because it does not include prorated start and stop time. Visualizing is easier done when it is based on the feet to be traveled rather than on a per pace basis. The distance specified or allowed should be the actually necessary path, not a straight line measurement. This makes the per foot method harder when obstructed conditions are encountered, as the true path length is harder to determine.

While the MTM data for walking is far from complete, the discussion given here will permit establishment of usable times for the average walking situation. More research may be desirable. A final point is that the walking data should not be applied where unusual conditions prevail or when the operator does not fully control his walking rate. Such *process time* indicators suggest that stopwatch time study rather than MTM data should be used.

DATA CARD INFORMATION

MTM time data has been given with the discussions of Body, Leg, and Foot Motions. In practice the analyst will ordinarily use the data as compiled on the official MTM card as shown in Table 2.

It will be noted that the card has been arranged in condensed fashion, primarily by grouping motions that require the same time values. Note also that tentative time values, such as obstructed and loaded walking times, have been omitted from the card pending clarifying research.

Table 2. Body, Leg, and Foot Motions
(MTM Data Card—Table IX—Body, Leg, and Foot Motions)

DESCRIPTION	SYMBOL	DISTANCE	TIME TMU
Foot Motion—Hinged at Ankle.	FM	Up to 4″	8.5
With heavy pressure.	FMP		19.1
Leg or Foreleg Motion.	LM —	Up to 6″	7.1
		Each add'l. inch	1.2
Sidestep—Case 1—Complete when	SS-C1	Less than 12″	Use REACH or
leading leg con-			MOVE Time
tacts floor.		12″	17.0
		Each add'l. inch	.6
Case 2—Lagging leg must	SS-C2	12″	34.1
contact floor be-		Each add'l. inch	1.1
fore next motion			
can be made.			
Bend, Stoop, or Kneel on One Knee.	B,S,KOK		29.0
Arise.	AB,AS,AKOK		31.9
Kneel on Floor—Both Knees.	KBK		69.4
Arise.	AKBK		76.7
Sit.	SIT		34.7
Stand from Sitting Position.	STD		43.4
Turn Body 45 to 90 degrees—			
Case 1—Complete when leading	TBC1		18.6
leg contacts floor.			
Case 2—Lagging leg must contact	TBC2		37.2
floor before next motion			
can be made.			
Walk.	W-FT.	Per Foot	5.3
Walk.	W-P	Per Pace	15.0

GENERAL APPLICATION RULES

Rules of application pertinent to each of the Body, Leg, and Foot Motions have been given in the discussion of each. Most of these rules have been formulated by considering the facts that: (1) The body motions are gross movements involving the heavier muscles of the worker; (2) the times for body motions are usually longer than for any manual motions that can be made concurrent with body motions; and (3) a distinct manner of using the body occurs when heavier loads are handled by the worker.

Regarding the first point, use of the heaviest muscles obviously will require the greatest expenditure of energy per unit of effective output. This will result in greater fatigue per unit of working time. No reasonable management expects their employees normally to incur more than a nominal amount of fatigue during the working hours; continued over-fatigue can only result in a net loss of efficiency for the company itself with attendant higher costs. The day when it was believed profitable to unfairly over-burden workers has passed; in addition the actions of those who might want to be unfair are now restricted in this matter by years of labor negotiation and social legislation. The logical outcome of the foregoing facts is that either excessive use of body motions is avoided through providing adequate material handling and other worker aids, or else some means for recovery from fatigue is permitted for jobs in which a large amount of body motion is unavoidable. The latter takes the form of rest periods, special cycle allowances at stated intervals, and permission for the worker to refresh himself during the working day.

In view of the foregoing, the methods analyst has a clear responsibility to specify methods, where possible, that minimize use of the body motions that are especially fatiguing. In this way he will implement more effective work patterns as well as meet the moral and legal requirements assigned to management. Armed with knowledge concerning the body members acting and the required time for each body motion, he is ideally equipped to achieve these aims. He can, sometimes, devise methods which employ less fatiguing body motions to attain equal work results. An example of this is provision of a roller conveyor to relieve the worker of the Bends, Stoops, Kneeling, and Walking usually found when moving heavy tote boxes.

The use of pedals and leg-actuated buttons in place of hand operated mechanisms is another example of a fatigue reducing measure; however, as pointed out previously, they must be used judiciously. Heavy pressures or light short movements can be applied easily by the foot—often easier than by hand.

The second point mentioned alludes to limiting body motions and over-lapping body motions that could or might be made concurrently with manual motions. The MTM analyst either should not require the use of such combinations of motions or else be sure that he has fairly allowed time for the true occurrences he finds. Short Reaches and Moves are almost always limited out by body motions; although it is possible for them to blend into body motions or begin while a body motion is ending. In the latter event, only that portion of the Reach or Move which has not been overlapped should be written separately, usually as a Type II motion, and time allow-ance permitted. For instance, the Reach (or part of it) to a part made during the last step of walking forward toward it can reasonably be limited out.

Body motions may themselves overlap and limit one another. Bend and Turn Body can be performed together if weights are not being carried. A step may be taken so as to overlap with either bending or arising from a Bend. A Leg Motion is often used to bring the feet together as a worker performs a Sit; Sidestep can also be used in this manner. However, care must be taken in such analysis. A Leg Motion would not be limited out, for instance, when used to cross the legs after sitting, to return the body to a place prior to sitting, or to shove a chair with casters to a required location.

Another factor is that, although any given body motion might be limited out, it will nevertheless provide a degree of assistance to the long reach or move that is limiting.

When the analyst is in doubt as to whether manual or body motions limit, or which of several concurrent body motions predominates, he should generally perform the motions himself and note the ease or difficulty —particularly the state of body balance—with which they can be combined. Remember, always, that the *normal* operator at *average performance* levels is the standard against which the difficulty of motions or their combinations is gaged, and body balance must be preserved during performance of all *normal* body motions.

Finally, the special manner of handling heavy loads should guide the MTM engineer in assigning body motions. Any manual Moves connected with this topic will, of course, involve the use of weight factors as discussed in the Move Chapter. In addition to this, the heavier loads require making the Moves separately from the body motions, in other words, such Moves are seldom overlapped or combined with body motions. They occur both before and after body motions required during handling of heavy weights. The worker tends to Move the heavy object to within a few inches of his body before he is balanced enough to make the body motion. He will then Move the object away from his body before he performs further motions with it following completion of body motions. Both of these Moves with weight must be separately allowed. Also, it is hard to avoid using some variety of body motion if the weight is moved more than very short distances; such weights are seldom moved as far as light objects without either body assistance or a definite body movement to aid the action.

No adjustments are made in the description or time for individual body motions used in handling weights; nothing similar to weight factors for manual motions pertains to body motions. The handling of heavier loads will dictate the use of different kinds of body motions rather than noticeable changes in the elemental motions themselves. The reason is that the body or trunk muscles are the heaviest, strongest parts of the body, but are less adapted to different kinds of actions than are the manual members. If any doubt exists in the MTM analysis of heavy transports, the best approach is to use stopwatch time study instead of MTM body motions. For long range solution of such work study problems, probably the best approach would be to take a motion picture and analyze the film for accurate general data which will augment the available MTM data.

SUMMARY

Body, Leg, and Foot Motions

Description	Symbol	Column	Reminders
BODY MOTIONS			
Sit down from standing erect	SIT	RH	In front of seat
Stand up from sitting position	STD	RH	To standing erect
Sidestep, only one foot moved	SS–C1	RH or LH	Blank for distance
Sidestep, both feet moved	SS–C2	RH or LH	Blank for distance
Turn Body, only one foot rotated	TBC1	RH or LH	Trunk revolves only
Turn Body, both feet rotated	TBC2	RH or LH	Trunk revolves only
Bend the trunk at waist or hips	B	RH	Feet remain fixed
Stoop, with legs aiding the bend	S	RH	Feet remain fixed
Arise from Bend	AB	RH	To standing erect
Arise from Stoop	AS	RH	To standing erect
Kneel on One Knee	KOK	RH or LH	Other thigh horizontal
Kneel on Both Knees	KBK	RH	The "prayer" position
Arise from Kneel on One Knee	AKOK	RH or LH	To standing erect
Arise from Kneel on Both Knees	AKBK	RH	To standing erect
LEG AND FOOT MOTIONS			
Leg Motion pivoted at knee and/or hip	LM–	RH or LH	Blank for distance
Foot Motion about ankle, heel, or instep	FM	RH or LH	Distance no factor
Foot Motion with heavy pressure	FMP	RH or LH	Very fatiguing act
Walk a number of paces (fill in blank)	W–P	RH	Forward or backward
Walk a number of feet (fill in blank)	W–FT	RH	Forward or backward
Walk through or with obstructions	W–PO	RH	Analyze obstruction effect on walking

QUESTIONS

1. Write the motions and time values for a machinist who picks up a 20-pound tray full of cutting tools from a shelf below his knee level with both hands and returns it to the waist-high shelf of a tool crib 100 feet away and to the left of his working position. The original shelf is to the right of his working position and about two paces away from it.

2. Each time the operator of a six-spindle drill press moves his drill jig to the next spindle, about 16 inches away, he slides it on the press table and per-

forms a certain body motion. What is this motion, and how much time does it add to the cycle between the first and sixth spindles inclusively? If he slides the drill jig on the table to the starting spindle to reload it after removing the drill part, what body motions and times will be normally used? Could the motion between spindles be analyzed differently than in your first answer? If so, what would this latter motion be? Why might no time be allowed for the balancing body action involved in the complete motion sequence for this motion possibility?

3. A number of questions in this text included body, leg, and foot motions that were not a required part of the answer in earlier chapters. Refer back to these questions and supply the missing body motions:

   a. Question 4. in the Apply Pressure Chapter.
   b. Question 5. in the Apply Pressure Chapter.

4. An office worker seated close to his desk is writing with a pen when a vital paper is blown by the ventilating fan so that it lands under his desk below the right-hand drawers and about 18 inches back from the front edge of the desk, which is shoved close to a corner of the room. Isolate all body motions he will likely employ to retrieve the paper until he is back in his chair writing again in his original position. Try to write these motions and include all manual motions you would reasonably expect to occur, assuming the pen is dropped on the desk. Finally, assign time values to the motion pattern you have written.

CHAPTER 18

Motion Combinations

Chapters 7 through 17 presented in detail descriptions of the basic motions defined in the MTM system and traced their development from origin to present status. These are the "building blocks" of the MTM system; the next task for the student is to learn how to connect them into a unified whole. This must be accomplished before any useful results can be produced through his study of the entire Methods-Time Measurement system. It is the purpose of this chapter to set forth the connections existing among the basic human motions.

The problem facing the reader is that of learning to co-ordinate the mass of somewhat discrete data concerning each motion of the MTM system to obtain time values for complete motion patterns. Intimate knowledge of the subject of Motion Combinations covered in this chapter will enable a skilled analyst to write MTM motion patterns, assign appropriate time values, and evaluate the effectiveness of the sequences and/or tasks involved in the majority of manual work cycles. He can, therefore, employ a powerful tool for management purposes, applying it to a whole gamut of industrial engineering problems.

To gain full appreciation of the highly logical and practical MTM data on motion combinations, the reader must be able to quickly and accurately: (1) recall and apply the individual motions and all factors connected with them; (2) structurally unite such motions with due account for the variables affecting their union; and (3) interpret the resulting methods-time data for the many uses to which a finished MTM analysis can be put. When lacking full confidence with respect to Step (1), the reader should *review and re-examine* the individual motion chapters. How to take Step (2) is the direct subject of this chapter. Application chapters to follow will delve more deeply into Step (3) so that the reader's understanding will become well-rounded and reliable for work measurement purposes.

THE LIMITING PRINCIPLE

The reader is familiar with the concept of a performance time required and allowed for each of the individual MTM motions. Also, the concept of combined motions, which was introduced in the Turn chapter, explained the meaning of "limiting" motions and times as well as the converse of "limited" motions and times. The method and logic by which time data is assigned to the many possible motion combinations is yet to be presented. The first step is to extend the reader's knowledge of the Limiting Principle.

Maynard, Stegemerten, and Schwab stated a very important and basic principle as follows:

> In performing industrial operations, it is usually undesirable to have only one body member in motion at a time. Two or more body members should usually be in motion simultaneously if the most effective method for doing the job is to be used . . . . If two or more motions are combined or overlapped, all can be performed in the time required to perform the one demanding the greatest amount of time, or the limiting motion.[1]

Although the general character of motion combinations can thus be described rather simply, the study and evaluation of their occurrences are the most complex aspect of any work measurement system, including time study and motion study in the sense known before the advent of pre-determined times. A myriad of variables and subtle differences in both the motions and their attendant time requirements makes difficult both the isolation and systemizing of data into a reliable form.

It has been generally recognized by most authorities in the work measurement field that the MTM system contains the most complete, practical, and research-based data on motion combinations that exists. Indeed, most other systems are woefully weak in this aspect of motion-time data; and useful data on motion combinations is, after all, the focus about which successful methods work and accurate time determination revolves in almost a primary manner. Some attempts to approach this most basic problem have been included in some of the other pre-determined time systems. Whether their data rests on reliable research or on pure judgment and estimation is difficult to ascertain without more public information on their motion combination rules and how they were developed.

The main source of MTM motion combination data is *A Study of Simultaneous Motions*,[2] which reports the results of over two years of intensive laboratory and industrial study of the problem. The reference includes a discussion and analysis of other pre-determined time systems'

---

[1] By permission from *Methods-Time Measurement* by Maynard, Stegemerten and Schwab. Copyright, 1948, McGraw-Hill Book Co., Inc.

[2] R.R. 105 (See Ch. 5).

handling of motion combinations which the reader will find worth investigating. However, this research and others[3] indicated a wide area yet to be investigated in this subject. Although the information in this chapter is relatively comprehensive, it is by no means offered as final or complete data.

Not only is it evident that additional studies should be made to completely investigate the effect of one motion on another in a combination, but it is also true that any inaccuracies in defining basic motions and/or their characteristics could affect motion combinations time-wise. The latter is true because the time for any motion combination will be that allowed for the individual motion in the combination which is limiting. For an example of possible inaccuracies in basic motion data, the following statements concerning motions and motion times have been given previously:

(1) The performance time of a Reach or Move exhibits proportionality between the time and the distance traveled.

(2) The acceleration time for a motion equals the deceleration time.

(3) Between the periods of acceleration and deceleration, the velocity of a motion achieves a relatively stable, constant value.

These are known not to be completely precise and exact statements of what occurs, and further research might change them slightly. Certainly, these ideas contribute an additional effect which complicates the study of motion combinations with statistical and analysis problems of a high order. However, the data presented in this chapter is practical and has proved reliable in thousands of applications.

The practical significance of the motion combination data is easy to state: It would be almost impossible to write the method in terms of pre-determined motions without this information. Even with the mass of data to be presented here, the analyst will at times find unanswered questions which he can solve for the present only by using his best judgment based on full knowledge of the variables here discussed and clarified. Perhaps one of the major contributions of MTM to the field of pre-determined times consisted in pinpointing for the first time exactly what the variables are and providing practical rules or procedures by which a fairly adequate accounting of them can be made in motion patterns. No substantial information of this nature existed until the MTM Association work was first published.

Let the problem of motion combinations be stated as follows: It is possible, during the same time span, for the left members of the body (or the entire body itself) to perform one, two, or even more basic motions while the right members complete only one single motion; the reverse is

[3] R.R. 108 and R.R. 112 (See Ch. 5).

also true for cases when the left members perform the limiting motion. In such cases, the procedure is to apply the relatively simple rule to allow or assign on the pattern only the longest time combination of basic motions. However, this is practically always complicated by the question as to whether a particular combination can be performed by the operator under the imposed conditions with the presence of major degrees of motion overlap.

The MTM system bases its practical rules on defined breakpoints which were somewhat arbitrarily selected from the mass of data evaluated in the research—this being a practical necessity because of the limits of present knowledge. The MTM analyst is cautioned, however, not to allow his thinking on motion combinations to be confined or restricted by the limits imposed by these categories, since a multiplicity of analytical approaches can exist to data which actually varies on a continuum. He should rely instead on full understanding of the variables discussed here and exercise independent judgment only *when required.*

While categorical definitions for the prevalent types of motion combinations are given in the next section, together with rules for determining the "limiting" and "limited" motions and time, the analyst should base his thinking on the ideas contained in the following general definition paraphrased by the authors from Research Report 105 as follows:

A motion combination may be defined as a complete single motion or a sequence of motions by one or more body members accompanied by a complete or partial motion or sequence of motions by other body members or by the complete absence of motion by all other body members.

Consecutive motion consists of a succession of unitary motion combinations, while combined, simultaneous, and compound motions as later defined are comprised of two or more concurrent motions involving either one or more body members. Because of this complication, no practical time results will be possible unless certain categorized rules given in this chapter are carefully applied and followed whenever they are applicable.

TYPES OF MOTION COMBINATIONS

The possibilities include three distinct categories, together with a fourth that is actually a composite of the second and third.

Consecutive Motions

DEFINITION: *A consecutive motion combination occurs when the same or different body members sequentially perform a series of individual, complete motions involving no overlap or pauses between motions.*

Perhaps the greatest error a work analyst can make in dealing with consecutive motions is to regard them as discrete entities that lack any essential connection, and can therefore be strung together like a necklace of beads at random. Such is not the case. A consecutive sequence of motions, when properly understood, will be considered as a special combination of motions subject to limitations no less important than the limits governing other motion combinations.

The basic supposition of all pre-determined time systems is: *The time required by a series of consecutive motions is the sum of the times for the individual motions in the series.* The validity of a total time based on this axiom depends on whether or not the following two necessary connections between each individual motion are met: (1) conformance of the individual motions with the limitations of the basic definitions that account for the preceding and following motions; and (2) that the resultant effect of the motions on the objects involved is physically logical and reproducible.

As an example of the first requirement, recall that the definitions for Reaches and Grasps included restrictions on the kind of Reach that must precede a given type of Grasp. For instance, full accounting for the muscular, mental, and visual control involved in selection time from a jumbled pile can be made only by the use of an R–C prior to the G4 Grasp employed. Another example of where a definition connects motions is the necessity for an M–C to precede the positioning of an object; the object must be brought very close to the final destination before the short motions comprising Position really begin. Many other such connections can be found in the chapters on each individual motion.

Common sense and logic indicate that objects affect and are affected by a given MTM motion in definite physical ways. This is the essence of the second requirement stated above. It is obviously a physical impossibility to perform a Move with a hand that has just released the only object previously held. The only logical motion that could follow would be a Reach. Likewise, as noted in the Turn data, the empty hand cannot perform a T90L, nor can the motion following a T90L be a Reach. At least an RL1 must intervene before a Reach is physically possible. Many such examples of the second requirement above could be stated, and reasoning alone should convince the reader that limitations such as these on individual motions may be imposed automatically by the objects and the workplace.

Subject to the limitations mentioned, almost any series of consecutive motions can be executed. The symbols and method of assigning times is shown in the examples below. The motion is recorded in the proper left- or right-hand column on the analysis form, following the rules given for each motion in earlier chapters. The times for each motion are then inserted in the TMU column and these are totaled for the time required by the entire consecutive combination. Note that each motion is written on a separate line of the motion pattern.

Example 1: An adult using both the left and the right hand in a consecutive motion-sequence to give a child a cinnamon ball.

Description	LH	TMU	RH	Description
Wait		12.9	R10C	To mixed candy in dish
		9.1	G4B	Select cinnamon ball
↓		12.2	M10B	Candy from dish
To child's hand	R6B	8.6		Hold candy
Grip child's palm	G1A	2.0		↓
Hold child's palm		10.6	M8B	Bring candy to palm
		2.0	RL1	Drop candy into child's
Total TMU		57.4		palm

Example 2: Dyeing Easter eggs using consecutive motions.

Description	LH	TMU	RH	Description
To hardboiled egg	R16B	15.8		Hold dipper
Pick up egg	G1A	2.0		│
Egg toward dipper	M16C	18.7		│
Place in dipper (with care)	P1SD	11.2		│
Let go of egg	RL1	2.0		↓
Wait		11.8	M8C	Carefully place egg in
Total TMU		61.5		Easter dye

It is obvious that this annual operation can be done with consecutive motions, although other methods are also possible.

Combined Motions

DEFINITION: *A combined motion combination occurs when two or more motions are performed by **the same body member** during the time required by the limiting motion.*

Note that this definition specifically excludes consecutive motions. To illustrate simply, a Turn or Regrasp combined with a Move clearly shows that combined motions are non-consecutive.

Combined turns, as previously discussed, brought out the many variables present with motion combinations of this type—such as assistance, measurement of the variables integral with each motion and as affected by being combined, and the method or convention of showing the limited and limiting motion(s) and time. The reader can best learn to distinguish combined motions by context or by sight.

The normal possibilities of dual combined motions can be listed as at right. While other combinations can and do sometimes occur, these are found with greatest frequency. The possibilities of triple combined motions are, however, harder to list because they occur more rarely and often require a special dexterity based on repetition of handling certain objects in certain ways. One common triple, however, is a Turn and Regrasp combined with a Move.

M with G2

R with T or RL

M with T or RL

The time required by a set of combined motions is that for the individual motion in the set that consumes the greatest time and limits out the others. While there is no absolute rule by which one can, upon examination only, decide which of the motions is limiting, knowledge of the relative time values of the individual motions is useful and will often save the analyst the necessity of referring to the data card to aid his decision, even though the data card is the only authority to consider for a sure answer.

The symbol conventions and times for combined motions are recorded on the work form as follows:

One line of the form is used to record each motion in the set, although the order in which they are listed is not important. The reason the order means nothing is because all motions in the set occur within the same time interval and also that a bracket is used to set off the combination from preceding or following motions of the pattern. Without this bracket, it might at times be difficult to tell at a glance whether the motion(s) limited out (identified with a slanted line) was combined with the motion above or below it; the bracket removes this doubt.

The time for the limiting motion is shown in the TMU column, with a horizontal dash being shown in this column to indicate a time that is limited out. The right- or left-hand column will, of course, help identify the body member which performed the combined motions. The slanted line through the limited out motion(s) also helps identification.

While combined motions can be illustrated as a set apart from preceding or following motions, the place they have in a work pattern and their purpose is more obvious if the examples include the combined motion set in a sequence of other motions. The descriptive columns also help promote clarity. The examples which follow are of this type.

Example 1: The familiar toss aside motions shown in the Move chapter are used here to cull dead blooms from pansies in a flower pot.

Description	LH	TMU	RH	Description
Hold stem of pansy		14.4	R14B	To dead pansy
		2.0	G1A	Grip dead flower
		4.0	D1E	Pull off stem
		8.6	⎛M10Bm	Toss flower aside
		—	⎝R̶L̶1̶	Open fingers
		4.7	mR4E	Hand overtravel
Let go of stem	RL1	2.0		Wait
Total TMU		35.7		

Example 2: A triple combined motion employed by many people in returning pencils to their shirt pockets. Note the G3 properly shown in the receiving hand column.

Description	LH	TMU	RH	Description
Obtain pencil from RH	G3	5.6		Let go of pencil
Pencil toward pocket	M12C⎞	15.2		Wait
Shift grasp	G̶2̶ ⎟	—		
Preorient tip	P̶6̶0̶S̶ ⎠	—		
Locate to shirt pocket	P1SE	5.6		
Total TMU		26.4		

Simultaneous Motions

As generally used in work measurement, simultaneous motions are any combination of motions done at the same time by more than one body member. As will be seen later in this section and the following one on compound motions, this general idea can include combinations ranging from the extremely simplified situation covered in the restricted definition next given to very complex combinations which include multiple motions with overlap and involve many body members. For reasons which will shortly be apparent, however, the MTM system approaches the interpretation of simultaneous motions on a categorical basis to permit the development of practical tables to aid the analyst in describing and timing such combinations. The categories are of the simpler variety but the reasoning may be extended to more complex cases after the simpler kinds of simultaneous motions become familiar to the reader.

DEFINITION: (*A Simple Simultaneous Motion Combination*)

A simultaneous motion (simo) combination occurs when a single, complete motion by one body member is performed and during the same time interval another body member performs a single, complete motion which consumes the same or less time.

For convenience in discussion, the terms "limiting member" and "limited member" have been coined to describe, respectively, the body members acting in the same order as in the definition above. The time for the limiting motion, as found from the individual motion data already given, is the performance time allowed for a simo combination. Understanding of simultaneous motions, however, requires that the actions of the *limiting and limited members* be clearly delineated from both the motion and time standpoints.

The *limiting member,* which by the Limiting Principle controls the time, always performs a basic or elemental motion (as previously defined in the MTM procedure) that completely fulfills all the conditions and requirements of any given Type I, II, or III motion and will consume the time which the MTM elemental motion data has pre-determined for it. In this sense, the analyst may conveniently regard the limiting motion in an isolated manner. The time for a pattern would be correct as long as the limiting motion was included in the proper place.

It is in *describing* the action of the *limited member* that the explanation of simo motions becomes more involved. The reason is that present application rules are based on the idea that the limited member will ordinarily be assigned only one motion which requires the same or less time than does the limiting member.

In order for the analyst to gain some insight into the simo variables, however, it is necessary that he know at least the rudiments of the limited action of the combination. Clarification of this type will be given here; but, for readers who desire further data and have a theoretical bent, the discussion of motion overlap and symbolic plotting of it is well covered in R.R. No. 105 and *A Research Methods Manual*[4] available from the MTM Association. Basically, the application simplification given above avoids the motion and time complication actually present in simo motions due to overlapping and interaction phenomena. While recognition and evaluation of these factors are essential for research evaluation, the practical analyst has no way by which to account for them in arriving at assignable times for simo occurrences. Perhaps progress in this deficiency will be a future advance of motion analysis that will come from further research by the MTM Association and others.

In truth, however, the researcher or statistician investigating simultaneous motion must recognize this to be a practical arbitrary approach that enables the analyst to make concise choices from the data which has been developed regarding motion times. With this reservation in mind, the theoretician can conduct research that may be codified into "simo tables" which give practical answers when followed, even though they do not reflect fully the precise nature and interaction of the two motions being combined in a simultaneous manner. The regular MTM analyst will not ordinarily con-

[4] R.R. 107 (See Ch. 5).

cern himself beyond this level of theory, being content to leave the complexities to the theorists and researchers. He applies the working rules represented by the "simo tables" with an understanding of the variables—to be discussed—and leaves the question of statistical accuracy in the hands of the people who have considered the true factors and reflected the practical interpretation in the "simo tables" developed.

According to the restricted simo definition, the limited member, the same as for the limiting member, performs a single, complete motion which requires the same or less time for its performance. Actually, however, the true performance of the limited member may include complete or partial motions and/or motion sequences. It could consist of a single, complete motion as noted by the restricted definition. It could also consist of partial increments of two motions, both of which overlap the limiting motion at the beginning and end of the limiting action. One or more complete motions, together with a partial motion comprises another possibility. An additional possibility would be one complete motion with two partial motions overlapping the limiting motion. The present simo data and rules cover only the first case mentioned, which is the reason for the restricted simo definition. An approach to handling the other cases will be given under "compound" motions presented later. In any event, the time for the limited member's action will not be allowed, since it is the limited time of the combination. This is the same idea meant when MTM analysts speak of the limited motion being "limited out" of time inclusion.

With this introduction to simo motions, further discussion will be deferred to more complete elaboration on the variables in a later section of this chapter. It is worthwhile, however, to present the symbol conventions here. Both motions in the simo combination are recorded on the same line of the analysis form, with the left and right columns reflecting the handedness involved. The limited motion is encircled, unless it is identical to the limiting motion, and the time for the limiting motion is written in the TMU column. Omitting the circle for identical motions is merely a saving of clerical time in pattern writing, since the simo time is not affected by adding it. Use of this data is obvious in the following example which involves seasoning eggs with salt and pepper.

Seasoning the breakfast staple by this method should improve its tastiness in a matter of little more than five seconds. Note that the simo Moves limited are either of shorter distance than the limiting Move or else require less time than the Turn employed. Circle omission is also well illustrated. The convention for writing multiple frequencies of individual motions is also exemplified in the shaking action, where four short Moves in each direction require the time for a single Move to be multiplied by eight as indicated by the numeral 8 in the No. column.

Description	No.	LH	TMU	RH	No.	Description
To pepper shaker	R10B		11.5	R10B		To salt shaker
Obtain shaker	G1A		2.0	G1A		Obtain shaker
Shaker toward plate	M6B		12.2	M10B		Shaker to plate
Hold			7.4	T135S		Turn top down
↓			36.8	M2B	(8)	Salt egg 4 shakes
Shaker to plate	M4B		7.4	T135S		Turn top up
Turn top down	T135S		7.4	M4B		Shaker out of way
Pepper egg 4 shakes	(8)	M2B	36.8			Hold
Turn top up	T135S		7.4			↓
Shaker to table	M10B		12.2	M6B		Shaker to table
Let go of shaker	RL1		2.0	RL1		Let go of shaker
Total TMU			143.1			

Compound Motions

DEFINITION: *A compound motion combination occurs when, during the same time interval, one body member performs either a single or combined motion while another body member executes a combined motion or more than one motion in a consecutive series.*

Either of the body members may be the limiting member, as may be determined by sequential application of the Limiting Principle to each member individually and then a reapplication of the Limiting Principle *between* the limiting motion(s) of the individual members.

The concept just defined has often been referred to in other MTM writings as "simultaneous and combined," which tacitly recognized that another motion combination besides consecutive, combined, or simultaneous exists.

For ease of explanation, it is well to assume that the body members in question are the left and right hands and to base the discussion on the right hand being the member first mentioned in the definition for compound motions. Logical deduction may be then used to isolate these compound possibilities:

(1) The RH does a single, complete motion while the LH performs a combined motion involving two or more individual motions.

(2) The RH does a single, complete motion while the LH performs a consecutive series of two or more individual motions which together take equal or less time than the right-hand motion.

(3) The RH does a combined motion that includes two or more individual motions while the LH does a combined motion comprised of two or more individual motions.

(4) The motions of the RH and LH may include any of these three compound actions with the additional feature of overlap of partially completed motions.

To see where this concept fits in, it is helpful to continue the listing to show that all other possible combinations have been previously defined;

(5) The RH may perform consecutive motions while the LH is idle or holding. The ordinary definition of consecutive motion confined to one body member fully describes this case.

(6) The RH does a combined motion while the LH holds or waits. This instance fulfills all the restrictions of the definition for combined motions.

(7) The RH does a single, complete motion while the LH also performs a single, complete motion. This accords with the restricted, practical definition of simultaneous motions described earlier. The reason for restricting simo motions to this case now becomes clear.

Case four (4) introduces the complication of motion overlap. For practical purposes, overlap must be evaluated in terms of the RH performing a sequence which may include both single and combined motions while the LH can perform a like sequence. (Not strictly confined to the limits of the compound motion definition.) In other words, a compound motion in the general sense may be considered as the combination of entire sequences in both hands, during the same time interval, that cannot be separated into other motion combinations due to overlap—the only requirement to be considered as a compound set being that the sequence in each hand begins and ends at the same instant of time. No limiting or time allowance rules have been pre-determined for this most general of all motion combination cases; in a real sense either hand may be considered limiting so long as the entire sequence is included in the total time allowed.

To show the application of the Limiting Principle to compound motions, the first three cases listed will be discussed in detail since they are the ones of practical value which have not already been discussed or where the solution is not obvious. The Limiting Principle says that the analyst must first examine each body member separately to determine which of the motions is limiting and apply the conventional symbols accordingly, and he then should examine the resulting limiting motions in each member in terms of simultaneous rules. Or:

(1) The lone RH motion is limiting for that hand. One of the motions comprising the combined set in the LH is limiting. The limiting RH and limiting LH motions are then considered as a simo combination, with the time resulting from this step being the total compound time.

Example: LH   TMU   RH

M8C	?	M10B
T60S		
G2		

The finished result will appear like this:

M8C	12.2	M10B
T60S	—	
G2	—	

RH analysis: The lone M10B requiring 12.2 TMU is obviously limiting. *LH analysis:* The M8C is 11.8 TMU, the T60S is 4.1 TMU, and the G2 is 5.6 TMU. The M8C is thus limiting. *Simo analysis:* The M10B in the RH limits the M8C in the LH, so a circle is used to limit out the LH motion.

In the finished analysis, the steps taken above are obvious by the conventions used to show limited motions. The dashes indicate that the T60S and G2 are not allowed. The encircling of the limiting motions of the LH analysis shows the result of the simo analysis.

(2) The lone RH motion is limiting. The consecutive motions in the LH require less total time than the RH motion. Considering the simultaneity, the RH by definition will always limit in this case of compound motion.

Example: LH   TMU   RH

G1A	?	R22B
M4B		
RL1		

The analysis result will be:

G1A	20.1	R22B
M4B	—	
RL1	—	

RH analysis: The single R22B is limiting with a time of 20.1 TMU. *LH analysis:* Adding the time for the three motions gives 2.0 + 6.9 + 2.0 or 10.9 TMU total. *Simo analysis:* The motion in the RH limits the consecutive sequence in the LH, which is encircled to show its limited status.

Note here that the absence of slanted lines or a bracket makes it clear that the LH motions were not combined. (They are actually physically impossible to do combined in this example.) The dashes show that no time was allowed for the components of the simo LH sequence written on succeeding lines of the form.

(3) While care must be exercised that this case includes individual motions that are really possible to perform in the manner written, such cases do appear rather frequently in actual motion patterns. The combined motions in the RH and LH will have their respective limiting motions, which then may be analyzed for the simo effect.

Example: LH   TMU   RH   *RH analysis:* The T90S of 5.4 TMU
                                              is limiting over the 4.9 for the M3A.
M8B)   ?   /T90S   *LH analysis:* The 10.6 TMU for the
G2)   (M3A   M8B limits out the G2 of 5.6 TMU.
The end result is: *Simo analysis:* The LH limits.
M8B)   10.6   (T90S
_G2_)   —   (M3A

The use of the conventions should be obvious by now, and
they clearly show the limiting process used in getting the
answer.

Novices to MTM sometimes ask why the limited motions are shown in
a methods analysis, since they do not determine the time for the motion
combination.   It is because the limited motions may be essential in providing a complete and understandable methods record on which the time
was based.   The superiority of methods description afforded by MTM in
contrast to time study is partially due to this inclusion of limited motions
in the pattern.   However, it is equally unnecessary to be extreme in the
use of symbolism by including every small motion that might conceivably
be a part of a given pattern.   For instance, a short R–E to balance the
motion rhythm or provide working space for the other hand need not be
shown; contrarily, safety requires that an R–E to remove the hand from
the operating area of a punch press ram must be shown.   Also, minor
turns (less than 30 degrees) made combined with reaches and moves—
especially where their occurrence is either obvious by the work conditions
or they are non-essential—can be omitted.   It is only important to show
limited motions that definitely affect the method or impart essential actions
to the objects where these factors would otherwise not be obvious from
the context.

General Definition of Simultaneous Motion Combinations

As noted after item (7) under Compound Motions, the complications
of overlap and interaction time have not all been evaluated from the
standpoint of limiting or time allowance rules.   No approved research
results or practical application procedures presently exist to handle overlapping combinations, so MTM patterns cannot adequately recognize or
indicate overlap at this date.   While it is therefore impossible now to give
full data for the general case of motion combinations, it is nevertheless
possible to attempt a full definition.   By way of summarizing the reader's
thoughts on types of simultaneous motion combinations, then, the authors
offer this definition of the most general type:

DEFINITION: *A general simultaneous motion combination occurs when
one or more body members perform a complete or partial single motion,*

*motion sequence, and/or motion combination during the same time interval
in which one or more other body members perform a complete or partial
single motion, motion sequence, and/or motion combination.*
This definition covers all of the possible types of combinations previously
discussed. It also describes such complex situations as where one hand
reaching toward a fixed object is assisted by a Sidestep and partial turn
body while the other hand reaches, contact grasps, and partially moves a
tool into a position for subsequent usage. The generalized definition,
in a more particular way, presents a possible avenue of future thought
and analysis that may lead to more practical means of interconnecting
manual and body motions in motion patterns; the data on this concept
is rather sparse now, as noted in a later section of this chapter.

The present data concerning motion combinations given in the remainder
of this chapter can be applied by the reader if he fully appreciates the
meaning of the more detailed descriptions of the restricted definitions for
consecutive, combined, simultaneous, and compound motions presented
above.

CONTROL—THE KEY TO COMBINATION ANALYSIS

In the performance of work, two principal agencies are present—the
operator and the objects being handled. The key to what can, may, or
will happen when these agencies interact is the *control* involved. Control,
for this purpose, has a dual meaning. First, from the standpoint of the
operator—Of what kinds and amounts of control is the human mechanism
capable? Secondly, from the viewpoint of the objects—What kinds and
quantities of control do the various characteristics of the objects permit
and/or require? These questions, when answered separately, provide
clues which can be wedded by synthesis and categorization to yield answers
to the total problem of work control.

To evaluate the question of *object control,* the MTM analyst must rely
upon his powers of observation, his engineering or other technical background, and the use of measuring devices where appropriate—seasoned
with practical common sense and experience factors. Definitive rules and
guides are difficult, if not impossible, to establish because the objects can
range in size and characteristics from a pin head to a two hundred pound
sack.

The question of *human control* is better defined because it has been the
subject of very exhaustive investigation by psychologists, scientists, physiologists, and many engineers dealing in branches of the engineering art
that include the human problems of operation and direction. The mass
of MTM research on motions and their combination is basically grounded

to this orientation. The subtle differentiations in both the basic motions themselves and in the simo data all depend on control characteristics. In this respect, industrial engineering is certainly attuned to other fields of engineering that concern themselves so greatly with differing kinds of control and their characteristics.

General Control Factors

In general, the higher the degree of control in a motion, the more difficult it is to perform either alone or in combination. Conversely, motions requiring little control are readily accomplished either alone or with other motions. Research has also established a most important fact related to simultaneous motions—*The amount of control required tends to increase when a given motion is performed in combination with other motions.*

The control capability of an operator depends most directly on:

1. APTITUDE AND/OR SKILL. The muscular, nervous, and mental equipment of a worker obviously influence his initial control capability. When he has acquired general or specialized skill, however, this has the effect of improving his basic ability to control motions. While natural aptitude for coordination is basically an inherited trait, it is possible to train people to the point where additional coordinating ability is gained. This idea is obvious when considering the differences between amateurs and professionals in the athletic world; the striking disparity between them can be reduced by a regimen of training and supervision of the neophyte. A sandlotter is unlikely to have the basic ability of Babe Ruth, but he can easily be taught to swing his bat more effectively and attain greater hitting power and accuracy. A similar situation obtains in regard to the aptitudes and skills of industrial workers as reflected in their control capabilities.

2. PRACTICE. The discussion of output variables in Chapter 2 made clear the role of training and practice in increasing operator skill. The repetition, or practice, of motions has an influence on control even beyond what was noted above in reference to skill. Practice has such a marked effect on the question of simultaneity that the choices of simo performance are directly based, in part, on three categories that express the degree of practice the operator will likely have with the combination being decided. More discussion of this appears later.

3. WORKING CONDITIONS. Peculiarities or other properties of the workpiece and arrangement of the workplace may aid or inhibit the use of certain motion combinations. One of the major gages of this, discussed later, is the field of vision. Some motion combinations

obviously require that placement of the objects concerned occurs within the field of vision. In the MTM data, two categories for the field of vision aid choices of simultaneity. Other factors can also affect the methods or combination of motions used. Sharp projections that endanger the skin is an example. Such factors will be more fully explained in a later chapter dealing with the laws of motion economy.

Kinds of Control

The kinds of control involved in motions by an operator are not new to the reader, since they were listed briefly in the discussion of selection time in the Grasp chapter. At this stage, however, it is possible to be more precise and achieve greater understanding than was true at that point.

All of the three kinds of control listed here have been considered in the simo tables. Although lengthy discussion of them is possible, a practical condensation of each is more useful to the MTM analyst. Basically, the worker does his tasks by employing the muscles of his body in a mechanical manner, in much the same way as the components of a mechanism perform their functions to cause a whole machine to accomplish its assigned role in production. But even the machine must be fed input information by dial settings, electric signals, pneumatic action, and hosts of other ways. In this regard, the human "machine" utilizes the sensory information gathered—mainly by the eyes—and filtered through the "master control"— the brain—to direct and limit the action of the muscles in a most effective manner.

The kinds of control, accordingly, depend on the components of this action:

1. MUSCULAR. This includes the effort or muscular strain involved in starting and stopping the motion, keeping it on the proper path, and any accuracy or precision demanded by the kind and classification of the motion. These all influence simultaneity.
2. VISUAL. Eye motions are often used in a minor way when the only control demand is normal orientation of the operator. On the other hand, when exact discrimination. is the type of control required, the exertion of visual powers to control the motion is very high. The frequency with which the eyes transmit information to the brain obviously must be greater when the need for more precise direction of the muscles is present. In passing, it is also well to note that the muscles have the special faculty of kinesthetic sense which can take over the control functions initially provided by visual means when the control demands are of such nature that they permit it; sufficient leeway in the operating characteristics and much practice of certain

motion sequences tend to favor this possibility. The sense of touch, in such cases, must provide enough data about the surrounding conditions that the higher sensing ability of the eyes is not essential to control. For most instances where high control is needed, however, the visual avenues must be used and relied upon.

3. MENTAL. All work requires at least a modicum of mental control. Certain motions, such as Case C Moves or Positions, obviously require more mental control than others, such as Case E Reaches. This control factor covers simple decisions affecting the performance that must be made consciously, but in no way approaches that involved in the work elements known as set-up or plan. The mental control being described might be categorized easiest as the instantaneous coordination of the eye and muscles within the brain. Work that requires relatively more coordination is commonly called high control work. Conversely, mental coordination is minimal when the control demands of the work elements are low. Obviously, it is harder to combine two motions requiring high control than two involving low levels of control.

Variables in Control

A host of factors were taken into account in development of the simo tables. Many are of such detailed nature that they are not discussed at length in this chapter. However, the following list of questions reveal the nature of the variables that have influenced the simo answers to some degree:

1. At which portion of a motion is the control exercised? Normally, the higher degrees of control are exerted toward the end of a motion, the lower degrees near the beginning and the middle portions.

2. Do the degrees and/or types of control needed conflict? Remember that the left side of the brain controls the right side of the body, and vice versa so that dissimilar commands tend to produce difficult motion sequences. This touches on the law of motion economy regarding symmetrical motion paths. It is easier to perform motions whose directions tend to complement one another than motions having odd path configurations or paths of travel in opposite directions in relation to the body.

3. What effect do differences in the predominant purposes of the two simo motions have on their ease of performance? Obviously, one would expect similar purposes to cause easier motions, while divergent aims would tend to complicate matters.

4. Does the use of certain muscle groups involve special difficulties or does coordination suffer when certain combinations of muscle groups

are used together?   Much study of motor ability by medical and
psychological people has been devoted to this question.   Their
answers tend to be complex and cause one of the major difficulties
of simo analysis.

5. Does the speed and force of one of the motions affect the other of
the pair?   A partial answer to this is mentioned later under balancing
delay, but there evidently is an interconnection.   One reason why
more data for this problem does not exist is the experimental difficulty of measuring either the speed or force of motions directly.

6. What is the effect of preceding or succeeding motions on the control
demanded of the pair of motions being considered?   The many rules
and definitions which provide answers to this question in relation to
individual motions contrast with the paucity of information concerning the same problem under simo conditions.

It should be apparent from this list that many variables have been
considered and evaluated to some extent in arriving at the simo data; but
the need for much more detailed research to permit even better answers in
future data on motion combinations is also obvious.   Other variables not
yet isolated may well be as pertinent as these.

Degree of Control

In much of the preceding material, reference has been made to the
amount of control inherent in motions.   It is necessary to know the
degree of control for individual motions in order to intelligently combine
them.   For this reason, an attempt has been made to list the degree of
control in the general order of difficulty.   This data can be seen in Table 1,
where suggestive categories are used.   These should not be considered as
absolute or restrictive, but they do indicate where the motions usually fall
in the over-all scale of control.

Low control implies that they may be easily done with little or no
practice, and accordingly would tend to be easily performed simo with
other motions.   *Medium control* suggests that at least a moderate amount
of practice is needed, so that their presence in simo combinations could
either indicate an easy pair or one requiring practice—depending on the
performance conditions.   *High control* infers maximum utilization of all
three kinds of control, such that the motion can be done simo only with
difficulty unless high skill and much practice indicate otherwise.

The simo tables, to assure uniform interpretation by analysts of the
many combination possibilities, have generally been based on the degree of
control needed by each of the individual motions.   They can be roughly
checked by using the listing in Table 1 with these generalized rules:

Table I.   Degree of Control for MTM Motions

(Suggestive only)

Motions Made	Control Category		
	Low	Medium	High
Reaches	R–A R–E	R–B —	R–C R–D
Moves	M–A	M–B	M–C
Turns	Usually	—	—
Apply Pressures	, —	Usually	—
Grasps	G1 A G2 G3 G5 (Always)	G1B (Depending G1C— on the case of reach that precedes)	G4– — — —
Positions	None	P1SE	All others
Disengages	D1E —	D1D D2E	All others
Releases	Always	—	—
Eye Motions	— —	ET EF	— —
Body Motions	Some	Most	Some

A. Two low control motions can be done simo under almost any conditions

B. One low control motion can be normally done simo with a medium control motion under almost any conditions

C. One low control motion can usually be done simo with a high control motion under almost any conditions

D. Two medium control motions can be done simo if they occur within the area of normal vision, but they require practice (as later defined) if they occur outside the area of normal vision

E. A motion of medium control can be done simo with one of high control within the area of normal vision if practice has been had; it is difficult to combine these simultaneously outside the area of normal vision

F. Two high control motions are difficult to perform simo under almost any conditions, normally they must be considered as uncombined.

Exceptions to these rules obviously will occur for two reasons: First, because the rules themselves are only approximations; and secondly, because the control listings for the individual motions are also only suggestive categories. In instances where extreme control is required, the performance of motions in a simo manner would obviously be very unlikely. At the other end of the scale, however, it would seldom be that uncontrolled motions could not be combined simultaneously. Remember that control varies on a continuum, and assigning breakpoints at all is an arbitrary procedure at best. Application of these rules will, however, permit practical answers in most instances of need.

SIMULTANEOUS MANUAL MOTIONS

Recall from all the background information previously given that control is the key to simultaneous coordination of motions. More specific factors will now be discussed that lead to an explanation of how the simo tables disclose whether a given pair of motions can be done simultaneously.

In actual usage, the analyst must choose, with the aid of the tables, whether the higher or both motion times must be allowed for two motions being considered as possibly simo. This is regardless of the number of categories by which to judge which class of combination—as next discussed —is correct for the pair of motions being considered. In effect, this limitation leaves *two choices;* either the pair can be done simo and the longer of the two motion times is allowed, or else it cannot be done simo and both times must be allowed because the motions are really consecutive. As for notation, the first choice requires that the motions be listed on the same line of the analysis form, while the second will necessitate writing them on successive lines.

The simultaneous motion tables existing at present cover only the manual motions. The research necessary to arrive at this state of knowledge was very complex and took much time; even so, these tables in no way represent final, unchangeable answers. To extend the knowledge of simo motions, and to further inquire into the even more complex compound motions in greater detail, will require a major effort in future researches. The benefits to be derived from proper usage of the present tables for manual motions, however, are sufficiently large so that when used with prudent judgment they can help solve a host of work measurement problems beyond the immediate concern of writing simo patterns.

General Classes

Simo manual motions can readily be classed in three ways—identical, similar, and dissimilar. The latter two can be subdivided respectively into three and four sub-classes each. All of this data is given in Table 2 and is self evident upon critical examination. The three classes, their features, and examples are all included in the table and are discussed in detail in a later section.

Table 2. Classes of Motion Combinations

Class of Combination	Features			Examples		
	Kind of Motions	Class or Distance	Case of Motion	LH Motion	TMU Allowed	RH Motion
IDENTICAL	Same	Same	Same	(1) R5A	6.5	R5A
				(2) G1A	2.0	G1A
				(3) M6B	8.9	M6B
SIMILAR	Same	May differ	May differ			
Subclass A	Same	Same	Different	(R10A)	12.9	R10C
Subclass B	Same	Different	Same	(M10B)	13.4	M12B
Subclass C	Same	Different	Different	(1)(R10A)	12.9	R12B
				(2)(G1A)	9.1	G4B
DISSIMILAR	May differ	May differ	May differ			
Subclass A	Different	Same	Same	M4A	6.1	R4A
Subclass B	Different	Same	Different	(M4A)	6.4	R4B
Subclass C	Different	Different	Same	R14B	14.4	(M6B)
Subclass D	Different	Different	Different	P2SE	16.2	(G2)

DEFINITIONS OF THE CLASSES

IDENTICAL —Identical simultaneous motions are the same as to kind, class, and case for both members

SIMILAR —Similar simultaneous motions are the same as to kind, but may differ as to class and/or distance and case between the two members

DISSIMILAR—Dissimilar simultaneous motions are always different as to kind, but may be the same as to class and case between the two members acting.

Note in the examples that the simplification of the limiting convention for identical—omitting the circle around whichever of the two motions is limited in the theoretical sense—makes no difficulty in assigning times or describing the motion occurrence.

Table Categories

Interpretation of the manual simo tables shown at the end of this chapter depends on knowledge of the two means or factors by which the combinations are listed to show which motion pairs are possible, probable, or the converse. These two factors are the field of vision and the degree of practice. In addition, there are several special variables which influence the observation of motions and the choice of pairs as possibly simo rather than the manner in which the tables are used directly.

A. *Field of Vision.* The principal means of control—visual, muscular, and mental—must all be exerted in space; but only the visual control is limited in respect to the location in space of the motions being controlled. This is due to the inability of the eyes to cover an area effectively that much exceeds the Area of Normal Vision. This area, as was explained in the Eye Motion chapter, provides a rough guide to the visual span of an operator during simo performance. It was defined as a 4-inch diameter circle located 16 inches from the eyes within which objects can be seen without shifting the line of sight.

If two motions being performed are terminated within 4 inches of each other at around 16 inches from the eyes, maximum visual control is possible; therefore, the likelihood of simo performance is favorable. If the endpoints are not within this distance proportion, and visual control is needed, it is less likely that the two motions can be simo. To distinguish this factor in the simo data, the tables include separate columns for motions ending Within the Area of Normal Vision (denoted by W) and Outside the Area of Normal Vision (denoted by 0) in all cases where visual control is an important variable. In choosing the proper column for field of vision, the MTM analyst automatically accounts for visual control in simo motions.

B. *Degree of Practice.* The basic assumption is made in the simo tables that the worker will have ample practice on long production runs and highly repetitive cycles to develop his best degree of skill; whereas under jobbing conditions or short production runs, he will not gain sufficient practice to achieve simo performance. The tables are constructed to permit a choice of simultaneity, therefore, that depends on the degree of practice the analyst anticipates will be applicable to the motion pattern in which the motions being examined occur. The three categories are:

E—*Easy* to perform with little or no practice. Such motions can be done simo, so only the longer of the two motion times should be allowed in the motion pattern.

P—*Practice* is required in at least a reasonable degree before the two motions can be simo. If the analyst decides there is enough opportunity for practice, he will show the motions simo and allow only the longer of the two times. If he decides, according to the basic rule given above, that practice cannot be enough to effect simo performance, he will show the motions consecutively and allow both motion times.

D—*Difficult* combinations, even after long practice, indicate that the analyst should almost always write the motion pair in a consecutive manner and allow both motion times. Of course, he might justify such combinations as simo when above average operators are observed or where exceptional practice and training are found on unusual jobs under highly repetitive conditions. Since the MTM standard is for average operators under average conditions, however, he will almost never decide for simo when the tables show a difficult combination.

It is obvious that the simo *tables must be used with judgment* when deciding whether the degree of practice permits simultaneous performance.

Included in the judgment of degree of practice should be the effects of lot size, cycle length, and pattern complexity. A good operator can learn with practice to do progressively more simo combinations; he can also reduce the case, type, or class of a given kind of motion or even eliminate certain motions entirely. Experience with similar motion sequences on other jobs will tend to carry over to newer tasks. For these reasons, the total lot size alone will not always correctly show the degree of practice to assign. Also, standards resulting from analysis of large lots or high production may be too "tight" for subsequent lots small in size, or smaller lots produced after a notable time lapse since the larger lot was run. Similarly, a long cycle will require much more practice to learn than a short one because there is less opportunity to repeat each motion sequence in the cycle. When the motion combinations or the individual motions are of the more difficult or complex varieties, a greater amount of practice will be needed to achieve equal skill and simo ability compared to a pattern involving only simple motions and combinations.

Additional insights regarding the degree of practice required to achieve basic MTM motion standards may be found in an MTM research report.[5] Specific MTM research data on how simo motions affect learning[6] is also available from the MTM Association. These are part of the current MTM research project, discussed in a later chapter, which shows that inexperienced operators may require thousands of cycles to attain the MTM standard times.

C. *Other Factors:* Personal differences in the ability of individual workers or groups of operators, particularly in aptitudes, will affect the decision of whether to allow simo or consecutive performance. The motions possible are directly affected by the distances and arrangement of the workplace, as well as the equipment and tools provided. Good facilities favor the assigning of simo combinations, so the work analyst should either improve the facilities or else realistically be fair to the operator by not assigning simo motions when the facilities are unfavorable. Besides these rather general

[5] R.R. 112 (See Ch. 5).

[6] "The Effect of Simultaneous Motions on Learning", by Stanley H. Caplan and Walton M. Hancock, *Journal of Methods-Time Measurement*, Vol. IX, No. 1, MTM Association for Standards and Research, Ann Arbor, Michigan, September–October 1963.

decision factors, there are two special variables which the analyst must sometimes evaluate during simo analysis.

One of these is called *balancing tendency*. For the simultaneous similar class of motion combination, of the type shown in Subclass B in Table 2, the MTM research showed that when the motions in the two hands differ only in distance, the motions tend to balance each other as to time needed. Actually, the hand traveling the shorter distance will tend to delay slightly, while the hand going the longer distance will tend to speed up slightly. Both hands therefore tend to arrive at their destination together. This means that the actual time taken for the combination will lie between the limiting and limited times, although the difference between the actual time and the limiting time due to balancing tendency is too small in most cases to change the time allowance in practical usage. This does indicate, however, that the decision of Easy—where permitted by appearance of a Practice designation in the simo tables—will be favored if this type of simo similar combination is encountered.

Interaction time is the other special variable that affects the simo decision from the table categories. This concept covers the observed cases where several motions appear to be done simo, but which are difficult to perform simo according to the data tables. What is actually occurring is similar to the action of Moves against a stop discussed and illustrated in the Move Chapter, where it was shown that double Moves sometimes occur even though the second Move is too short for the eye to observe directly. Reliance on a "rule of thumb" developed by the researcher viewing each motion picture frame was shown to provide proper analysis for such cases. For example, an operator may appear to be doing two M7C simo outside the area of normal vision, which is difficult according to the tables. Without knowing about interaction time, the analyst would incorrectly assign both times, or 22.2 TMU. The research showed this combination to require 12.1 TMU. Simo performance would require the time for only one M7C of 11.1 TMU, which is low. Knowing about interaction time would cause the analyst to record the proper motions and assign times as shown below. This obviously gives a better answer that is on the safe side of the actual time. The M6B can be done (with practice) out of vision with the M7C, so that the simo rules are not disregarded by this analysis.

LH	TMU	RH
M6B	11.1	M7C
MfC	2.0	
Total	13.1 TMU	

SIMULTANEOUS MOTION TABLES

Two sets of simultaneous motion data exist in the MTM system. One is the very detailed information that resulted from the MTM researches. In order to permit handy reference in a condensed form to fit the MTM data card, the other set of data was developed. Actually, these tables differ mainly in degree of preciseness and the detail of coverage of the simultaneous manual motions. The data card table, because it is condensed, includes more cases in one listing and is thereby more conservative. It will sometimes indicate a higher degree of simo difficulty for a pair of motions than will the detailed tables. In addition, some simo combinations cannot be found separately listed in the condensed table; but they are readily found in the detailed table, which covers almost all possible combinations between the manual motions.

Detailed Tables

The detailed tables can be found on five sheets at the end of this chapter. They will be found easy to use once the reader becomes familiar with the coding and the motions covered by each table. Remember, when consulting the tables, the analyst decides either that the motions can be simo or that they will not be simo under the visual and practice conditions pertaining to the motion pattern in which the two motions concerned appear. If they can be simo, he will record the motions on the same line of the analysis form and allow only the longer time; if not, he will write the motions on successive lines and allow both motion times.

The coding used to indicate practice conditions is as follows: the intersection of the row for one of the motions and the column for the other motion, displays a blank space for *easy* combinations; the intersection is marked with an "x" when the analyst has a pair of motions that can be simo *with practice,* and he must decide accordingly; and motion pairs that are *difficult* to do together are distinguished by a solid black area.

When the combination occurs within the area of normal vision, one of the motions is read in the column labeled "W." If the motions end outside the area of normal vision—more than 4 inches apart by definition —the column headed "O" is used. In cases where the field of vision has no bearing on simultaneity, the columns are either labeled "ALL" or the heading is omitted.

Note that the Case B Moves are subdivided into two classes. The basis for such a division appears in the definition for M–B as follows: "Move object to *approximate* or *indefinite* location." Apparently, some differences in the ability of operators to perform B Moves simultaneously depend on a distinction between the precision with which the end point of the motion path of an M–B can be associated. Separate rows and columns for each class of Case B Move therefore appear in the detailed simo tables. In symbols, the approximate case is often written M–Ba while the indefinite distance is shown as M–Bi. This listing should involve no difficulty of interpretation so long as the analyst is careful to decide which kind of Case B Move he has to evaluate.

Other special distinctions in the tables can be seen. Turns are considered as either approximate or exact in most of the tables; a further subdivision is made for Turn with Disengage depending on the degrees of Turn being greater or less than 90 degrees. Release has a general rule that shows it is easy to perform simo with any other motion. A note for Apply Pressure indicates that special analysis is needed when deciding whether it can be simo. There is a difference for Disengage that depends on the presence or absence of care. And finally, Grasp-Grasp combinations may require reference to several notes that make the simo decision depend on the type of reaches preceding the grasps.

Examples: 1. R–B with R–C. This combination is easy in vision, but will require practice out of vision.
2. R–D in one hand with an exact Turn in the other hand. To do this within the area of normal vision requires practice, and it is difficult to do out of vision.
3. M–Bi and G4. This can be done easily regardless of visual conditions.
4. G1C in combination with D2. This is always difficult to do simo.
5. P3SE with RL. Release can always be easily done simo with any other motion.

The answers given provide information with which the analyst can apply his knowledge of the variables in simo performance to reach a decision.

Data Card Tables

Table X of the MTM data card is reproduced in Table 3.

Note that in this table, the intersections for Difficult are in heavy black as they are in the detailed tables. Generally, it is easiest when using this table to enter the right-hand column with the motion nearest the top of the column and then read the row headings to the left until the intersection desired is found. For instance, the quickest way to find an R–B and G1C combination is to find Reach B in the right-hand column, follow that row to the left until it intersects with the row heading for G1B and G1C, and discover there that the two motions are easy in vision but require practice out of vision. When attempting to enter the table from the top headings, time will be lost because of the manner in which the listings are made.

The column headings labeled "W" and "O" refer, as do the detailed tables, to the field of vision. Those headed "E" and "D" refer to easy and difficult handling categories as they normally pertain to positions and disengages, that is, they are the ending letter for the symbol. For instance, in the P1S column, there are two sub-columns so marked; the left one is used for P1SE and the right one for P1SD.

At the bottom of Table 3 (Table X of the data card) are listed some guide rules that help decide simo for combinations not listed in the table. It is obviously much easier to use the detailed tables when instances such as this are found, but the data card (usually carried) may often be the only information source the MTM analyst has available when he must

Table 3. Table X of the MTM Data Card—Simultaneous Motions

make a simo decision. Remember that the condensed tables have the utility of being conveniently available with the rest of the MTM motion data; they are not intended to provide final answers in every case, but they do offer a convenient form and location of data. To make sure that the answers are generally on the safe side, check any doubtful combinations by reference to the detailed tables:

Examples: 1. R–B with R–C. Easy in vision, practice out of vision; this answer is the same as found in the detailed tables.

2. R–D in one hand with an exact Turn in the other. The

special note says this is not easy because the Turn is controlled, but whether it requires practice only or is difficult cannot be found on the condensed table. This is a case where the detailed table gives an answer more enlightening than the Data Card table.

3. M–B and G4. The card shows this to require practice in vision and to be difficult out of vision. Because the "indefinite" could be identified on the detailed tables, the answer there was more liberal—it said this combination was easy. Notice, however, that the M–Ba answer for the detailed tables agrees with the condensed tables.

4. G1C in combination with D2. The data card agrees with the detailed tables that this is a difficult combination to perform.

5. P3SE with RL. The answer here also agrees—this is easy to do.

This comparison should make obvious both the advantages and limitations of the data card simo tables in relation to the detailed tables. It is better and more correct to use the detailed tables when they are readily available, but the data card must often be relied upon in practical situations where the detailed tables cannot be carried or located easily.

Simo Analysis by Class of Combination

If the MTM engineer has a firm grasp of the general rules on which the answers are based, he can often save time by not having to look at either set of simo tables. These are given here grouped by classes as they were defined earlier in Table 2.

Identical and Similar Combinations:

REACH-REACH. In most cases, identical Reaches are easily done simo in vision, but require practice out of vision. The main exception is that identical Case C and Case D Reaches require practice in vision and are difficult out of vision. Another exception is that, for identical R–A and also identical R–E, the vision field makes no difference, as they are always easily done together. For the similar class cases, the same general rules hold except that the C and D Reaches should be looked up in the tables to be certain of the answers.

MOVE-MOVE. In vision, similar or identical combinations are all easily simo with the exception that the identical Case C requires practice. Out of vision, most combinations require practice except that C Moves of the identical class are difficult to do simo. Recall in this particular case, however, the analysis earlier given for interaction time.

TURN-TURN. Approximate turns (relatively uncontrolled) are easily simo regardless of the field of vision. Identically exact Turns, however, require practice in vision and are difficult out of vision.

GRASP-GRASP. Generally, the tables should be consulted for Grasp combinations, because of the variety of answers. Note that G1A is always easily performed simo with other Grasps, and this is also true for G2 and G5. Identical G4 cannot be done simultaneously; both Grasp times must be allowed. Similar Grasp combinations including G4 result in various answers. The reason is that search and select control is needed for each hand that makes a G4, so the operator must concentrate on one hand at a time. G3 is by definition a kind of grasp where simultaneity does not come into question. Identical G1B and G1C in vision are easy when preceded by R–A or R–B, but are otherwise difficult. Identical G1B and G1C out of vision require practice when an R–A precedes, but are otherwise difficult. For other similar combinations, no rule can substitute for looking into the simo tables.

POSITION-POSITION. For average operators, identical P1SE are easy to do simo. All other identical or similar Position combinations are difficult to do.

DISENGAGE-DISENGAGE. All identical or similar combinations not requiring care can be done simo, but all other possibilities are difficult.

RELEASE-RELEASE. Release is easily done simo with any other motion.

APPLY PRESSURE-APPLY PRESSURE. Although each case must be examined, these combinations tend to be easier if the pressures are applied in the same direction by like body members. All other cases either require practice or are difficult, the latter being especially true when unlike body members are used in different directions.

Dissimilar Combinations:

REACH-MOVE. Case A and B Reaches may be easily simo with any case of Move within the normal vision area; out of vision, they normally require practice. All R–E can be easily performed with any case of Move regardless of visual bounds, since the eye will follow the Move rather than the Reach. Case C Moves in vision require practice to combine with R–C and R–D; it is difficult to make these combinations out of vision. Most other possibilities require practice.

REACH-TURN OR MOVE-TURN. If the Turn is approximate, it will be easy to combine with any case of Reach or Move. When it is controlled, however, the need for practice or the difficulty of combining depend mainly on the field of vision and the relative control in the Reach or Move.

REACH-GRASP. Simultaneous performance is easy for any case of Reach with G1A, G2, and G5. Practice is needed to combine G1B with controlled Reaches, and either practice or difficult choices are possible for G1C with controlled Reaches; either of these Grasps are easily done with low control Reaches. Case A and E Reaches are easy with G4, Case B in vision requires practice, and all other G4-Reach combinations are difficult.

MOVE-GRASP. With G1A, G2, and G5 any Move can be easily combined. Practice is needed for M–Ba out of vision with G1B and G1C, most M–C require practice with either of these Grasps, but G1B and G1C can otherwise be easily done together with Moves. G4 can be easily performed with M–A and M–Bi, but it is difficult to Select Grasp with most other Moves.

TURN-OTHER MOTIONS. Approximate Turns are easily done with all other motions except Disengage. Exact Turns, however, are usually difficult to combine.

APPLY PRESSURE-OTHER MOTIONS. The remarks given for identical and similar simo combinations hold here, except that dissimilar combinations involving AP are less likely to be easily done unless special conditions are true.

RELEASE-OTHER MOTIONS. Again, Release is easy to do with any other motion.

POSITION-OTHER MOTIONS. Generally, it is difficult to combine Positions with most other motions, although some cases can be done with practice. The only frequent exception to this occurs with P1SE, but even these are usually difficult to combine with other motions involving higher control.

DISENGAGE-OTHER MOTIONS. Some Disengages of the D1 and D2 classes can be readily performed with certain Reaches and Moves of lower control categories. In almost all other combinations, Disengage is difficult to do simo. It is never simo with Positions, and seldom with any kind of Grasp.

Special Notes:

Sometimes people uninitiated in work measurement think that by using both hands at all times together production will be doubled. With knowledge of the extensive simo data, it is extremely obvious why this is ordinarily impossible. Not all of the right and left hand motions can be simo. Because of this, it is considered good if 20 to 35 per cent productive increase results from changing an operation to two-handed, other things remaining the same. Of course, double, triple, and other multiples of the original production can result from complete methods revisions based on design of parts, tooling, layout, and the like; but increases due to maximum simo usage alone are generally more limited.

Remember that all of the simo data given is predicated on the capability and dexterity of average operators. It is readily understandable, therefore, that highly skilled workers with much practice can perform motion combinations that apparently belie the simo data. For example, an average worker may perform two Case B Reaches simo and follow these with non-simo G1B; whereas a highly skilled operator may change this to two simo R–A followed by simo G1B. Positions that require practice, or are difficult, to achieve simultaneously by the average worker may actually be readily done by experts; the expert may even find ways to eliminate entirely the Positions considered. The MTM standard, to repeat for emphasis, is applicable to *average* workers exerting *average* skill and effort under *average* conditions.

Occasionally, an MTM analyst observes motions being performed partially simo. If the appropriate simo table indicates the motions can be done simultaneously, this is the method which should be specified. However, if the chart does not indicate this, the partial simo should be considered as due to above average operator skill and non-simo motions should be assigned and allowed.

SIMULTANEOUS BODY MOTIONS

Some remarks concerning the likelihood of combining body motions with each other and with manual motions were made in the last chapter. The comments here provide additional information.

The fact that body motions generally are time consuming, and therefore limit out manual motions concurrently performed, is the main point to remember. It is not usual that simo motions can be done with body actions involved. It is fairly common, however, to find combined motions involving the body, and compound motions with body action included are also encountered. Since no tables have been developed to provide ready information—this is another area which research should cover in the future—these general concepts can be applied with judgment in the analysis of body, leg, and foot motions where simultaneity appears worth investigating:

1. During body motions, it is essential to maintain a certain degree of balance. Because the manual members are frequently used to provide stabilizing and restraining action, they are often unavailable to perform productive motions themselves.

2. Heavier objects are usually handled by manual motions to bring them close to the body before body motions are made; additional manual motions are then needed to move them away from the body prior to performance of succeeding manual motions. If all such

motions are recognized and analyzed, rules previously given should be sufficient to arrive at reasonable performance times.

3. Grasps to pick up objects in conjunction with body motions are usually performed only after the body action has been completed.

4. The motions of the right side of the body are controlled by the left half of the brain, and vice versa. Dissimilar commands in regard to kind of motion or direction of motion path to each side of the body will tend to result in confusion, destroying effective action. Also, different body members controlled by the same half of the brain must be given harmonious commands if successful motions are to ensue.

These ideas indicate that much is yet unknown about the human body in spite of the large amount of data on human motions available from existing research. When an MTM analyst must record body motions, therefore, it is wise practice to observe more than one operator if possible so that he will not be misled by special ability of the first operator he was watching. In addition, when body motions are being visualized, an experienced analyst will usually try out the various motions himself to see whether motion combinations he has in mind are possible.

SUMMARY

The four kinds of motions combinations are:	Consecutive Combined Simultaneous Compound
The three classes of simo motions are:	Identical Similar Dissimilar
The main basis to judge motion combinations is:	Control
The main practical factors in simo data are:	Degree of Practice Field of Vision

There is no substitute for practical judgment when analyzing motion combinations.

Index to Detailed MTM Simultaneous Motion Tables*

Page	Motion	In Combination With
373	Reach	Reach. Move. Turn. Grasp.
374	Reach	Position. Disengage.
374	Release	All other motions.
374	Apply Pressure	No definite rules.
375	Move	Move. Turn. Grasp.
376	Move	Position. Disengage.
375	Position	Position. Turn. Disengage.
376	Turn	Turn.
376	Disengage	Disengage.
377	Disengage	Turn.
377	Grasp	Grasp. Turn. Position. Disengage.

* The Detailed MTM Simultaneous Motion Combination Tables (sheets 1 to 5 on the following pages) differ from the condensed table (Table 3, page 366) mainly in degree of preciseness and detail of coverage as stated on page 364.

Detailed MTM Simultaneous Motion Table—Per Research Report 105

SHEET NO. I		SIMULTANEOUS REACH							
IN COMBINATION WITH		R-A		R-B		R-C		R-D	R-E
		W	O	W	O	W	O	W	O	ALL

R E A C H	R-A			⊠		⊠		⊠		
	R-B	⊠		⊠		⊠		⊠		
	R-C	⊠		⊠		■		⊠	■	
	R-D	⊠		⊠		⊠		⊠	■	
	R-E									

M O V E	M-A	⊠		⊠		⊠	⊠	⊠		
	M-B APPROXIMATE	⊠				⊠	⊠	⊠		
	M-B INDEFINITE									
	M-C	⊠		⊠		■	⊠	■		
	M-Bm					⊠		⊠		

T U R N	APPROXIMATE									
	EXACT	⊠		⊠		■	⊠	■		

G R A S P	G1A									
	G1B			⊠		⊠	⊠	⊠		
	G1C			⊠		■	⊠	■		
	G2									
	G4		⊠	■	■	■	■	■		
	G5									

☐ SHOWS COMBINATIONS THAT CAN BE DONE EASILY WITH LITTLE OR NO PRACTICE.
ALLOW ONLY THE LONGEST OF THE TWO TIMES FOR COMBINATION.

⊠ SHOWS COMBINATIONS THAT REQUIRE PRACTICE FOR SIMULTANEOUS PERFORMANCE.
ALLOW BOTH TIMES FOR JOB SHOP OR NON-REPETITIVE CONDITIONS.
ALLOW ONLY THE LONGEST OF THE TWO TIMES FOR HIGHLY REPETITIVE CONDITIONS.

■ SHOWS COMBINATIONS DIFFICULT TO PERFORM EVEN AFTER LONG PRACTICE.
ALLOW BOTH TIMES UNLESS EXCEPTIONAL PRACTICE AND TRAINING ARE FOUND ON UNUSUAL JOBS UNDER HIGHLY REPETITIVE CONDITIONS.

W - WITHIN AREA OF NORMAL VISION (NOT OVER 4"APART AT 16" FROM THE EYES).

O - OUTSIDE AREA OF NORMAL VISION (OVER 4"APART AT 16" FROM THE EYES).

Detailed MTM Simultaneous Motion Table—Per Research Report 105

SHEET NO. 2				SIMULTANEOUS REACH				
IN COMBINATION WITH				R-A	R-B	R-C	R-D	R-E
POSITION	CLASS 1	S	ALL		⊠	■	■	
		SS	E		⊠	■	■	
			D	⊠	■	■	■	⊠
		NS	ALL	⊠	■	■	■	⊠
	CLASS 2	S	E		⊠	■	■	
			D	⊠	■	■	■	⊠
		SS	E	⊠	■	■	■	⊠
			D	■	■	■	■	■
		NS	E	⊠	■	■	■	⊠
			D	■	■	■	■	■
	CLASS 3	ALL	ALL	■	■	■	■	■
DISENGAGE	CLASS 1		E			⊠	⊠	
			D			■	■	
	CLASS 2		E			■	■	
			D		⊠	■	■	
	CLASS 3		ALL	■	■		■	

RELEASE	ALWAYS EASY TO PERFORM SIMO WITH ANY OTHER MOTION.

APPLY PRESSURE	NO DEFINITE RULE CAN BE GIVEN. FOR ANY COMBINATION, THE ANALYST SHOULD EITHER OBSERVE IT OR TRY IT HIMSELF TO DETERMINE WHETHER THE COMBINATION IS EASY, REQUIRES PRACTICE, OR IS DIFFICULT TO PERFORM. TIME ALLOWANCE WILL BE MADE TO ACCORD WITH DECISION.

Detailed MTM Simultaneous Motion Table—Per Research Report 105

SHEET NO. 3 — SIMULTANEOUS MOVE

IN COMBINATION WITH		M-A		M-B APPROXIMATE		M-B INDEFINITE		M-C		M-Bm
		W	O	W	O	W	O	W	O	ALL
M O V E	M-A		X	X				X		
	M-B APPROXIMATE		X	X				X		
	M-B INDEFINITE									
	M-C		X	X				X	■	
	M-Bm									
T U R N	APPROXIMATE									
	EXACT		X	X				X	■	
G R A S P	G1A									
	G1B			X				X		
	G1C							X	■	
	G2									
	G4		X		■			■	■	
	G5									

SIMULTANEOUS POSITION

IN COMBINATION WITH		CLASS 1				CLASS 2 ANY SYMMETRY	CLASS 3 ANY SYMMETRY
		S		SS	NS	ALL	ALL
		E	D	ALL	ALL		
P O S I T I O N	P1SE ONLY		■	■	■	■	■
	ALL OTHER		■	■	■	■	■
T U R N	APPROXIMATE						
	EXACT	■	■	■	■	■	■
DISENGAGE		■	■	■	■	■	■

Detailed MTM Simultaneous Motion Table—Per Research Report 105

SHEET NO. 4				SIMULTANEOUS MOVE				
IN COMBINATION WITH				M-A	M-B APPROX.	M-B INDEF.	M-C	M-Bm
P O S I T I O N	CLASS I	S	ALL					
		SS	E					
			D					
		NS	ALL					
	CLASS 2	S	E					
			D					
		SS	E					
			D					
		NS	E					
			D					
	CLASS 3	ANY SYMM.	ALL					
D I S E N G A G E	CLASS I	ALL						
	CLASS 2	E						
		D						
	CLASS 3	ALL						

IN COMBINATION WITH		SIMULTANEOUS TURN		
		APPROXIMATE	EXACT	
		ANY	W	O
T U R N	APPROXIMATE			
	EXACT			

IN COMB. WITH		NO CARE	CARE REQUIRED
D I S E N G A G E	NO CARE		
	CARE REQUIRED		

SIMULTANEOUS DISENGAGE

Detailed MTM Simultaneous Motion Table—Per Research Report 105

SHEET NO. 5		SIMULTANEOUS GRASP								
IN COMBINATION WITH		G1A	G1B		G1C		G2	G4		G5
		ALL	W	O	W	O	ALL	W	O	ALL
G R A S P	G1A									
	G1B		NOTE I	NOTE II						
	G1C				NOTE I	NOTE II				
	G2									
	G4									
	G5									
T U R N	APPROXIMATE									
	EXACT									
P O S I T I O N	CLASS 1 — S — ALL									
	CLASS 1 — SS — E									
	CLASS 1 — SS — D									
	CLASS 1 — NS — ALL									
	CLASS 2 — S — E									
	CLASS 2 — S — D									
	CLASS 2 — SS — ALL									
	CLASS 2 — NS — ALL									
	CLASS 3 — ANY SYMM. — ALL									
E N G A G E D I S	CLASS I — ALL									
	CLASS 2 — ALL									
	CLASS 3 — ALL									

GRASP NOTES

I. EASY WHEN PRECEDED BY R-A OR R-B, OTHERWISE DIFFICULT.

II. PRACTICE WHEN PRECEDED BY R-A ONLY, OTHERWISE DIFFICULT.

IN COMBINATION WITH		SIMULTANEOUS DISENGAGE		
		CLASS I	CLASS 2	CLASS 3
T U R N	90° OR LESS			
	OVER 90°			

CHAPTER 19

Motion Patterns —
Methods Evidence

The visible evidence of Methods-Time Measurement analysis is the recorded motion pattern. ˙While mental application of the data and decisions regarding work analysis based on knowledge of the data are valuable and have their place, employment of MTM in this manner does not produce a record which preserves or substantiates the work method and/or resultant time standard. Only by writing the motion pattern can this most valuable of all MTM functions be effected.

The first eighteen chapters of this book have given the reader all the motion information and data he needs to write motion patterns. Each MTM motion together with all known related factors has been described in detail. Chapter 18 covered the means by which motions can be combined into useful patterns. Included in the explanation of motion combinations were several illustrative type examples of motion patterns for shorter work elements.

However, little detail has been given previously concerning the procedures, cautions, or other factors incident to the writing of motion patterns. This chapter, therefore, is intended to show how the MTM motion data and motion combination knowledge can be coordinated into motion analyses that comprise the practical, useful aspect of MTM in its final form. Although it sometimes is seemingly laborious, the "paperwork" stage of MTM analysis—writing motion patterns—is the key to maximum benefits from use of the techniques. The astute reader will wish to know, for this reason, every possible aid to quick, accurate writing of motion patterns that will reduce the effort of recording without leaving doubt in the mind of the persons who read his pattern as to his intentions or decisions regarding the work method.

WHAT ARE MOTION PATTERNS?

DEFINITION: *A motion pattern is the recorded evidence of the motion analysis of a work method at the element, sequence, or task level that provides lingual and/or symbolic information in a condensed form which fully and clearly delineates the means of performing the work in a manner permitting precise* **reproduction of the method.**

To be consistently successful in solving the many problems of work measurement, an MTM analyst must fully understand the characteristics of motion patterns. He can do this only if he is able to practice his art with full awareness of *what* he is doing, *why* he is doing it, *how* it may be done, *where* it is best done, and *who* is affected or a valid party to what is being done. Note how the five basic questions used by the industrial engineer are as applicable to evaluating the engineer himself as they are to evaluating the work he is studying.

A motion pattern is a useful evaluation device solely because it answers for anyone reading it, in compact form, the five basic work study queries. It is adequate only to the degree with which it faithfully and completely mirrors the method employed (or to be used) in performing the work analyzed. This concept does not deny that time determination is a necessary and useful part of the motion pattern, but it nevertheless places emphasis on the motions and descriptions—with the time values being an added feature. It is of little worth for an analyst to overly concern himself about time determination if he has insufficient ability or confidence in writing the motions on which, when employing a pre-determined time system, the time must necessarily be based. Assigning and computing the time values on a motion pattern are primarily clerical in nature, most of the true methods engineering having been achieved prior to this point.

To appreciate the place and importance which motion patterns can hold in the chain of events that create production, remember that one of the *prime* functions of industrial engineers—perhaps their most utilitarian one —is to develop and write processes. Industrial engineers, in cooperation with any other concerned specialist, staff, or executive personnel in the plant, must perform the vital step of processing. Starting with the design blueprints and the bills of materials (often called the "Bible of Production") as basic data, they must play a vital role in translating this data into a finished product ready to be shipped to the customer.

To help illustrate the importance of this essential step in the manufacturing enterprise, the following three definitions are quoted from A.S.M.E. Standard No. 106 entitled "Industrial Engineering Terminology":

PROCESS ENGINEER:

An individual qualified by education, training, and/or experience to prescribe efficient production processes to produce a product as designed and who specializes in this work. This work includes specifying all the equipment, tools, fixtures, and the like that are to be used, and often, the estimated cost of producing the product by the prescribed process.

PROCESSING:

n. 1. The act of prescribing the production process to produce a product as designed. This may include specifying the equipment, tools, fixtures, machines, and the like required, the methods to be used, the workmen necessary, and the estimated or allowed time.
2. The carrying out of a production process.

PROCESS:

n. 1. A planned series of actions or operations which advances a material or procedure from one stage of completion to another.
2. A planned and controlled treatment that subjects materials to the influence of one or more types of energy for the time required to bring about the desired reactions or results. Examples include the curing of rubber, mixing of compounds, heat treating of metals, machining of metals, and the like.

Inherent in many of the acts and functions thus defined is the necessity and desirability of evaluating human performance. *This implies that work measurement is essential to adequate processing and will both aid and measure it for the many industrial parties who are interested in profitable manufacture.* The implication, indeed, is closer each day to being an absolute fact as products and production technology become increasingly complex. The day when persons other than qualified industrial engineers can successfully design processes that will meet the competition of other vendors is rapidly passing; the growing demand for all types of engineering effort and skills is ample evidence of this truth.

To continue the reasoning, any valid work measurement procedure must be directly related to all the major factors in production. It must aid their attainment and give practical clues to better ways of doing things. The efforts of all technical, staff, and executive departments in the plant impinge on the worker as he makes the product, so that correct and complete analysis of his work requires attention to how the aims of these departments are served and contribute to the success of the business. Such analysis must reflect all the factors the industrial engineer must face and choose from, both in developing and in improving productive processes. Most of these factors, concisely listed in the definitions above, can definitely be shown to be an integral part of the working methods. *The motion pattern is the most evident proof and picture of the work method contained on any piece of paper in the entire factory.* Motion patterns, therefore, are important to the degree with which they properly mirror productive factors. As practiced in the techniques associated with Methods-Time Measurement, this kind of reflection in motion patterns is extremely well done.

Having regarded the general picture presented above, it is easier to look more closely at the connection of motion patterns to and with processes. The industrial engineer aids his work by subdividing his processes into components that are increasingly finer as follows: Operations, Sequences, Elements, and Motions. For example, the *process* may be that of producing conventional washing machines. The *operation* in question might be the assembly of the wringer. This would include the *element* of inserting the lower rubber roll into the drive barrel and bearing blocks. All of the *motions* needed to perform this task element would be analyzed by MTM to provide a record of the method of inserting the roll. From such a motion pattern would spring all the information and data from which the work analyst would proceed to institute, guide, and improve good washer production. Patterns, taken in the correct order and frequency, therefore, add up to processes. Actually, the work instruction sheets given the foreman and operator—often called Process Sheets—are easily written from motion patterns merely by transposing the pattern data into common shop language and descriptive words the operator can understand.

A motion pattern is basically built from the MTM motions that account for what, how, and where the operator performs the part of the process under human control; to be complete, it must also include pertinent information covering "process time" that is under the control of other agencies and factors. When the rate or time for performing the element covered by the pattern is controlled by, say, the cycle time of a machine, this must be obtained by time study or calculated by some alternate method —the MTM data covers only the manual time. It is, therefore, obvious that pre-determined times do not supplant time study. In fact, certain essential features must appear in analyses by either technique. For example, both must include necessary sketches of parts and/or workplace layouts, identification of tooling and equipment, and similar data which aids in providing a complete picture of the work being done. A technique like MTM, instead of supplanting time study, requires the integration of time study into the total analysis task.

What Patterns Show

Basically, the only thing a pattern of motions can show is a *method.* True, the attendant time is also a part of the written pattern, but such time is meaningful only to the extent and completeness with which the pattern accurately and truly describes a given method. However, writing the correct motions does not guarantee that the times will be correctly applied, or that there is complete lack of error in the pre-determined times; nevertheless, the time could not be correct unless the proper motions have been written. This emphasis on the method employed to do a task is basic to good MTM analysis, and from it springs most of the benefits of

MTM usage. Although it is possible to use the methods information gained from proper MTM usage and attitudes without even bothering to write the motions, recording is essential to later verification, checking, and modification as required. For instance, whenever research shows the need for revision in time values for motions in a pattern that has been correctly analyzed with the older time data, it is very easy to determine a new, more accurate time without affecting the method in any way.

Because methods are the principal feature shown by motion patterns, it is essential that the concept of method be crystal clear to an analyst. A method is a *way* of performing work—how the operator uses his muscles, eyes, and other faculties—along with any machinery, tools, etc.—to perform a useful or required task. An MTM pattern permits very fine distinctions along this line. An element might consist of twenty motions that include a P3SSD. Redesign of a part or a fixture might change this *one motion* to a P1SE. Although only this motion might be changed in the pattern, technically and for time purposes the pattern represents a new method. In actual use of MTM, such single motion changes in highly repetitive, short cycle jobs are frequently productive of significant cost savings. In the example given, 46.5 TMU would be saved each time the element was performed; this means that .028 minutes multiplied by the frequency of that element in a total task would be the saving of labor resulting from merely reducing the positioning time involved. As cited here, this example therefore shows that calling such a change in a pattern a new method is highly logical and justified.

While the MTM procedure is supported by more publicly documented research than any pre-determined time system, its practical application is assured only by suitably trained analysts. This does not imply that such analysts when observing the same operator together will write identical motion patterns. Some minor differences in the allowed motions may well appear. However, unless the analysts have made gross errors, their total allowed time will be practically equal. Perfectly valid reasons explain this situation. No two people can physically occupy the same vantage point for observation, and therefore logically they cannot see things exactly alike. Also, average operators normally employ minutely differing methods and motions during successive cycles of a given task, since they are not automatons. In addition, certain of their motions may at times be extremely difficult to classify, which clearly indicates possible honest differences between analysts when they exercise their judgment as to the true motion classification for an observation. In spite of all these factors, proper application training including guided practice will enable analysts to write valid motion patterns with minimal differences. Finally, the practical effect of such differences upon the allowed time usually will be of such small magnitude as to be well within accepted time study limits.

The MTM neophyte will learn from practice that a well written motion pattern provides precise answers to the basic industrial engineering questions that should be answered when any work is analyzed. How the patterns show these answers will be described in the next section, but the questions answered are:

1. *What* is the worker doing? *What* happens to the workpiece and/or parts?
2. *When* does he do it? *When* is the exact time in the cycle to do a certain act that will achieve the purpose of the work?
3. *How* does it get done? *How* does the worker use himself, the tools, the equipment, and the parts to get the job done?
4. *Where* on the workplace, the assembly, the parts, or the tools does the worker direct his actions? *Where* do the workpieces go during the task?
5. *Why* are certain actions taken or certain motions used? *Why* is one motion, rather than another closely similar, used in the working method?

It is obvious that if a motion pattern can answer these questions, there will be little doubt in the mind of anyone reading it concerning the analyst's interpretation of the method, and this can readily be checked against actual performance for verification, detection of changes, and clues to operator skill.

Insofar as machine time or process time are concerned, the motion pattern, by times and word descriptions, can show only what function they serve or add to the progress of the work being done. Whether such time was properly determined can be checked only by retiming that portion of the cycle by any of the numerous means and devices described in a later chapter specifically pertaining to time study. It is also sometimes possible to calculate such times based on known factors and data.

Finally, a motion pattern provides for future reference a concise compendium of facts regarding the task analyzed and comprises the best known type of methods record at the present time. Evidence, legal proof, time changes easily verifiable, detection of errors and difficulties in the task, the need for tools, and many other features are recorded in a form permitting easy confirmation or reconstruction of the method for any desired purpose. Any task described in a motion pattern can be resumed easily and/or reinstated following even long lapses of time since the task was discontinued. The value of such detailed methods records is unquestionably great for practicing work analysts and others.

All of these facts comprise a powerful justification for using MTM instead of time study.

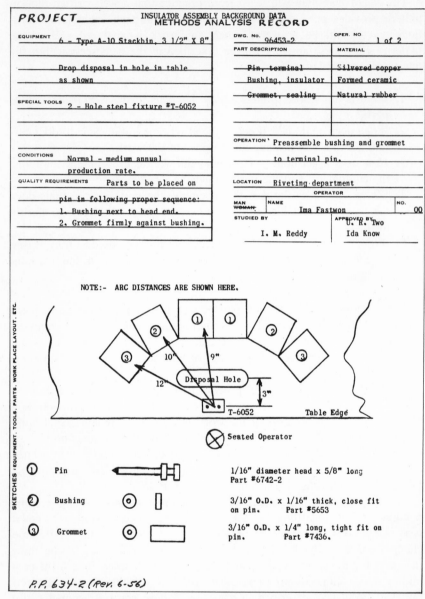

Fig. 1. Background data for insulator assembly analyzed in Fig. 2.

How Motion Patterns Show Facts

Perhaps the easiest way to portray the means by which a motion pattern shows the various facts cited in the last section is by analysis of an actual

PROJECT _____   METHODS ANALYSIS CHART   PART No. 96453-2

PART _____ INSULATOR ASSEMBLY _____ DATE _____ 7/26/56 _____ OPER. No. 1 of 2

OPERATION _____ Assemble bushing and grommet _____ ANALYST _____ C. I. Kno _____ SHEET No. 1 OF 1

DESCRIPTION — LEFT HAND	No.	L H	TMU	R H	No.	DESCRIPTION — RIGHT HAND
A. OBTAIN PINS, PLACE IN FIXTURE						
to pin supply		mR6C	7.2	mR6C		to pin supply
			9.1	G4B		select one pin
select one pin		G4B	9.1			
pin to fixture hole		M9C	12.7	M9C		pin to fixture hole
orient head down	2	G2	--	G2	2	orient head down
			21.8	P2SD		push into hole
push into hole		P2SD	21.8			
let go of pin		RL1	2.0	RL1		let go of pin
			83.7	TMU		TOTAL ELEMENT A
B OBTAIN, ASSEMBLE BUSHINGS						
to bushing supply		R10C	12.9	R10C		to bushing supply
			12.9	G4C		select one bushing
select one bushing		G4C	12.9			
bring to pin shaft		M10C	13.5	M10C		bring to pin shaft
preorient in fingers	2	G2	--	G2	2	preorient in fingers
push onto pin		P2SD	21.8			
			21.8	P2SD		push onto pin
let go of bushing		RL1	2.0	RL1		let go of bushing
			97.8	TMU		TOTAL ELEMENT B
C. OBTAIN, ASSEMBLE GROMMETS						
to grommet supply		R12C	14.2	R12C		to grommet supply
			12.9	G4C		select one grommet
select one grommet		G4C	12.9			
bring to pin shaft		M12C	15.2	M12C		bring to pin shaft
preorient in fingers	2	G2	--	G2	2	preorient in fingers
			48.6	P3SD		push onto pin
push onto pin		P3SD	48.6			
			147.4	TMU		TOTAL ELEMENT C
D. ASIDE ASSEMBLY IN HOLE						
get new hold - all parts		G2	5.6	G2		get new hold - all parts
pull assembly from hole		D2D	11.8	D2D		pull assembly from hole
assembly to dispose hole		M3Bm	3.6	M3Bm		Assembly to dispose hole
drop into hole in table		RL1	-----	RL1		drop into hole in table
			21.0	TMU		TOTAL ELEMENT D

P.P. 634-1 (Rev. 6-56)

Fig. 2.   Motion analysis of insulator assembly.

pattern. Figure 1 gives all the background data for an Insulator Assembly that is made by the motions analyzed in Fig. 2. This data is a necessary part of the motion pattern. A summary for the operation is shown in Fig. 3. Before proceeding, it is suggested that the reader familiarize himself with the two figures in detail. Bear in mind the previous remarks while doing this, since the following discussion will thereby be more meaningful.

Before proceeding with a discussion of the motion pattern itself, it is important that the data given in Fig. 1 be explained to show how vital it is to the meaning of the method and resulting time standard based upon it. Why this is so is also evident from the definition for method contained in A.S.M.E. Standard 106:

METHOD:

> n. 1. The procedure or sequence of motions used by one or more individuals to accomplish a given operation or work task. 2. The sequence of operations and/or processes used to produce a given product or accomplish a given job. 3. A specific combination of layout and working conditions; materials, equipment, and tools; and motion pattern, involved in accomplishing a given operation or task.

Logically, if a method subsumes a *specific* layout together with the materials, tools, and equipment pertinent to the method, any change in these factors indicates, at least in some degree, a different method or slightly different motions needed.

To substantiate a given method, therefore, requires the use of factual data, sketches, photographs, blueprints, and even models that clearly depict the essential features of the layout and job conditions which affect the method. The means employed will naturally be suited to the degree of precision required in the standard and the expected difficulty of supporting the standard; background information could even be recorded to the extent of making motion pictures which critics would find extremely difficult to refute. With these remarks, the significance of the data in Fig. 1 should be apparent upon examination. A word of warning—it is far too easy and all too frequent that work analysts bypass or neglect this stage of analysis, and find later that it is the key to unanswered questions which embarrass them. The few extra minutes of analysis and recording time are well invested. In fact, the thinking and effort to clearly discern these factors in a job even lighten the work of motion recording and analysis. It is likewise obvious that changes in any of these factors that might justifiably affect the method can easily be checked and evaluated at any later date. The value of such data can therefore be great.

Referring now to Fig. 2, there are natural divisions of the motion pattern which answer the basic questions raised in the preceding section. These will be pointed out and discussed in the same order previously used:

1. *What?* The description columns—left hand and right hand—when properly written show with distinct, specific words what is happening during the elements. There are a few good rules to follow that help achieve this aim. Origins and destinations of Reaches and Moves, since they represent the major manual displacements, should be noted

N.	ELEMENT DESCRIPTION	ANALYSIS CHART REF.	ELEMENT TIME TMU	CONVERSION FACTOR .0006 LEVELED TIME .05022	15 % ALLOWANCE	ELEMENT TIME ALLOWED minutes	OCCURRENCES PER PIECE OR CYCLE	TOTAL TIME ALLOWED min.
A	Obtain pins, place in fixture		83.7		.00753	.05775	1	.05775
B	Obtain & assemble bushings		97.8	.05868	.00880	.06748	1	.06748
C	Obtain & assemble grommets		147.4	.08844	.01327	.10171	1	.10171
D	Aside assembly in hole		21.0	.01260	.00189	.01449	1	.01449
	TOTALS		349.9	.20994		.24143		
	ALLOWED RATE			497.0 pieces per hour or .12072 min. per piece				

PROJECT_____ OPERATION SUMMARY   PART No. 96453-2
INSULATOR ASSEMBLY   1 of 2
PART _____   DATE _____ OPER No. ____
OPERATION Assemble bushing & grommet   ANALYST C. I. Kno   SHEET No. 1 OF 1

P.F. 647-D (Rev. 6-56)   TOTAL TIME ALLOWED PER ____

Fig. 3.   Operation Summary of elements for insulator assembly.

by "from" and "to" designations.   The object, part, tool, or other material on which the action is exerted should be identified by words that leave no doubt in the reader's mind.   It is wise to use shop terms and nomenclature, as well as to differentiate between similar or successive parts by finer terms or number references such as "first," "second," etc. As soon as parts lose their identity in units produced, it is necessary to refer to them as assemblies. Naming the assembly is also required when more than one assembly is included in the same element. It is unnecessary to repeat in the description columns the words such as "Reach, Move, etc." describing what the operator does in the way of motions, since the symbol columns tell this precisely and in much better defined manner. In summary, the description columns tell *what* happens to the objects, *where* it happens on the workplace layout, and *how* the tools and equipment are used.

2. *When?* This question is answered by the order in which the elements are displayed, the succession between the motions, and the frequencies that show repetition of either motions or elements. As long as a pattern shows the complete method, there is no doubt as to when things occur. Sometimes, when a pattern merely contains a collection of necessary elements, not necessarily in their proper order—as when used to develop standard data, for instance—this feature is less obvious until recourse is made to the summary of elements such as appears in Fig. 3. In actual practice, it is usual to find this summary on a separate form rather than at the bottom of the motion pattern.

3. *How?* The columns labeled LH and RH containing the MTM motion symbols are used to show precisely how the operator does the work. The condensed, shorthand system which the symbols represent are already quite familiar to the reader from earlier study of previous chapters. To write the same information in words and numbers would require prohibitive space, which emphasizes the necessity and economy of the MTM system of symbols. The symbol conventions also show the application of the Limiting Principle as discussed in Chapter 18. A properly written motion pattern must be carefully edited from the standpoint of which lines are used to record the symbols, since this convention and uniform practice becomes a great aid to interpretation when different readers consider the patterns written by different analysts.

4. *Where?* Part of this answer is provided by the pattern itself, as was noted in the remarks concerning the descriptive columns. But it is even more important to this answer to refer to the workplace layout and the parts prints or sample parts, since a visual aid is worth many words.

In spite of this general fact, however, the finer distinctions of location are often inherently found in the motion symbols and carefully worded descriptive columns. Developing skill in designation of locations is one of the more difficult features of motion patterns for the neophyte to learn; his best success in analysis requires, however, that he attend to this matter at the very beginning of his MTM practice. There are two general ways to show workplace layout distances. Blueprint type dimensions from reference lines usually indicate that the distances shown are actual measurements on the projection given. A more frequently used strategy, however, is to employ arrowed lines radiating from the operator symbol and between parts that show, instead, the allowed Reach and/or Move distance (including arc distance) in any motions made between the locations. With this practice, it is easy to reconcile the motion symbols and layout. Where the method record warrants it, however, it might be desirable to show both types of layout for future reference.

5. *Why?* Answering this query amounts to defining the purpose of any given motion and differentiating it from other motions closely similar. The purpose of a motion is partly defined by the symbol itself (because of the MTM definitions which the symbol represents) and partly by key words in the descriptive columns. The differentiation feature is revealed by the class, case, and/or distance assigned to any given kind of motion indicated in the symbol column.

That the MTM motion pattern fully answers all the basic work study questions in a concise and clear manner is apparent from the discussion above. Remember, though, that these remarks apply only to well-written patterns; patterns lack methods value to the degree in which they depart from the criteria of good patterns just enumerated.

MOTION PATTERN MECHANICS

With the nature and desirable characteristics of motion patterns clearly in mind, the next problem is how to reduce motion analysis to a systematic approach. This section will give both general and specific ideas toward solving this problem.

MTM Working Forms

Paperwork of any kind can be systemized most readily when prepared forms adequate for the task and flexible enough to handle the range of situations are utilized. Accordingly, MTM practitioners make use of four general types of forms; the following illustrations are typical of the forms adopted by many firms and industries applying MTM. They are available at nominal cost from the MTM Association.

1. Since the method always depends on the conditions and surroundings during its performance, a Methods Analysis Record such as shown in

Fig. 4 should be made a part of each pattern written. The principal exception to this suggestion occurs when standardized workplace layouts, tool designs, and other factors in the process have been developed in detail and assigned coded symbols. In this case, reference to the symbols on one of the other forms might lessen the need for the Methods Analysis Record. The divisions of this form are obvious from the printed designations. Figure 1 is an example of this form filled out for the Insulator Assembly.

2. To meet the need for quick recording of much information in a minimum space when observation type studies are made, Methods Engineering Council's Form No. 205 is shown in Fig. 5. Note that the descriptive columns are missing from this form, and it is generally used as an expedient during study, with transposing of the data to a Methods Analysis Chart being the next step in the work. This form is intended to record the motions actually observed—what the operator *is* doing, not what he *should* be doing. For this reason, performance rating space is provided to permit rating of the operator. This, in turn, may affect the value which the analyst places on the operator's actual motion pattern when he transposes the data to the succeeding form, which shows average operator motions for standard purposes. This form obviously is the closest approach to conventional time study forms, both in format and manner of usage. For this reason, it will not be further discussed; the essentials of its usage are covered equally well in a later chapter showing the time study procedure in detail.

3. The form which actually displays the motion pattern, commonly known as a Methods Analysis Chart is seen in Fig. 6. A completed example of this form was seen earlier in Fig. 2. Further discussion in this chapter revolves principally around this form. It is used directly for studies of the visualization type, and also for studies based on indirect observation. Indirect observation consists of viewing the actual job to note key facts and complete the Methods Analysis Record, with the actual motion analysis and recording being done away from the job. It has the advantage of minimizing interference with the work and operator, while permitting writing of the motion pattern for standards purposes without the extra recording needed when the form in Fig. 5 is used. Also, as previously mentioned, the Methods Analysis Chart is normally used following the form for direct observation in order to complete the descriptive portion of the method and to write the *average* motion pattern rather than the motions used by one certain operator. The Methods Analysis Chart is, therefore, in all respects, the key MTM form.

4. After the MTM engineer completes a number of Methods Analysis

PROJECT _____   **METHODS ANALYSIS RECORD**

EQUIPMENT		DWG. No.		OPER. NO.
		PART DESCRIPTION		MATERIAL

SPECIAL TOOLS

OPERATION

CONDITIONS

QUALITY REQUIREMENTS

LOCATION

OPERATOR

| MAN WOMAN | NAME | | NO. |

| STUDIED BY | APPROVED BY |

SKETCHES (EQUIPMENT TOOLS, PARTS, WORK PLACE LAYOUT, ETC.

P.P. L.74-2 (Rev. 6-56)

Fig. 4.   Methods Analysis Record form (see Fig. 1).

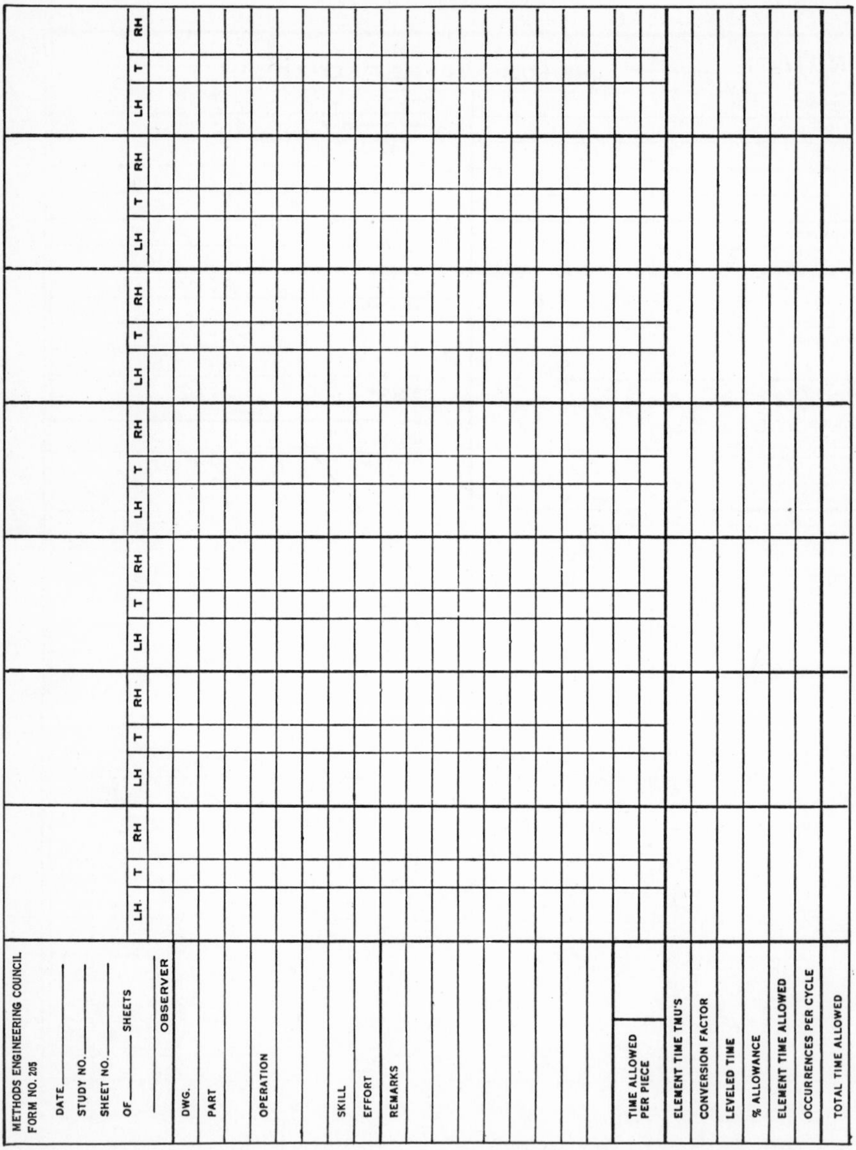

Fig. 5. Sample form for observation-type studies.

PROJECT_____		METHODS ANALYSIS CHART				PART No. _____	
PART_____			DATE_____			OPER.No. _____	
OPERATION_____			ANALYST_____			SHEET No_____OF___	
DESCRIPTION — LEFT HAND	No.	L H	TMU	R H	No.	DESCRIPTION — RIGHT HAND	
P.P. 634-1 (Rev. 6-56)							

Fig. 6. Methods Analysis Chart for recording motion pattern (see Fig. 2).

Charts, he normally wishes to summarize the data resulting and develop the time standard for a complete operation or process. The Operation Summary form generally designed as in Fig. 7 fulfills this need. Essentially, it compactly collects data from many motion

				CONVERSION FACTOR					

PROJECT _____ **OPERATION SUMMARY** PART No. _____

PART_____ DATE_____ OPER No. _____

OPERATION_____ ANALYST_____ SHEET No. _____ OF____

NO	ELEMENT DESCRIPTION	ANALYSIS CHART REF.	ELEMENT TIME TMU	CONVERSION FACTOR		ELEMENT TIME ALLOWED	OCCURRENCES PER PIECE OR CYCLE	TOTAL TIME ALLOWED
				LEVELED TIME	% ALLOWANCE			

P.F. 647-D (Rev. 6-56)   TOTAL TIME ALLOWED PER_____

Fig. 7.   Operation Summary form used to summarize elements (see Fig. 3).

patterns and represents the finished data derived from the total analysis of an operation (refer to Fig. 3 for example). This form is such as to permit its usage to summarize time studies also, as is sometimes done by practicing engineers.

Familiarity with the format and content of these four basic analysis forms will assist the MTM analyst in his work, and permits the paperwork to be systemized.

Elemental Division

When considering the mechanism by which industrial engineers are able to analyze even highly complex work routines, one striking feature stands out. This is the old and obvious truism, sometimes lost sight of in these modern days of high pressure and exciting variety: A man can see only one thing at a time and understand it. A corollary statement might well be: A man can think only one thought at a time clearly. Any reasonable or logical use of a man's powers in analysis requires recognition of these concepts and adaptation of them to the problem at hand. The difficulty of divided attention, for example, is found in conventional time study because the analyst must almost simultaneously (1) observe the work, (2) observe and operate the timing device, and (3) record the details of timing. This is a basic reason why such study is often inadequate, poorly done, or arrives at unwarranted conclusions unless employed by an analyst well versed in the intricacies of time study and experienced in the art of close observation. The MTM procedure differs from this in that attention need be, indeed should be, directed to only one factor of the total analysis task at any given instant. Among the features of the procedure that permits this desirable state is the means or method of subdividing tasks into elements for MTM motion study.

Having determined the general orientation to a process and divided it into operations and sequences, the analyst must next decide what elements should be chosen and define their starting and stopping points in the work cycle. Skill in this part of his effort will greatly simplify his work, increase the value of his finished analysis for many uses of methods and times, and result in a truer picture of the work being analyzed. There are a number of good principles which, when known and properly understood, shorten the time needed to develop such skill.

To begin the exposition of these principles, consider next three additional definitions from A.S.M.E. Standard 106 as follows:

ELEMENT:

n. A subdivision of the work cycle composed of a sequence of one or several fundamental motions and/or machine or process activities, which is distinct, describable, and measurable.

ELEMENT TIME:

The term used to indicate either the actual, observed, selected, normal, or standard time to perform an element of an operation.

ELEMENT BREAKDOWN:

> The subdivisions of an operation each of which is composed of a distinct, describable, and measurable sequence of one or several fundamental motions and/or machine or process activities.

The fineness of breakdown of operations into elements is thus not limited by the commonly accepted definitions. Furthermore, practicing work analysts know well that the current and future demands of work study indicate the need for ever more finely divided elements and correspondingly adequate description or identification of such elements. In this respect, MTM has superior advantages over time study. It permits complete freedom as to the point at which the element is split and revision of that point later without affecting the method in any way. It also gives keys— in the right- and left-hand descriptive columns on the analysis form—as to the most appropriate name for the element, because the principal action or effect during the element is pinpointed with one or more of the motions included. Length of element, while optional, should generally be suited to the particular work studied; one widely accepted opinion is that an MTM element should be limited to 12-20 motions or less for maximum ease of analysis. Even if elements of such length include many motions of high time value, they will be unlikely to total more than 100–200 TMU and are usually less than 100 TMU. Note that even 100 TMU is only .060 minutes. Most time study men agree that timing with a decimal minute watch cannot evaluate accurately elements requiring less than .02–.03 minutes; elements are commonly selected to require few instances where less than .10 to .15 minutes are recorded. Thus, MTM elements certainly permit finer element breakdown than do time study elements.

Another sometimes vexing problem with work elements concerns their identification as constant or variable, together with the cause of any variation. A constant element requires the same performance time on each and every occasion it may be repeated in the task of which it is a part. The time for such elements is constant chiefly because the method for the element does not change with added occurrences and/or the motions comprising the method do not contain any variable factors, such as differing distances. Variable elements, on the other hand, may require unlike performance times on each occurrence in the task. The time variation may be due to employing a different method to accomplish the purpose of the element, or else the length, case, and class of motions used may include variable factors that are not the same in time influence at each repetition of the element. Especially in time standards and time formula work it is important that the analyst be able to determine constancy or variability and detect reasons for any variation.

If constancy or variability are not recognized when the length and/or defined content of an element is initially determined, much wasted effort and difficult manipulation can result in later usage of the element. With MTM, these problems are minimized because the breakpoints between elements can be revised at any stage of the analysis without much effort; rewriting of the known motions into more convenient groupings is easily done. In addition, with each MTM motion and its frequency shown, one cause of element variability is readily pinpointed. Also, the motion symbols and verbal descriptions in the pattern yield obvious clues as to any cause of variation; the length, case, and class of the motion can all be examined for variability conveniently.

Time differences in time study elements are less readily explained and justified. The time variation might be that which could normally be expected, although the degree of variation—especially when slight but nonetheless significant in the standard—is often difficult to justify or suspect. The analyst would most likely scrutinize distances for readily detected causes of time variation, but he would find it difficult to isolate the cause in a time study element if this hypothesis did not prove fruitful. Accordingly, it is not as easy to initially establish or later revise the content of time study elements as it is for MTM elements; nor can the classification or analysis of time study elements be as thorough and defensible in regard to constancy or variability. This would be especially true if the element in question had the same name as another element covering an entirely different method of doing the task, since the time difference shown by the watch yields no real clue to the reasons why the method differs.

The MTM convention for separating the elements and how and where to write the name of the element is well-illustrated by Fig. 2. Space of at least one line is left at the end of the preceding element—often used for totaling the time for that element—and the next element name is written in capital and underlined to make it easily distinguished from the rest of the pattern. Of course, many alternate ways of doing this are possible and used, but conformity to such a convention would aid transmission of information between MTM analysts.

The Frequency Problem

In the experience of many MTM instructors, one of the more vexing problems for people learning MTM is determining and assigning frequencies to motions, motion series, and repeated elements. It would be wasteful of analysis time, analysis forms, and the time of any party reading an analysis if each and every motion, series of motions, or job element were chronologically listed singly in an analysis. Such repetitive writing could well destroy much of the effectiveness of the MTM technique simply due to the increased laboriousness of the analyst's work. Motion economy principles should certainly be used by the analyst who hopes to get them adopted in the job he is studying!

The frequency problem can be greatly minimized by a number of intelligent attacks upon it, which will be described briefly in this section. But first, it is well to show the mechanics by which frequencies are indicated on a study.

When single motions or motion combinations are immediately repeated in the work, a numeral to show the frequency is written in the "No." column (or columns) on the analysis form. Note, for example, the double frequencies of G2 in the first three elements shown in Fig. 2. This indicates that, on the average, several regrasp motions will be performed while bringing objects to the assembly nest for insertion. The same columns are equally usable for cases where motion series appear; such a series would be common in running down a bolt with the fingers. The series of Reach, Grasp, Move and/or Turn, and Release could be repeated any number of times within an element, depending mainly on the number of threads on the bolt and the distance it must be advanced into the threaded hole. It could vary also with the possible need to repeat the series more than once for a complete revolution of the bolt. In any event, whatever frequency is decided as appropriate would be shown by numerals in the "No." columns on the analysis forms.

When whole elements are repeated in a given task, several means can be used to account for the extra time involved. A new element could be written, with a note of its identity to a preceding element, and the total element time copied from the earlier analysis. Or, the frequency could merely be multiplied at the point where the element is totaled and reference to the proper place of the repetition inserted in later stages of the analysis. The most usual place, however, in which to account for element frequency is in the column on the Operation Summary form headed "Occurrences per Piece or Cycle." In Fig. 3, for instance, the unitary frequency of each element in a total cycle is shown by "1" numerals in this column.

In any of the cases cited, of course, the motion, motion series, or element time values would be multiplied by the frequencies to obtain total task time.

Many MTM neophytes, while knowing where and how to indicate frequencies on their analysis, still experience difficulty in deciding the proper frequency to assign. Logic, common sense, and experienced judgment must be used in this decision; and it is quite common to find that the greatest source of error in task time by newcomers to MTM analysis is caused by their lack of these attributes at that stage of their experience. One good reason for this difficulty is that often frequencies are not constant, but vary with each cycle of the task; the need for reaching an assignable figure requires practice and knowledge of the task being studied, as well as familiarity with the various ways in which frequencies can be ascertained and/or what may usually be expected. The fact that an observed instance may differ from what would be proper to allow for the average operator in the finished analysis is a further complication.

The most obvious way to determine frequency is by direct counting as the work is done, with or without a counting device to aid when the frequency is high. Averaging of a sufficient number of cycles would then provide a reasonable expectancy of the correct count. Sometimes physical factors suggest directly the proper frequency, as would be true for the case of the bolt cited earlier. In many cases, application of the principles of applied mechanics, particularly where the hand action is on mechanical devices involving gear or similar ratios, will benefit the analyst if he is familiar with them. Ratio analysis and other statistical means (described in a later chapter) can be employed occasionally to derive mathematical approaches to critical frequencies. The practical analyst will often find that estimation will yield the best answer, particularly if this is checked with the foreman, worker, or another analyst. It is evident that practice with all of these techniques will help the analyst in his problem.

Another factor with series of motions is that the frequency might not be the same for each and every motion in the series. To illustrate, if the worker had hold of the bolt before he started tightening it, the Reach and Grasp in a series like that earlier noted would be assigned a frequency one less than that allowed for the Move and Release motions. A further case in which the analyst without experience could err occurs when a tool is used that requires alternate approaches and departures from the work-piece. For instance, to hammer four blows could require—depending on conditions preceding and following the Moves written for the hammer blows—three, four, or five upstrokes; in any event there would be four downstrokes. Close observation and discernment of changes in the direction of motion must be relied upon to catch such frequency variations.

It is noteworthy that many of the frequency problems here discussed would never be encountered in time study simply because single motions are not evaluated in that procedure. Much of the frequency problem is buried in an element which is merely variable by the watch reading. On the other hand, the knowledge of frequency resulting from MTM analysis often provides one of the very best keys to method improvement; reducing the frequencies associated with motions, series of motions, and elements by various strategies is often one of the most time-saving tactics that can be utilized in work measurement.

A word of caution. Accounting for frequencies can be overdone in terms of analysis cost. This is especially true for "occasional" elements, which are often best handled by allowances, variances, or standard element times that apply to all infrequent occurrences of a given type and description. An "occasional" element could comprise minor setup, minor tool care, tagging, tabulating of pieces produced, etc. that covers necessary work which does not occur each and every time the complete work cycle is performed. When such work should be written into a pattern in detail, or when it should be handled by an alternate scheme is another instance where judgment and experience help the analyst greatly.

Synthetic Elements

Many times in the work of engineers, the use of synthesis helps achieve answers when direct facts or the limitations of their definitions do not permit them to give unequivocal answers to problems. In a sense, the employment of synthesis is a major difference between the successful engineer and one who becomes mired in a morass of uncertainty, indecision, and inability to reconcile facts with the necessity for a practical, workable answer. Synthesis, as used here, implies that the result or answer given is a reasonable approximation, although strict interpretation of the procedures and rules under which the answer was obtained would not warrant the given result. The use of such synthesis is a highly legitimate procedure provided the analyst does not fool himself into unbounded faith in the result or refuse to revise his decision in the light of new facts or better technology on the problem at hand; successful engineers have no qualms at using synthesis properly when it is appropriate and provides answers that apparently check against performance.

In work measurement, synthetic elements, motions, and motion equivalents are all basically a means of reducing analysis time and achieving answers which are required but do not merit extensive study or precision. For example, it is possible to argue endlessly whether a hesitation or shifting of the fingers in handling an object is one kind of MTM motion or another. The real problem, oftentimes, is to allow sufficient time in the motion pattern if the shifting is legitimately necessary to the job. If an analyst finds that, for given occurrences of this type, assigning of several Regrasps covers the time, he is using appropriately a synthetic equivalent motion. An equivalent motion is one that does not precisely delineate by definition or actual occurrence the action taking place, but which does have a pre-determined time which seems correct for the action. It sometimes happens that minor planning pauses can be covered in this way, particularly when the time is too short to catch on a stop watch as normally used for process time. Hosts of cases where such synthesis can be applied advantageously could be cited. It should be sufficient to refer, however, to the usage of synthesis in the theories of Grasp, Position, and Disengage given in those respective chapters. Even the definition for an AP1 includes the idea of its differing from an AP2 by "a regrasp or its equivalent."

The analyst must always remember, when employing synthesis, that his analysis is open to question and must sometimes be defended and the allowed time demonstrated to be correct. While disputants to an analysis will seldom question the assignment of a motion which complies fully with basic MTM definitions, they will often provide much argument on synthetic motions which the analyst should be prepared to meet.

Most firms using MTM have compiled series of equivalent motions commonly accepted in their own usage as being time savers. Many of such equivalent motions and/or typical motion sequences are peculiar to certain trades, lines of activity, and the practice of certain crafts. An instance is the set of sewing motions widely used in the needle trades employing MTM. Lists of equivalent motions and typical motion sequences of a more general applicability are available from many MTM consultants and firms using MTM. All such synthetic devices are a strategy by which to reduce MTM analysis time, particularly where experience and validation by stop watch check have shown the device to give reliable answers. However, no claims to such devices being official MTM data are valid unless the MTM Association has sanctioned the particular synthesis through validated research.

Another use of synthesis consists in using special code schemes to indicate in motion patterns motion series that are extremely common in a given type of work. This device is merely a logical extension of the idea of pre-determined times. It must be used with caution, however, because there is a danger of assigning such coded equivalents when they do not apply or of bypassing good methods study due to the habit factor in usage of coded elements.

Clerical Aspects

Another saving in MTM analysis time results from judicious use of less skilled and lower pay personnel to relieve the MTM engineer of some of the clerical detail in pattern writing. The whole problem here is what can safely be delegated without sacrificing the effective methods work of the MTM analyst. The answer to this will depend somewhat on whether the study is of the observation or visualized type. It will also vary depending on what the constants and variables in the task and the motions might be. There are several items on an MTM analysis, however, which can safely be delegated to a properly trained clerk or technician.

One of these is the insertion of captions on the forms, particularly when a large number of analysis sheets for a given job must be labeled identically. Another is the insertion, totaling, and extending of time values on the analysis and summary sheets. Posting of standard elements to master sheets is another possibility. This means of reducing the demands on the MTM analyst is worthy of wide acceptance, as it has been successfully used in many places. The whole concept is based on the idea that the method record sheet and actual motion analysis and description requires the talent and attention of an MTM engineer, while the remainder of the total job of finishing the work analysis is primarily clerical in nature. The completed study returned to the engineer can always be checked and revised, if necessary, to assure the efficiency of the clerical help utilized.

SUMMARY

The crux of good MTM usage consists in the writing and recording of good motion patterns that mirror the working method accurately. There are many skills which are a part of this task and which are essentially available only from an adequately trained MTM analyst. This is one good reason why application experience is absolutely basic to make knowledge of MTM theory and data meaningful for the MTM student. On the other hand, parts of the analysis task that can be removed from the shoulders of the MTM analyst should properly be assigned to technical or clerical personnel capable of performing them.

CHAPTER 20

Current MTM Research — Learning Curves

This chapter reports the learning curve research project of the MTM Association at the University of Michigan. This research is a natural outgrowth of the fact that attainment of task standards based on predetermined motion times assumes experienced operators. It was designed to find how long the typical operator will take to attain the experience necessary to meet an MTM task standard. This effort is a notable example of the future trend in work measurement progress. The project already has yielded new data and a useful methodology by which to approach the traditionally difficult operator learning problem. A means of constructing learning curves based on the MTM motion pattern for an operation has resulted. Such curves applied to the problems of operator selection and training offer hope of improving work design and job analysis in a professional manner.

The authors of this text feel that an overview of work measurement progress is essential to achieving a proper perspective on the research herein reported. Traditional methods of measuring operator performance have relied principally upon observing and/or visualizing what the operator will or should do to accomplish the various elements of the working task. The worker was considered as a "muscle machine" and prime attention was directed towards his output characteristics. To the extent that such approaches neglected to evaluate the input characteristics of the operator and the feedback effect of the task requirements upon the operator, they did not fully explain or measure the complete worker-task system. Significant interactions which may affect both the immediate and long range production performance have not been sufficiently understood. Particularly because total system approaches to work design promise direct benefits to the worker by easing his task through better matching of job and worker requirements, truly engineered work measurement has needed production oriented human factors research results. The required research and application techniques involved in this fresh approach to human performance are much more penetrating and sophisticated than earlier procedures. Yet they further such traditional goals as the human and humane emphasis in work measurement promoted over the years by Dr. Lillian M. Gilbreth and other work design pioneers.

This expansion of work measurement horizons therefore is a logical development toward more effective industrial engineering in the evaluation and design of production systems utilizing human beings. It takes advantage of the firm analysis base established when the availability of predetermined time systems advanced the field from the confines of conventional time study into a higher stage of development. The rise and spread of predetermined time systems with their increased capacity for objective methods design broadened the scope of work analysis by better motion and time measurement. Similarly, current efforts to develop practical industrial engineering techniques from the work of industrial psychologists over the years will benefit work measurement and analysis. Among the anticipated benefits are solutions to many of the human equation unknowns which always have interested work analysts. Application of tools developed by quantifying human factors in a practical way should help to routinize much of the evaluation process now dependent upon personal opinion and intuitive policy.

THE NATURE OF LEARNING CURVES

The exact nature of learning curves—what they are and what they are not—is crucial to clear thinking about them. Because industrial managers and their technical staffs have necessarily been dealing with operator learning and training problems for many years without the benefit of definitive research data, a multitude of misleading ideas have surrounded these topics. Therefore, at the outset, it is important to understand the true nature of learning and to exclude from the subject consideration of topics not properly within this class of information.

Only Individuals Can Learn

The first widespread misconception to be clarified is that organizations or groups can learn. *Only individuals can learn,* since learning is a mental development of a living organism based on the experience of adjustment to the sensory environment. Organizations or groups, as such, merely reflect the sum total of the performances of their individual members; they mirror their *members'* learning rather than themselves having the capacity to learn. However, the mutual success enjoyed by organizations and groups can create the most favorable *environment* in which their individual members can efficiently learn and thereby contribute to the combined success of the group. For example, what has frequently been called "learning" for an assembly crew or assembly line group actually is the increase in performance resulting because each line station worker progressively learns his station task. Assuming all line stations are fully loaded, the line can perform only as fast as its slowest member permits. Hence, the pivotal learner for line "learning" really is one individual. As soon as this worker learns to perform faster than the next slowest member, the latter becomes the pivotal learner, and so forth. In this progressive sequence, it seems as though the assembly group *per se* is learning; whereas only the cumulative learning of the currently slowest worker can significantly affect the productivity of the line. To reiterate, only individuals are capable of the human process called learning.

As a result of the foregoing, performance and/or efficiency curves for an industry, organization, or group should be excluded from consideration under the topic of learning curves. Instead, the proper names— performance, production, experience, training, or efficiency curves—should be used to describe the graphical plotting of produced units, time per unit, cost per unit, etc. for such groups. The basic reason is that such curves represent far more variables than merely those properly associated with learning. They are influenced by all facets of production, not just learning.

When learning is being considered, the most fruitful line of inquiry is that which attends to behavioral changes of the individual learner. Having available the individual learning curves will permit the productive improvement of individual jobs. As replications and extensions of this process over a range of jobs occurs, the performance of an organization or group will tend to be upgraded. The heart of the new research is the correct placement of emphasis and measurement upon the individual.

Learning Defined

Learning was defined in the MTM research as the improvement in performance (reduction in cycle time) resulting from practice in the reinforcement region. For the reader to understand this definition and appreciate its precise simplicity, some discussion of the nature of learning is deemed necessary by the authors.

A great many authorities have defined learning in their own way. This is to be expected because of variations in the personal backgrounds of the definers and also because the definition is addressed to different audiences. Perhaps one of the more cogent, complete descriptions is that by Julius Kling of Brown University partially quoted[1] as follows:

---

[1] *Funk & Wagnalls Standard Reference Encyclopedia,* Standard Reference Works Publishing Company, Inc., New York City, 1961.

The term "learning" is used in experimental psychology to refer to the relatively permanent changes in behavior which result from conditions of practice. As such, learning is distinguished from behavior changes due to fatigue (which are temporary changes) and from changes due to maturation or growth. . . .

Extensive studies of retention and forgetting suggest that the passage of time, by itself, is of but slight importance in causing forgetting. Instead, interference with the learned material from previous and subsequent learned materials, and failure to reinstate the appropriate stimulus conditions for the retention test, seem to account for the greater part of forgetting. . . .

A considerable portion of learned behavior is of the type called classical conditioning, first investigated by the Russian psychologist Ivan Petrovich Pavlov. . . .

A second form of conditioning is called instrumental conditioning because the acquired response operates upon the organism's environment to modify it in some fashion and is instrumental in determining subsequent trains of events. . . .

More complex forms of learning (discrimination, problem solving, concept formation) seem to depend largely upon instrumental conditioning principles. . . .

Note that the classical Pavlov learning is frequently called the STIMULUS → RESPONSE syndrome. Instrumental learning, often called the RESPONSE → REINFORCEMENT syndrome, is a companion principle. These two principles are the primary basis of modern-day programmed learning.

However, the key to a successful stimulus is perception. In fact, stimuli frequently are classed according to the kind of percept they represent. Again, a partial quote[2] of Julius Kling is enlightening:

Perceiving is the immediate, active organization and interpretation of sense data. . . .

Research has revealed that perceiving has several interesting characteristics, of which the following are noteworthy: (1) Perceiving is selective. . . . (2) Percepts are organized. . . . (3) Percepts display constancy effects. . . . (4) Perceiving is an active process of adding to the sense data. . . .

The authors organize these thoughts into the following definition:

Perception is the active response to sensory input by a process of adding selective, organized, and relatively constant information or data to the mental consciousness of an observer. Memory is the recall and recognition of previously processed sensory perceptions from mental storage to the immediate consciousness.

Based on the above discussion of the nature of learning, the viewpoint of those interested in work measurement concerning the subject can be stated rather well. The learning of manual work is a combination of classical and instrumental conditioning achieved by the practice of motor skills made significant by perceptual input within the information processing capability of the learner. This leads directly to two classifications of manual learning—threshold and reinforcement.

[2] *Ibid.*

Until the perceptual capacity of the manual learner has progressed, usually by a process of instruction followed by trial and error practice, to the point at which he can perform a task unaided and without hesitation, his performance will be in the threshold area.   Having crossed this barrier into the reinforcement region, the manual learner repeats enough task cycles to develop automaticity in his movements.   When the rate of cycle performance reaches that required by an average operator with average skill and effort under average conditions, the standard (MTM) time has been achieved.

The MTM Learning Curve Project was designed to evaluate the reinforcement learning portion of the total learning process described above.   The researchers have developed a practical technique, based on the MTM system, of determining the required number of cycles to achieve the MTM standard for a task.   This powerful new work measurement tool is described in the remainder of this chapter in sufficient detail to enable an MTM analyst to greatly broaden his work design capability.

MTM LEARNING CURVE RESEARCH

The MTM Learning Curve Project sponsored by the U.S.-Canada MTM Association at the University of Michigan is currently continuing in its third phase.   The results from the first and second phases were reported[3] in 1963 and 1965 respectively.   These reports and allied literature (see the list at the end of this chapter) provided a practical procedure by which to determine the learning time for an MTM pattern and shed considerable light on the qualitative nature of manual learning in the reinforcement region.   The consequences of these findings necessitated a continuation of the project into further areas.   As these areas, notably those of operator selection and training, are explored and further developed they undoubtedly will yield additional practical data and procedures.   These will help work measurement analysts to better accomplish their primary task of work design and specification

Before the learning curve research began in 1962, about three years of effort had been concentrated on developing the Electronic Data Collector (EDC) which is described in Chapters 5 and 22 of this text.   The first extensive application of the EDC was on the learning research.   The EDC was essential to both recording and electronic computer analysis of the type of data needed in this project.   Signals from transducers appropriately

---

[3] Phase I : R.R. 112 (See Ch. 5).
Phase II: R.R. 113 "Learning Curve Research on Manual Operations: Phase II, Industrial Studies;" by Walton M. Hancock, Robert R. Clifford, James A. Foulke, and Leonard F. Krystynak; Ann Arbor, Michigan; 1965.

situated within the workplace layout to electronically define motion break-points were converted for time recording on punched paper tape. This tape was processed for extensive analysis by electronic computer. The computer program output was in the form of numerical data, regression equations, and scatter plots of cycle time versus number of cycles—visual material upon which the equations produced by the program could be plotted for analysis. The extreme mass of data accumulated could not have been recorded or analyzed efficiently without the EDC. In addition, analysis errors were reduced to a fraction of those possible from manual processing of the data, which would have taken the researchers vastly longer before they could reach their conclusions.

The literature list at the end of this chapter shows that the project findings were shared with the profession as soon as possible during each phase. This sharing with other researchers and persons having industrial interests in the project provided much useful feedback at each stage of the research. Such feedback helped to arrive at the practical learning curve procedure to be described herein, and it also facilitated cooperation during the second —industrial study—phase of the project. This over-all approach and professional openness is the direct opposite of procedures which impeded work measurement progress before the advent of the MTM system. As the project continues, cooperative efforts between industrial engineers and other personnel within allied disciplines are being actively encouraged. Therefore, this project represents a new maturity in the work measurement field.

It will not be possible to reproduce here the large amount of data and information covered by the extensive literature. Instead, the authors will summarize the salient points and provide all the material needed to apply the experimental results to the extent they are presently available.

Project Phase I

The laboratory study established the basic nature of learning curves in the form of single-handed regression equations for individual MTM motions. These indicated the direction required in subsequent research. A most important question—learning behavior for simultaneous motions—was deferred to Phase II experimentation.

To assure the selection of typical operators, all were pre-tested with the Purdue Pegboard.[4] This also provided a standard measure of their skill levels readily comparable to extensive data available from industrial users of this widely-known test. This measure was shown in Phase II to correlate highly with initial performance, although it proved to be a poor indicator of the final performance levels. This indicated the need for additional measures of skill levels for hiring and job placement purposes.

[4] Available from: Science Research Associates, Chicago, Illinois.

For a number of reasons, the Phase I experiments were limited to 1,000 cycles of each task. The subject motivation was kept at a high level, as was reflected in consistent achievements of incentive pace performance. Also, each operator was provided sufficient instruction and initial practice to cross the threshold into the reinforcement learning area prior to recording of the desired learning data. They also were urged to attain their fastest performance of the general method without incurring excessive fumbles. Otherwise, no rate goal was given nor were the subjects informed concerning their efficiency or performance rate. A useful conclusion was that speed and the fumble rate are interrelated even when the operator does not know his rate of performance.

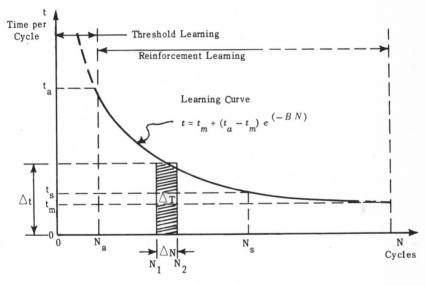

T = Time to perform N cycles

t = Time per cycle

t_a = Time for first reinforcement cycle

t_s = Standard time per cycle

t_m = Minimum cycle time

$B = \dfrac{1}{N}$ when $t = \dfrac{t_a}{e} = 0.36788\, t_a$

N = Number of task cycles performed

N_a = Cycles to cross threshold

N_s = Cycles to reach standard time

e = Natural (or hyperbolic) logarithm base
  = 2.71828

$\dfrac{1}{e} = 0.36788$

Elemental Area $\triangle T = \triangle N\,(\triangle t) = \triangle N(t) = (N_2 - N_1)\left\{ t_m + (t_a - t_m)\, e^{\left[-B\,(0.5)(N_2 + N_1)\right]} \right\}$

Fig. 1.   Generalized negative exponential learning curve.

Actual reduction in cycle time (the measure of learning in this research) was observed for all subjects. This learning resulted from subtle methods changes, even at the *micro* level, which the urge for faster cycles and sensory changes caused the operators to make. That is, reduction in the total cycle times due to pace and to individual motion times which vary because of methods changes together account for much of the learning under repetitive performance conditions. An interesting fact was that initial learning was more rapid for low-skill motions, but high-skill motions were improved more in the later stages of reinforcement practice. Subsequent investigation showed that although motions interact highly during the early stages of learning, continued practice causes them to become essentially independent except for the type of interactions defined within the MTM systems. All of these results confront directly some of the basic problems associated with predetermined motion times and tend to more firmly establish their validity on a research basis.

The next considerations are the mathematical properties of learning curves and their ease of application by users in the field. Figure 1 displays a generalized negative exponential curve which most nearly matches the smoothed learning curves resulting from *manual* learning. The accompanying notation makes all too obvious the complications which application of such curves would present. Not only are exponential mathematics less widely understood than would be necessary, but also they are laborious and do not permit easy manual computation. On the other hand, linear regression lines of the type shown in Fig. 2 greatly reduce this application problem to manageable proportions. The research showed by least squares analysis that linear regression lines provided results as good as the exponential curves for learning in the 1,000 cycle range. Therefore, such equations were used in subsequent project analysis.

Project Phase II—Laboratory

Actually, Phase II work began long before the Phase I results were published. Based on earlier MTM research,[5] additional laboratory work concerning the learning behavior for simultaneous motions—a topic deferred to Phase II as indicated earlier—was performed during 1962. The results[6] of this work, accomplished by the report authors along with Messrs. James A. Foulke and Kenneth R. Eaton, Jr., have implications for both the Learning Curve Project and the general subject of simultaneity during manual performance. Although the important learning aspects were assimilated into the Phase II results, the indications for further simultaneous

[5] R.R. 105 (See Ch. 5).

[6] "The Effect of Simultaneous Motions on Learning," by Stanley H. Caplan and Walton M. Hancock, *Journal of Methods-Time Measurement*, Vol. IX, No. 1, MTM Association, Ann Arbor, Michigan, September-October 1963.

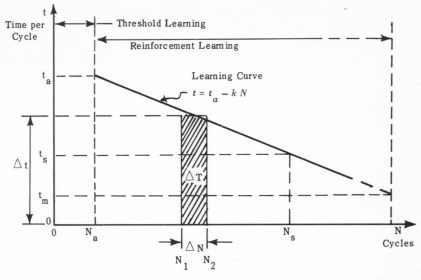

T = Time to perform N cycles

t = Time per cycle

t_a = Time for first reinforcement cycle (intercept of regression line)

t_s = Standard time per cycle

t_m = Minimum cycle time

N = Number of task cycles performed

N_a = Cycles to cross threshold

N_s = Cycles to reach standard time

k = Slope of the regression line

Elemental Area $\Delta T = \Delta N (\Delta t) = \Delta N(t) = (N_2 - N_1) \left[t_a - k \, (0.5)(N_2 + N_1) \right]$

Fig. 2.   Generalized linear regression learning curve.

motion research may perhaps prove equally vital to future work measurement progress.

Using the same general approach and instrumentation similar to that described for Phase I, but also retesting several subjects after a lapse of two months, the experimenters concluded that the observed learning was not due solely to an increased degree of simultaneity. Rather, *most* of the performance improvement accrued primarily from the number of cycles performed by the subjects. Also established was the need for differing regression equations to cover single-handed and dual-handed learning. However, the ability of linear regression equations to reflect simultaneous learning was seen to be relatively equal to the previous findings for single-handed learning. All of these conclusions were essential to Phase II progress.

Further Phase II work is summarized in R.R. 113 (see Footnote 3). It involved both additional laboratory effort by the R.R. 113 authors and three extensive industrial studies to be described later. To promote clarity on the curve development itself, the additional laboratory work will be described first.

As a consequence of the preliminary simultaneous motion investigation already considered, additional experiments were conducted to determine regression equations for simo performance. Analysis of these equations and those from Phase I for best fit to the experimental data led to a decision to express the results in two linear regression lines for each manual learning curve. Refer again to Figures 1 and 2 while this is explained. Although Phase I indicated that linear regression lines correlated reasonably well with negative exponential curves over the total learning period, this conclusion leaves unsolved a practical requirement for applying learning curves to actual operations. This requirement is that point values on a learning curve must reasonably reflect the true performance time at any chosen number of cycles throughout the cycle range. Basically a single linear regression expression does not meet this requirement because of the more rapid learning at early stages of practice than at later stages. This behavior is better represented by exponential curves. Analysis revealed, however, that the advantages of linear expressions could be retained with more adequate satisfaction of the practical requirement by using two linear equations to approximate the exponential behavior. The breakpoint selected by comparative analysis was at 500 cycles. Therefore, the elemental MTM learning curves are stated in two equations: 0 to 500 cycles and 500 to 1,000 cycles. Accordingly, the equations finally developed cover four conditions:

1. Single-handed in the 0 to 500 cycle range.
2. Simultaneous in the 0 to 500 cycle range.
3. Single-handed in the 500 to 1,000 cycle range.
4. Simultaneous in the 500 to 1,000 cycle range.

The learning equations were further refined by adjusting them to a unit time basis. That is, assuming that the learning rate for a given case of motion is essentially constant[7] throughout the range of distance for that motion, the learning equations were normalized to a basis of one TMU. To illustrate this procedure, consider the following laboratory data expression for an R10A: $10.51 - 0.00288(N)$, TMU. When this is divided by 11.3 TMU—the MTM standard for an R10A—it becomes: $0.930 - 0.00025(N)$, per TMU. This expression then applies for each TMU assigned to an R__A in an MTM pattern. If this expression is multiplied by the sum of the Case A Reach time included in an MTM analysis, it will yield the learning equation for the R__A elements of the pattern. However, the particular expression selected to show this normalizing process was further adjusted by the "revolving" procedure next described to establish

[7] This assumption was partially justified in R. R. 113.

the actual final equation for single-handed, Case A Reaches in the 0 to 500 cycle range.

When the learning data points were expressed in two linear regression lines, most of the lines did not meet at the 500-cycle point as would be necessary to permit totalizing performance time up to any point in the 0 to 1,000 cycle range. The potential usage of learning curves for labor estimating purposes requires that such totalizing should be technically correct. For this purpose, the essential feature is that *the area should remain constant* under the 0 to 500 cycle curve, even though its end points might be shifted to *both* better approximate the initial point of the true exponential curve *and* match the starting point for the 500 to 1,000 cycle curve. See Fig. 3 for the method of "revolving" the 0 to 500 cycle curves

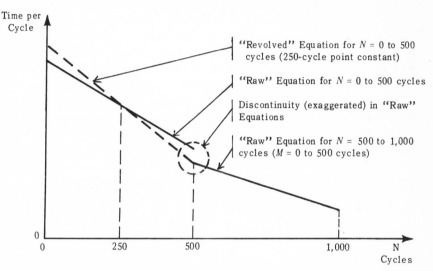

Fig. 3. Method of "revolving" the 0 to 500 cycle regression curves about the 250-cycle point to meet the 500 to 1000 cycle curves at the 500-cycle point.

to satisfy these requirements. It is useful to understand this calculation at a later point in the learning curve procedure. To illustrate the operation, the R—A equation from the last paragraph is used. Here the single-handed, Case A Reach equation in the 500 to 1,000 cycle range was: $0.854 - 0.000150\ (M)$, where $M = (N - 500)$. It is desired to "revolve" the $0.930 - 0.000250(N)$ curve to meet the 0.854 point at 500 cycles. Calculating the 250-cycle point yields: $0.930 - 0.000250(250) = 0.930 - 0.0625 = 0.8675$, per TMU. The difference from the starting point of the 500 to 1,000 cycle line is: $0.8675 - 0.854 = 0.0135$. Dividing by 250 cycles gives a "revolved" slope of: $0.0135 \div 250 = 0.000054$. Then adding the 0.0135 figure to the 250-cycle point value gives: $0.8675 + 0.0135 = 0.881$. By combining the intercept and slope values, the "revolved" equation becomes: $0.881 - 0.000054(N)$, per TMU. This is the final equation for single-handed, Case A Reaches in the 0 to 500 cycle range. The same procedure was used to derive all other 0 to 500 cycle regression lines.

For simultaneous regression lines where experimental data was not available, it was established that a factor of 1.2 applied to the intercept value of the single-handed equation would be satisfactory. This factor was a compromise based partly on the data from the preliminary simo investigation and partly on the subsequent Phase II simo experiments.

The final regression equations appear on the worksheet which is part of the procedure detailed in the next major section. These equations predict the manual learning for a 120 per cent operator; because they reflect the highly motivated, very favorable laboratory conditions of performance. To adjust the equations back to a 100 per cent performance, the intercept values must be multiplied by 1.2. Also, the slope to the cyclic breakpoint must be determined from applying the "revolving" procedure outlined above when the equation is in the 0 to 500 cycle range. This calculation also will be illustrated in the next section.

Among the basic equations used to develop the composite learning curves for an MTM pattern, as described in the next section, are several identified by "Remainder Motions." These special regression expressions were developed to cover all the kinds, cases, or classes, and types of MTM motions which are not specifically identified with other equations. Included are all the motions for which learning data were not experimentally determined: Turn, Apply Pressure, Release, Disengage, Eye Motions, and Body Motions. These equations were normalized based on the residual learning not included within pattern calculations for the motions having known elemental learning curves. To properly weight the averages for the known motions, a general expression was derived based upon the relative frequency of occurrence for Reach, Grasp, Move, and Position. The values used for relative frequency were approximations from data generated by Ulf Åberg[8] and John E. Mabry;[9] they represent industrial averages.

With the final elemental equations for manual learning developed, the research progressed to the industrial validation phase. This work is discussed under the next topical heading. Concurrent with the industrial effort, further laboratory analysis was undertaken to develop a learning prediction method. The composite learning curve technique which resulted from this combined effort is covered in the next section. All during Phase II experimentation, laboratory and industrial work was directed toward the major

[8] R.C.R. No. 1 (See Ch. 5).

[9] Staff Industrial Engineer, U. S.—Canada MTM Association. His report is as yet unpublished.

questions of operator selection and training.   These subjects also are considered in a later section.

Project Phase II—Industrial

The purposes of the industrial study were to validate the laboratory findings and to discover any additional factors requiring recognition in the development of composite learning curves, based on MTM patterns, by which actual learning behavior could be predicted.   Because such investigation would reveal more by comprehensive study of a few operations typical of the industrial spectrum than by a large relatively homogeneous sample, only three intensive studies were made.   However, these three included manual-machine, inspection, and clerical-machine operations besides the desired experimental factors.   Following description of the particular studies—MACE, TRW, and GEICO—the common results which most directly influenced the composite curve development will be discussed.

1. *MACE*.[10]   Performed by the report authors at a Michigan plant which chose to remain anonymous (hence the code name MACE), this study covered the manual loading and unloading of fragile ceramic parts on an automatic grinder which limited the operating cycle time.

   The short-cycle MTM pattern of 130.8 TMU was repeated 1,100 to 1,700 times by four men and four women differing in job backgrounds and having no experience on the type of task studied.   During selection, each volunteer was given the Purdue Pegboard test and their medical history was checked.   They were instructed on the grinder operation; but the standard parts handling method, which involved a high degree of simultaneity, was not revealed.   Although the experiment was conducted in a production area on a regularly used machine, the standard method was protected by prohibiting subject communication with regular operators.   Recycling of a piece was not permitted and no performance indication except an eventual confirmation on having attained the correct method was provided.   The recognition and disposal of scrap parts was left up to the operator, but the average production scrap rate was allowed in evaluating the performance data.

   The study records comprise a motion picture and recording of the stopwatch times required to complete five cycles.   Due to no particular attempt to motivate the subjects, the performance level averaged about 100 per cent for all subjects.   Therefore, the laboratory equations were modified by the method previously mentioned.   The effects of medium and long breaks on learning were checked during this

---

[10] "An Industrial Study of Learning," by Robert R. Clifford and Walton M. Hancock, *Journal of Methods-Time Measurement,* Vol. IX, No. 3, MTM Association, Ann Arbor, Michigan, January-February 1964.

study, as later described.   During the breaks, the subjects were kept in remote sections of the plant to safeguard the learning conditions of the experiment.

Thus, the MACE study essentially tested novices to the task having differing backgrounds, ages, sex, and having no particular motivation in a manner which permitted comparison of learning differences with minimal effects from extraneous variables.   In other words, the only controls imposed were those necessary to avoid confounding the test results.   As to kind of operation, it typified manual-machine processes which are most prevalent in today's mechanized industry.

2. *TRW*.[11]   This study at the Cleveland, Ohio plant of Thompson Ramo Wooldridge, Inc. (TRW) involved the inspection of a triangular sheet metal block in a lever-operated gaging fixture with two dial indicators. Part delivery was from a supply chute in a pre-oriented condition, while drop disposal into holes in the worktable separated scrap from good parts.   Although within the factory, the operation was isolated from the regular inspection department as a control upon the method used.   The method was divulged motion by motion so that such full oral and demonstration type instruction could be tested.   To provide motivation, the subjects were told to work as fast as possible without excessive fumbles—which also permitted a correlation of fumble rate during learning.

All task elements were under full manual control of the six operators, of whom four were female.   Two women had no inspection experience, two men had a year or less, and the remaining women had more than a decade of such experience.   However, despite their differing backgrounds, their Purdue Pegboard scores were about equal and a short intelligence test showed a five-to-one spread.   The import is that their initial manual ability was essentially the same but their mental aptitudes definitely were unequal.   The sample therefore provided a definite mixture of skill levels, sex, and ages which should be typical of inspection operators.

During performance, the threshold was defined as the completion of five successive cycles without trial and error or referral to instructions, after which recording began.   Every fifth cycle was recorded for the first 100 cycles, every tenth cycle for the next 300 cycles, and every 25th cycle thereafter.   All subjects performed 1,000 to 4,000 cycles except that the skilled operators stopped at 2,000 cycles.   The MTM pattern was of medium simultaneity with a short cycle of 94.8 TMU.   Periodic short breaks were scheduled and short fatigue breaks

[11] "Experiment in Operator Learning at TRW," by Russell R. Paine, *Journal of Methods-Time Measurement*, Vol. IX, No. 4, MTM Association, Ann Arbor, Michigan, May–June 1964.

were granted upon request. Due to the instruction and motivation, the average performance level of 120 per cent matched the laboratory pace, so that the elemental learning equations did not require pace adjustment.

To summarize the TRW study conditions, it tested operators of different ages and sex from the novice to the expert skill level with high task motivation on a standardized method following full oral and demonstration type instruction. The operation was typical of industrial inspection tasks.

3. *GEICO.* This study, not as yet separately published, was named from the initials of the Government Employees Insurance Company. Performed in Washington, D.C., it involved a clerical-machine operation typical of life insurance work, namely, calculating the policyholder rebate for a policy cancelled prior to the termination date. Mr. William M. Bellman of GEICO joined with Messrs. Robert R. Clifford and Leonard E. Krystynak of the University of Michigan to conduct the study.

All six subjects were new clerks selected by the normal personnel tests of the company. Each was fully trained on the task with a programmed learning device, although the device was discarded after the third cycle because all operators had crossed the learning threshold. Competition was high as indicated by the average performance of 120 per cent, thus the laboratory learning curves were directly applicable as to pace.

The rebate calculation included clerical entries on working forms, finding such information as the prorata percentage of rebate, and calculating the rebate data on an automatic desk calculating machine. Although the calculation generated some process time, a more important learning factor in its usage was the replication of calculating motions in almost identical groups of four due to the four types of policy coverage. This repetition actually increased the learning practice on the calculating motions. Each subject was timed on 10 different policies, with the MTM cycle time of 3,150.4 TMU qualifying the work as long cycle. Also, while the simultaneity was fairly low, the usage of eye time was very high. This was a fortunate choice in the composite learning curve development, as will be seen later.

During the first six cycles, four observers were used. One counted eye usages. The other three used TMU watches to isolate the total cycle time and the time for each step in the task procedure. However, on the remaining cycles, one observer counted eye usages and took total cycle times on the stopwatch. Operator behavior also was noted by the observer at all times. Each operator performed an average of 150 cycles.

Essentially, then, the GEICO test covered inexperienced operators with uniform programmed instruction and good motivation on a standard method typical of clerical-machine work in the insurance industry.

By reviewing the condition variables in the three studies, the potential derivation of composite learning curves can be discerned. Based on the study results, since the experimental design deliberately covered the range and scope of variables, it was possible to isolate the major influences on operational learning in actual industrial environments. The variables and their evaluation therefore are now discussed as a prelude to the composite curve description in the next section.

A summary of the industrial sample data is given in Table 1. Reference to these data will be helpful in gaining an understanding of the discussion of the industrial results. The over-all general result of the industrial studies, at first, was that the plotted actual performances were not sufficiently predicted by the linear elemental equations from the laboratory studies. In general, the number of cycles to standard correlated well with the prediction. However, it was apparent that some aspect of learning besides the manual improvement demonstrated in the laboratory occurs in the industrial context. This was highlighted by initially longer performance cycles than would be expected from the 0 to 500 cycle regression lines. Also, the rate of learning to standard appeared to be more rapid and uniform in the actual situation than in the laboratory. Therefore, the industrial variables were analyzed to ascertain which of them contributed the major portion of the discrepancy.

Two variables eventually proved to be the principal factors requiring recognition in the adjustment of the laboratory curves to improve their predictive powers. When these factors were applied, the actual industrial curve prediction was transformed from seemingly poor to the degrees shown on the last line entries in Table 1. These two variables were the *sensory-information processing* behavior and the *personal characteristics* of the operators. The best measure of the first of these proved to be the eye usage during the operation. In this context, one eye usage is considered to be an Eye Travel and Eye Focus sequence upon the workpiece or some feature of the workplace. As learning was achieved, the eye usages were progressively reduced to the number included in the standard, with the simultaneous acquisition of kinesthetic control due to concurrent muscular practice. Apparently the sensory-information processing capability of the operator shifts with practice from reliance on external clues to internal direction by mental and manual procedures. In view of this, several principles must be recognized. First, any composite learning curve must account for eye usage functioning. Second, the personal characteristics of an

Table I. Data Summary of Industrial Sample

Study Variables	Industrial Study		
	MACE	TRW	GEICO
Type of Operation	Manual-machine	Inspection	Clerical-machine
MTM Standard Cycle, TMU	130.8	94.8	3,150.4
Replications per Subject	1,100 to 1,700	1,000 to 4,000 (except 2,000 for skilled subjects)	150 (average)
Standard TMU per Subject	143,880 to 222,360	94,800 to 378,200	572,560
Number of Subjects	8	6	6
Standard TMU per Study	1,151,040 to 1,778,880	568,800 to 2,269,200	3,435,360
Sex of Operator	4 male, 4 female	2 male, 4 female	2 male, 4 female
Age Range, Years	18 to 50	22 to 62	17 to 18
Work Experience, Years	0 to 21(none on task)	0 to 15 (on task)	Essentially None
Type of Experience	Differing	Differing	Not Applicable
Manual Ability Score (Purdue Pegboard Assy.)	34 to 47	36 to 46	45 to 86
Mental Test Score (Wonderlic Form B)		6 to 30	
Type of Task Instruction	Minimal (Trial and Error)	Maximum Oral and Demonstration	Full Programmed Learning Device
Average Subject Pace	100%	120%	120%
Eye Usage (in Final Standard)	Low	Low	Very High
Simultaneity (in Standard)	High	Medium	Low
Break Periods Studied	Medium, Long	Short, Medium	None
Other Factors Studied	Scrap Rate	Fumble Rate	Eye Usage
Aircraft-Type Curve "Learning Rate"	92.0%	89.3%	86.8%
Fit of Actual Performance to Composite Curve	Good	Excellent	Very Good

operator are crucial both to his current performance predictability and to his capacity to maintain predicted performance as time passes, creating aging effects which eventually cause his complete failure as a source of productive manual energy.

Essentially, the composite curve development covered in the next section applies the results of eye usage analysis to achieve a practical learning prediction method. The personal characteristic problem, however, was only partially solved in the Phase II effort. More details concerning this major variable will be found in the section entitled Operator Selection and Training. Also, the ongoing research effort (Phase III) which is directed at the problem is described in the section entitled New Aspects of Project. Accordingly, the remainder of this section discusses the results concerning all other variables evaluated in the three industrial studies.

The authors believe that environment affects learning mainly in two respects, namely, in relation to the operator's concentration and motivation on the task. Concentration aids learning, and environment conducive to it provides a freedom from distractions and annoyances which liberates the mental faculties for more efficient sensory-information processing. Another facet of a favorable environment is that the physical powers are not strained by over- or under-stimulation from the physiological standpoint. However, the tolerance to unfavorable environments is determined by the degree of motivation. Remembering that a productive environment includes one's co-workers, the total effect can itself become a source of motivation or vice versa. Unfavorable environments can be surmounted under high motivation conditions, albeit at a physiological price. Generally, a worker is more sensitive to such environmental factors during learning periods than when performing habitually a task already fully learned.

Apparently, the sex of the worker makes no major difference in the learning rate. However, age is an important factor in both motor fitness and the sensory-information processing ability in relation to learning. The effects of aging are complex and the MACE report[12] includes an extensive discussion of them, to which the reader should refer. In essence, the learning rate usually declines with increasing age. However, individual characteristics suggest caution in the application of generalities to specific individuals.

Training and experience both seem to most directly concern the rapidity with which an operator crosses the learning threshold and the rate of continued improvement displayed in the reinforcement area. Extensive and careful instruction pays dividends in reducing the costs of learning. However, more data is needed in this area to permit definitive statements. This data also is being generated in continuing research. Nevertheless, the net

12 *Op. Cit.* (Footnote 10)

effect of both training and experience is to bring established sensory-information processing channels and existing muscular coordination to the immediate task, provided it is not too dissimilar to the tasks on which the training and experience have been gained. This phenomenon is known as "transfer learning," which permits quicker attainment of the needed skill in learning a new task. The recentness of the appropriate training and experience also affects the amount of transfer learning which is effective.

The job requirements themselves have a direct bearing on the amount of learning required. Job requirements include the length of cycle, the number of cyclic elements, the degree of control required in motions and the kind of motions themselves, the information content or perceptual and/or kinesthetic loading included, the number of choices within the task elements, the degree to which sequential elements are related or provide clues to the next step, and the physical variables of the workpiece and workplace. As learning progresses, subtle methods changes which improve performance increasingly become accomplished unless job requirements interfere with this process. Another aspect of the question is the degree of simultaneity, which requires different learning rates than is the case for single-handed methods. However, from the MTM standpoint manual learning now can be explained by the laboratory regression equations, while the sensory-information processing requirements are largely accounted for by the eye usage function of the composite curve method. Of course, it is expected that refinements and new application rules will emerge from further research; but the existing procedure appears to be capable of explaining the major learning effects regarding job requirements.

Short (15 minutes or less), medium (overnight or one-day), and long (a week or more) breaks in the routine of learning, as examined in the MACE and TRW studies, have a diminishing effect on performance as the number of completed cycles increases. The effect appears to be negligible for short and medium breaks after full learning has been achieved, although longer breaks may have residual effects. However, the learning rate after short breaks is more rapid than before, so that the performance rate soon overtakes the trend of the original learning as though no break had occurred. Two practical procedures are suggested by this information. The learning should start as early as possible in the working shift to allow attainment of as much learning as possible before the shift ends, thereby minimizing the loss of production due to the break period decrement in short-term memory between daily shifts. Thus, attention to the scheduled job lot quantities may help avoid learning penalties by keeping the orders in amounts that can be finished within the shift.

Recognizing that in addition to material reasons the scrap rate is partly due to operator actions on the workpiece (especially in conjunction with any machine involved) and partly due to the efficiency with which the operator perceives actual defects present, it appears that the rate of learning is affected by the scrap rate in the same general way as by short breaks. A scrap part interferes with the learning process briefly, but a recovery in the learning rate may be expected after disposal unless the scrap rate becomes excessive. Also, learning tends to lessen both the manual errors and the non-recognition of bad parts which are integral factors in the scrap rate. That is, the scrap rate should tend to reduce as higher degrees of task learning are reached. Similar conclusions also apply to the fumble rate, and for similar reasons.

COMPUTING MTM LEARNING CURVES

In this section, the heart of the chapter insofar as practicable learning curve data is concerned, consideration starts with the elemental regression equations resulting from the Phase II laboratory effort. How the Phase II industrial results affected the composite learning curve development is first described. This is followed by the current MTM Learning Curve procedure. To show how the procedure is applied, several comparable examples are computed and analyzed for the training effects of an actual industrial methods improvement. Interestingly for this recent procedure, the example methods improvement was made more than a dozen years ago, yet the MTM patterns on which it was based are all that is needed to permit application of the MTM learning data. The power of such a tool should be obvious to the reader.

Composite Curve Development

The key to the composite curve development proved to be the mathematical function which describes the eye usage behavior previously described. In terms of operator performance, the number of eye usages is gradually reduced as the sensory-information processing channels gain efficiency from practice to the point at which the minimal or ultimate number of eye usages specified by the MTM pattern is achieved. Previous to this research, no definitive way to determine this junction existed. However, based solely on the motions of the MTM pattern, the manual learning equations from the laboratory can be used to define this junction—the number of cycles at which the MTM standard is achieved. In other words, if one could plot the eye usage function based on its intersection with the manual learning function, it should accurately represent the composite effect of learning the MTM pattern. It would consider the combined results of the operator's gain in manual efficiency with the accompanying reduction in the necessity for visual guidance of those motions subject to kinesthetic control. The means of achieving this desirable condition involved high-order mathematical analysis aided by the computer. However, the net result is readily explained in terms of graphical functions.

To permit the development, several questions had to be answered. First, what is the proper mathematical function to describe the eye usage behavior? The fortunate inclusion of eye usage observation in the Phase II industrial studies provided this answer. The algebraic function can be expressed accurately in the negative exponential form of:

$$y = k\,(x)^{-a}$$

where y = the number of eye usages (ET + EF, as previously defined)
    k = a constant coefficient for the operating conditions
    x = the number of cycles in the reinforcement learning area
    a = a constant exponent related to the rate of learning.

Now, since the value of y reduces exponentially as shown, it becomes necessary to answer a second question. What is the *ratio* of the final to the initial value of y under typical industrial conditions? This result from the industrial data was a value of 2.5; i.e., the operator will use his eyes 2.5 times as much at the start of reinforcement learning as he will after meeting the MTM standard.

With this data, it would be possible to establish the beginning and MTM standard junction points of the eye usage function. However, for the curve to be most useful, a simple calculating method to obtain intervening points was needed. Here, a traditional rule of the *so-called* aircraft learning curves was used. These *performance* curves are of the negative exponential type, and several accepted techniques of simplifying their calculation are well defined. The rule is that the required cycle time is reduced by a constant percentage for each point at which the amount of production (or number of cycles performed) is doubled. Of course, aircraft-type curves normally are plotted in the forward direction starting from the known or anticipated initial cycle time; however, the endpoint is not known except by experience on comparable production runs. This defect would not be present for the eye usage function. In fact, the eye usage function could be plotted in the reverse order. Starting with the known number of cycles required to attain the MTM standard (from the manual equations), and by determining the value k which represents the TMU per cycle at the start of reinforcement learning, the curve could be generated backwards to its intersection with k. This circumstance permitted analysis which established that the constant percentage, or learning rate, of the eye usage function could be expressed as:

$$P\,(\%) = \text{antilog}_{10}\,[\,(0.30103)\,(-a)\,].$$

Therefore, all obstacles to plotting the continuous eye usage function had been removed.

The only other equations needed, a matter of algebraic analysis, were relationships for computing the values of a and k. The proper equation for the exponent a turned out to be a function of the eye usage reduction ratio (2.5) and the number of cycles both to the learning threshold and to the MTM standard:

$$a = \frac{\log_{10} 2.5}{\log_{10} x_2 - \log_{10} x_1} = \frac{0.39794}{\log x_2 - \log x_1}$$

where x_2 = the number of cycles to the MTM standard
and x_1 = the number of cycles to the learning threshold.

Similar investigation showed that coefficient k could be computed by the relation:

$$\log k = \log S + a (\log x_2)$$

where S = the total TMU in the MTM pattern, with the other symbols being as previously defined.

Unfortunately, computing the values of a, k, and P all involve logarithmic calculations. Although many analysts in the field are either unfamiliar or have forgotten their former practice with this kind of mathematics, no good substitute scheme of computing these values can be offered at the present time. The analyst simply needs to review or become educated to logarithmic manipulation if he wishes to apply the MTM learning curve data. However, for this kind of mathematical quantity, the computations are not difficult.

Now all of the preceding information needed to be tested in the industrial environment. Therefore, the MACE, TRW, AND GEICO actual learning curves were each plotted on the same graph as the composite learning curves which matched each study condition. Of course the term "composite learning curves" implies a particular graphical orientation of the eye usage function and the two linear manual functions as depicted in Fig. 4. When the industrial data curves were superimposed on this type of plot, agreement as entered in the last line of Table 1 was obtained. In other words, the composite curve method is a very good predictor of actual industrial learning. Operator performance was sufficiently close to the eye usage function developed in this manner to be considered as essentially equivalent. Therefore, the composite curve approach has been adopted as the proper means of computing and constructing MTM learning curves. Details of applying the composite curve method have been embodied in the procedure which is presented next.

The procedure for computing and plotting an MTM Learning Curve, examples of which will be given later, is as follows:

Step I. Be sure the MTM motion pattern is properly written and that all symbol conventions, especially those concerning limiting of motions,

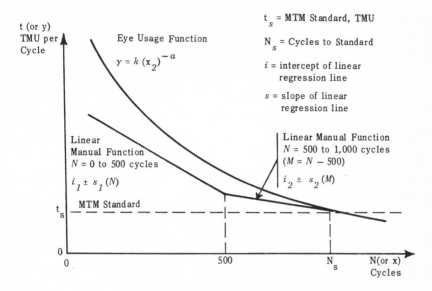

Fig. 4.   Idealized composite learning curve method developed by MTM research.

have been correctly indicated. Correct pattern writing is crucial to the results from this procedure, so a check first is very worthwhile.

Step II. Fill out the MTM Learning Curve Worksheet for $N = 0$ to 500 cycles (see Fig. 5) as follows:

A. Examine each line of the motion pattern for the limiting motion.

B. Summarize the time for each kind and case of limiting motion element in the pattern and enter the appropriate TMU totals in the third column of the worksheet.

C. Multiply the third and fourth columns of the worksheet and enter the extensions in the last column.

D. *Algebraically* sum the last column of the worksheet to determine the unadjusted Composite Learning Equation for 0 to 500 cycles.

Step III. Fill out the MTM Learning Curve Worksheet for $N = 500$ to 1,000 cycles (see Fig. 6) as follows:

A. Copy the entries in the third column of the previous worksheet into the third column of this worksheet.

B. Multiply the third and fourth columns of the worksheet and enter the extensions in the last column.

C. *Algebraically* sum the last column of the worksheet to determine the unadjusted Composite Learning Equation for 500 to 1,000 cycles.

MTM LEARNING CURVE WORKSHEET (N = 0 to 500 cycles)

MTM Elements	Hands	TMU in Pattern	Manual Learning Equations	
			Unit Basis	Pattern Basis
R_A	One		$0.881 - 0.000054(N)$	
R_E	Simo		$1.170 - 0.000290(N)$	
R_B R_C R_D	One		$0.864 - 0.000251(N)$	
	Simo		$0.946 - 0.000119(N)$	
M_A	One		$0.982 - 0.000152(N)$	
	Simo		$1.178 - 0.000185(N)$	
M_B	One		$0.491 + 0.000087(N)$	
M_C	Simo		$1.090 - 0.000336(N)$	
G1A	One		$2.365 - 0.001270(N)$	
	Simo		$2.915 - 0.001670(N)$	
G1B,G1C G2 G3	One		$0.763 + 0.000104(N)$	
	Simo		$1.010 - 0.000128(N)$	
G4	One		$1.667 - 0.000334(N)$	
	Simo		$2.255 - 0.000430(N)$	
P1SE	One		$2.000 - 0.000199(N)$	
	Simo		$2.558 - 0.000576(N)$	
P1SSE	One		$1.195 + 0.000802(N)$	
	Simo		$2.208 - 0.000579(N)$	
P1NSE	One		$1.934 - 0.000749(N)$	
	Simo		$2.208 - 0.000579(N)$	
P21S	One		$0.940 - 0.000091(N)$	
P22S	Simo		$1.205 - 0.000273(N)$	
Remainder Motions	One		$1.130 - 0.000446(N)$	
	Simo		$1.573 - 0.000650(N)$	
COMPOSITE LEARNING EQUATION				

Fig. 5.   MTM Learning Curve Worksheet for $N = 0$ to 500 cycles.

MTM LEARNING CURVE WORKSHEET (N = 500 to 1,000 cycles)
($M = N - 500$)

MTM Elements	Hands	TMU in Pattern	Manual Learning Equations	
			Unit Basis	Pattern Basis
R_A	One		$0.854 - 0.000150(M)$	
R_E	Simo		$1.025 - 0.000149(M)$	
R_B R_C R_D	One		$0.739 - 0.000093(M)$	
	Simo		$0.887 - 0.000093(M)$	
M_A	One		$0.905 - 0.000058(M)$	
	Simo		$1.086 - 0.000058(M)$	
M_B	One		$0.534 - 0.000016(M)$	
M_C	Simo		$0.922 - 0.000093(M)$	
G1A	One		$1.730 - 0.000430(M)$	
	Simo		$2.080 - 0.000430(M)$	
G1B,G1C G2 G3	One		$0.789 - 0.000149(M)$	
	Simo		$0.946 - 0.000149(M)$	
G4	One		$1.500 - 0.000256(M)$	
	Simo		$2.040 - 0.000086(M)$	
P1SE	One		$1.900 - 0.000028(M)$	
	Simo		$2.270 - 0.000017(M)$	
P1SSE	One		$1.596 - 0.000346(M)$	
	Simo		$1.918 - 0.000208(M)$	
P1NSE	One		$1.560 - 0.000155(M)$	
	Simo		$1.918 - 0.000208(M)$	
P21S	One		$0.895 + 0.000013(M)$	
P22S	Simo		$1.068 - 0.000008(M)$	
Remainder Motions	One		$0.943 - 0.000145(M)$	
	Simo		$1.240 - 0.000176(M)$	
COMPOSITE LEARNING EQUATION				

Fig. 6.   MTM Learning Curve Worksheet for $N = 500$ to 1000 cycles.

Step IV. Determine the following Pace Correction Ratio (*PCR*):

$$PCR = \frac{120}{\text{Observed or Expected Pace, \%}}$$

> Note: The usual value of the denominator for an MTM standard basis will be 100. However, any desired pace basis can be chosen. The basis entered here will affect the results from this entire procedure. If the chosen pace basis is 120%, no correction is needed, so the *PCR* will be 1.00.

Step V. Adjust the intercept and slope values of the equations determined in Steps II and III as follows:

  A. Multiply the *intercept* value of the equation from Step III by the *PCR* determined in Step IV. This will give the adjusted Composite Learning Equation for 500 to 1,000 cycles. Note that the slope of the regression line will remain unchanged.

  B. Multiply the *intercept* value of the equation from Step II by the *PCR* determined in Step IV. Subtract from this value the intercept found in Step V-A. Then divide this difference by 500 to determine the adjusted slope.

  C. Using the adjusted intercept and slope values determined in Step V-B, write the adjusted Composite Learning Equation for 0 to 500 cycles.

Step VI. Examine the two equations resulting from Step V. Choose the one which intersects the TMU time value of the MTM pattern. Note that this will be the one with the smallest intercept value which is greater than the MTM standard time. Using the chosen equation, solve for M or N. If M is found, add 500 cycles to determine the value for N. The value for N is the predicted number of cycles to standard at the selected pace basis.

Step VII. Establish or estimate the number of cycles to the learning threshold. Then determine the eye usage function as follows:

  A. Calculate the exponent value a with the following equation:

$$a = \frac{0.39794}{\log x_2 - \log x_1}$$

  where x_2 = cycles to standard from Step VI.
  and x_1 = cycles to learning threshold.

  B. Calculate the value of coefficient k with the following equation:

$$\log k = \log S + a (\log x_2)$$

  where S = total TMU in the MTM pattern.
  and x_2 = cycles to standard from Step VI.
  and a = exponent from Step VII-A.

    C. Based on the symbol values determined in Steps VII-A and VII-B, write the eye usage function as follows:

$$y = k(x_2)^{-a}$$

Step VIII. Determine the per cent slope, P, of the eye usage function with the following equation:

$$P = 100 \text{ antilog}_{10} \left[(0.30103)(-a) \right]$$

where a = exponent from Step VII-A.

Step IX. Calculate the plotting points on the eye usage function curve, based on the *decimal* value of P from Step VIII and the coefficient k value from Step VII-B as follows:

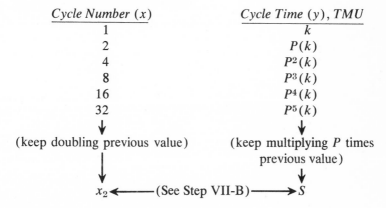

Cycle Number (x)	Cycle Time (y), TMU
1	k
2	$P(k)$
4	$P^2(k)$
8	$P^3(k)$
16	$P^4(k)$
32	$P^5(k)$

(keep doubling previous value)   (keep multiplying P times previous value)

$x_2 \longleftarrow$ (See Step VII-B) $\longrightarrow S$

Step X. Plot the MTM Learning Curve as follows:
    A. Establish a horizontal axis and select a scale for the number of cycles (x or N) to be plotted.
    B. Establish a vertical axis and select a TMU per cycle scale (y or t) which will permit plotting the required cycle times.
    C. From the y axis, plot a horizontal line for the value S (see Step VII-B) and label it "MTM Standard."
    D. Plot the x and y values found in Step IX and connect the points with a smooth exponential curve. Label this curve "Eye Usage Function" and also write nearby the equation established in Step VII-C.
    E. Plot the regression line determined in Step V-A and label it "Manual Function (500 to 1,000 cycles)." Also write nearby the expression determined in Step V-A.
    F. Plot the regression line determined in Step V-C and label it "Manual Function (0 to 500 cycles)." Also write nearby the expression determined in Step V-C.

G. Indicate somewhere in the upper right space the note "Threshold = x_1 cycles," using the value of x_1 from Step VII-A.

H. All other desired identifying items may be added to complete the MTM Learning Curve. For example, the pace basis (see Step IV) may be noted on the curve plot.

Step XI. As desired, apply the following equations to determine the indicated information at any desired number of cycles up to the standard:

Where a = exponent from Step VII-A.
   k = coefficient from Step VII-B.
   x_1 = cycles to threshold from Step VII-A.
   x = desired number of cycles selected.

A. Total TMU through the xth cycle:

$$\frac{k}{1-a}\left[(x)^{1-a} - (x_1)^{1-a}\right]$$

B. Average TMU per cycle through the xth cycle:

$$\frac{(\text{Step XI-A value})}{(x - x_1)}$$

C. Cycle time, TMU, at the xth cycle:

$$\frac{k}{(x)^a}$$

D. If the MTM pattern is dual, i.e. when two pieces are produced for each cycle, the TMU per piece will be: 0.5 (Step XI-C value)

Future development in the direction of simplifying application of the MTM Learning Curve data already has started. In R.R. 113, a method of developing *average* learning curves for groups of operations having similar characteristics within an industrial group is reported. However, the method there described is contingent upon industrial data not at present completely determined or widely accepted. Therefore, the interested reader is urged to study R.R. 113 for such information.

Examples of MTM Learning Curve Computation

Two comparable MTM patterns (contained in this textbook since the original edition) have been selected to illustrate the application of the MTM Learning Curve procedure just described. In Fig. 2 of Chapter 28 is an MTM analysis of an old method used for an insulator assembly. It is essentially a single-handed method with a poor layout requiring 207.4 TMU per piece or cycle. During this example, it is called the *old method*.

In Fig. 2 of Chapter 19 is a revised method for the same insulator assembly. It has been made highly simultaneous with a much better workplace design requiring only 175.0 TMU per piece (albeit, a cycle time of 349.9 TMU). This is called the *improved method* during the example.

The composite curve calculations will be shown in parallel columns for easy comparison. In the interest of brevity, the first column will identify the procedural step being shown. Thus, the calculations will show only the information not readily apparent from the procedure itself, as just given. Table 2 is the illustrative example in full.

Comparing the two methods is facilitated by the wealth of quantitive learning data available from the procedure. Although the old method takes 350 cycles less than the improved method for the operator to reach the MTM standard, basically due to less simultaneity, the improved method produces twice as much per cycle. Therefore, by the time the old method reached standard, the improved method—although still not up to standard —would have produced about eight more pieces. This latter figure can be obtained by evaluating the improved method at 1,933.8 cycles and comparing the production. In other terms, by the time the old method reached standard, the improved method already would have saved an average of 34.6 TMU per piece even though its ultimate potential was still not attained.

Another basis of comparison would be the cost for a given job lot quantity. For example, the typical order quantity actually was about 1,000 pieces. From Step XI-A, assuming a labor rate of $2.00 per hour ($.00002 per TMU), the labor cost of the lot by the two methods would be $5.84 and $5.03. Therefore, the improved method would save $.81 on this order quantity, provided a new operator was used with either method. If a similar ordering situation prevailed 41 times, the cost of making the methods change would be recovered. This can be seen by examining Item E in Fig. 1B of Chapter 28, showing that the change would cost $33.20. Quantitative information of this nature never before has been readily computed in work measurement practice. Such cost figures, however, are a natural outgrowth or progression from the detailed performance predictions possible with the MTM Learning Curve method.

Still other comparisons would be possible by applying the data in Step XI of Table 2. However, in addition to the learning data itself with its value for understanding the training problem, the comparisons already presented amply demonstrate the utility of the MTM Learning Curve data. It is fully expected that usage of the information in this chapter for a time in the field will generate many additional applications toward solution of practical production problems. If such developments should be coupled with many of the higher order operations research and computer routines, it is not difficult to imagine the sophisticated but financially sound routines which could result.

Table 2. Dual Example of MTM Learning Curve Computation

Procedure		Old Method	Improved Method
Step I		Pattern examined and considered acceptable.	Pattern examined and considered acceptable.
Step II		See Fig. 2 of Chapter 28 and Fig. 7 of this chapter	See Fig. 2 of Chapter 19 and Fig. 8 of this chapter
Step III		See Figure 9 of this chapter and spotcheck the calculations for practice.	See Fig. 10 of this chapter and spotcheck the calculations for practice.
Step IV		Because example is from a daywork plant: $$PCR = \frac{120}{100} = 1.2$$	Because example is from a daywork plant: $$PCR = \frac{120}{100} = 1.2$$
Step V	A	$(1.2)(192.120) - 0.016142(M)$ $= 230.544 - 0.016142(M)$	$(1.2)(331.017) - 0.026527(M)$ $= 397.220 - 0.026527(M)$
	B	$(1.2)(206.037) =$ 247.244 -230.544 $500 \overline{)\ 16.700}$ 0.033400	$(1.2)(397.000) =$ 476.400 -397.220 $500 \overline{)\ 79.180}$ 0.158360
	C	$247.244 - 0.033400(N)$	$476.400 - 0.158360(N)$
Step VI		Standard = 207.4 TMU. This intersects the Step VA equation. Therefore: $M = \dfrac{230.544 - 207.4}{0.016142}$ $= 1,433.8$ cycles $\underline{+\ 500}$ $N = 1,933.8$ cycles to standard for a 100% operator	Standard = 349.9 TMU. This intersects the Step VA equation. Therefore: $M = \dfrac{397.220 - 349.9}{0.026527}$ $= 1,783.8$ cycles $\underline{+\ 500}$ $N = 2,283.8$ cycles to standard for a 100% operator
Step VII	A	$x_2 = 1,933.8$ cycles Estimate $x_1 = 50$ cycles $a = \dfrac{0.39794}{\log 1,933.8 - \log 50}$ $= \dfrac{0.37974}{3.28641 - 1.69897}$ $= 0.25068$	$x_2 = 2,283.8$ cycles Estimate $x_1 = 50$ cycles $a = \dfrac{0.39794}{\log 2,283.8 - \log 50}$ $= \dfrac{0.39794}{3.35866 - 1.69897}$ $= 0.23976$
	B	$S = 207.4$ TMU $x_2 = 1,933.8$ cycles $a = 0.25068$ $\log k = \log 207.4 +$ $0.25068 \log 1,933.8$ $= 2.31681 + 0.25068\,(3.28641)$ $= 3.14065$ $k = $ antilog 3.14065 $= 1,382.5$ TMU per cycle	$S = 349.9$ TMU $x_2 = 2,283.8$ cycles $a = 0.23976$ $\log k = \log 349.9 +$ $0.23976 \log 2,283.8$ $= 2.54394 + 0.23976\,(3.35866)$ $= 3.34922$ $k = $ antilog 3.34922 $= 2,234.7$ TMU per cycle

(continued on next page)

Table 2 (continued).   Dual Example of MTM Learning Curve Computation

Procedure		Old Method		Improved Method	
Step VII (continued)	C	$y = 1,382.5\ (x_2)^{-0.25068}$		$y = 2,234.7\ (x_2)^{-0.23976}$	
Step VIII		$P = 100\ \text{antilog}\ \big[(0.30103)(-0.25068)\big]$		$P = 100\ \text{antilog}\ \big[(0.30103)(-0.23976)\big]$	
		$= 100\ \text{antilog}\ (-0.07546)$		$= 100\ \text{antilog}\ (-0.07217)$	
		$= 100\ (0.84048)$		$= 100\ (0.84690)$	
		$= 84.048\%$		$= 84.690\%$	
		So this is an 84.0% learning curve, about the same as for the simultaneous method.		So this is an 84.7% learning curve, about the same as for the single-handed method.	
Step IX		$k = 1,382.5$ TMU per cycle		$k = 2.234.7$ TMU per cycle	
		$P = 0.84048$		$P = 0.84690$	
		$S = 207.4$ TMU		$S = 349.9$ TMU	
		$x_2 = 1,933.8$ cycles		$x_2 = 2,283.8$ cycles	

Cycle Number (x)	Cycle Time (y), TMU	Cycle Number (x)	Cycle Time (y), TMU
1	1,382.5	1	2,234.7
2	1,161.9	2	1,892.6
4	976.6	4	1,602.8
8	820.8	8	1,357.4
16	689.9	16	1,152.2
32	579.8	32	975.8
64	487.3	64	826.4
128	409.6	128	699.9
256	344.3	256	592.7
512	289.3	512	502.0
1,024	243.2	1,024	425.1
1,933.8	207.4	2,048	360.0
		2,283.8	349.9

Procedure		Old Method	Improved Method
Step X		See Figure 11 of this chapter.	See Figure 12 of this chapter.
Step XI	c o m m o n	$a = 0.25068$ $k = 1,382.5$ TMU per cycle $x_1 = 50$ cycles $x = 500;\ 1,000;\ 1,500;$ and 1,933.8 cycles selected for evaluation	$a = 0.23976$ $k = 2,234.7$ TMU per cycle $x_1 = 50$ cycles $x = 500;\ 1,000;\ 1,500;$ and 2,283.8 cycles selected for evaluation
	A	Total TMU through the selected cycle: <u>Sample</u> calculation for cycles to standard (x = 1,933.8): $(1-a) = 1 - 0.25068$ $\quad\quad\quad = 0.74932$ $\dfrac{1,382.5}{0.74932}\big[(1,933.8)^{0.74932} - (50)^{0.74932}\big]$ (continued on next page)	Total TMU through the selected cycle: <u>Sample</u> calculation for cycles to standard (x = 2,283.8): $(1-a) = 1 - 0.23976$ $\quad\quad\quad = 0.76024$ $\dfrac{2,234.7}{0.76024}\big[(2,283.8)^{0.76024} - (50)^{0.76024}\big]$ (continued on next page)

Table 2 (continued).   Dual Example of MTM Learning Curve Computation

Procedure		Old Method		Improved Method	
Step XI (cont'd.)	A	= 1,845.0 (290.13 − 18.75) = 500,690 TMU total through the 1,933.8th cycle		= 2,939.5 (357.60 − 19.57) = 993,640 TMU total through the 2,283.8th cycle	
		x	Total TMU	*x*	Total TMU	Half-Value
		500	159,690	500	273,730	136,865
		1,000	291,990	1,000	503,480	251,740
		1,500	407,990	1,500	706,090	353,045
		1,933.8	500,690	2,283.8	993,640	496,820
	B	Average TMU per cycle through the selected cycle:		Average TMU per cycle through the selected cycle:	
		x − x_1 = $(x - x_1)$		x − x_1 = $(x - x_1)$	
		500	50	450		
		1,000	50	950		
		1,500	50	1,450		
		1,933.8	50	1,883.8		
		500 50 450		500 50 450	
		1,000 50 950		1,000 50 950	
		1,500 50 1,450		1,500 50 1,450	
		1,933.8 50 1,883.8		2,283.8 50 2,233.8	
		Cycles	Avg. TMU per Cycle	Avg. TMU per Piece	Cycles	Avg. TMU per Cycle	Avg. TMU per Piece

MTM LEARNING CURVE WORKSHEET (N = 0 to 500 cycles)

MTM Elements	Hands	TMU in Pattern	Manual Learning Equations	
			Unit Basis	Pattern Basis
R_A	One	10.5	$0.881 - 0.000054(N)$	$9.251 - 0.000567(N)$
R_E	Simo		$1.170 - 0.000290(N)$	
R_B R_C	One	15.6	$0.864 - 0.000251(N)$	$13.478 - 0.003916(N)$
R_D	Simo	14.2	$0.946 - 0.000119(N)$	$13.433 - 0.001690(N)$
M_A	One		$0.982 - 0.000152(N)$	
	Simo		$1.178 - 0.000185(N)$	
M_B	One	35.1	$0.491 + 0.000087(N)$	$17.234 + 0.003053(N)$
M_C	Simo	13.5	$1.090 - 0.000336(N)$	$14.715 - 0.004536(N)$
G1A	One		$2.365 - 0.001270(N)$	
	Simo		$2.915 - 0.001670(N)$	
G1B,G1C G2 G3	One		$0.763 + 0.000104(N)$	
	Simo	11.2	$1.010 - 0.000128(N)$	$11.312 - 0.001434(N)$
G4	One	34.9	$1.667 - 0.000334(N)$	$58.178 - 0.011657(N)$
	Simo		$2.255 - 0.000430(N)$	
P1SE	One		$2.000 - 0.000199(N)$	
	Simo		$2.558 - 0.000576(N)$	
P1SSE	One		$1.195 + 0.000802(N)$	
	Simo		$2.208 - 0.000579(N)$	
P1NSE	One		$1.934 - 0.000749(N)$	
	Simo		$2.208 - 0.000579(N)$	
P21S	One	70.4	$0.940 - 0.000091(N)$	$66.176 - 0.006406(N)$
P22S	Simo		$1.205 - 0.000273(N)$	
Remainder Motions	One	2.0	$1.130 - 0.000446(N)$	$2.260 - 0.000892(N)$
	Simo		$1.573 - 0.000650(N)$	
COMPOSITE LEARNING EQUATION			$206.037 - 0.028045(N)$	

Fig. 7.   Step II for old insulator assembly method.

MTM LEARNING CURVE WORKSHEET ($N = 0$ to 500 cycles)

MTM Elements	Hands	TMU in Pattern	Manual Learning Equations	
			Unit Basis	Pattern Basis
R_A	One		$0.881 - 0.000054(N)$	
R_E	Simo		$1.170 - 0.000290(N)$	
R_B R⁻C R⁻D	One		$0.864 - 0.000251(N)$	
	Simo	34.3	$0.946 - 0.000119(N)$	$32.448 - 0.004082(N)$
M_A	One		$0.982 - 0.000152(N)$	
	Simo		$1.178 - 0.000185(N)$	
M_B	One		$0.491 + 0.000087(N)$	
M_C	Simo	45.0	$1.090 - 0.000336(N)$	$49.050 - 0.015120(N)$
G1A	One		$2.365 - 0.001270(N)$	
	Simo		$2.915 - 0.001670(N)$	
G1B,G1C G2 G3	One		$0.763 + 0.000104(N)$	
	Simo	5.6	$1.010 - 0.000128(N)$	$5.656 - 0.000717(N)$
G4	One	69.8	$1.667 - 0.000334(N)$	$116.357 - 0.023313(N)$
	Simo		$2.255 - 0.000430(N)$	
P1SE	One		$2.000 - 0.000199(N)$	
	Simo		$2.558 - 0.000576(N)$	
P1SSE	One		$1.195 + 0.000802(N)$	
	Simo		$2.208 - 0.000579(N)$	
P1NSE	One		$1.934 - 0.000749(N)$	
	Simo		$2.208 - 0.000579(N)$	
P21S	One	179.4	$0.940 - 0.000091(N)$	$168.636 - 0.016325(N)$
P22S	Simo		$1.205 - 0.000273(N)$	
Remainder Motions	One		$1.130 - 0.000446(N)$	
	Simo	15.8	$1.573 - 0.000650(N)$	$24.853 - 0.010270(N)$
COMPOSITE LEARNING EQUATION			$397.000 - 0.069827(N)$	

Fig. 8. Step II for improved insulator assembly method.

MTM LEARNING CURVE WORKSHEET (N = 500 to 1,000 cycles)
($M = N - 500$)

MTM Elements	Hands	TMU in Pattern	Manual Learning Equations	
			Unit Basis	Pattern Basis
R_A	One	*10.5*	0.854 − 0.000150(M)	*8.967−0.001575 (M)*
R_E	Simo		1.025 − 0.000149(M)	
R_B R−C R−D	One	*15.6*	0.739 − 0.000093(M)	*11.528−0.001451 (M)*
	Simo	*14.2*	0.887 − 0.000093(M)	*12.595−0.001321 (M)*
M_A	One		0.905 − 0.000058(M)	
	Simo		1.086 − 0.000058(M)	
M_B	One	*35.1*	0.534 − 0.000016(M)	*18.744−0.000561 (M)*
M_C	Simo	*13.5*	0.922 − 0.000093(M)	*12.447−0.001256 (M)*
G1A	One		1.730 − 0.000430(M)	
	Simo		2.080 − 0.000430(M)	
G1B,G1C G2 G3	One		0.789 − 0.000149(M)	
	Simo	*11.2*	0.946 − 0.000149(M)	*10.595−0.001669 (M)*
G4	One	*34.9*	1.500 − 0.000256(M)	*52.350−0.008934 (M)*
	Simo		2.040 − 0.000086(M)	
P1SE	One		1.900 − 0.000028(M)	
	Simo		2.270 − 0.000017(M)	
P1SSE	One		1.596 − 0.000346(M)	
	Simo		1.918 − 0.000208(M)	
P1NSE	One		1.560 − 0.000155(M)	
	Simo		1.918 − 0.000208(M)	
P21S	One	*70.4*	0.895 + 0.000013(M)	*63.008+0.000915 (M)*
P22S	Simo		1.068 − 0.000008(M)	
Remainder Motions	One	*2.0*	0.943 − 0.000145(M)	*1.886 − 0.000290 (M)*
	Simo		1.240 − 0.000176(M)	
COMPOSITE LEARNING EQUATION			*192.120 − 0.016142 (M)*	

Fig. 9.   Step III for old insulator assembly method.

MTM LEARNING CURVE WORKSHEET (N = 500 to 1,000 cycles)
($M = N - 500$)

MTM Elements	Hands	TMU in Pattern	Manual Learning Equations	
			Unit Basis	Pattern Basis
R_A	One		$0.854 - 0.000150(M)$	
R_E	Simo		$1.025 - 0.000149(M)$	
R_B R⁻C R⁻D	One		$0.739 - 0.000093(M)$	
	Simo	*34.3*	$0.887 - 0.000093(M)$	*30.424 − 0.003190 (M)*
M_A	One		$0.905 - 0.000058(M)$	
	Simo		$1.086 - 0.000058(M)$	
M_B	One		$0.534 - 0.000016(M)$	
M_C	Simo	*45.0*	$0.922 - 0.000093(M)$	*41.490 − 0.004185 (M)*
G1A	One		$1.730 - 0.000430(M)$	
	Simo		$2.080 - 0.000430(M)$	
G1B,G1C G2 G3	One		$0.789 - 0.000149(M)$	
	Simo	*5.6*	$0.946 - 0.000149(M)$	*5.298 − 0.000834 (M)*
G4	One	*69.8*	$1.500 - 0.000256(M)$	*73.290 − 0.017869 (M)*
	Simo		$2.040 - 0.000086(M)$	
P1SE	One		$1.900 - 0.000028(M)$	
	Simo		$2.270 - 0.000017(M)$	
P1SSE	One		$1.596 - 0.000346(M)$	
	Simo		$1.918 - 0.000208(M)$	
P1NSE	One		$1.560 - 0.000155(M)$	
	Simo		$1.918 - 0.000208(M)$	
P21S	One	*179.4*	$0.895 + 0.000013\ (M)$	*160.563 + 0.002332 (M)*
P22S	Simo		$1.068 - 0.000008(M)$	
Remainder Motions	One		$0.943 - 0.000145(M)$	
	Simo	*15.8*	$1.240 - 0.000176(M)$	*19.592 − 0.002781 (M)*
COMPOSITE LEARNING EQUATION			*331.017 − 0.026527 (M)*	

Fig. 10. Step III for improved insulator assembly method.

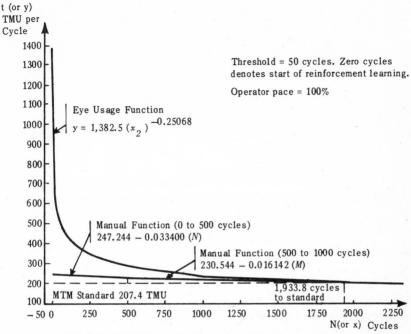

Fig. 11.   MTM Learning Curve for old insulator method.

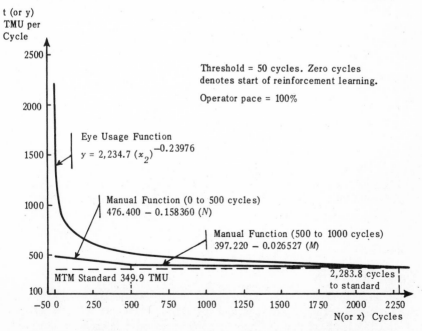

Fig. 12.   MTM Learning Curve for improved insulator assembly method.

OPERATOR SELECTION AND TRAINING

As identified in the discussion of Phase II results, the principal operator factors in industrial work are their sensory-information processing behavior in conjunction with manual requirements and their personal characteristics. At quite some length, the MTM procedure which evaluates the first set of factors has been explained and illustrated. Therefore, attention now is turned to the personal characteristics problem.

Perhaps the most important aspect of personal characteristics in relation to job performance is that they uniquely describe the capability of the operator to accomplish both the manual and sensory-information processing activity required by the task. That is, each worker brings to the task his own inherent methods kit of muscular and analysis tools. The difficulty is that very little quantitative data is available to answer two vital questions when the worker is assigned to the task. First, what personal skills and capacities really are essential to any particular task? Definitive data and information are needed to permit correlating the job parameters and the human energy or motive power—in both motor and control aspects—available to assign to the job. Second, assuming that the required human attributes necessary for a job can be isolated, what measures of the operator are meaningful and useful in specifying that he possesses those attributes? Here, without doubt, is focused the justification for selection and evaluation measures of human performers. Of further interest is the variation of such measures in real time for a given individual, since people are dynamic and subject to change due to both feedback from the job and many other factors such as aging and training.

All of these knotty problems were recognized during the Phase II effort as having prime research potential. Some useful work already done in this area is reported under the next topic. However, investigation accomplished so far merely sharpened the need for more extensive basic research of the kind described in the next section. The emphasis in such investigation is to clarify which operator characteristics most affect productive learning and their numerical relationship to the learning rate. However, the practical tools sought are test measures to be used as a basis of worker selection and assignment to assure the matching of job and personal characteristic requirements.

Selection Tests

For selection tests to be meaningful, the attributes they are intended to measure must be clearly defined and specified. Then care must be taken to design the tests so that, in fact, the measures do reflect those attributes. These guide rules were applied during the MTM Learning Curve research.

They also provide a natural division for discussing the personal characteristics problem.

Basically, operator attributes can be classified as physiological, psychological, and sociological. Each of these has many facets, few of which are presently quantified to the extent desirable for work measurement. Despite decades of psychological research and testing, most of the information and data currently available cannot be directly applied to industrial operator performance without their interpretation by capable professional personnel. A definite need exists for objective, relatively simple decision criteria which can be used by less highly trained work measurement personnel to economically solve human factors problems in productive situations. It must be understood, therefore, that the following discussion is tentative in nature and will be subject to revision from further research results.

To the present time, the status of human attribute measurements may be roughly summarized as follows. Physiological attributes, being most amenable to direct measurement, have been much studied and much is known concerning the physical capabilities of the human body. Obviously, this is true largely because of the necessities of modern medical practice and even because of the essential requirements of space flight, undersea exploration, and similar feats involving current technology. The data were indispensable to the attainment of such objectives. Unfortunately, the simple workaday needs in this area of physiological measurement are only beginning to be met. That is, behavioral measurements of the human body and in relation to specific task requirements in actual working environments are very recent in origin. However, they do hold much promise, as the MTM Learning Curve research already has shown. As for psychological attributes, they certainly have been measured. But the amount and quality of measurement have been less than for the physiological attributes. Also, psychological measures have not yet been adequately related to predicting individual task performance. The principal exception to this statement is in the design of educational tests which rather well predict scholastic potential. Finally, to be most candid, the measurement of sociological attributes still remains in the primitive stages. Here too, definite hope has appeared on the horizon in very recent years, although the social environment in productive groups has obtained scant attention despite the desperate need during this era of labor unrest. Therefore, in brief, the measurement of human attributes insofar as providing useful data for human work measurement purposes has been woefully sparse, mainly qualitative, and unmatched to the needs of modern productive technology.

Despite the foregoing statements, one can at least describe the general nature of these attributes and nominally specify what is included in each category. This will be attempted in the following paragraphs.

Physiological Attributes concern a number of basic concepts. The first is the physical equipment of the worker—age, sex, size, weight, presence and development of musculature and sensory organs, absence of deformities and handicapping features, etc. Next is motor fitness as exemplified by dexterity, muscle condition, and the like. Third is neural fitness as typified by reaction time. Then there is the large area of sensory acuity: visual, auditory, olfactory, gustatory, and tactile. Also included are internal sensory functions such as kinesthetic sense which operate to give directive and orientation powers to the worker. Fifth is the general state of health which could determine job performance. And finally, but perhaps one of the more important, the amount and kind of manual experience. All of these physiological attributes may well have vital influence on the learning ability and continuing performance of the industrial worker.

Psychological Attributes include a somewhat analogous list of concepts. Education and training are vital factors in the mental equipment possessed by the worker. Basic intelligence, or the capacity to learn, certainly plays an important role. Decision ability could be the control limit on the performance of mental tasks and even some complicated manual tasks. Another large area is mental acuity: memory span, recoding ability, learning rate, and similar traits which reflect the sensitivity and coherence of the mental processes. Fourth, motivation could determine job performance to the same extent possible for the general state of physical health. Finally, conceptual experience certainly is as vital for mental tasks as is manual experience for motor tasks, with the amount and kind largely defining the starting point of job training. That each of these psychological attributes has a bearing on task performance, the amount and nature being at present largely unverified, is reasonably certain.

Sociological Attributes involve much of intra-personal and group dynamics in productive effort. Competition can spark or dampen productive effort. The positive or negative aspects of participation will influence job satisfaction and productivity. Obviously, the effects of management and labor union policies will either help or hinder the worker's effectiveness due principally to the effects upon his social behavior. Both formal and informal supervisory impact can be classed as a sociological factor in productivity. Finally, both individuals and groups possess social experience which aids or inhibits the initial and continuing success of an enterprise. When the day arrives in which sociological attributes in the industrial environment have been properly understood, progress in increasing productivity should be wonderful to behold.

With so many attributes for which predictive measures could be developed, a limited number were selected during Phase II research for test design and evaluation against a known performance task standard. The standard was a short-cycle simulation from Phase I research.[13] Choosing of the particular measures was based upon the following criteria:[14]

1. Motor Ability. Motor response tests should be as basic as possible, i.e., require no sensory input.
2. Mental Processes. Mental response tests should:
    a. be basic
    b. be as independent of attitude and emotion as possible.
    c. be independent of motor ability.
3. Recoding Ability. The measure of recoding ability must simulate a general industrial situation.
4. All measuring devices must be non-verbal, portable, easily administered, and involve testing time short enough so that the subject will exhibit essentially no learning during test sessions. The non-verbal requirement was included to minimize, as much as possible, both education and cultural differences.

The same source[15] provides the following two definitions pertinent to the predictive measures chosen:

Decision ability . . . is the ability to make discriminatory choices between two or more alternatives.
Recoding ability . . . is the ability to "chunk" information and thereby reduce the amount of time necessary to obtain sensory information. An example of chunking is a situation where a person gets a cue and then knows what to do for a whole series of events. One person may require more cues than another even though he has fully learned the operation.

Additional factors in the test design were the most immediate application potential and the availability or ease of building suitable measuring devices. However, future research will explore the use of other measures and devices. Also, the predictive power of the selected measures and devices in relation to performance tasks which are non-experimental is a topic for future research.

While the Phase II tests are only listed here, they are completely described in the research report[16]. Motor ability was tested by devices which measured Cranking Speed, Tapping Speed, Lateral Sliding Speed, and Purdue Pegboard Dexterity. The latter test involved right hand only, left hand only, both hands simultaneously, and assembly cycle modes of performance. Mental processes were measured by Numerical Aptitude and Verbal Facility tests commercially available from the Psychological Corporation plus a specially designed card deck which provided a Decision Rate test. Recoding ability was predicted by a Puzzle Assembly Learning Rate test de-

[13] R. R. 112 (see tootnote 3).

[14] R. R. 113 (see footnote 3).

[15] *Ibid.*

[16] *Ibid.*

veloped for the purpose. The reader is referred to the report for the interesting description and illustration of these various tests.

The performance data from these tests were analyzed in various combinations against the chosen standard for predictive power. Analysis was accomplished by an electronic computer program which produced multiple regression correlation coefficients. That is, the effect of each test upon the predicted standard performance of any given subject or the subjects as a group was gaged against a chosen level of statistical significance and accepted or rejected in various combinations by the computer program. The results are quoted[17] as follows:

The correlation coefficients, based on the last 50 cycles of the performance task in our learning experiments, are quite high relative to the coefficients usually obtained in personnel tests. In addition, the use of multiple predictive tests, each of which is designed to measure a "basic" characteristic of an individual, enables one to rearrange the coefficients of the regression equations to obtain a good predictor which is a function of the type of operation to be performed by a person. For example, decision ability is probably much more important and, therefore, should have a higher coefficient in an inspection task than motor ability. However, in a shoveling operation, motor ability is probably of more importance than decision ability. The recoding test would probably be the most important where the performance of varied tasks requiring rapid learning is expected of the individual.

Of course, it would be desirable for people to excel in all of the tests; but, where the available labor cannot supply enough people with this potential, selection procedures must be established based upon the requirements of the job or jobs the employees are expected to do.

Since the MTM system contains elements having different sensory requirements, the relative frequency of occurrence of the various elements probably is a very good indication of the varying amounts of decision, motor, and recoding requirements. For example, the existence of a large number of Positions and Case C Moves and Reaches might be a good indication that the decision content is high and that a high decision rate score would be necessary to obtain the best performance.

Since these tests were only exploratory in nature, the desired selection tests and procedures cannot at this time be considered as finally established. However, this excellent start toward the measurement of human attributes in a manner which allows one to predict task performance represents a fresh approach to the problem. The expansion of this approach in ongoing research promises to eventually provide the desired practical tools for operator selection on the basis of personal characteristics essential to known job requirements.

Performance and Training Implications

Besides the Phase II work toward selection test development, the MTM Learning Curve research also provided certain clues and indications re-

[17] *Ibid.*

garding performance behavior and training requirements for industrial operators. Some data resulted from each of the three industrial studies and the rest came from the laboratory experiments of the Phase II effort. Much of this information is woven into appropriate places throughout this chapter. However, somewhat random discussion of such topics not previously mentioned is now given to complete the account of the project.

Although many factors interact to determine the makeup and practical effect of operator experience, it is worthwhile to consider the matter from several standpoints which shed light on the learning process. Certainly enough age is necessary to possess the desired quantity and quality of experience; but age is not synonymous with experience. Perhaps much erroneous thinking can be corrected by illuminating the false assumption that length of service and physical seniority, per se, confer the necessary experience upon a person. Actually, all too often, this assumption is a shield for some who merely outlast their competitors while never really gaining either the amount or kind of experience which the job requires. Because of this, a test may well appear to show the "experienced" worker —perhaps never adequately trained or held to account against realistic standards—to be less able than a young, eager worker less skilled at deceptive performance. A natural conclusion, therefore, is that the "experienced" worker is suffering from the effects of aging; but in fact the poor result may only be due to his ingrained attitude.

Research essentially confirms that pure motor ability does not deteriorate *solely* due to age. The apparent performance reduction then must be due to some form of decline in the sensory-information processing ability. Remembering that this ability is subject to conscious mental control, at least part of the decline can be explained by the diminuation of desire or determination as the years roll by with humdrum monotony in the same job. In other words, a predisposition against learning at any age is only accentuated as age increases. This may well explain why the outlasted competitors have long since gone on to better jobs, which itself creates further dampening frustration that becomes reflected in mental resistance where a learning situation is presented. Thus to put any performance data regarding either experience or age into proper perspective, the preceding concepts must be recognized.

With the foregoing qualification, the phenomena of transfer learning and the effects of aging on performance as related to operator experience become easier to understand. Certainly the regard or concern over quality of work and the loss in flexibility due to ingrained habits which are characteristic of more experienced workers are valid. Also, the ability to compensate or avoid errors—which may slow the performance—is more highly regarded by an experienced worker. Practice in safe procedures which often are more time-consuming is an additional performance factor related to the known lower rates of industrial accidents for older workers. So all of these factors may help explain why learning may be less efficient and rapid for experienced workers than for newer personnel who are trying hard to prove themselves.

Besides all the above factors, substantial reasons exist why experience and aging may be paramount considerations in a learning situation. These are best expressed by the following series of selected quotes from the MACE report:[18]

A rather obvious difference between an experienced and an inexperienced operator in a highly repetitive job is the new operator's dependence upon the eyes to direct each sequence of the operation. . . . the experienced operator rarely looks. . . . because of a developed ability to replace dependence on the eyes with increased awareness of the spatial orientation of the workplace. . . . the sensory shifts from eyes to the other senses occurred at progressively increased numbers of cycles with increasing age.

. . . younger subjects were more likely to detect an obviously inferior piece and reject it. They did not ponder whether or not to keep it because it might have passed inspection but scrapped the piece instead. When the older people did detect a bad piece, it took them much longer to decide what to do with it or where to put it. . . . regardless of age the people who were not used to making decisions about the quality of the product they handled rejected parts less frequently than those previously mindful of quality.

. . . the aging process occurs in the nervous system and decreases the rate at which it can process the information fed into the system. . . . older people, who require more information because of both decreased rate of processing and predisposition to quality, also receive the information at a slower rate. Assuming single channel capacity, the effect may be partially multiplicative. That is, if more information is required and is received at a slower rate, the reaction to the information will be slowed. This would affect the over-all decision reaction. This may also offer an explanation of the delay in sensory shift by the older people.

If we consider a person starting to work at a new job, his initial manipulations in the operation will be eye directed and will require constant shifting of the eyes to gather the information necessary to perform the task. Beginning the first time the operation is performed and continuing through each successive cycle, the rest of the body becomes more and more accustomed to the workplace and the positions occupied in the particular workplace by the elements which are part of the operation. This development of the kinesthetic cues adds more and more information to the total available from which the central processing system may select that necessary to do the task. The following is a suggested explanation of what occurs. If we consider that the input information per unit time from the eyes is reduced in older people because of perception losses, then the information building up from the kinesthetic cues will facilitate the operation up to the point at which the information processing capacity of the individual is reached. The psychological theories of single channel processing with apparent multiplexing would indicate that at this point the information input

18 *Op. cit.* (Footnote 10).

will continue to grow in amount, but will not be processed at any greater rate. At such a time that the input from the kinesthetic receptors is sufficient to perform any segment of the operation, the eyes will no longer be necessary for that part and can be used for greater concentration in another area. This is the sensory shift in its first noticeable form.

If the younger people perceive the information from both the eyes and the kinesthetic receptors and can translate this information into reactions at a faster rate, then we suggest that the younger people obtain more information from the workplace and job per cycle of operation. The younger subjects are therefore able to reduce the amount of high order information necessary from their eyes and rely on the processing of the more second order information from the kinesthetic receptors. We further suggest that, as the younger people are able to process the information at the higher rate, they are able to more quickly store the pertinent information about the orientation of their workplace and will thus need fewer cycles in which to gain the necessary confidence in the information received from their lower order senses. For this reason more repetition of the information is needed by the older people before their confidence is established because of predisposition to quality (with slow decision time), and this in turn requires a longer period of time or practice.

We have thus returned to the explanations of the effect of age on the motor processes as being dependent on the central system and not really a function of the body member.

. . . . no substantial difference in performance existed between experienced people, old or young, but a substantial difference in performance was found between the inexperienced old and the young people either experienced or inexperienced.

Thus, if we compare the performance of an older person of long experience with the younger people, we should find that the older person can do a comparable job. This comparison was not true, however, for the inexperienced people. The question arises as to what happens. . . . when experienced people are placed on an unfamiliar job.

Briefly, it appears that experience can compensate for the aging process in familiar operation sequences, but learning new operations and motion patterns is retarded with increasing age. It is suggested that a decreased frequency of job changes should accompany increasing age.

The effect of variable amounts of training is partially a function of job "insight" during the so-called threshold period and method shifts during the conditioned learning period. Insight can be accompanied by shifts in the method. This is not always the case but, unless the operator is trained in the proper method at a level sufficiently detailed to assure thorough understanding, the continuous shifts in method . . . will hamper attempts to obtain efficiency with new operators.

It can thus be concluded that experience can compensate for age but only if the operator has had a sufficiently diversified working career, such that no single member of the body has suffered unequal aging processes.

To summarize the effect of prior experience on the learning of a job:

A. Experience of some type, preferably in a situation similar to the new operation, results in a carry-over of skills which enables the operator to gain insight into the operation much sooner than a person with no experience.

B. Prior knowledge of the operation carries the concept of insight to its highest point by reducing the threshold portion of the learning curve to a minimum.

C. Experience of a type which contains a dormant state will reduce the ability to shift from one operation to another."

NEW ASPECTS OF PROJECT

As emphasized throughout this chapter, the scope of the MTM Learning Curve research is such that it is still in progress. Proper closing of the chapter, therefore, requires indicating to some extent the nature and direction of the ongoing effort. In passing, many indications have been given of topics and areas considered incomplete and subject to further investigation. However, the Phase III effort also involves certain experimentation not previously mentioned, which will be described here. Some of this directly concerns learning processes, while the remainder involves technical questions which must be resolved to increase the reliability of performance measurement and prediction generally.

Several experiments are extending the work of developing measures and devices for determination of human attributes. Kinesthetic learning or ability certainly deserves an adequate form of predictive measurement. The same is true for precision learning, which pertains to the learning of controlled motions used for precise location or location to limited tolerances of working objects. Since recoding ability is basic to the sensory-information processing capability of an operator, it also justifies further investigation. Allied to the entire research project is simultaneous behavior, for which more regression equations should be developed and which needs much additional analysis for complete understanding. Some thought also has been given to discovering the requirements of training in the threshold learning area. All of these activities are directly related to learning phenomena and thus logically extend the research frontiers.

A special form of learning interaction between operators effects the attainment of standard performance on assembly lines. This raises the question of line balancing techniques and procedures. These are under consideration for experimentation either under the project for learning aspects or as a potential project to follow the learning research. Another observation during this project has been the need for more quantitative assessment of the acceleration-deceleration characteristics of manually controlled motions. This experiment is in the developmental stage and promises implications beyond learning relationships, since the basic design of any predetermined time system rests on certain assumptions regarding these characteristics.

Basic data which permits predictive correlation of manual motions with physiological requirements also needs enlargement to permit better specification of the personal characteristics essential to a defined task. Topics included under this subject are the effective work performed by the operator and the influence of fatigue on task performance or of the task requirements of fatigue. This whole area also could prove to be of sufficient proportions to justify a separate project.

It is quite evident from these remarks that both the current MTM research and the research it could spawn are quite extensive. The need is great for such research to improve both MTM and work measurement generally. Automation alone provides incentive to accelerate such human behavior research. Also, such research would continue the now-established tradition of work measurement inquiry into production problems via the scientific method.

MTM LEARNING CURVE LITERATURE

Although a departure from the format of other chapters, this section is included because the reader wishing to inquire more deeply into the research project will be aided both by isolation of the sources and their arrangement into chronological order of publishing.

1. "A Description of the Electronic Data Collector and the Methods of its Application to Work Measurement," by Walton M. Hancock and James A. Foulke, *Research Information Paper No. 1*, MTM Association, Ann Arbor, Michigan, 1961.
2. "Effects of Learning on Short-Cycle Operations," by Walton M. Hancock and James A. Foulke, *Research Information Paper. No. 2*, MTM Association, Ann Arbor, Michigan, 1961.
3. "New Research Techniques in Work Measurement," by Walton M. Hancock, *Proceedings—12th Annual National Conference*, American Institute of Industrial Engineers, Detroit, Michigan, May 1961.
4. "The Effects of Learning on Short Cycle Operations," by Walton M. Hancock and James A. Foulke, *Proceedings—10th Annual MTM Conference*, MTM Association, New York City, October 1961.
5. "A Description of the Electronic Data Collector and the Methods of its Application to Work Measurement," by James A. Foulke and Walton M. Hancock, *Journal of Industrial Engineering*, Vol. XIII, No. 4, American Institute of Industrial Engineers, New York City, July–August 1962.
6. "A Laboratory Study of Learning," by Walton M. Hancock, *Proceedings—11th Annual MTM Conference*, MTM Association, New York City, September 1962.

7. "Learning Curve Research on Short-Cycle Operations: Phase 1, Laboratory Experiments," by Walton M. Hancock and James A. Foulke, *MTM Research Report No. 112,* MTM Association, Ann Arbor, Michigan, 1963.

8. "Pinpointing Operator Learning Time," by Walton M. Hancock, Third International MTM Conference, New York City, September 1963.

9. "The Effect of Simultaneous Motions on Learning," by Stanley H. Caplan and Walton M. Hancock, *Journal of Methods-Time Measurement,* Vol. IX, No. 1, MTM Association, Ann Arbor, Michigan, September–October 1963.

10. "You Can Reduce Training Losses," by Walton M. Hancock, A. T. Kearney & Company Seminar, Chicago, Illinois, November 1963.

11. "Progress Report on Learning Curve Research," by Walton M. Hancock, *Journal of Methods-Time Measurement,* Vol. IX, No. 2, MTM Association, Ann Arbor, Michigan, November–December 1963.

12. "An Industrial Study of Learning," by Robert R. Clifford and Walton M. Hancock, *Journal of Methods-Time Measurement,* Vol. IX, No. 3, MTM Association, Ann Arbor, Michigan, January–February 1964.

13. "Experiment in Operator Learning at TRW," by Russell R. Paine, *Journal of Methods-Time Measurement,* Vol. IX, No. 4, MTM Association, Ann Arbor, Michigan, May–June 1964.

14. "Results of Industrial Phase of Research on Learning," by Walton M. Hancock, 12th Annual MTM Conference, New York City, September 1964.

15. "Tests to Predict Worker Total Performance," by Robert R. Clifford, 12th Annual MTM Conference, New York City, September 1964.

16. "Independence of MTM Elements," by John A. Muckstadt, 12th Annual MTM Conference, New York City, September 1964.

17. "Learning Curve Research on Manual Operations: Phase II, Industrial Studies," by Walton M. Hancock, Robert R. Clifford, James A. Foulke, and Leonard F. Krystynak, *MTM Research Report No. 113,* MTM Association, Ann Arbor, Michigan, 1965.

PART III

Time and Work Study Basics

CHAPTER 21

Fundamentals of Time Study Observations

SPECIAL NOTE TO MTM READERS:

SUCCESSFUL FLOOR MTM STUDIES DEPEND UPON
UNDERSTANDING THESE CONCEPTS AND PROCEDURES

The Methods-Time Measurement procedure can be of great assistance to the industrial engineer in situations which require the traditional procedures of time study and motion study. In any work study the analyst needs to recognize basic motions, motion patterns, and motion combinations. Knowledge of MTM makes this part of his task relatively easy.

However, the reverse is also true. Traditional time study is an essential part of MTM analysis of work in a number of ways. Time study is used directly to determine process time which occurs in an MTM pattern. Even more important, however, are the procedural rules and guides to analyst conduct which have resulted from years of successful time study. These work well and their correct usage is even more essential for MTM studies when direct observation of operator performance is involved. The reason why greater fidelity to correct time study practices is necessary during MTM studies is the fact that the TMU is a much finer time unit than is usually employed in conventional time study. Therefore, incorrect procedures can result in larger relative errors in the final work study time standards.

The first step in a time study is to record general data relative to the operation being studied. This procedure is exactly the same as that followed in an MTM study; the general data section of the time study observation sheet and the MTM work study sheet look essentially identical. The next step in a time study is to divide the operation into short elements easily recognizable as to starting and stopping points, again similar to MTM procedure, and the analyst is aided in this by a knowledge of MTM.

Finally, the elements are timed with a stop watch, the operator's performance is rated, and the rating is applied to the elapsed time values to determine the select or normal time.

It was mentioned in the MTM procedure that process time must be determined with a stop watch. Process time in either system, therefore, means the establishment of a *time study element*. When a lever is activated to start a machine, the finish of the activating motion is the starting point of the operation or element called process time. Process time then continues until the machine has completed its cycle of operation. It must be evaluated because of the need to determine the limiting time. Four cases are possible. If necessary motions requiring less time can be performed while the machine runs, the process time is limiting and the manual time only provides needed information about the work accomplished during the process time. When no necessary motions can be accomplished during the process time, this limiting time determines the "attention time" of the operator to the machine. Third, if the manual time is limiting, the process time shows that no additional "attention time" is needed. Finally, in borderline cases where it is questionable whether the process or manual time is limiting, careful stop watch study of the process time may be of critical importance.

TIME STUDY EQUIPMENT

The equipment required for time study work is relatively simple. The principal items are as follows:

TIME STUDY WATCH OR OTHER TIMING DEVICE

PENCIL   TIME STUDY OBSERVATION BOARD

SPEED INDICATOR   TIME STUDY OBSERVATION FORMS

The speed indicator often needed to obtain machine speeds can be a simple turn counter which, when used with a stop watch, permits determination of revolutions per minute or may be a tachometer which indicates revolutions per minute directly.

A typical time study observation board is shown in Fig. 1. This type of board is considerably more convenient than the standard clip board sometimes used which may or may not include a holder for the stop watch. Its special design also makes it superior for MTM floor studies.

Time study observation forms vary in format, but almost all provide (a) a section for recording general data, (b) an area for sketching the workplace, parts, etc., and (c) a section in which to record the work elements and applicable times. A typical completed form is shown in Fig. 2. More detailed data concerning this study will be stated later.

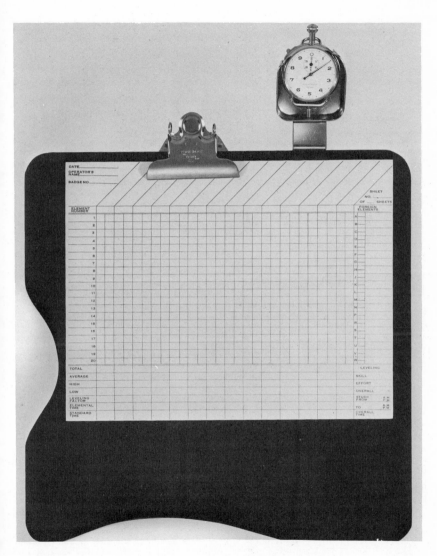

Fig. 1.   Single time study board ready for use.
Courtesy of Meylan-Stopwatch Corp.

STUDY No. _985276-3_ DATE _8-21-52_

OPERATION

DRILL HOUSING & RING ASSY.

DWG. 985276 SUB. 3

DEPARTMENT	OPERATOR		MOULD	DIE	STYLE	ITEM
1100 RIVETING	MAN NAME T. BREWER No. 2466		PATTERN	INS. SPEC.	L. SPEC.	SUB.

PART DESCRIPTION: MACHINED HOUSING WITH LOOSE END RING (LAMINATED) MATERIAL PHENOLIC-ALUMINUM

EQUIPMENT: DELTA 6-SPINDLE GANG DRILLPRESS & MANUAL INDEX BARREL DRILL FIXT WITH DETENT STOPS

MACHINE TOOL No. ANX-57

SPECIAL TOOLS, JIGS, FIXTURES, ETC. ALL DRILLS & STEPDRILLS ARE CARBOLOY TIPPED, STEPDRILLS: ① .152" C'SINK 150° to .312", ③ .098 C'SINK 100° to .176", ⑤ PILOT ∅

CONDITIONS C'SINK 82° to .279"
GOOD CONDITIONS, INCL. ADEQUATE LIGHTING & EASY INDEXING OF DRILL FIXT

OBSERVER HENRY COOP   APPROVED BY JIM DANDY

No.	ELEMENTS	SMALL TOOL NOS. FEED SPEED, DEPTH OF CUT, ETC	ELEMENTS TIME ALLOWED (BOTTOM LINE OTHER SIDE)	OCCUR-RENCES PER PIECE OR CYCLE	TOTAL TIME ALLOWED
1	OBTAIN PARTS, PLACE ON SPINDLE		.343	1	.343
2	LOAD FIXT, PREPARE TO DRILL		.913	1	.913
3	17 HOLES @ SPINDLE ①	.312" STEPDRILL	3.143	1	3.143
4	4 HOLES @ SPINDLE ②	9/16" STD. DRILL	.482	1	.482
5	1 HOLE @ SPINDLE ③	.640" DRILL	.216	1	.216
6	4 HOLES @ SPINDLE ④	.176" STEPDRILL	.507	1	.507
7	9 HOLES @ SPINDLE ⑤	.279" STEPDRILL	1.126	1	1.126
8	2 HOLES @ SPINDLE ⑥	.219" DRILL	.170	1	.170
9	SLIDE FIXT BACK TO START		.091	1	.091
10	UNLOAD DRILL FIXT		.500	1	.500
11	UNLOAD DRILLED HOUSING		.258	1	.258
12	AIR CLEAN DRILL FIXT		.230	1	.230
13	REPLENISH RING SUPPLY		.219	1/5	.044
14	MOVE STORAGE TRUCKS		.690	1/55	.013

SKETCH

BAY 3,

LOADING TABLE

DRILL PRESS SPINDLES

⑥ ⑤ ④ ③ ② ①   FIXT.   WOOD FIXT.

RAILS

20"
61"   40"

TRUCK

AISLE

RINGS

TIME ALLOWED, SET UP (BY SETUP MAN)   EACH PIECE ➔ MINUTES TOTAL 8.036

REMARKS: 1. DRILL FIXT INDEXING BY CAM LEVERS AGAINST DETENT STOPS WITH MANUAL BARREL ROTATION.
2. CHIPS BLOWN BY AIR CLEAN EXHAUSTED BY SUCTION HOOD BEHIND SPINDLES ① & ②
3. APPROX. VOLUME 29,500 PER YEAR
4. ELEMENTS 3 THRU 8 INCLUDE STARTING & STOPPING DRILLS AND ALSO INDEXING OF DRILL FIXTURE.

OBSERVATION SHEET

Fig. 2A.   Completed time study observation form.   (Back)

Fig. 2B.   Completed time study observation form.   (Front)

TIMING DEVICES AND THEIR OPERATION

While a simple stop watch will suffice for ordinary time study work, the importance of evaluating human performance in the advancing industrial technology over the past six decades has led to the development and use of many different timing devices for time study.

Stop Watches

Figure 3 illustrates a plain decimal-minute stop watch. It is started by moving slide (A) toward the stem and stopped by moving the slide away

Fig. 3.   Decimal minute "snapback" stop watch.
Courtesy of Meylan Stopwatch Corp.

from the stem. Pressure on crown (B) resets the hands to zero. The large hand makes one revolution per minute to cover one hundred dial divisions; each division, therefore, shows 0.01 minutes. The small hand completes one revolution in thirty minutes, with the dial markings showing one-minute intervals. This type of watch is used more than any other for time study work and is adapted to both the continuous and snapback methods of recording.

In the continuous method of time study, the watch is kept running from the beginning to the end of the operation; and the analyst quickly notes the position of the hands at the completion of each operation element and records the reading on the time study observation sheet. In the snapback method of recording, the hand is reset to zero after the completion of each operation element.

A decimal hour watch is shown in Fig. 4. The large dial is graduated into 100 divisions, each representing 0.0001 hours. The large hand makes

Fig. 4. Conventional decimal hour stop watch with "time out" feature.
Courtesy of Meylan Stopwatch Corp.

one revolution in 36 seconds or 0.01 hours. The small hand revolves once for each 30 revolutions of the large hand, so the 30 dial divisions show 0.01 hours each. The method of operation is the same as for the decimal minute watch.

The split-hand watch shown in Fig. 5 has two large hands. Successive presses of crown (B) will start both hands, stop them, and return them to zero. Pressing pin (A) holds the one hand at whatever prior position it attained, but allows the other hand to continue its progress. The advantage of this watch is that the time study analyst can then record the time shown by the stopped hand while the next element is being timed. The dial divisions are 0.01 minutes, with one revolution showing 1.00 minute. A second pressure on pin (A) causes the stopped hand to instantly catch up with the moving hand and continue with it. The timing process proceeds in this manner to the end of the study. The upper small hand registers minutes (up to a total of 30) and runs continuously, while the lower small hand accumulates seconds (up to 60) in a like manner. This type of watch is not adapted for snapback recording. Another variation of this watch has a series of numbers about the border of the dial which gives the

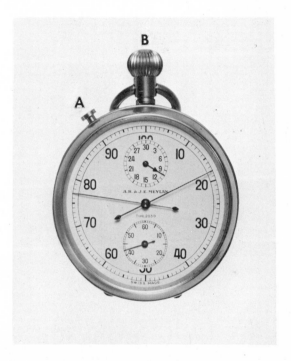

Fig. 5.   Split-hand (double action) decimal minute stop watch.
Courtesy of Meylan Stopwatch Corp.

pieces per hour represented by each main dial division to reduce the task of converting times (up to one minute) to hourly production rates.

Another type of stop watch—often called a "wink" watch—is shown in Fig. 6. Successive crown depressions start, stop, and reset both hands to zero. It is designed for timing brief operations where extreme accuracy is required. Each division of the large dial represents 0.001 minute with each complete revolution of the large hand equalling 0.100 minute (or 6 seconds). Each graduation of the small dial, therefore, equals 0.100 minute; up to three minutes can be accumulated for each time the crown is depressed.

Many other types of stop watches are available. They feature either variations and/or combinations of these basic designs or other distinctive capabilities. Their design shows the responsiveness of alert manufacturers to the needs of work analysts. An example, which also illustrates the essential unity of time study and predetermined motion study approaches, is the TMU watch. It appeared soon after MTM gained prominence, with the purpose of facilitating process timing and over-all cycle time checks during MTM floor studies. The convenience to the analyst of avoiding

Fig. 6.   Decimal minute (0.001) "wink watch" precision timer.
Courtesy of Meylan Stopwatch Corp.

conversion of observed process time intervals to the new TMU time unit was quickly recognized. After all, the TMU involves only a decimal point variation from the traditional decimal hour time unit which had been used on stop watches for decades before MTM was developed.

Multiple Stop Watch Mechanism

Several multiple watch holders have been designed to enable the analyst to time operations more effectively; one example is shown in Fig. 7. When the first watch is set at zero, and the second stopped at any point other than zero, the third watch is in motion. Depressing the lever as the first

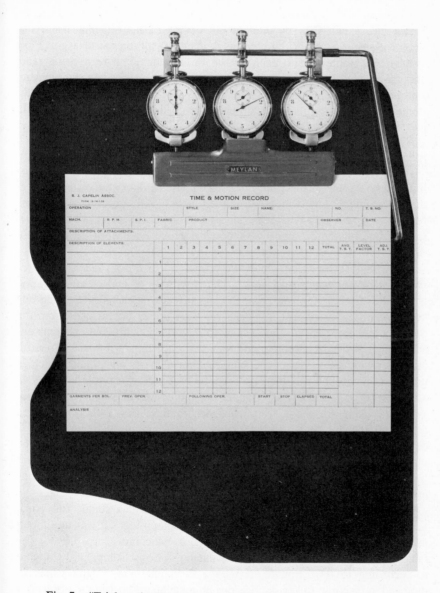

Fig. 7.   "Triple action" special time study board with multiple timers.
Courtesy of Meylan Stopwatch Corp.

element begins starts watch No. 1, resets No. 2 at zero, and stops watch No. 3. At the end of the first element, the lever is again depressed. This stops watch No. 1, simultaneously starts No. 2, and resets No. 3 at zero. Watch No. 1 can then be read at the observer's convenience while the second element is being timed; this sequencing of the watches may be repeated indefinitely, with each of the three watches in turn being read while stopped. This feature facilitates reading and recording the element time and makes "clock watching" less necessary, which frees the analyst's attention somewhat for closer observation of the work being timed. It also makes reading to the nearest 0.01 minute practical.

Time Recording Machines

A variety of time recording machines have appeared to "mechanize" time study. Some of these are intended for use in floor studies, because of their portability, and will be described here. All are similar in some respect to a research-type recorder called the Kymograph, which is described in Chapter 22 along with other research-type work measurement devices.

The Marstochron was originally described in Vol. 97 of *Factory Management and Maintenance* magazine. The beginning or end of an operation is recorded by pressing two keys, the end of each element by pressing one key. With this instrument, the observer need not divert his eyes from the operator and there are no time values to record. Operational elements are established prior to the timing, and recorded on a standard form. Pressure on either key depresses a type bar, making a mark on a tape which is moving at a constant rate beneath the type bars. Normally the tape moves at either 10 or 20 inches per minute depending on the motor drive used. When the tape travels at 10 inches per minute, one inch of the tape represents 0.1 minute, and 0.1 inch equals 0.01 minute. Elapsed time is determined by scaling the tape. Also, the tracks on the tape must be matched with the previously-written element listing to ascertain the element times. Both of these chores can be onerous unless the cycle is short and has few elements.

Another device is known as the WETRFAC, which stands for Work Element Timer and Recorder for Automatic Computing. It was developed in cooperation with the International Business Machines Corp. (IBM) for factory time study usage by R. R. Donnelley & Sons Company. Capable of recording to 0.01 minute, it uses a 5-channel paper tape which is punched in response to key depressions on a keyboard held in the observer's hand. A cart contains the power supply and an IBM electric typewriter which can be used simultaneously to automatically produce a visual record of the operation. The punched recorder tape is converted to IBM punched cards for computer analysis. Another Donnelley device for automeasurement of crude elements in production timing is called AFTR, for Automatic Frequency and Time Recorder. Also, IBM produces a variety of automatic production recording systems with various timing features.

A newer time recorder called Accro-Fac is a product of Gar Wood Industries, Inc. It has a capability of 0.001 minute elements from a completely portable device having a self-contained power supply. Pinpoint holes are burned by condenser discharge into a revolving electro-sensitive paper disc, which rotates at selected speeds from ¼ through 4 revolutions per minute. The nine discharge stylii contacting the paper disc move spirally and are actuated for burning when the observer depresses nine coded keys on a hand-carried keyboard either singly or in combinations to represent work elements. Also part of the equipment are a Pace Simulator to provide the observer with a calibrated tempo for operator comparison, a Decoder which permits direct reading of the recorded discs in any chosen time units, and some calibrated rings which assist conversion of the direct readings to normalized times.

Electronic Timers

A number of timers have been developed which use electronic circuitry and computer principles. Most of these are research-type equipment, as described in Chapter 22. Among these, the Electronic Data Collector (EDC) used for the industrial phases of MTM Association research is the only truly portable device. This usage justifies its mention here as at least a potential means of floor time study, although special instrumentation of the workplace would be needed to permit such an application.

Motion Pictures

A motion picture camera can be used for time and motion study work as outlined in Chapters 4 and 22. The same equipment can also be used to make training films, a more common application in industry. Another use is for permanent visual records of operations, methods, tools, layouts, etc.

THE SUCCESSFUL TIME STUDY

A listing of the major steps in a complete time study follows; all are discussed in this chapter except steps 8, 9, and 10, which are covered in other chapters. The asterisked steps apply equally well when making floor MTM studies.

*1. Receive the request for a time study
*2. Obtain the cooperation of the departmental foreman
*3. Select an operator and obtain his cooperation
*4. Determine whether the job or operation is ready for study

*5. Obtain and record all general information about the operation and the operator

*6. Divide the operation into elements and record a complete description of the method

7. Observe and record the time taken by the operator and/or machine to perform each element of work

8. Rate the operator's performance

9. Determine the required allowances

10. Determine the allowed time standard for the operation.

I. Receive the Request for Time Study

A majority of the requests for a time study or a floor MTM study in most plants originate with the foreman. Others who may request a study would be the plant manager, chief industrial engineer, manager of the time standards department, production control supervisor, cost accountant, union steward, etc. Study requests should be in writing and specify at least the operation to be studied, its location in the plant, and the reason for the request. Request forms often are designed and used for this purpose. In many plants the foreman is responsible for seeing that operations are running satisfactorily prior to a floor study. This does not relieve the industrial engineer or time study analyst of his responsibility to determine whether the job is ready for study, that the best methods are being used, etc. The practice of assigning this responsibility to the foreman is gradually being eliminated by its transfer to the industrial engineer.

2. Obtain the Cooperation of the Departmental Foreman

The human elements in either a time study or an MTM analysis are as important as the technical elements. Such studies may not be successfully concluded if the engineer fails to obtain the cooperation of the foreman, the union steward, group leader, the operator, or anyone else in a position to undermine any good work of the engineer.

The engineer should exert himself to be cooperative and enlist the foreman's aid. This does not imply submissiveness to any whim of the foreman; but it does mean that he must not be arbitrary, merely insisting on his way as being correct. He must always endeavor to state reasons for his opinions concerning the job and/or operation and endeavor to "sell" them—not force them on concerned individuals.

More than technical competence is needed by the engineer for success in work measurement; his personality is of extreme importance.

Assuming that the foreman is already familiar with time study procedures and has requested the study, it will not be necessary to explain to him why the study is being taken, how it is developed, how the results are to be used, etc. Generally foremen, union stewards, etc., in plants with a time study department have gone through a training period which introduced them to the rudiments of time study and/or MTM studies, the reasons for taking them, the use of results, etc. This is not always true for the operators to be studied.

If the foreman has not requested the study or is unaware of the specific reason for the study, he obviously should be told. This will promote his cooperation by keeping him fully informed of all activities concerning his department. Requesting his assistance in selecting the operator to be studied also stimulates cooperation. In addition, he may offer valuable advice toward properly accomplishing the study.

3. Select an Operator and Obtain His Cooperation

If only one operator is performing the operation, there is no choice in the matter. If more than one operator performs a given operation some choice is open to the foreman and the engineer in selecting the operator to be studied. The aim should then be to select a worker as nearly normal or average as possible. With time studies, it is sometimes essential to study more than one operator.

Unlike a visualization MTM study, it is impossible to establish a watch time for a particular operation until after an operator has been trained to perform the operation and it is being performed at the time of the study. Any studies prior to adequate training are seldom accurate enough for the establishment of work standards used in either a measured daywork or a wage incentive plant. In fact, they are of little genuine value for any purpose. Therefore any operator to be time studied should be well trained and working at a reasonable pace—the nearer to average the better. This requirement is less essential for MTM floor studies. In addition, the operator should preferably be a cooperative employee who has been studied on other occasions. These ideal conditions cannot always be attained.

The foreman should introduce the engineer to the operator selected. The engineer should then explain the reasons for the study and generally encourage the operator to discuss his work. This will help establish harmony between the operator and the analyst. However, personal familiarity should be avoided in favor of an objective relationship. Discussion of the operation engenders a valuable mutual understanding that will assist the engineer in his next task of determining whether the job is ready for time study, as well as in the obtaining and recording of pertinent information in Step 5.

Involved in the discussion with the operator are the many reasons for requesting time studies and/or MTM studies. For a new job, it is usually for establishing a time standard for a wage incentive plan, a standard cost system, or a measured daywork standard; but it could also be to check the method of performing an operation. Another reason for such studies might be to determine the adequacy of an existing standard, especially if the operator is earning far above or far below standard; involved in this reason is a need to determine whether the method was changed to enable the operator to produce far above standard or whether he is just a superior operator. If the operator cannot meet the established rate, possibly the method used for the task has changed, the conditions of the equipment and/or surroundings have deteriorated, or he is merely a poor worker. Obviously, any reasons for not meeting the rate that the operator could be responsible for cannot be stated bluntly to the operator as this would likely create antagonism between the engineer and the operator. Such antagonism would make a successful time study virtually impossible; however, it is still possible to make an MTM analysis of the job, although the MTM analysis would be in jeopardy if operator acceptance of results is required. Since MTM is not primarily being discussed at this point, however, the problem must be approached solely on a time study basis—which is to prevent such antagonism from developing.

If the operator is performing consistently above standard, one possible approach might be for the engineer to explain that he is not there to increase the rate but only to check the method on which the rate depends—if the method is correct, the rate will remain unchanged. This is usually a valid statement in incentive plants. In non-incentive plants, changes in rates have less importance or significance to the operator and he usually accepts willingly any rate change due to changed methods, mistakes in a prior study, etc. Fairness to both the operator and the company should always be stressed, this being true regardless of the wage plan in effect; the existence of incentive pay only sharpens issues to a greater degree—money is at stake! To operators failing to attain the rate and/or an incentive bonus, for example, the approach can be made by the engineer that management may have specified a method which makes it impossible to meet the rate and that they are willing to re-evaluate it and correct any errors revealed by the study.

The reputation of an engineer who consistently antagonizes operators will follow him throughout the shop and eventually his services will become worthless to management and its industrial engineering department. In fact, the effects of one or more such men who are allowed to continue their work will eventually undermine faith in the entire industrial engineering department to such an extent that essentially an entire turnover of its personnel might be required to restore the department's value. Obviously personality plays an important role in any industrial engineering operation.

Lack of cooperation by the worker frequently presents special hazards in those cases where it is necessary to determine the level of his performance, so that diplomacy on the part of the analyst is essential to both the company's and the worker's interests. Performance evaluation is necessary to the establishment of a time study standard and it provides data for analyzing and/or explaining differences between workers.

4. Determine Whether the Job or Operation Is Ready for Time Study

This step of the procedure includes a discussion of the operation or task between the process engineer and/or the departmental foreman. The justification of any of the reasons for requesting and/or making the study can be explored. Other concerned individuals often are logically included for portions of this discussion. The final decision occurs after discussion of the job with the operator.

This phase of a study also blends into Step 6 which involves dividing the operation into elements. During these preliminary discussions with the process engineer, foreman, or operator, the analyst should discover their ideas of the various elements of the work and record them on a memorandum pad for future reference. As each element of the operation is later established, he should ascertain the reasons for its presence and decide whether a better way could be devised or if it could be performed more adequately and efficiently at some other stage in the operation than the point at which it is presently being performed.

The five common questions asked to test and/or determine the validity and economics of the elements are:

WHAT?   WHY?   WHERE?   WHEN?   HOW?

In addition, the analyst should ask other questions similar to the following:

(1) Can the operation or certain elements be eliminated?

(2) Might the operation or element be performed better at another point in the work cycle?

(3) Can any machine speeds involved be safely increased without adversely affecting the cost of the operation, such as reduced tool life, etc?

(4) Would design or other changes in tooling reduce the cycle time?

(5) Does the equipment operate satisfactorily?

(6) Is the quality of the product being produced as desired? Is it too low or excessively high?

(7) Might minor revisions of the product design facilitate its production?

(8) Is the operation safe for the operator?

If the analysis of the operation reveals only minor desirable changes, they should be installed promptly; and after limited practice by the operator, the time study can proceed in a normal fashion. If major changes resulting in method improvement are indicated, then more time will be required to install the changes. The operator should in this case be given adequate training time for any new sequence of work elements before the time study proceeds—such waiting is not necessary with an MTM floor study.

With MTM floor studies, the data obtained during the actual study often makes possible very significant methods improvements—improvements that either could not or normally would not be discovered with the time study approach.

5. Obtain and Record General Information

During the time study analyst's discussions with the process engineers, foremen, and operators concerned (Steps 2, 3, and 4), he should record on his time study analysis form all general information pertinent to the job. Various companies use different forms, however all are somewhat similar to the form shown in Fig. 2. Also, the floor MTM analysis forms have a section similar to the top half of Fig. 2, which is the portion of the form concerned in this step. The general information sections ordinarily include, but are not limited to the following:

Date	Assembly or Part Number
Name of Operation	Applicable Drawing Numbers
Name of Operator	Material Numbers and Specifications
Name of Foreman	Tool Numbers and Specifications
Name of Analyst	Plant Location of Operation (usually by
Department Number	building, bay, and column numbers)
Machine Number	Sketch of Workplace and its Layout
Operation Number	Purpose of the Study

As was discussed in Chapter 19 for MTM studies, there are many reasons why it is essential to include this data on the study form. Its principal value as a method record, as well as its making possible better use of the study results for standard data and proof-of-rate validity, is great compared with the slight extra time required by the analyst to include it. Sometimes, due to time pressure or laziness, analysts greatly reduce the value of their study by omitting such data. It is false economy for managers to reduce analysis cost by any policy that does not insist on recording such data. Overcoming a deficiency of such data can cost much more than the initial amount required to obtain it. This step is therefore important.

It is important to accurately detail the relative location of all tools and materials on the workplace layout to facilitate good work element descriptions and to attain a reproducible working method. Do not underestimate the importance to either good MTM study or adequate time study of sketching the workplace layout in the place provided on the analysis form.

6. Divide Operation into Elements and Record Complete Description of Method

The following are some of the principal reasons why an operation should be divided into short elements and each of them timed separately:

A. Operators do not always work at the same tempo or with the same effort throughout an entire work or operation cycle. Such speed variations can be detected only if separate elements are timed. This also permits individual performance ratings to be applied to each element of the job when adjusting each element time. The analyst will quite often find this necessary.

B. Timing of an entire job or operation precludes analysis of the operation to discover what elements actually take excessive time. It is true that many studies show no excessive time on any given element of an operation. However, it is equally true that many operations timed element by element show later that certain elements apparently require excessive time. Separate analysis of these elements will often disclose the reason for the excessive time, and corrections can then be made to eliminate it.

C. Establishing times for the various elements permits the eventual establishment of standard data. This will, in turn, make possible the elimination of unnecessary time studies. This development will be described in a later chapter.

D. The best description of any operation includes any and all minute details. The minimum requirement for this task is to describe each work element. These descriptions can thereafter be used for training new operators and other purposes.

Note that elements of the operation which occur regularly are listed first on the observation sheet followed by those that occur only a few times. More about handling this type of situation will be said later in the text.

Dividing the operation into elements that are easily timed is greatly aided by knowledge of MTM fundamentals and procedures. Reach can logically be combined with Grasp as an element or Grasp can be combined with Move as an element. Position and any separate Moves associated with the final Position of an object, such as a long insertion, can be treated as an identifiable element and easily timed. The main limiting factor (at least for a decimal-minute watch) is the 0.02 to 0.03 minute minimum time which can be recorded, as agreed by most time study men.

Three general rules should govern the division of an operation into time study elements. They are as follows:

(1) The elements should be of as short duration as can accurately be timed.

(2) Constant elements should always be separated from variable elements. The elements should be so established that no element will contain both a work element that is variable in time requirements and another work element that is constant in time requirements.

(3) Machine and/or "process" time should always be segregated. This means that when the operator continues to perform work after the machine has started, a necessary notation must be made on the study sheet to identify the start of the machine time. The completion of machine time must likewise be identified. It is obvious that, if the operator continues to work, the time study analyst must be able to identify and continue to record the time for any manual work elements which extend into the actual machine time.

General rule No. 1 is a very practical one. Referring to MTM procedure, it is obvious that if elements are selected which consume less time than that required to read and record (which is approximately 0.027 decimal minutes or 45 TMU), it will be impossible to time them at all. Elements of 0.02 to 0.03 decimal minutes are a commonly accepted practical minimum.

Separation of constant elements from variable elements as required by rule No. 2 is logical for several reasons. Once time has been established for any constant element, it need never again be timed unless the work conditions differ; it provides excellent material for the establishment of standard data. Also, the breakpoints between elements—where one element ends and the next begins—should be readily distinguishable by the analyst's senses. Sounds and relationships of objects are often used to aid the analyst to discern breakpoints.

In a similar manner, the time for variable elements must be kept separate. For example, the variables in the case of a metal removal machine (such as a lathe, mill, etc.) are usually governed by spindle speed, rate of tool feed, type of tools, material, etc. If enough data can be obtained concerning a variable element, it can generally be plotted or a formula developed so that times for any future work with that type of variable can be established without actually going to the machine to time the operation.

It will be relatively easy for an analyst trained in MTM procedures to decide which manual elements of the operation can be defined as constant or variable because of the knowledge he has gained regarding the variable factors in fundamental manual motions.

The amount of space available for listing the various elements on a time study form is limited: however, it is very important that the descriptions be complete enough so that a stranger picking up the study could easily identify each element, the tools and equipment associated with each element, and any other pertinent information that might be needed to establish in the future whether or not changes had occurred.   If room is not available in the space provided for element descriptions, a more complete description can be given in the space reserved for general comments.

A number of examples of poorly defined elements as contrasted with better descriptions are now listed to more clearly indicate the need for good descriptions and how they can be achieved.

Poor Descriptions	Better Descriptions
Pick up part	Pick up part No. 6W50 from tote-pan No. 1
Pick up soldering iron	Pick up 200 watt soldering iron from holder
Drill hole	Drill ⅛″ dia. hole ½″ deep
Pick up screwdriver	Pick up No. 1 ratchet screwdriver
Turn turret	Turn turret 2 positions
Paint cover	Paint outside of cover with Paasche air brush
Glyp terminals and screws	Glyptal the 5 completed terminals and 4 screws with nuts holding terminal board

A comparison of the descriptions above will readily indicate why any issue could easily be confused if a stranger to the operation, or even the original analyst, returned after six months to check on changed conditions using the poor descriptions as a reference.   Being specific avoids later difficulty, and is well worth the small additional recording time required.

7. Observe and Record Element Times

A time study analyst should stand in a position so that he can easily bring directly into his field of vision the three things demanding his attention: the operator, the watch, and the time study sheet.   The photograph in Fig. 8 illustrates the proper method of holding the board and a good position for the analyst with reference to the operation being timed.

The analyst's position should not only permit him to observe the operator but, more particularly, the hands and the actual operations being performed.   It is preferable to be located a few feet behind the operator to avoid interference or in any way distracting the operator's attention from his work.   In general, the analyst should blend into the background as much as possible.   If the operator stands at his work, then the analyst should always stand while making the observation.   If the operator is seated, it is permissible under certain conditions for the analyst to be seated during observation.   However, standing will give some extra advantage in observing the operations being performed.

There is usually a natural resentment by most operators against an analyst who settles himself comfortably into a seat to watch them work.

It is difficult enough to gain the confidence of the worker without jeopardizing it by apparent laziness on the part of the analyst. It is also a recognized fact that a person is more alert when he is standing than when he is sitting. Work study certainly demands the maximum amount of alertness and concentration and this, in itself, should be sufficient reason to stand while making observations.

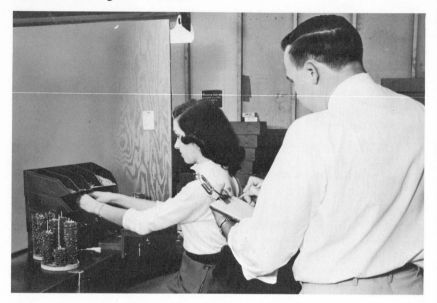

Fig. 8.   Time study analyst properly equipped in correct stance.
Courtesy of The Magnavox Company.

It was mentioned that some exceptions to standing occur. This certainly would be true when timing an office operation, since the majority of such workers are usually seated. It might also be true for a coil-winding department or a female electronic assembly department. In any event, the analyst's objective should be to conform as closely as possible with those among whom he is working and do his work in a manner causing a minimum of disturbance to normal conditions.

To the uninitiated, it may seem an impossible task to time elements as short as have been discussed in this chapter. It is no more difficult to accomplish this task than that of making a detailed MTM study. Recall that when first considering the recognition of various Reaches, Grasps, Moves, etc., it seemed like an impossible task to correctly identify each motion a person made during an operation and thereby establish time values for the elements and the total operation. With full understanding and adequate practice, however, a good analyst achieves surprising skill at isolating MTM motions or obtaining short watch readings.

The necessary timing can be done by close attention to the timing device and the operator. However, since even the shortest elements as described and identified in a time study do not reveal the minute details covered in a fundamental MTM study, it is important for the time study observer to learn the art of minimizing attention to the timing function alone. The timing can approach automaticity if he utilizes the distinctive sounds frequently accompanying the beginning or the ending of many of the elements found in a time study. Such sounds aid the observer in taking his readings. Representative sounds are the starting of the machine, the stopping of the machine, a shaft dropping into place in a jig, the cover of the jig being snapped into position, etc. The analyst should train himself to detect such sounds, thereby freeing his attention somewhat so that he can discern better the operator's method and its variations.

Elements such as "blow chips out of jig," "replace empty tote box," "lubricate die," and other similar operations that occur infrequently should always be considered specific parts of the operation and should be timed. Such elements are normally listed last on the time study form. In timing such elements it is necessary to obtain, in addition to the time required for the specific operation, data concerning the frequency of occurrence of each such element. Obtaining this data may involve an all-day time study, or the use of a memo-motion study (use of a timer-operated camera to take photographs at specific intervals throughout the day), or a ratio-delay study (a statistical analysis based on random observations). Both of the latter procedures are discussed in other chapters.

There are four commonly used methods of reading a stop watch. These are (1) *Continuous timing*, (2) *Repetitive timing*, (3) *Accumulative timing*, and (4) *Cycle timing*.

Continuous Timing

In this method, the watch is allowed to run continuously from the beginning to the end of the observation period. The position of the hands on the watch at the termination of each element is mentally noted and recorded, but obviously this reading does not indicate the elapsed time for the element. Elapsed times can be secured only by subtracting successive readings. This additional clerical work can be performed by comparatively low-salaried clerks and thereby does not greatly increase the cost of the study.

One of the advantages of the continuous method—the one most used traditionally—is that the exact sequence of elements is always shown, since the watch runs for the entire length of the study. It is also quite easy to rationalize the study with the operator if he has any questions to raise after it is completed. This cannot always be done with the snapback method (see below), since sequence identity is lost and the time study analyst may be criticized unjustly as having limited out some of the foreign elements by merely not recording them. It is also possible to unfairly criticize the analyst as having unduly shortened the time for certain elements by too early snapback and thereby establishing a tighter standard than would have resulted from correct procedure. Such criticisms can never in honesty be leveled against the continuous method of timing. Due to the necessity of reading the watch quickly, individual element times could be somewhat in error; but the total task time would certainly be truly shown by continuous timing.

The exact clock starting time of the time study should always be recorded on the data sheet as well as the clock time at the completion of the study. The total elapsed time can then be compared to the total stop watch time to determine whether the stop watch reading is approximately correct. Stop watches are normally more delicate than an ordinary watch and should therefore be checked frequently.

Repetitive Timing

Repetitive timing is commonly known as the snapback method. At the termination of each element, the watch is read and, at virtually the same instant, the hand of the watch is reset (snapped back) to zero by depressing the crown of the watch.

In this method of timing, the observer is enabled to record the time for each element directly on his observation sheet. This means that he can note variations in the performance time for any given element quite easily, even during the study. It has an additional advantage in that no clerical work of subtraction to get element times is involved, such as must be done for the continuous method of timing.

Repetitive timing has been used successfully, but it does have decided disadvantages. Most time study men prefer instead the continuous method of timing an operation. An appreciable amount of time is lost in the act of resetting the hand of the watch to zero at the termination of each element. This introduces an error which may approach 5 per cent excess time if most of the elements are of very short duration and the remaining elements are not of any substantial length. The error is reduced only if a certain balance exists between long and short element times.

Another criticism leveled at the snapback method of timing is that the time study analyst may neglect to record foreign elements by merely stopping the watch until the regular sequence is resumed. He can do this by keeping the crown depressed until he wishes to resume timing. This produces an incomplete study which is not good for either the worker or the Industrial Engineering Department. Of course, this is a question of honesty and does not of necessity occur as a standard feature of the snapback method. Since only the elapsed times are recorded, a study made by this method does not present a clear picture of the sequence in which elements are performed. This is one distinct advantage that is obtained when continuous timing is used.

Accumulative Timing

The accumulative method of timing also permits the direct reading of the time for each element. It makes use of two or more stop watches mounted closely together on the observation board with their crowns contacted by a lever mechanism which resets all watches at the same instant. When the first watch is started, the second watch is automatically stopped; when the second watch is started, the first watch is stopped. Both watches must then be reset to zero immediately after being read; this action makes unnecessary the subtractions which are required in the continuous method. It also overcomes some of the criticisms ordinarily leveled at the snapback method, but still does not offer all the advantages of the continuous method.

The time study board shown in Fig. 7 and described earlier in this chapter permits a variation of the procedure above by adding a third watch. This relieves the analyst of the task of resetting the watches to zero as a separate operation because each depression of the lever starts one watch, stops the preceding one for reading, and resets the following one ready to time.

Cycle Timing

A method of timing seldom used, but one that permits measuring short times accurately, is known as the cycle method. It uses the snapback type of watch shown in Fig. 3. When this watch is used for repetitive timing, the slide on the side of the case is moved toward the crown to start, with all subsequent action being achieved by successive depressions of the crown. For cycle timing, however, the slide is moved to start the watch (after reset to zero by the crown) and then moved away from the crown to stop the watch when desired. Any portion of a cycle can thus be read as a continuous time shown by the stopped hands. The portion of the cycle which the analyst wishes to omit (as well as any foreign elements occurring) can be left out of the partial cycle timing by activating the slide both ways as desired.

Cycle timing relies on the algebraic principle of addition to isolate short times. By deleting in turn, as described above, the time for each element from the partial cycle time taken, the analyst obtains a series of partial times. The rules for addition and subtraction can be applied to algebraic expressions for these partial times to isolate any or all pure element times desired. For example, if three elements compose a cycle with total time T, the following set of equations can be solved for each element, using the cycle timing method:

1st reading

$$a + b + c = T = 0.46 \text{ min.}$$

2nd reading

$$a + b = t_1 = 0.42 \text{ min.}$$

3rd reading

$$a + c = t_2 = 0.23 \text{ min.}$$

Deducting the 2nd equation from the first,

$$c = 0.04 \text{ min.}$$

Substituting in the 3rd equation,

$$a = 0.23 - c = 0.23 - 0.04 = 0.19 \text{ min.}$$

Subtracting the 3rd equation from the 2nd equation,

$$b - c = 0.42 - 0.23 = 0.19$$

and

$$b = 0.19 + c = 0.19 + 0.04 = 0.23 \text{ min.}$$

Checking in the first equation,

$$0.19 + 0.23 + 0.04 = 0.46 \quad \text{or} \quad 0.46 = 0.46$$

This method is arithmetically laborious and is seldom used except for special conditions. It is even harder physically to employ because of the extra effort required to operate both the slide and the resetting crown during observation.

The term "cycle timing" or "cycle check" is also sometimes applied to the practice of making rough checks of over-all times for a cycle or operation. In this case, the term obviously has a different meaning. Such checks are used for rough checks of operator performance, labor content evaluation, etc.

8. Rate Operator

Unless the operator was rated during longer elements of the study, it will now be necessary to establish and record a performance rating for the operator. The procedure for doing this, whether element by element or for the job as a whole, has been discussed thoroughly in Chapter 6. Record either the "speed rating" or the rating for each of the four factors affecting over-all performance; that is skill, effort, conditions and consistency. Consistency should actually be rated after the time study analyst notes the variation of element times while summarizing the study in the office as described in Chapter 6.

9. Determine the Required Allowances

A complete discussion of this subject is quite involved and is a part of Chapter 23. Suffice it to say here that some adjustment of time study and/or MTM studies are required by the engineer to account for the operator time spent because of personal needs, miscellaneous delays, fatigue, etc.

10. Determine the Allowed Time Standard for the Operation

This also involves a somewhat detailed discussion included in Chapter 24. The computations involved are similar, however, to those shown in Fig. 2 of this chapter, which is discussed next.

A COMPLETED TIME STUDY EXAMPLE

Reference was made earlier to the time study example in Fig. 2, but detailed discussion of the steps and factors in a completed time study was deferred to this point. With all of the preceding information, the reader is now in a better position to appreciate the details of the work and attach the correct interpretation to remarks made here concerning the various aspects of the example.

To begin the story, note that Fig. 2 is in two parts. Figure 2A shows the "back" side of the time study form and contains all background data, the sketch of the workplace in this case, and the calculations for the completed time standard based on this study. Also, in the space for remarks, extra information may be listed if there is not enough room on the front of the study and no assigned place elsewhere on the form for data which should be recorded. Figure 2B shows the elemental breakdown, the recorded watch times, the computed elemental times, all extraneous times and interruptions which could affect the standard, and finally calculation of the allowed times entered on the standard calculation on the back of the form. Most of the remaining remarks regarding this study concern the "front" side of the time study form.

It is worthwhile at this point to clarify one thing about time study forms. Many companies design their own forms, and may even design forms to be most convenient for certain departments or lines of work. While this results in certain definite advantages—justified if the number of time studies to be taken with the form is sufficiently large—it does involve printing problems and the services of someone in or out of the organization who has the necessary skill in graphic art work. For this reason, many management consultants have developed standard time study forms which are adaptable to a wide range of application with minimum loss of convenience and saving the printing and design problem. The form shown here, (available at modest prices from Methods Engineering Council in Pittsburgh, Pa.) has probably gained the widest acceptance of any form on the market. Any standardized form adaptable to a wide variety of work will necessarily involve economy of space; this creates the problem of careful recording and small writing which the analyst can best solve only through experience in taking time studies.

Discussion earlier concerned the nature and content of the elements, and the listing of these for this study can be found at the top row of the form. One technique not illustrated here is the method of handling repeating elements. The best way to record them is to assign a new element number and refer back to the element it repeats in the word listing; another means is to merely note in the listing that a certain numbered element is repeated. With either scheme, the elapsed times for a repeating element are all totaled in the first column in which the element appears and the number of readings is shown as the total number of occurrences in all columns.

Note next that each column is subdivided into two columns headed "T" and "R." The "T" columns are used to show the elapsed element times. These are computed after the observations are complete—usually back in the office. Most analysts also find it convenient to use a colored pencil to record the elapsed times to afford contrast with the watch readings recorded in the "R" columns. It is customary, to help overcome the space deficiency, to record the full minutes of a watch reading only when the minute value changes; the readings between these recordings are self-evident as to the minute by examination.

The way the line numbers are used will vary with the method of recording employed. This example shows the recording of complete cycles, one per line, so that the watch readings proceed to the right on any given line; this constitutes the *accumulative* method of timing. With this listing, the "T" columns are computed by subtracting from the value of the watch reading in the "R" column for that element the watch reading in the "R" column for the preceding element. This is true for all except the first reading of the watch for the first element—here the watch reading is the elapsed time for the element in question. If the element elapsed times are extremely short, it is often more convenient to proceed vertically down a column and catch the watch reading for that particular element each time it occurs; this would require usage of the "snapback" timing method. When one of the elements was completely timed, the analyst would then proceed to the next column in turn and repeat the process; the elapsed times in this case would be equal to the "R" value for any given line and element. "Snapback" timing can also be used in conjunction with cycle recording on the same line, but it is more difficult to successfully complete the writing of watch times during short elements.

In the right columns labeled "Foreign Elements" are listed the data needed to adjust the element watch readings or "R" values for the effect of interferences in the study or for extraneous occurrences which it is desirable and proper to omit from the time standard. Here, a column coded alphabetically is used to provide a key to the element and line where the foreign element occurred. If the foreign element can or should be timed, this is recorded in the next column. The beginning of the foreign element is listed on the lower double line and the ending on the upper line. These two readings are then subtracted to obtain the "T" value listed in the next column. The description column identifies the nature and details of the foreign element involved, since this data is vital in determining whether the time, if recorded, should be included in the study or not. Frequently, time study analysts use the foreign element space to record "occasional" elements and time them; but in this example two "occasional" elements are recorded as elements 13 and 14. Such choice of techniques is often dictated by the limits of recording space and the nature of the elements involved.

In case an over-all performance rating is made for the study, the bottom of the right columns provides space for the factor rating and their numerical values. This particular rating space is designed for usage of the LMS rating system described in detail in Chapter 6. When it is feasible and desirable to rate each and every element in the study, the individual ratings are listed instead on the line near the bottom of the form labeled "Rating (S.E.C. & CY.)." For this example, an over-all rating of E1E1DD was used, which would mean that the operator was considered as performing at 91 per cent of the desired standard conditions of skill, effort, conditions, and consistency. Accordingly, this factor is listed once on the rating line and the leveling factor of 0.91 listed on the line below. If the individual elements were rated, the line below would show instead the particular numerical rating value for the LMS rating listed immediately above for. that element.

In the following detailed discussion of the example, the place to look is given by the line number and element column of the time study form. Several major time study tehniques are illustrated here, and they merit separate comment.

Line 1, Elements 1 and 2 and Line 5, Elements 8 through 10: When for any reason a watch reading is missed or the analyst was not able to record it properly, this fact is shown by the symbol "M" in the "R" column. Naturally, the "T" values cannot be found for such elemental cycle values, nor will the time for the following element be found reliably. For this cause, the dash (–) is shown in the appropriate "T" columns and these dashes indicate reduction of the number of occurrences used to compute the average element times at the bottom of the form. Evidently, the M listed for Line 1, elements 1 and 2 was due to the fact that the analyst did not start the watch until the beginning of element 3; accordingly, the "T" value for element 3 is valid. The "T" value for Line 5, element 11, however, is not considered valid because the analyst was not sure whether he started the watch just as element 11 began or slightly earlier; no "T" value is therefore shown in that place.

Line 3, Element 3: Symbol A here shows that a foreign element occurred; the foreign element was timed and recorded at the right-hand side as having been time out to instruct the cementing operator who was working near to the drilling operator being studied. Since this instruction took 0.26 minute, the "T" value for Line 3, element 3 was computed as follows: The subtraction of the "R" value of 14.57 for element 2 from the "R" value of 17.89 for element 3 shows a total elapsed time of 3.32 minutes from the end of element 2 to the end of element 3. The "T" value for element 3, however, must be reduced by the instruction time of 0.26 minute as recorded for foreign element A. The "T" value for element 3 is thus correctly listed as 3.32 minutes less 0.26 minute, or 3.06 minutes.

Line 3, Element 11: Note that a double time recording is used here. Refer to element 14 to discover what happened at this point. Note B for element 14 shows that, out of sequence, the operator stopped element 11 before it was completed at 21.00 minutes, took 0.60 minute to move a storage truck, and then returned and completed element 11 as the watch showed 21.72 minutes. The "T" value for element 11 is therefore computed as follows: The upper "R" value of 21.72 minutes minus the 20.84 minutes "R" value for element 10 shows a total elapsed time of 0.88 minute. To obtain the "T" value for element 11, it is necessary to first find the "T" value for element 14. The "R" value for element 14 shows it was completed at 21.60 minutes, while the bottom "R" value for element 11 shows element 14 began at 21.00 minutes; accordingly, element 14 would take 0.60 minute as mentioned earlier. When this time is subtracted from the total elapsed time of 0.88 minute, the result is the "T" value of 0.28 minute for element 11.

Line 4, Elements 7 and 12: These are examples of instances where it was not possible to determine the adjustment time for the foreign elements noted as C and D at the right of the form. While the readings were used to list "T" values, examination of these values when the calculations on the bottom of the form were being made led to the conclusion that these times were out of range. The "T" values were therefore encircled to show that they were discarded in computing the average element times. It is also instructive to examine the other two places in this study in which foreign element C occurred. In Line 6, element 3 the talking evidently did not interfere with the drilling operator's time enough to justify discarding the "T" value recorded there; whereas for Line 7, element 10 the talking made the "T" value almost twice as long as others for the same element, so that the "T" value recorded there was discarded. Such usage of a circle to denote discarded times for these reasons or because— even without knowing exactly why—the "T" value is unreasonably high or low is a universal practice in time study techniques.

With the detailed explanations given above, the reader should be able to continue through the rest of the recorded times and figure what happened and how the elapsed element times listed were computed. A properly written time study must always permit complete accounting of all watch readings taken and also explain any discrepancies which can be attributed to assignable causes through the use of notes or foreign elements.

It can readily be seen that a high degree of skill and concentration is needed by a time study man since all of the recording techniques illustrated in the example are accomplished while he is also reading the watch and attending to the actions of the operator. Until a man gains mastery of the art, time study appears to require the use of three hands and three pairs of eyes! With practice in aligning the watch and recording sheet with the line of sight to the worker as shown in Fig. 8, however, the neophyte suddenly arrives at a state of skill in which the work of taking a time study seems entirely natural and readily accomplished.

The computations for allowed time at the bottom of the study are rather evident from the titles of the lines. Perhaps it would help to tell why the lines for minimum and maximum "T" values are included. There are two principal reasons. First, examination of the minimum and maximum in contrast to the average time will reveal whether any additional "T" values should be established by further study or whether others should be discarded and encircled, in which case the average would be recomputed. The key is that the average should be fairly close to the average of the minimum and maximum values listed. Such information helps the analyst decide whether an extremely high or low "T" value, whether or not he can determine the cause, is better discarded. The second reason is that when LMS ratings are applied to each individual element, knowledge of the range of data in comparison to the average value helps the analyst to assign the proper rating for consistency. Remember that consistency as a rating factor in the LMS system accounts purely for the mathematical variation of the data, and this rating is determined solely on that basis at the time the study is summarized. The cause of the variation, however, was discussed in Chapter 6. The final step on the front page of the study is to add the allowances and transfer the allowed times to the rear of the form for computation of the standard.

To summarize this discussion of the example time study, note that almost all the computation work can be assigned to properly trained clerical help. It is essential to use a trained time study analyst for taking the study and recording all the "R" values shown. Computing the "T" values and filling in the bottom of the form, however, can be done by a clerk equipped with calculating devices if he is given proper guidance. It is also good practice for the analyst to have a look at the finished computations to satisfy himself that the clerk has done his work correctly and no gross or apparent errors in arithmetic or interpretation of the analyst's recording will cause the final standard to be incorrect.

CHAPTER 22

Analysis Procedures and Techniques

Much thought and effort by the industrial engineer must precede most work studies, particularly those involving functions or departments that have not previously enjoyed the benefits of labor standards. If the labor standards are to be established on clerical work, for instance, automatically included in the prestudy tasks are those of analyzing all related paper work, its flow, and all paper forms used by the operators.

Labor standards should not be established until the work has been simplified. This is vital to reliable results. The broadest possible interpretation must be placed on the word *work*. Not only are the tasks performed by the people to be studied involved, but also all *related* work. Related work in a factory operation usually involves material handling; this, in turn, involves plant layout. Preceding and subsequent operations to the task to be studied must also be considered. Often work can be eliminated by rearranging operations. For example, drilling locating holes in a casting may sometimes be eliminated if operations are properly sequenced to locate from required machined surfaces and/or holes.

Often, organizational study is also a prestudy requirement in clerical situations, since many clerical tasks can be eliminated or simplified merely by changing the department where the work is done. For example, the industrial engineering department should be informed of delays affecting production. If delay reports originated by the foremen are routed through the industrial engineering department, no summary report from the accounting department is required; otherwise a daily report to the industrial engineering department by others summarizing such occurrences is usually needed.

It is not intended here to discuss in detail the analysis and solution of these broad problems, since they could encompass several volumes. The more prevalent analytic techniques used, however, will be presented.

CHARTING

The most convenient and much used technique for analyzing operations is to develop a picture of the work being done or to be done. A chart is the industrial engineer's picture. There are various kinds of charts and he must choose the one which enables him to do the best possible job of methods analysis and improvement. Properly used, these charting techniques can substantially decrease the amount of time required to analyze a given task. The more common types of charts used by the industrial engineer will be presented. In addition, a few of the more specialized types will be shown to aid the reader in devising his own special varieties.

Cautious and sound judgment should be exercised as to the amount of detail that is included in any given analysis. Charts of more than one kind are not usually necessary to arrive at a good answer in the shortest time. On the other hand, a variety of charts applied to the same problem can be of inestimable value in analyzing the more complex operations.

Operation Process Chart

The ASME definition of an operation process chart is as follows: "An operation process chart is a graphic representation of the points at which materials are introduced into the process, and of the sequence of inspections and all operations except those involved in material handling. It includes information considered desirable for analysis such as time required and location."[1] An operation process chart clearly shows the sequence of all operations, inspections, time allowances for each operation and inspection and, in addition, the flow of all materials concerned with the charted manufacturing process.

The operation process chart is essentially a blueprint of a manufacturing process. These charts are therefore of value either in designing a new manufacturing process or improving an old one. A sample operation process chart is shown in Fig. 1. The small circles denote an operation while the small squares denote an inspection.

All charts should be carefully identified as to title and all other pertinent information. This additional information generally includes, but is not restricted to, the following: assembly number, drawing number, process description, present or proposed method, date, name of person doing the charting, chart number, department, etc.

Vertical lines indicate the general flow of the work, whereas horizontal lines denote the introduction of material either purchased as a finished

[1] Extracted from ASME Standard 101 entitled *Operation and Flow Process Charts*, 1947, with permission of the publisher, The American Society of Mechanical Engineers, United Engineering Center, 345 East 47th Street, New York, New York 10017.

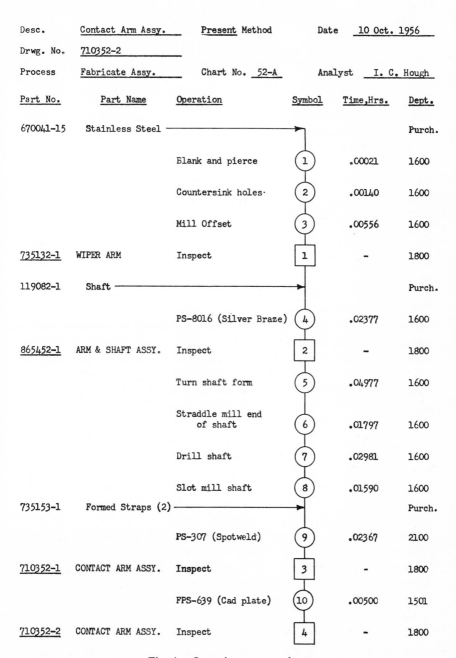

Desc.   Contact Arm Assy.   Present Method   Date   10 Oct. 1956

Drwg. No. 710352-2

Process   Fabricate Assy.   Chart No. 52-A   Analyst   I. C. Hough

Part No.	Part Name	Operation	Symbol	Time,Hrs.	Dept.
670041-15	Stainless Steel				Purch.
		Blank and pierce	1	.00021	1600
		Countersink holes·	2	.00140	1600
		Mill Offset	3	.00556	1600
735132-1	WIPER ARM	Inspect	1	–	1800
119082-1	Shaft				Purch.
		PS-8016 (Silver Braze)	4	.02377	1600
865452-1	ARM & SHAFT ASSY.	Inspect	2	–	1800
		Turn shaft form	5	.04977	1600
		Straddle mill end of shaft	6	.01797	1600
		Drill shaft	7	.02981	1600
		Slot mill shaft	8	.01590	1600
735153-1	Formed Straps (2)				Purch.
		PS-307 (Spotweld)	9	.02367	2100
710352-1	CONTACT ARM ASSY.	Inspect	3	–	1800
		FPS-639 (Cad plate)	10	.00500	1501
710352-2	CONTACT ARM ASSY.	Inspect	4	–	1800

Fig. 1. Operation process chart.

product or as a part or an assembly upon which work has been performed within the plant.

Whenever possible, the chart should be so constructed that the vertical flow lines and the horizontal material lines do not cross. Should it be necessary to cross these lines, the conventional practice to show that no juncture occurs is to draw a small semi-circle in the horizontal line as shown in Fig. 2.

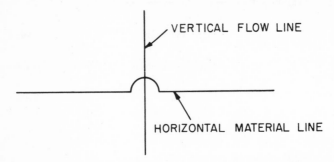

Fig. 2. Convention for crossing lines on an operation process chart.

Each operation and inspection should be numbered chronologically for identification and reference purposes. An examination of the sample operation process chart illustrates one means of accomplishing this task. If desired, an "O" can be used as a prefix or suffix to the operation numbers and an "INS" to the inspection identification numbers.

Flow Process Chart

The ASME defines a flow process chart as a "graphic representation of the sequence of all operations, transportations, inspections, delays, and storages occurring during a process or procedure, and includes information considered desirable for analysis such as time required and distance moved."[2]

The flow process chart contains much more detail than an operation process chart and consequently is not adapted to showing the complete manufacturing details of a complicated assembly. It is used primarily to show the manufacture of one component. This chart is especially valuable in revealing hidden costs, such as unnecessary distance traveled, unnecessary delays, temporary storages that are not required, etc. These nonproductive periods are highlighted and the analyst should note these and eliminate them wherever possible. If they cannot be eliminated they should be reduced to an absolute minimum.

It should definitely be understood that merely producing a chart will

[2] *Ibid.*

not improve an operation. It merely helps to find places where a given process could possibly be improved.

The sample flow process chart illustrated in Fig. 3 requires the same general identification details as the operation process chart.

The meaning of the flow symbols are relatively self-explanatory; however the standard symbols and their ASME definitions[3] are shown in Fig. 4.

Noting distances of five feet or less normally is not required. However, if the process is such that short moves represent a significant cost factor, then they should be recorded in addition to the longer moves. Normally, distances are not measured but rather estimated from known physical distances within the building. A common reference guide for distance in an industrial building is the column spacing, which is generally known for each building.

It is important to note the amount of delay time and storage time. The longer a part lays in storage or is delayed, the more inventory value it accumulates.

Flow process charts are sometimes used in plant layout work; in fact, they are almost a necessity where the processes are complex. However, the engineer will find that a flow process chart is not essential to make the majority of the layouts ordinarily required for the less complex processes in an industrial plant.

Man and Machine Process Chart

The man and machine process chart is used to show the exact time relationship between the element working cycle of the man and the operating cycle of his machine(s). This chart is used primarily to study, analyze and improve a given work station rather than an over-all process or series of operations.

The facts are so presented that possibilities for the fuller utilization of both idle man and idle machine time are evident. Many machine tools are either semi- or fully automatic and hence the operator is often idle for a portion of the working cycle. The proper utilization of this idle time leads to improved efficiency of production. It is common practice to have one employee operate two or more semi-automatic or fully automatic machines.

One method of constructing a man and machine process chart for two machines is shown in Fig. 5. It should be constructed in a manner similar to the previously discussed charts and contain like identification data. The reader will notice that this type of chart is drawn to scale, which requires that the analyst select a distance (usually in inches) to conform with an appropriate time unit so that the chart will be properly arranged in the space available on the paper being used. The longer the cycle time of the operation, the shorter will be the distance per unit of time. Cross-

[3] *Ibid.*

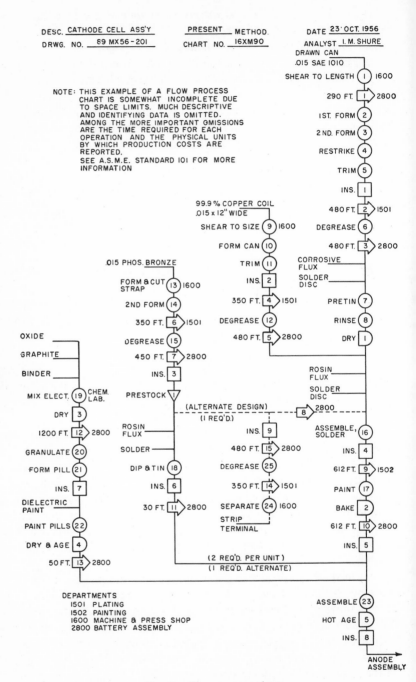

Fig. 3. Flow process chart.

SYMBOL	NAME	DEFINITION
 ◯	Operation	An operation occurs when an object is intentionally changed in any of its physical or chemical characteristics, is assembled or disassembled from another object, or is arranged or prepared for another operation, transportation, inspection, or storage. An operation also occurs when information is given or received or when planning or calculating takes place.
 ⇨	Trans- portation	A transportation occurs when an object is moved from one place to another, except when such movements are a part of the operation or are caused by the operator at the work station during an operation or an inspection.
 ▢	Inspection	An inspection occurs when an object is examined for identification or is verified for quality or quantity in any of its characteristics.
 ◗	Delay	A delay occurs to an object when conditions except those which intentionally change the physical or chemical characteristics of the object, do not permit or require immediate performance of the next planned action.
▽	Storage	A storage occurs when an object is kept and protected against unauthorized removal, shown by inverted triangle.
 ◲	Combined Activity	When it is desired to show activities performed either concurrently or by the same operator at the same work station, the symbols for those activities are combined, as shown by the circle placed within the square to represent a combined operation and inspection.

When unusual situations outside the range of the definitions are encountered, the intent of the definitions summarized in the following tabulation will enable the analyst to make the proper classifications.

CLASSIFICATION	PREDOMINANT RESULT
Operation	Produces or Accomplishes
Transportation	Moves
Inspection	Verifies
Delay	Interferes
Storage	Keeps

Fig. 4.   Process chart symbols.*

* Extracted from A.S.M.E. Standard 101 *Operation and Flow Process Charts,* published by The American Society of Mechanical Engineers, United Engineering Center, 345 East 47th Street, New York, N. Y. 10017.

NOTE: THE BACKGROUND DATA FOR THIS CHART, ALSO MUCH OF THE TEXT MATERIAL, WAS GIVEN BY COURTESY OF MR. DON KANE, SUPERVISOR OF METHODS AND STANDARDS, ARGUS CAMERAS, INC., ANN ARBOR, MICHIGAN.

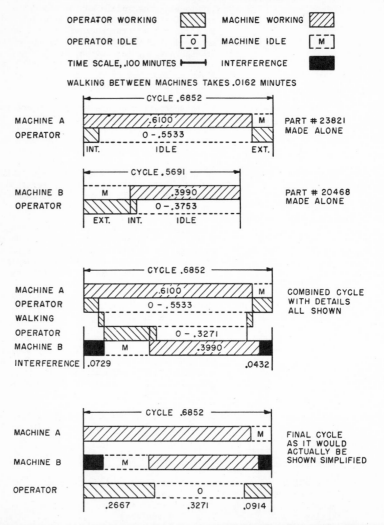

SUMMARY-ALL TIMES DECIMAL MINUTES	WORKING TIME				IDLE TIME		MACHINE INTERFERENCE
	EXTERNAL	INTERNAL	WALKING	TOTAL	MINUTES	PERCENT	
MACHINE A	(.0752)	(.0567)	—	.6100	.0752	11.0%	—
MACHINE B	(.1701)	(.0237)	—	.3990	.1701	24.8%	.1151
OPERATOR	.2453	.0804	.0324	.3581	.3271	47.9%	—

Fig. 5. Man and machine process chart. (Normally produced on graph paper for ease of scaling.)

hatched lines under each heading denote operator and machine working time, differentiated by the slope of the hatching. Idle time is shown as dotted spaces, using the symbol "O" for the operator and "M" for the machine. Machine interference is shown as a black space.

Accurate element time values are necessary for the construction of the man and machine process chart. The time values shown in Fig. 5 are select times; but such charts can properly, in certain cases, represent allowed time, which will include, in addition to the select time, allowances for personal time, fatigue, and unavoidable delays. Note that inclusion of allowances will reduce idle time and increase interference time. If the times are reduced to reflect incentive pace, the effects will be opposite to those stated. It is also usual procedure to show total working time, total idle time, and grand total (cycle) time for each machine and for the operator on the chart.

The considerations involved in producing these charts appear elementary to the novice. This is far from the truth. Usually the first thing to be determined in a multiple machine assignment—the usual end result of a man and machine process chart—is the work load of the operator for a given job. Using a mill as an example, the operator must do certain operations to load and unload the part on the mill—this is the external work. That is, the work is external to the automatic cycle of the mill. He then will engage the start button and the machine cycle follows. During the machine cycle he may be required to gage the part previously run—this is the internal work or that internal to the machine cycle. The diagram below illustrates the three components mentioned.

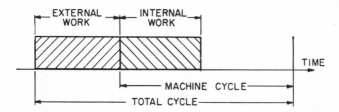

From the diagram, the total cycle to mill this part is the time for external work (part of which may precede and the rest follow the machine time) plus machine cycle time. Of this total cycle to mill the part, the operator is working during the external and the internal portions. The work load is defined as the percentage of these two elements to the total cycle:

$$\text{Per cent work load} = \frac{\text{external} + \text{internal}}{\text{external} + \text{machine cycle}} \times 100$$

Once the work load is established for a given machine, it is possible to begin to define the number of machines an operator should run. *It must be*

remembered that machines cannot only be overmanned; they can also be
undermanned which, from the standpoint of economics, is just as important.
In the case of overmanned machines, the utilization of the machine is high;
but the labor cost may also be too high. In the case of the undermanned
machine, the labor may be at a minimum; but the machine utilization may
also be very low, causing a loss of available capacity—and idle capacity
costs money.

If an operator has less than a 100 per cent work load he obviously has
idle time. The fourth work load component, idle time, may be added to
the previous diagram as shown below.

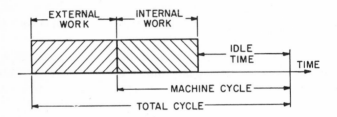

Idle time involves labor cost along with the external and internal work.
At this point, however, it is known how much the work performance is
costing and how much idleness in the operation is costing.

If leveled time study data or MTM pattern data were used to determine
the external and internal elements of a job, and these normal times were
used to calculate the work loads for a multiple machine assignment, an
incorrect work load would likely ensue in an incentive plant. Recall that
in an incentive system, it is not expected that the operator will be working
at a normal pace, but at some higher rate, commonly called an incentive
pace. Therefore, in such plants a more realistic or true work load is based
on the expected incentive pace of the operator. To obtain such correction,
the external and internal elements must be factored to reflect the expected
pace. This pace is usually the average pace at which a group of operators
would be working under an incentive system (115 to 130 per cent of
normal). The net effect is to increase idle time and decrease machine
interference, which might make possible assignment of another machine to
the operator. Note that a man-machine cycle less than 0.3109 minute
could be added to the tasks of the man in Fig. 5. This time plus the extra
0.0162 minute for walking equals the total operator idle time of 0.3271
minute.

A most important result and/or consideration in developing a man and
machine process chart is the determination of the interference created by
virtue of more than one machine running at the same time. The novice's
first reaction is—why worry about interference between machines? The

answer is that it affects the possible output and therefore the incentive earning of the operator for his labor. Interference can be defined as that loss of machine operating time that occurs when one machine stops at the end of its cycle for servicing by the operator, while at the same time a second machine stops for the same reason and the operator obviously is unable to service both machines at the same time. This interference is inherent in multiple machine assignments and causes a loss of production that would not occur if the operator were tending one machine. The operator must be paid for this loss of production. The interference value for planned multiple machine assignments can be determined by the use of man and machine process charts as shown in Fig. 5, where the value is 0.1151 minute total.

The above are some of the more obvious and important considerations in producing these charts. There are related, complex considerations in establishing the work standard for the operator, such as the addition of all applicable time elements, the application of allowances, etc. Suffice it to say in this regard that it can now be accomplished; to treat this item in detail is not deemed necessary by the authors.

An analyst will find many occasions which appear to include an appreciable amount of idle man time. He should be careful not to draw a quick conclusion that this is uneconomical since, under many conditions, it is better to have the man idle rather than a piece of expensive equipment. Over-all costs, including that of the facility, must be considered in drawing final conclusions.

Gang Process Chart

The gang process chart is a variation of the man and machine process chart. Industrial engineers will occasionally encounter processing situations of such magnitude that it is not a question of how many machines the operator should handle but, rather, a problem as to the number of operators needed to man the machine effectively. With this slight variation, it is exactly the same kind of chart as a man and machine process chart.

Left and Right Hand Operator Process Chart

The left and right hand MTM analysis previously described in this text represents one variety of this type of process chart. Another variety utilizes element time study descriptions and may or may not contain conventional flow chart symbols.

Miscellaneous Flow Charts

Just as some machine tools are more efficient than others for some specific operation, so are some analysis tools better than others for certain purposes. Figure 6 illustrates in condensed form the following additional miscellaneous

NOTES – Organizational units usually are coded by letters A, B, C, D, etc.
and identified by legend at the top and/or bottom of the chart.
Operations, on the other hand, are commonly identified by numbers.
For the graphical symbols employed, see Fig. 4 of this chapter. They
can be shaded only, connected by lines, or both may be used.
All descriptive terms should conform to the convention and detail
normally required in all management charts.

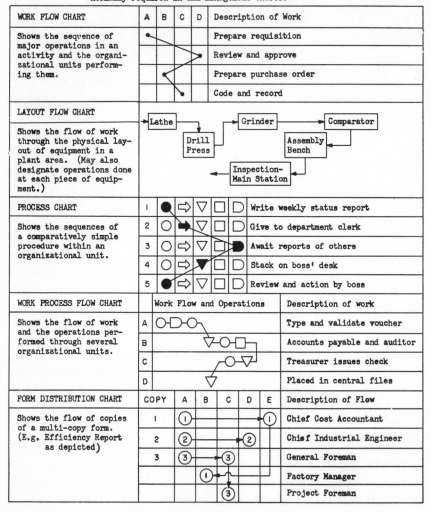

Fig. 6.   Miscellaneous flow charts.

types of flow charts: work flow chart, layout flow chart, process chart, work process flow chart, and form distribution chart.

The general purpose of each of these charts is shown on the left side of the space allocated to each type of chart with the general configuration of the chart given to the right of the statement of purpose and/or application. Obviously, a complete chart will take up one or more pages and must contain the proper identification as outlined for the previously detailed descriptions.

Flow Chart Summation

All industrial engineers should be familiar with the various types of charts described so that they can use these valuable tools in the most intelligent manner. They will also find occasions justifying variations of these charts to better analyze certain problems. Within the business world, many adaptations of the flow charting principles have been devised which are more valuable for certain specific purposes than the generalized flow charts described in this text. For example, Fig. 7 illustrates a specialized flow chart devised to analyze punch card and accounting machine problems. An analyst should carefully determine the problem he wishes to solve, then select or devise the chart which will help him most in its analysis and solution.

NEW PRODUCTS[4]

When new products are introduced into a department and/or plant, industrial engineering labor additional to that already described is obviously required. The steps which are normally followed are outlined to show the student how work measurement fits into the scheme. These steps, however, involve not only work measurement and the type of chart analysis just described, but other important industrial engineering tasks.

1. Drawings, bills of materials, samples of product, and other available data are thoroughly examined and studied to determine the product designer's intent and the general composition of the product.
2. Decisions are made as to which parts used in the apparatus are to be manufactured and which are to be purchased. This decision is usually based on economics—can it be made for the same or less cost than when purchased? Entire books have been written on what factors require consideration in arriving at the correct "make-buy" decision. Suffice it to say that, at least, all real costs associated with purchasing the part are to be compared to all real costs of manufacturing the item. Sometimes it even pays to buy partially finished parts and complete them in the plant. This entire effort often involves obtaining outside vendor quotations to compare with estimated make costs. Associated with *purchase cost* is the vendor price, necessary quantity over-order due to in-plant losses, vendor tool costs (if any), transportation expense, incoming inspection labor, incoming inspection gages and test equipment, etc. Associ-

[4] For additional information see: *The New Product,* by Delmar W. Karger, The Industrial Press, New York City, 1960.

PUNCHED-CARD ACCOUNTING MACHINE PROCESS ANALYSIS

COMPANY Abig Corporation   CHART NO. Ex-1234

LOCATION Metropole, Pennsiana   PAGE NO. 1 OF 1 PAGES

DEPARTMENT Factory Payroll   PREPARED BY A. Countant

PROCESS Weekly Direct Labor Payroll   DATE 25 Sept 1956

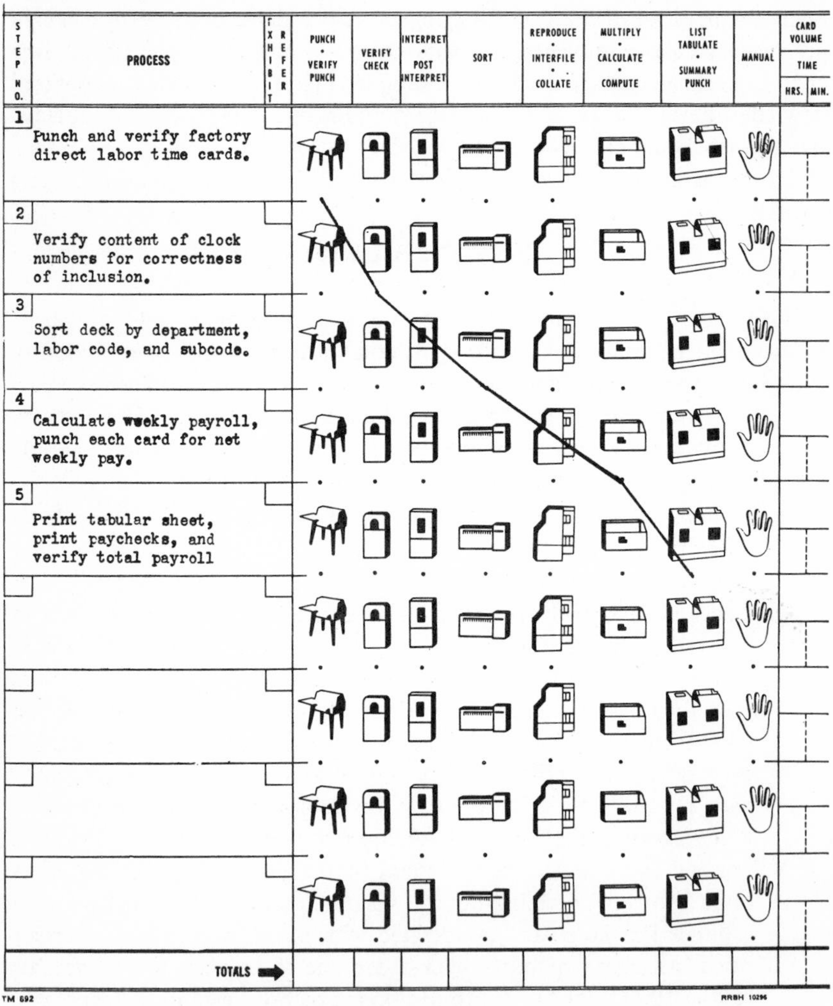

STEP NO.	PROCESS	TX HIBEIR THENEIR	PUNCH · VERIFY PUNCH	VERIFY CHECK	INTERPRET · POST INTERPRET	SORT	REPRODUCE · INTERFILE · COLLATE	MULTIPLY · CALCULATE · COMPUTE	LIST TABULATE · SUMMARY PUNCH	MANUAL	CARD VOLUME / TIME (HRS. MIN.)
1	Punch and verify factory direct labor time cards.										
2	Verify content of clock numbers for correctness of inclusion.										
3	Sort deck by department, labor code, and subcode.										
4	Calculate weekly payroll, punch each card for net weekly pay.										
5	Print tabular sheet, print paychecks, and verify total payroll										

TOTALS ➡

Fig. 7. Process analysis chart for punched-card accounting machine.

ated with *make cost* is purchased raw material (or partially finished part) cost, including all of the above associated factors for buying the part, labor to make the part, overhead (sometimes only the variable overhead is used for these comparisons), tools, gages, test equipment, etc.

3. The parts and/or assemblies are processed. Writing operator instruction sheets is part of this step and sample instruction sheets or processes are illustrated in Figs. 8 and 9.

    If MTM and/or Standard data is used in processing, time requirements are also obtained and recorded. This is a major advantage in such efforts. MTM can also help assure that the correct method is specified at the onset of production, particularly when methods based on engineered workplace layouts are enforced in actual production.

4. The determination of required tools, gages, test equipment, etc., is concurrent with the processing step. These must be ordered from the concerned functions responsible for providing this equipment.

5. The tools, gages, test equipment, etc., either must be ordered from outside vendors or constructed in the plant. After receipt and/or construction they must be trial run and corrected if found to be operating unsatisfactorily.

6. The layout of the plant must often be altered to make possible economical manufacture of the new product. This should occur preferably during the procurement of material, tools, test equipment, etc. Plant layout is another major function of the industrial engineer that cannot be covered in this text.

7. Once the above steps have been accomplished, it is usually advisable to make a small amount of the apparatus (2 to 50 pieces) on what is commonly known as a "pilot run" basis. Set-up men, group leaders, and/or a few skilled operators normally make the pilot run quantity and during this effort prove out the tools, processes, test equipment, etc.

8. Upon successful completion of the pilot run, production operators are assigned to the work and the training operation begins. Often, hundreds of employees are involved and good processes, departmental layouts, workplace layouts, tools, etc., are extremely important and necessary to keep training costs to a minimum.

9. Establishment of time standards is the next step if standard data and/or MTM was not used in the processing step. Time study cannot normally be utilized until this stage of events has been reached.

10. Methods improvement and/or methods enforcement, combined with ascertaining adequate operator performance, is the final step. This

PRINT PROCESS SHEET P1290

PROCESS NUMBER	⊗ 639606-2	MODEL NO. ARN-6		B.M. NO. 8094	CODE 120	PIECES/SHIFT ⊗ 1576
						PIECES/HOUR 204

PART NAME **R.F. OSC. CASE - STAMPING**   PROC. ENG. FHB   JOB ORDER 61270   DATE 8-17-56   LINE BALANCE   TOTAL SELECT TIME .256

DEPT. 1100   OPER. 4 of 4   USED IN ASSEMBLY NO. 639808-2   STD. ENG. FHB   PAGE 1 of 2

REFERENCE DRAWING NOS. 639606, 639808, 800206   TYPIST   P.R.

FATIGUE T. & C.	10 %
PERSONAL	3 %
UN. DELAY	2 %
TOTAL ALLOWANCE 15%	.038
TOTAL ALLOWED TIME	.294

PROCESS CHANGES				TOOLING AND FIXTURES		TOOLING AND FIXTURES	
DATE	CHKD. BY	SEQ.	CHANGE DESCRIPTION	SEQ.	MACHINE, TOOL OR FIXTURE	SEQ.	MACHINE, TOOL OR FIXTURE
10-22-56 FHB			REVISED PER ECN-20802		SLIDE FIXT (INSIDE) T# GA-F-694-A		SLIDE FIXT (OUTSIDE) T# GA-F-694-B
					DUMMY INKING CASE		DUMMY INKING CASE
					REQ'D STAMPS PER MARKING PRINT		REQ'D STAMPS PER MARKING PRINT

WORKPLACE LAYOUT

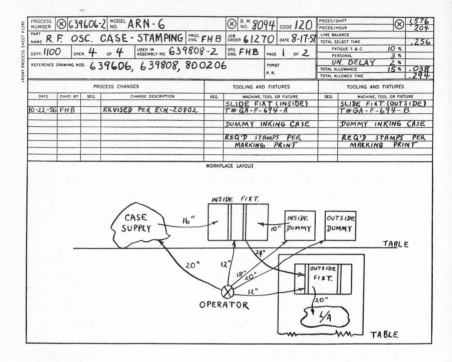

MECHANICAL PROCESS SHEET P1256A

PROCESS NUMBER	⊗ 639606-2	OPER. NO. 4	PART NAME R.F. OSC. CASE	⊠ - STAMPING	PAGE NO. 2	MODEL NO.	⊠ ARN-6

SEQ. NO.	QTY.	B.M. ITEM NO.	PART NO.	PART DESCRIPTION	LEFT HAND	DESCRIPTION OF OPERATION — STAMP CAN PER PRINT	RIGHT HAND	SELECT TIME SH./MIN.
1	1		639606-2	(OPER. 3)	OBTAIN CASE, POS ON INSIDE FIXT		RETURN HAND, ASSIST, RL	.049
2					PUSH CAN BOTH WAYS ON SLIDE TO STAMP BOTH ENDS INSIDE		WAIT, GR CASE	.033
3					ASSIST, RL, HAND ASIDE		CAREFULLY REMOVE CASE FROM INSIDE FIXT, POS ON OUTSIDE FIXT	.041
4					WAIT		PUSH CAN BOTH WAYS ON SLIDE TO STAMP BOTH ENDS OUTSIDE	.033
5					WAIT		CAREFULLY REMOVE CASE FROM OUTSIDE FIXT, L/A TO DRY ON STACK WITH CARE, RL CASE, RETURN HAND TO START	.037
6	AR		800206-1	STAMP INK	AFTER EVERY 4 CASES STAMPED, USE DUMMY CASE ON INSIDE FIXT TO RE-INK (PRORATED)			.020
7					SAME AS SEQ. 6 FOR OUTSIDE FIXT RE-INK			.020
8					ALLOWANCE TO INK DUMMYS; CHECK BAD STAMPS, CLEAN OFF AND RESTAMP AS NEEDED — 10% OF TOTAL ABOVE			.023

P/U—PICK UP   R—REACH   GR—GRASP   RL—RELEASE   POS—POSITION   L/A—LAY ASIDE

Fig. 8. Manual process instructions.

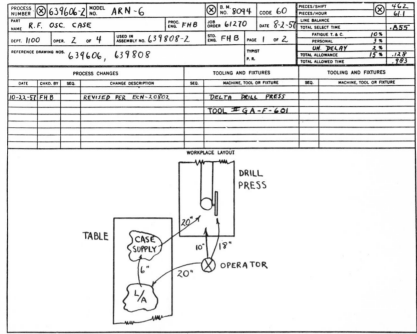

PROCESS NUMBER	⊗ 639606-2	MODEL NO. ARN-6		B.M. NO. 8094	CODE 60	PIECES/SHIFT		⊗	462
						PIECES/HOUR			61.1
PART NAME R.F. OSC. CASE			PROC. ENG. FHB	JOB ORDER 61270	DATE 8-2-51	TOTAL SELECT TIME			.855
						LINE BALANCE			
DEPT. 1100	OPER. 2 OF 4	USED IN ASSEMBLY NO. 639808-2		STD. ENG. FHB	PAGE 1 OF 2	FATIGUE T. & C.	10%		
						PERSONAL	3%		
REFERENCE DRAWING NOS. 639606, 639808				TYPIST		UN. DELAY	2%		
				P. R.		TOTAL ALLOWANCE	15%		.128
						TOTAL ALLOWED TIME			.983

PROCESS CHANGES				TOOLING AND FIXTURES		TOOLING AND FIXTURES	
DATE	CHKD. BY	SEQ.	CHANGE DESCRIPTION	SEQ.	MACHINE, TOOL OR FIXTURE	SEQ.	MACHINE, TOOL OR FIXTURE
10-22-51	FHB		REVISED PER ECN-20802		DELTA DRILL PRESS		
					TOOL # GA-F-601		

WORKPLACE LAYOUT

DRILL PRESS

TABLE

CASE SUPPLY

20"

10" 18"

6"

20"

⊗ OPERATOR

L/A

9-55 CM 63083 ● DITTOFORMS ●

MECHANICAL PROCESS SHEET P1256A

| PROCESS NUMBER ⊠ 639606-2 | OPER. NO. 2 | PART NAME R.F. OSC. CASE ⊠ | | | PAGE NO. 2 | MODEL NO. ⊠ ARN-6 |

DESCRIPTION OF OPERATION
DRILL 4 HOLES IN 2 BRKTS & 2 INSERTS

SEQ. NO.	QTY.	B.M. ITEM NO.	PART NO.	PART DESCRIPTION	LEFT HAND	RIGHT HAND	SELECT TIME 2MD MIN.
1	1		639606-2	(OPER. 1)	OBTAIN CASE, POS IN DRILL JIG, HAND ASIDE	HOLD JIG LID, CLOSE, RL	.040
2					POS JIG UNDER DRILL, HOLD	ASSIST LH GR LEVER AND LOWER DRILL	.041
3					DRILL 1ST HOLE (PROCESS TIME)		.150
4					RELOCATE DRILL JIG TO 2ND HOLE, HOLD	RAISE DRILL WAIT, LOWER DRILL	.028
5					REPEAT SEQ. 3 ONCE FOR 2ND HOLE		.150
6					REPEAT SEQ. 4 & 5 TWICE FOR 3RD & 4TH HOLES		.356
7					RL JIG, R TO CASE	RAISE DRILL, RL LEVER, OPEN JIG LID	.030
8					REMOVE CASE FROM JIG, SHAKE & BLOW OUT CHIPS, L/A CASE ON TABLE	HOLD JIG LID OPEN	.060

P/U—PICK UP　　R—REACH　　GR—GRASP　　RL—RELEASE　　POS—POSITION　　L/A—LAY ASIDE

Fig. 9.　Machine process instructions.

is a continuing effort that should not cease as long as the product is being manufactured. Even if the method originally established is very good, the appearance of new technology, equipment, etc., will often permit major cost reductions. Obtaining adequate operator performance is discussed in a later chapter.

MISCELLANEOUS DEVICES USED TO ANALYZE MANUAL OPERATIONS

Just as MTM and/or time study must often be associated with other types of engineering effort, it is also true that these two techniques are sometimes replaced or supplemented by other types of work study. This is especially true when fundamental research is made or where peculiar kinds of work are involved.

Again, it would be impossible to adequately cover all of the specialized work study techniques. It will only be possible here to briefly describe the better known methods. If more information is desired or needed, other works dealing with these subjects should be consulted. These specialized devices and/or techniques again emphasize the importance of the over-all subject of "work measurement."

Standard Industrial Engineering 16mm Motion Picture Equipment

In a few of the better equipped industrial engineering departments, motion picture equipment will be available to study work measurement problems. Its use in industry for work measurement is essentially confined to very high volume operations that involve complex, high-speed movements. The actual need for this equipment is rare, especially if MTM knowledge is available.

The method of usage is approximately parallel to the method used to establish the MTM data. To use it effectively requires a reasonable knowledge of photography so that adequate, detailed pictures are obtained. Many specialized books on photography are already available for reference and should be consulted prior to using this method of work analysis. The manufacturers of motion picture equipment will also be glad to assist in selecting and applying their equipment.

Essential equipment will include the following:

1. Constant speed (preferably adjustable) motor driven camera. Lens should be as good as possible. The ideal camera will be equipped with a lens turret permitting quick changes. If possible, it should be equipped with one very good, high-speed, general purpose lens

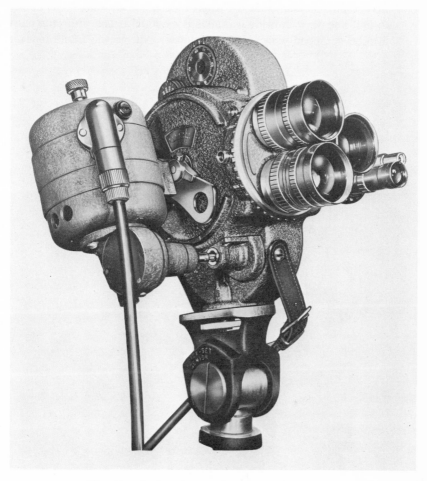

Fig. 10.   Typical time- and motion-study camera.
Courtesy Bell & Howell Co.

plus a telephoto lens and a wide angle lens. A typical 16 mm camera
for time study work is shown in Fig. 10. It has a capacity of 100
feet of film and speed settings of 500, 750, 1000, 1500, 2000, 3000,
and 4000 frames per minute.

2. A substantial, easily adjustable tripod.
3. Exposure meter.
4. Several photo flood lamps with reflectors and stands.
5. A film viewer, splicer, and rewinder.
6. Titling equipment.
7. An adjustable speed projector, equipped with a governor, plus a device

that permits manual frame by frame indexing of the film. The ability to halt and view individual frames is essential. The projector must also be equipped with a frame counter. An electric frame indexer

Fig. 11. Adjustable speed projector with frame count and indexing features.
Courtesy Bell & Howell Co.

is another handy adjunct to such equipment. A projector of the type indicated is illustrated in Fig. 11.

8. A Microchronometer is a useful, and often required, device. It is a high-speed, synchronous electric motor driven clock with a large face. The one shown in Fig. 12 has its finest divisions in 0.0005 minute (one "wink"). Each revolution of the large hand shows

Fig. 12. Microchronometer.
Courtesy Lafayette Instrument Co.

0.05 minute. By placing the clock in the viewing area of the camera, an analyst can very accurately determine elapsed time for each frame (if frame count timing is not used) and also the elapsed time per work cycle directly from the film.

The same camera equipment can also be used for making training films. This is a more common use for such equipment in industry. Another common use is in producing film records of the method, etc.

Extreme High-Speed Motion Analysis Cameras

The complex and advanced technology of this century has given birth to many new, unique, and outstanding devices. One of these is the ultra high-speed motion analysis camera that was originally developed to help solve many complex mechanical motion problems. It can also be adapted

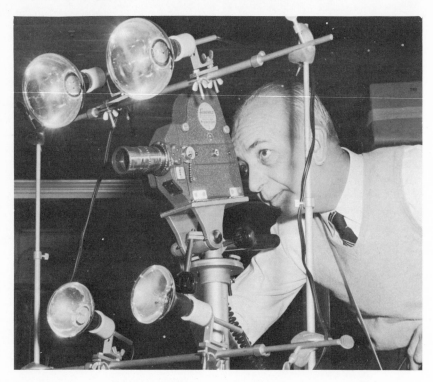

Fig. 13. High-speed motion analysis camera.
Courtesy Fairchild Camera and Instrument Corp.

to analysis of human motions of the kind work measurement considers. While various kinds of such cameras have existed in the laboratory, as special development models, it has only in recent times been possible to purchase commercial units such as the one illustrated in Fig. 13. Four speed ranges are available in the illustrated camera as follows: 32 to 200; 100 to 1000; 300 to 3000; and 500 to 5000 frames (exposures) per second.

Basic equipment might include the following items, although others may be added as budgets or problem situations dictate: high-speed camera; programmer mechanism; light stands and sockets; tripod; exposure meter;

four special 300-watt lamps; additional lenses; spare and/or extra motors permitting more than one speed range; and batteries.

Memo-Motion Studies

Memo-motion studies are made with a special camera providing adjustable interval timed exposures, say, one frame every half minute. Such a camera can be stationed at a remote point and aimed at either one operation or a whole department to determine frequency of delays, the kinds of

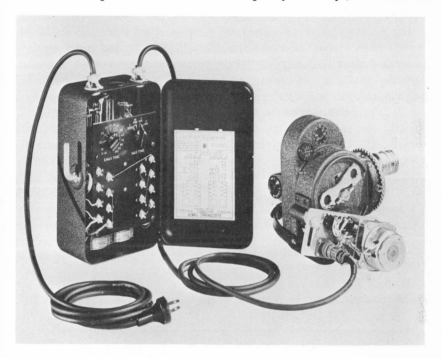

Fig. 14. Memo motion camera.
Courtesy Photovision Co.

delays, unusual occurrences, loafing, etc. By attaching a random signal generator, the equipment also can be used for ratio-delay studies (see Chapter 24) or other statistical studies of work situations. It is an obviously useful device of increasing popularity, since it reduces the amount of industrial engineering personnel and time required to determine the facts concerning items such as those mentioned. A list of equipment used for memo-motion studies might include: memo-motion study camera (a typical unit is shown in Fig. 14); camera tripod; exposure meter; film viewer, splicer, and rewinder; and projector (same type as used for motion studies).

Photo flood lamps and a titler are useful adjuncts, although lamps are normally not used since they usually adversely affect the study by changing the conditions surrounding the task being studied—the operators become greatly aware of the camera and cease performing in a normal manner. Another problem associated with memo-motion cameras is the distracting sound produced by the indexing mechanism attached to the camera and operated by the timer. The sound is quite noticeable in quiet areas and could adversely affect the study by continuously diverting the operator(s) attention to the device.

Kymograph

The Kymograph is an instrument developed by Professor Ralph M. Barnes while at the University of Iowa. It was designed and used in a research project to determine Therblig times and is therefore not commercially available. It consists of a paper tape moving at 2,000 inches per minute upon which electrically actuated pens draw jogged lines in a direction perpendicular to the travel of the tape to indicate motion breakpoints. The rapidly moving tape can measure times as small as 0.001 second. Obviously, means other than manual must be used to actuate the pens; the circuits controlling the pens are normally opened and closed by photoelectrically actuated switches or by mechanically operated limit switches.

Commercially available instruments using the same principle are now used to study machine usage and probably could be adapted to operate like the Kymograph.

Visicorder

Another time recorder actually used during the industrial phase of the MTM research on Apply Pressure[5] is the Visicorder (see Fig. 15). This

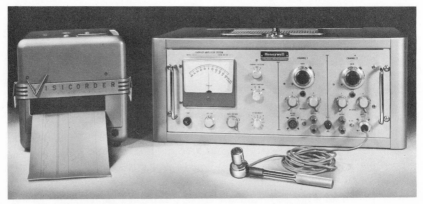

Fig. 15. Visicorder instrumented for Apply Pressure research.
Courtesy MTM Association for Standards and Research.

[5] R.R. 111 (See Ch. 5).

product of the Minneapolis-Honeywell Regulator Company provides a graphical analog record on photo-sensitive paper. It is a typical example of a multi-channel strip chart recorder. The scale in the direction of travel is 0.20 second or 5.56 TMU per inch. In the figure, a ratchet wrench is shown instrumented with a strain gage. The force signal is amplified in the carrier amplifier at the right and then fed into the Visicorder on the left. The force in this instance was recorded in a direction perpendicular to the time axis of the graph, using a scale of $\frac{1}{3}$ pound per inch. The recordings, similar to that visible in the figure, were visually interpreted by a reader. The resulting Apply Pressure data proved highly reliable, illustrating the capability of modern time recording devices.

Cyclegraph

The Cyclegraph was originally developed by the Gilbreths. Small electric lights are attached to the fingers, elbows, and head of the operator and, where desired, they can even be attached to the body. An ordinary still picture camera is then focused on the operator so that a time exposure made during a brief cycle of work records the path of each motion on the plate as a streak of light, thereby providing a permanent record of the path in two dimensions. This device is primarily of value in motion study, as it does not indicate time intervals. "Before and after" Cyclegraphs of motion study projects often make striking illustrations of the amount of motion reduction in a task which can result from a micromotion study.

Stereo-Chrono-Cyclegraph

If a Stereoscopic camera is used in a similar manner to the still camera in making a Cyclegraph, the picture obtained gives an approximation of the third dimension of the motion path. This is called a Stereo-Cyclegraph. When a plate is exposed throughout the duration of a work cycle with an ordinary still camera and the time elements are simultaneously recorded, the result is called a Chrono-Cyclegraph. If a stereoscopic camera is used in this manner, the result is called a Stereo-Chrono-Cyclegraph.

The time recording feature can be obtained photographically by installing an interrupter in the power circuit which flashes the lights off and on at a uniform rate per second. The photograph will then show a series of time dashes, instead of the continuous path of the regular Cyclegraph or Stereo-Cyclegraph. By counting the dashes, the elapsed time of motions in the cycle can be determined. A further refinement controls the power to the lights in such a manner that their brilliance either builds up gradually to a maximum or decreases to a minimum. This causes the dashes to be pear-shaped, so that they automatically provide an indication of the direction of motion being observed. A rotating disc in front of the camera lens has also been used to provide the flashes of light for timing purposes.

Multiflash Pictures

The multiflash technique, originally developed by Professor Edgerton of the Massachusetts Institute of Technology, employs a stereoscopic movie camera and a light flashed on and off at timed intervals. When these pictures are projected on a screen through a special lens and viewed with special polaroid glasses, a three dimensional picture with the flashes providing the timing is obtained. The authors know of no commercial equipment of this sort available at the present time.

Penetrating Screen

If a motion picture camera containing an electric drive motor that runs the film at a constant speed is utilized, it is possible by a double exposure technique to show motion paths in relation to a dimensionalized cross-sectioning, thus allowing exact linear and speed measurement.

In this process, a sheet of black paper (say 3' x 3') with white lines enclosing squares of convenient size (say 4") is set up in the plane of motions to be studied. A section of film is then exposed with the camera aimed at the squared paper—usually from an approximately perpendicular position. The cross-sectioning will then appear on the film, but the black background will make it possible to see the operation when a subsequent second exposure of the same section of the film is made—the camera being in exactly the same position when making the second exposure. Several such film sections, each with its own screening, can be taken from different directions simultaneously if a complex operation is being analyzed. Obviously, telephoto lenses are also useful for making such films.

Electronic Timers

Modern work study research generally utilizes electronic timing systems, punched card or paper tape or magnetic tape recording methods, unit record equipment (sorters, tabulators, etc.), and electronic computer analysis routines.

For example, the earlier photographic method used for MTM research which employed tedious manual film analysis and laborious hand computation has been virtually replaced by the Electronic Data Collector (EDC) shown in Fig. 16. This equipment was developed and constructed during 1958–61 to greatly accelerate the research program of the MTM Association, principally by Dr. Walton M. Hancock and James A. Foulke at The University of Michigan in cooperation with the Research Committee of the MTM Association. It automatically records on punched paper tape vast amounts of data to a time increment as small as 0.001 TMU, which is one-hundred-millionth of an hour. Various kinds of transducers (see Fig. 17) are used to instrument the workplace for motion sensing and thereby serve as input signal sources. These signals pulse-gate a quartz crystal oscillator, a precision electronic time reference. The timed pulses are totalized on an electronic counter. The counts also are recorded on punched paper tape to provide a permanent record when accompanied by the MTM pattern and photographs of the instrumented workplace. The paper tape is transcribed onto magnetic tape for high speed input to the electronic computer used to analyze the data and produce either conventional print-out or visual plots, which also become part of the permanent record. Not only is this system more accurate than motion picture film analysis, but it also has tremendous speed and vastly greater recording capacity. Another feature is its portability (see Fig. 16) which permits its usage on the factory floor during the industrial phase of MTM research. The EDC has been used in the Learning Curve research and on simo evaluation studies to date.

Fig. 16.   Electronic Data Collector (EDC) used for MTM research.
Courtesy MTM Association for Standards and Research.

To provide an informative record of the remarkable development rate for electronic timers since the first edition of this textbook, this section further elaborates on other well-known systems with notable features. All are basically research equipment, potentially adaptable to industrial usage, with promising prospects for future advances in work measurement. The results reported from usage of many of them already tend to indicate developmental trends in human factors topics such as fatigue measurement, quantification of the physiological cost of human work, sensory and perceptual limits, and psychomotor design criteria. Work measurement analysts anticipate results which will aid their analytical work, provide operator learning data, and unlock the secrets of superior training methods.

The staff of Pennsylvania State University has developed and constructed motion analysis equipment which utilizes limit switches to actuate electronic timing devices. Known as the Electronic Time Detector for Body Motions, it detects the start and finish of broad motions such as Reach or Move by apparently measuring the effect of body capacitance (electrical) of the study operator. Photoelectric devices are used as additional motion detectors. The time events are actually recorded on a moving tape in a manner similar to that described in this chapter for the Kymograph.

At the University of Wisconsin, Karl U. Smith and R. F. Wehrkamp built a timer called the Universal Motion Analyzer. It includes a panel on which are mounted detent knobs, toggle switches, push buttons, pull

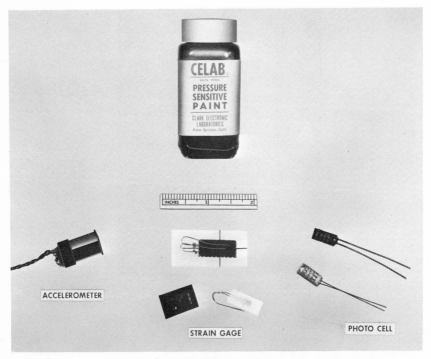

Fig. 17. Typical transducers used to instrument the workplace for research with MTM-EDC.
Courtesy MTM Association for Standards and Research.

latches, squeeze latches, and continuous knobs for dial setting. These objects are used to measure travel time versus manipulation time in a total cycle which includes reaches to and from the panel. It does not isolate individual motion times, but merely divides the total cycle time into the two components. Solenoid clutches controlled by the panel objects actuate electric timing clocks and other recording elements. The final recorder is a sequential interval time recorder devised by Mr. Smith and Gerald Rubin. It consists of 40 pens on four holders which inscribe a fixed speed decoder chart.

Dr. Gerald Nadler and Jay Goldman, while at Washington University in St. Louis, adapted the Doppler principle to human measurement in the UNOPAR—Universal Operator Performance Analyzer and Recorder. One statement of the Doppler principle is that a moving source of sound appears to change pitch as its velocity varies relative to a fixed listening point. When detected this change can be compared to a reference signal and the difference used to generate a signal proportional to the velocity of the sound source. The UNOPAR uses a Lorenz electrostatic speaker which is very small and light to avoid affecting normal operator motions, strapped onto the worker like a wrist watch. The speaker generates an inaudible supersonic signal of 20,000 cycles per second. Monitored by three sensitive microphones oriented to three orthogonal planes at 10-foot spacings from the working area, the signal provides the spatial vector components of the total velocity vector. By electronic processing, the individual vectors and vector sums of velocity, acceleration-deceleration, and displacement position can be generated for recording or plotting. One method of recording is a 3-channel real time magnetic tape which is analyzed in an analog computer. Another method uses a 12-channel oscillographic recorder to produce a record on paper moving at five inches per second. This requires visual interpretation, but it also permits force plotting. UNOPAR location accuracy is within one percent for a time measurement unit of 0.000133 minute.

A different usage of acoustical principles provides the inaudible pulses to operate the ETR—Electronic Time Recorder. This equipment was developed by Elwood S. Buffa at UCLA to measure human motions with 0.0001 second time units. The pulses are triggered by a device created by Christian Rand. This device is acutated when the subject, who is part of the circuit although not electrically connected, contacts sensitive objects on the workplace. After calibration against a 10,000 cycle per second time base oscillator, the pulse signal is electronically processed through five channels. Each channel has five electronic counting tubes and two mechanical counters. The left counter and the tubes show accumulated time up to 2,760 hours, while the right counter records occurrences up to one million. Recording by the observer is visual or photographic. Either travel time or manipulation time may be recorded by toggle switch selection.

A more mechanical approach which offers potential for fatigue measurement as well as indicating force-time relationships, utilizes the Lauru Platform. Lucien Lauru was a Frenchman who devised a rigid triangular platform on which the subject sits or stands while working in an otherwise normal environmental condition. The force reactions at platform suspension points are detected by piezo-electric quartz crystals which generate signals proportional to the pressures in the three component planes. The amplified signals electronically switch timing pulses which are converted to oscilloscopic displays that are photographically recorded by a 5-lens camera. Notable adaptations of the Lauru principles are the following. Lucien Brouha, M.D. has converted the platform signals for stylus pen recording. His work at the Haskell Laboratory of Dupont has yielded much basic physiological data of importance to work measurement. The Department of Anatomy at Oxford University modified the platform to measure the force reactions by strain gages attached to cantilever beams at the pivots. James H. Greene and W. H. M. Morris designed another version of the Lauru force platform at Purdue University. It utilizes linear-variable differential transformers (LVDT) as the pressure sensitive input devices. The LVDT sensing element is comprised of three toroidal coils over a magnetic core driven by the platform movements, with the primary coil being energized by a 2,000 cycles per second oscillator. Processing through a Brush Universal Analyzer converts the LVDT secondary coil responses into a paper tape record traced by pens. This Force Platform is so sensitive that it records the forces of the human heartbeat even when the subject is at rest.

The final example of electronic timers is the SEMTAR—for Sequential Electronic Motion Timer and Recorder. Developed by Dr. Stanley M. Block at the University of Minnesota, it uses transducer inputs in a manner similar to the MTM-EDC timer, although the electronic signal processing is different. Six or more transducer (photoelectric cell, microswitch, contact plates, etc.) inputs are recorded on 5- or 7-channel punched paper tape at 3,600 characters per minute. A master clock which operates electronically at chosen rates of 100, 500, or 1000 cycles per second gates the inputs to decade counters. This arrangement permits concurrent recording of both single-handed and simultaneous motions to an accuracy of 0.001 second or less. Dr. Block has used SEMTAR for cooperative MTM research, notably in evaluating simo and blind Grasps.

General Comments

Most of the devices just discussed, with the exception of the ordinary 16 mm motion picture camera equipment and the memo-motion equipment, can be classed as research equipment. They are not found in the ordinary industrial engineering or time and motion study departments. Even the exceptions stated come very close to being classed as research equipment insofar as industrial work study is concerned.

COMBINING MTM AND TIME STUDY

It would be inappropriate to leave the subject of analysis techniques without discussing MTM versus time study. The work measurement engineer is often required to make a choice between these two techniques.

Some of the more prevalent work study situations encountered in industry will be explored by first delineating the problem and then giving the more important reasons why time study and/or MTM should or can be used. In some cases there is little technical choice between them. Occasionally, entirely non-technical considerations—such as union attitudes—may force the choice of one or the other.

Recall that technical and non-technical considerations, with their advantages and disadvantages, have been discussed at various places in this text regarding both time study and MTM approaches to work study problems. The following discussion will merely review many of the previously stated considerations in a relatively organized manner and will be confined more to the technical, rather than the non-technical, aspects of the delineated work study problems. Direct answers to many problems of choosing the study technique will be provided. In addition, a review of this section can help the reader in deciding how to solve problems not listed here.

Operator Not Meeting Standards

The existing condition is that the operation has been processed, the standard set, etc., but the operator claims inability to meet the standards. The problem facing the engineer is to determine whether the standard is wrong for the process or if the operator is failing because of inherent poor ability, not following the process, deliberate malingering, or insufficient training and/or practice. Time study is the most commonly used technique in such situations, regardless of whether MTM or time study was used to set the standards. A time study will first be made to check the actual versus standard time. MTM training will then help the engineer most in reconciling any lack of agreement in the two times. The real questions to be answered in such cases are:

1. Is the specified method being followed? Are ineffective motions being substituted?
2. Have conditions changed? Are the method motions different to compensate for this?
3. Is the operator reasonably well trained? Was the method otherwise well instituted?
4. Is the operator working with average skill and effort? Does his rating correct the actual time back to standard?

5. Is the operator deliberately trying to avoid meeting the standard? Does notable lack of consistency in the stop watch readings point to malingering?

6. Is the standard satisfactory? Does obvious confirmation of the standard time show the problem to be non-technical instead?

Items 1, 2, and 3 can probably be answered best by MTM; however, time study could be used. Time study yields better answers in less time to the other questions. The clue as to which technique to use first is the fact that the watch readings provide a quick indication of whether further technical study is justified. Items 4 and 5 especially almost demand usage of the time study technique first. Lack of consistency in performance for each element would raise the suspicion that the operator is deliberately trying to fail. Consistency of poor performance, on the other hand, would indicate a lack of ability or insufficient practice; the supervisor could help in determining which of these is involved. If the definite cause still cannot be found a detailed MTM study should be made.

Both time study and MTM can serve to check the standard in this manner. However, MTM will provide the most accurate check for the manual parts of the process, while time study is essential to checking the accuracy of process times and it also provides quickest the first clues as to the proper course of action in resolving the operator's complaint.

If the task must be reprocessed and/or a new standard established, all of the previously mentioned factors regarding MTM and time study must be considered in making the choice between MTM or time study.

Low Volume, Non-Repetitive, Low Manual Labor Content Operations

Examples of this situation would be the operation of mills, lathes, etc., in a toolroom, maintenance shop, etc. What technique should be used to set the standard? How can measurement of such work be economical?

The technique to use is not clear. Time study is the usual approach; however, this means the job must be running. This, in itself, is not a major hindrance in many such cases, since time study of the machine time would be required even if MTM were used. The engineer would then, of necessity, be present during the performance of the manual operations anyway and could just as well use time study.

As the manual work content increases, the choice of MTM becomes more important. Also, a more important consideration then is the possibility and need for standard data, where MTM gains the advantage for reasons stated elsewhere in this text. Some firms have solved this problem by using MTM almost exclusively to build standard data and/or time formulas.

Actually, for the situation originally stated, the combined approach of MTM and time study will often prove most fruitful. Standard data, either by element or by task, can be developed to provide time standards for later recurrences of operations of this type. It must be recognized, because of the non-repetitive factor, that the expense of obtaining extreme accuracy with either technique is not warranted since a good approximation is sufficient. The best approach, therefore, seems to be estimation of the manual portions by simplified versions of MTM data and rough indications of the process times by stop watch checks of the few cyclical occurrences in which they appear. After such analysis on several occasions, reasonably useful standard data could be compiled.

High Volume, High Manual Labor Content Operations

Examples of this situation are: assembly operations, certain test operations, riveting operations, etc. Which technique should be used? How can they be combined?

Normally, MTM with time study of process times is the best over-all choice because:

1. The correct method can be established before starting the job. The process times can be recognized and determined by time study after the job is running.
2. The best technique for improving and/or establishing the method is MTM, while time study can provide over-all time checks to assure that no pertinent factors were overlooked.
3. MTM provides a sound labor standard, provided time study is integrated with it where appropriate.

Exceptions can always be found. For example, if engineering time is limited, an immediate standard is needed, and training time is virtually non-existent, then time study of a few cycles would generally provide a quite satisfactory temporary answer. This answer could then be improved later, when analysis time is available, by utilizing the approach indicated above that relies mostly on MTM procedure. This combined approach provides better processes, more accurate labor standards, helps in training the operator, and yields standard data with least over-all effort. Normally, more analysis time becomes available after an operation has run sufficiently long to be "debugged." Using the latter approach, the standard will also be more accurate.

High Volume, Low Manual Labor Content Operations

Examples of this situation are: rolling mill operations, automated machine tending, etc. Again, the question involves how to combine the two techniques in setting a labor standard, although main reliance here should be on time study.

Time study would definitely be needed to determine the machine time, which would be a high proportion of the total time. In the rather extreme examples mentioned, the manual labor content probably would have minimal effect on the standard. Time study would probably be combined with a ratio delay study on the two examples in order to determine delay time, adjustment time, set up frequency, etc.

However, MTM often can be very useful in answering such questions as how many stations one operator can adequately tend if the final answer, based on the time study data, is not certain. After time study discloses the over-all cycle time and/or the limiting time at each station, the motions needed by the operator at that station can be analyzed with MTM. An attempt to reconcile and balance this operator time against the limiting time at one or more stations can lead to greatly increased efficiency and better labor utilization. It is even possible to justify extensive mechanization of operations by this combined procedure.

High Volume, Intermediate Manual Labor Content Operations

When to use each technique in these situations cannot be clearly delineated. MTM loses some of its advantage as the manual work content of an operation decreases. However, any manual work in a high volume operation is worth evaluating; and if the manual work is at all complex, then MTM probably should be used to help set the method and standard on that portion of the work.

Related to this problem are such factors as whether the job is already running with an apparently satisfactory method. If so, then time study would appear to be a logical choice. If it were a new job, then it would appear to sway the decision to MTM.

The possibility of standard data development also enters. Standard data on manual work can normally be obtained more quickly and precisely with MTM, hence the amount and degree of complexity of the manual work guides the choice. Each situation merits individual evaluation.

Low Volume, Non-Repetitive, High Manual Labor Content Operations

Examples of this problem would be the assembly of small lots of special machines, jigs, equipment, etc. The following are possible considerations when deciding which technique to use:

1. If the work has not been started, and similar assemblies have not previously been produced, MTM is the only analytically sound procedure by which to establish any desired detailed methods and work standards prior to production.

2. If work has been started, and the task is relatively simple, it will obviously be faster and less expensive to use time study to establish a fairly accurate standard. It will also provide generally adequate information in these situations to aid sound methods improvement.

3. If the task is such that many elements will repeat on future assembly operations (such as fit 1-inch face, 20-tooth gear on shaft; position ¼–20 screw in hole, etc.), then MTM is by far the best technique since a simple analysis of one such element will provide accurate standard data for future occurrences of the element.

Summary of MTM Versus Time Study

It is evident that almost every work measurement situation encountered merits individual consideration in selecting the way to use MTM and time study. The advantages and disadvantages of each must be weighed in the decision.

MTM can claim the following major advantages:

1. Yields good labor standards with no necessity to view the actual operation.
2. Makes possible the establishment of good methods prior to the start of an operation and thereby cuts training time, yields minimum manufacturing cost, uses less over-all engineering time, etc.
3. Provides a scientific and practical tool for methods improvement of manual operations.
4. Provides valid data for standard data and/or time formulas from even one properly written motion pattern.

Time study has the following advantages:

1. When the job is running, it will provide the quickest labor standard. If standard data is not being developed, it will produce the standard at the lowest over-all cost.
2. It is a technique more universally recognized and understood by all concerned parties.
3. It provides the best data for analyzing operator performance levels.

Using these points as guides, it is possible to analyze most work study situations to arrive at a solution as to which technique to use. Remember, the real problem is not whether to use MTM *or* time study, but rather *when* and *how* to use *both*.

CHAPTER 23

Allowances and Variance Factors— Adjustment of Standards

It is the purpose of this chapter to clearly explain the relation of allowances and variance factors to time study and/or MTM work measurement standards. The subject of allowances and variance factors highlights the integral relationship between industrial engineering and management. This is because their specification and usage must definitely result from close cooperation and mutual understanding. The intimate connections between work measurement, the resulting labor time standards, the associated labor cost standards, and the reported actual production time and cost all have an important influence on the success of the enterprise. In fact, discriminating attention to allowances and variance factors is essential to achieving scientific management.

Unfortunately, the common usage of the phrase "allowances and variances" in both industrial engineering and cost accounting work has led to considerable confusion in the exact meaning of a labor standard. Some of the confusion is due to the use of the term "variance" in the cost accounting sense rather than with the accepted statistical meaning of "mean standard deviation." Also, the context and content of a labor standard differs depending on whether it is applied to operator performance, the labor cost of a production item, the labor estimate for pricing a new product, etc. The best way of solving this semantics problem is to carefully delineate the factual and procedural bases for the adjustment of work measurement standards to meet management requirements. However, this chapter will not attempt to give fixed answers or to identify every allowance and variance factor which could be encountered, but instead it will describe the more common instances in sufficient detail to enable the reader to make intelligent choices in their application.

Both scientific procedures and experience factors play important roles in determining which allowances and variance factors are to be recognized, identifying their causes and ways they can be controlled, obtaining their magnitude, and deciding where they should be placed in the standards structure. Managers seek guidance in these matters from the results of industrial engineering studies. The practices in this area vary with the management, the firm or company, the industry, and even the contractual relationships with labor. Specifying allowances and variance factors is at least as much an art as it is a science. However, no company can afford to neglect this chore just because it is difficult or because unanimity is impossible with the present knowledge about it.

To begin the explanation, consider what is included in the select or normal time obtained from either an MTM analysis or a time study. For purposes of discussing allowances and variance factors, this time may be considered as the *base standard*. The base standard is determined as outlined by Time Study Steps 1 through 8 in Chapter 21, or by completion of an MTM pattern as described in Chapter 19. It covers the performance-rated time required to accomplish all of the operational, task, and motion elements which have been included in the basis. To meet such a standard, the average operator would have to work continuously with average skill and effort under average conditions using the method specified in the base standard.

Now, any reason which justifiably prevents such ideal performance is a cause for adjusting the base standard toward a more realistic figure. The mechanism of adjustment is to increase the base standard either by adding a predictable or measurable time increment or, as is more common, by multiplying the base standard by a percentage factor which compensates for the additional time required by the justifiable cause. Such time or percentage adjustments are called *allowances*. Since these must be determined by engineering analysis, an allowance is basically an engineering device—the industrial engineer's "factor of safety" in methods design. Note in passing, however, that some of the causes for which increased time must fairly be allowed as designated by Steps 9 and 10 of the Time Study procedure in Chapter 21 would be best recognized by including their effects as elements in the base standard. When allowances have been applied to the base standard, the resulting figure is called the *allowed time* or *allowed standard*. In essence, this is the actual clock time an engineer would expect the average operator to require for the performance of each working cycle, if the total clock time spent on the work covered by the standard during a working day was divided by the number of cycles (units of production) completed during that day.

The allowances normally included by most analysts, with the approval of their managers, in the allowed time are (1) personal, (2) fatigue, and (3) minor unavoidable delay. In fact, this practice accords with the official

industrial engineering terminology definition. While each of these is discussed separately later, they are collectively called P, F, & D allowances.
In the ordinary situation, the total P, F, & D allowance ranges from 10 to
15 per cent or more. Many engineers and managers believe this is the point
at which to stop time adjustments for ordinary manual work situations.
While it is generally desirable to minimize the number of adjustments
applied to base standards, the actual conditions met in industrial situations
frequently do not permit such ideal procedure.

It is a widely accepted practice to exhibit the base standard (in time
and as a piece rate), the time or percentage allowance(s), and the allowed
standard (in time and as a piece rate) on the process or method description
sheet, which may or may not be placed in front of the operator. The authors
suggest that human relations purposes are best served by showing these
figures on the process sheet and by placing the sheet in front of the operator.

Consider next the subject of variance. *Variance* may be defined as the
difference between the actual performance time and the allowed standard.
Variance is basically a cost accounting concept which usually engages, with
obvious merit, the close attention of enlightened managers. In seeking to
control and reduce the amount of variance, they are taking the most constructive action possible in a standards program. Only when the variance
is zero has the allowed standard been achieved. Actually, some degree of
variance is unavoidable. Several alternatives are open to management in
evaluating and minimizing such variance.

One procedure is to isolate *all* identifiable causes of variance and then
apply appropriate adjustment factors (NOTE: It is *not* correct to call these
allowances, they are variance factors) against the allowed standard to cover
these causes. If all of the causes are associated with the operator, this might
be a feasible action. However, the causes frequently involve the work of
other persons whose actions affect the time required by the operator. Also,
it is usually impractical to isolate *all* of the causes of variance due to the
cost of measurement alone. Therefore, this strategy will work at best for
only part of the total variance.

A second approach is to go to the opposite extreme. This is to merely
use the allowed time as the total cost standard with no attempt to account
for the variance except when it is demanded on specific occasions. A certain
amount of effort can be avoided in this manner if no one demands explanation of the variance or if the variance is fortuitously low. On the occasions
when explanations are required, however, there will be maximum difficulty
in both isolating and quantifying the causes of the total variance. Usually
such occasions do not permit sufficient time for proper analysis of the
variance. In addition, this procedure violates good control principles and
could even be dismissed on the grounds that it is a shirking of management
responsibilities.

A more reasonable method of accounting for variance actually is a synthesis of these first two alternatives. That is, those variance causes amenable to analysis are examined to determine their nature, the probability of their occurrence and means of their routine control, and the magnitude of the adjustment factors which they justify. Normally, such adjustment factors are additive to provide a total multiplier—usually expressed as a percentage—or total time increment which is applied to the allowed time standard. After this partial (or designated) variance figure is obtained and added to the allowed time, thereby giving the *routed time* or *routed standard* shown as the final figure on the cost routing sheet, the remaining difference between the actual performance time and the routed time is considered as undesignated variance. This residual variance represents deviations in performance not normally or regularly encountered. As compared to the second approach above, it is smaller in magnitude and therefore more easily analysed to isolate occasional or special causes which must be explained on demand. Often it represents potential savings in productive operations. However, the designated variance factors should not be neglected as a source of savings; since new knowledge or technology often can be applied to reduce designated variance too.

Another way to think of allowances and variance factors is to consider allowances as operator time adjustments and variance factors as management or cost accounting time adjustments. In either case, the signal for corrective action is the routine efficiency report based on the process or cost routing. The two principal efficiency figures usually reported to managers and supervisors are:

1. *Operator Efficiency.* This may be reported for an entire division, department, assembly line, etc. without isolating the individual performance, or it can be developed for individual operators. It is the percentage ratio of the allowed time standard to the actual operator(s) production time:

$$\text{Operator Efficiency, } \% = \frac{\text{Allowed Standard}}{\text{Actual Operator(s) Time}} \times 100$$

2. *Total Efficiency.* This may be reported for the routed time of each process or part number or it may be generated for all the production covered by the cost routings in a division, department, etc. It is the percentage ratio of the routed time standard to the actual production time:

$$\text{Total Efficiency, } \% = \frac{\text{Routed Standard}}{\text{Actual Time}} \times 100$$

The remainder of this chapter discusses separately the most often recognized allowances and variance factors. Others are possible, however, and it is always a management function to approve their isolation and inclusion in the standard cost system.

PERSONAL TIME

Personal time is an allowance to cover the time required by such personal needs of the operator as going to the drinking fountain, trips to the rest room, etc. It is obvious that the operator cannot work throughout the day without absence from the workplace for short periods of time because of personal needs. The actual time required will vary with the workload, sex, age, temperature, humidity, etc. The amount of personal allowance is sometimes written into negotiated union contracts.

Personal allowances normally vary between 2 and 5 per cent of the base or select time standard. The amount of time required for personal needs can be determined by all-day time studies or by work sampling procedures (often called Ratio-Delay Study) covered in Chapter 24.

The industrial engineer starting to work in an established plant will normally find that the personal allowance has already been determined and need not again be established. Once established, it is almost always used as a matter of uniform plant policy for all work measurement studies.

FATIGUE TIME

The basic idea behind a fatigue allowance is that the slower pace at which an operator works towards the end of his shift is due to fatigue. When such an allowance is given, it tacitly concedes (some engineers are not aware of this) that this pace reduction cannot be properly taken into account when rating operator performance.

Many researchers have investigated fatigue and entire books have been written on the subject. Therefore, it is unfortunate that there is no unanimity of opinion concerning what, if any, allowance should be given to the operator to cover fatigue recovery time. Perhaps this is because the problem is basically medical and physiological in nature, and the necessary interdisciplinary attack upon it has only recently developed. One of the more promising sustained investigations aimed at quantitative evaluation of fatigue recovery time is that of Lucien Brouha, M.D. at the Haskell Laboratory of E. I. duPont de Nemours & Co. Many of the concepts in the following discussion are based on his book[1] and his speeches which have been heard by the authors.

[1] *Physiology in Industry*, by Lucien Brouha, M.D., D.Sc., Pergamon Press, New York City, 1960.

Perhaps the basic major cause of fatigue is the muscular effort required of the worker. However, another major contributor is "nervous tension" which induces fatigue by increasing the physiological load the worker must sustain. In Dr. Brouha's words: "There's no simple definition for fatigue. Some call it a negative appetite for activity—and usually for the activity that caused the fatigue." Such tension may be caused by the working pace, excessive noise, jarring or distracting vibration, rapidly alternating changes in the direction of motion, frequent interruptions, the need to concentrate on the object of attention or on the surroundings, physical or electrical or chemical dangers, the need to work safely and to maintain the safety of one's coworkers, etc. Such physiological, perceptual, and psychological loading needs to be evaluated for a practical measure of fatigue to be developed.

A number of parameters related to the degree of work intensity have been investigated by many researchers recently. An example is given in Table 1, which is Dr. Brouha's summary of data for oxygen consumption, energy expenditure (heat rate), and heart rate levels associated with various working intensities. However, any practical method of evaluating the physiological cost of work must be suited to easy floor study of the worker and his actual tasks. It cannot include the operation of complicated laboratory paraphernalia or the need for costly evaluation of the results such equipment may register. By these criteria, oxygen consumption and heat rate measurements appear to be more useful for methods laboratory usage in the design of workplaces, working tools, and motion patterns rather than for practical floor studies of worker capacity.

Table I. Workload Classification in Terms of Physiological Reactions
(Data from Dr. Brouha)

Workload Classification	Oxygen Consumption, liters per minute	Energy Expenditure, kilocalories per minute	Heart Rate during Work, beats per minute
Light	0.5 to 1.0	2.5 to 5.0	60 to 100
Moderate	1.0 to 1.5	5.0 to 7.5	100 to 125
Heavy	1.5 to 2.0	7.5 to 10.0	125 to 150
Very Heavy	2.0 to 2.5	10.0 to 12.5	150 to 175

Heart rate evaluation, however, may well prove to be the desired practical measurement tool. It requires only a timing device and counting, both of which are ordinary adjuncts of the work analyst. In fact, light telemetering equipment already is available to facilitate automatic recording of the heart rate during *both* working and resting periods. In the medical sense, heart rate is a measure of the cardiovascular reaction to physiological stress. It also correlates well with oxygen consumption and heat rate. Dr. Brouha summarizes this crucial point as follows: ". . . two of the main factors which determine the physiological adaptation to muscular activity are work load and heat load. At rather low levels of energy expenditure, the heart reactions are determined by the nature of the operation, its speed, its duration, and the environmental conditions. Jobs involving heavy labor, heat exposure, or a combination of the two, place a greater stress upon the worker. This stress is reflected by high cardiac reactions and a tendency to reach faster heart rates after successive work cycles, indicating that the recovery processes become less efficient as the shift progresses. . . . Thus, the pulse rate curve can be used as an index of the stress imposed upon the worker by his activity and the environment in which he performs it." Since it is relatively easy to employ the heart rate without restricting the worker's effort or motions and without imposing other restraints on his mobility, this measure offers much promise as a means of designing tasks for reasonable physiological cost and of evaluating fatigue levels.

Dr. Brouha and associates at the Harvard Fatigue Laboratory developed a method of assessing the stress level attained during work by measuring the pulse rate while the worker is recovering from the working energy expenditure. They constructed heart rate recovery curves by determining the pulse rate at intervals of 0.5 to 1.0, 1.5 to 2.0, and 2.5 to 3.0 minutes following the cessation of work effort. Typical curves of this type, arranged to show the effects of working intensity and environment are shown in Figure 1. The behavior of the pulse rate as it approaches the worker's resting level has been shown to be a fairly reliable predictor of fatigue, which

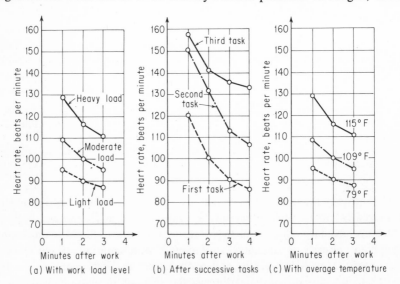

Fig. 1. Typical variation of heart rate recovery curves with working environmental factors (adapted from Brouha).

gives a clue as to whether the worker has been asked to perform a fair task and how much recovery time he needs to sustain the working level. These points are clearly indicated in the three parts of Fig. 1, as follows:

(1a) The heart rate recovery curve indicates the rapidity with which the pulse speed returns to its resting level. As the workload increases, the heart rate at the start of recovery is progressively higher and the total recovery time to the resting level also greatly increases.

(1b) The onset of fatigue can be predicted from the heart rate recovery curves. This is shown when satisfactory degrees of recovery are not attained between a series of successive work cycles or between a series of new tasks. The general behavior of the curves is similar to that described for the previous case. However, a noteworthy point arises here. It is not generally feasible economically to permit sufficient times throughout the working day for *complete* recovery before working periods are resumed. The resulting sustained effort does necessarily involve a progressive increase in the physiological cost to the worker. Therefore, a balance point between the physiological and economic factors should be sought. One way to minimize the source of such fatigue is to alternate light and heavy tasks. Another is to reduce the total fatigue potential during the day by careful scheduling of breaks for rest, lunch, etc.

(1c) The pulse recovery rate also can be used to evaluate the influence of environmental factors such as temperature, humidity, ventilation, etc. Here the effect of increasing average temperature on stress or fatigue is apparent. Again, the general behavior matches that described for the first case in Figure 1b. Regarding temperature and recovery, Dr. Brouha showed that recovery from fatigue is much more efficient in a special room with controlled temperature and humidity as opposed to resting for an equal time in the workplace area.

For the work analyst, the most vital question is the average heart rate at which a worker may be expected to maintain a healthy performance throughout the working day. This would give a measure of the "fair day's work" in physiological terms. Here appears a fortunate agreement between Dr. Brouha's data and the research of Charles Miller, M.D. and Mr. Harry L. Davis at the Human Factors Laboratory of Eastman Kodak Company. The latter research has been developing physiological data *during the working period* itself with the telemetering equipment previously mentioned. It has shown in actual industrial operations that no undue physiological penalty to the worker is incurred if the pulse level during working periods does not *consistently* exceed 110 to 120 beats per minute. Tasks designed to stay within 110 beats per minute average level therefore are within the "fair day's work" range. Also, the worker's complete overnight recovery from fatigue on such tasks is to be expected provided he is physically qualified for this level of work intensity. To summarize the concurring data of Dr. Brouha, he states from long experience that a safe stress level throughout the working shift is sustained, provided the sequence of working and resting periods is properly arranged, if his heart rate recovery method shows the first recorded pulse rate to be 110 beats per minute or less and the third recorded pulse rate is at least 10 beats per minute lower.

The principal conclusion from the discussion is that industrial tasks should be designed to safeguard the worker's health if meaningful work measurement is to be attained. Also, fatigue causes should be reduced where possible instead of relying upon allowances in the time standard and rest period variance factors to overcome the problem of fatigue.

All of this interesting information does provide some work design guidelines for evaluating and eliminating fatigue. However, it has not yet provided practical procedures by which the industrial engineer can establish fatigue allowances. At present, the rather vague traditional methods must serve until the continuing research of these investigators and others is translated into practical work measurement data.

The change in pace from the start to the end of a shift is more noticeable on individual operations than where a progressive assembly line is involved. On a progressive assembly line, it is not normal to change the pace during the day to compensate for fatigue. The conveyors run at the same speed or the timing bells ring at the same intervals throughout the day. The line pace or operation standard, however, normally includes a fatigue allowance. It is, therefore, reasonable to ask—if it is not necessary to vary the pace in a progressive assembly line, whether operating on standards containing such an allowance or not, why should a fatigue allowance be given on either progressive assembly operations or individual operations?

The answer to this question involves historical industrial practices. Recall that time study started early in the 20th century. In prior years, the physical exertion of the operator was considerable. In addition the plant surroundings were anything but uplifting. Hence, in the early days of time study when fatigue was a greater problem, the idea that a fatigue allowance was required became firmly established.

Today the opposite is true. Material handling devices to relieve the operator are found in almost every situation; plants are normally well painted, well ventilated, etc.; and every effort has been made by the manufacturing organization to install as many labor-saving devices as possible. Experience has proved the worth of such actions. Fatigue, therefore, is actually not as important a factor in the normal situation today as it was in the early days of time study, even though many plants are still using the allowance established many years ago.

While fatigue allowances may be much less important in the ordinary plant than in the early days of work measurement, the authors acknowledge that they are required under certain conditions. Also, *if* true rating is applied to the work of an *unfatigued* operator, then fatigue allowances may be valid.

Most industrial organizations have, over a period of time, determined for their operation the amount of allowance to be given to compensate for fatigue. Such allowances are usually based on some study, some experience factors, and probably some emotional concepts regarding fatigue. Union negotiations are also involved in their establishment, especially when variable fatigue allowances are used.

A fatigue allowance normally varies from 5 to 10 per cent, although some manual operations may actually require a considerably larger allowance. In some plants, the magnitude of fatigue allowances has been specifically identified in union contracts. In others, they have been standardized for various plant situations and the labor force is usually quite aware of their amount and would object strenuously if they were not included in the allowed standard. There are also plants where the amount of fatigue allowance is determined solely by the time study man; however, these latter situations are becoming rather rare.

Many plants have organized rest periods, during which time no employees in a department or in the whole plant are required to work and in most are not even permitted to work. It is common today to find such plant-wide rest periods, one in the morning and one in the afternoon. Both can be of the same duration or they may be unlike in period of time. The ordinary length of these periods varies form 5 to 15 minutes each.

If a plant has some exceptionally fatiguing operations, such as are found in a forge shop, the rest periods for such operations or for such departments usually vary from those found in the general plant so that the persons working on such operations have more frequent rest periods. Such rest periods in the usual plant situation have been established without concurrently bringing about a revision of the fatigue allowance.

In plants with no wage incentive plan, it is common practice to pay for the rest periods at the employee's regular hourly base rate. The situation in incentive plants is somewhat variable. In plants where the fatigue allowance has been incorporated in the time standard, the employees are sometimes not paid for the rest periods as such and the worker merely takes his fatigue allowance during the rest period rather than at intervals during the day.

REST PERIODS

When the morning and afternoon rest periods mentioned under the topic of fatigue time are covered by a separate time calculation, it is normally known as a rest period variance factor. It will be necessary to account for such time in any work measurement system. Since work activity ceases entirely during rest periods, the allowed time standards are not operative or do not apply during that span of time. Therefore a realistic cost standard requires a rest period variance factor. The commonly heard expression "rest period allowance" is therefore a misnomer and should be discontinued. Many analysts consider the rest period to partially cover some of the required personal and fatigue recovery time. For this reason, they may reduce the personal and fatigue portions of the P, F, & D allowances below the values they would otherwise assign when not using a rest period variance factor.

DELAY TIME

There are two basic kinds of delays, avoidable delays and unavoidable delays. The unavoidable delays can be subdivided into minor unavoidable delays and major unavoidable delays, the latter frequently being called "management" delays.

Delays that the operator makes or intentionally causes are classed as avoidable and should not be considered in determining the time standard for an operation. If such delays occur during a time study, they are identified as foreign elements and are eliminated from the study insofar as their effect on the time standard is concerned.

Other delays are often beyond the control of the operator. Assuming that the operator runs a machine, it is logical and obvious that the machine will not work forever without requiring attention. Motors burn out, clutches and parts wear out, etc. Also, the operator need not be working on a machine to experience unavoidable delays. Stock handlers can forget to keep a supply of parts available to an assembly operator. A fuse can burn out and cause the lights to go off, etc. Such delays not caused by the operator are known as unavoidable delays.

Unavoidable delay time can vary greatly both as to its ease of prediction and its amount. This is the main reason most standards systems separately identify and report such time as either major or minor. Major delays are characterized by their relatively long duration for a single operator or their effect on a large number of operators for shorter periods. They represent distinct, easily recognized events which result in the need for immediate management action to avoid sizable monetary losses. If the event cripples the plant, e.g. a major power failure, or is catastrophic in nature, the working force may be sent home for the remainder of the day. In this case, costs are still incurred due to idle time while investment and other costs continue to be charged or due to the loss of production which prevents shipments, etc. Of course, even a minor power failure caused by a blown fuse or tripped circuit breaker can idle many workers and on this basis be classified as a major delay. Here the remedy is relatively simple. The working force is retained on standby while the cause of delay is corrected. Nevertheless, the extra operating cost incurred to pay the idled workers must be covered in the cost standards. Such *major unavoidable delay* costs normally are included in the cost standard by using a *variance factor* to modify the *routed time* standard. On the other hand, minor delays are relatively short in duration, affect only one or a few operators, have a very short correction time, do not usually require corrective management action, etc. But they do cost something which generally can be charged off to the individual operator or task. Therefore, such *minor unavoidable delay* costs normally are covered by using an *allowance* (part of the P, F, & D allowance) to modify the *allowed time* standard.

Most plants with an established work measurement program in effect have determined the amount of minor unavoidable delay allowance required for the typical jobs in the plant covered by the program. This will simplify the task of the industrial engineer, whether he is applying MTM or time study. Minor unavoidable delay allowances are required for standards based on either type of study. Also, based on industrial engineering and cost accounting studies, the variance factor for major unavoidable delays may be an established figure. However, the magnitude of this variance factor is subject to periodic review and determination of a new value for a contract, bid, or fiscal period.

If minor unavoidable delay allowances have already been established for typical jobs, it is still necessary for the industrial engineer to analyze each given situation to determine whether the standard allowance will apply. When a new piece of machinery is installed it may require a greater or lesser allowance, depending on the type of machine, the complexity of the operation, etc.

For example, a machine delay allowance of 3 per cent might be adequate for the ordinary situation; but one firm found that five operators tending an automated line required a greater allowance of 13 per cent because of greater chance for the more complex machine to break down.

Delay allowances and variance factors can be determined by a series of all-day time studies or by means of a work sampling (ratio-delay) study. It is more common today to use the ratio-delay method since all-day time studies are quite expensive to take and yield results not appreciably more accurate.

TOOL HANDLING

Rather than attempting to establish directly the amount of time required by the operator in a given operation to keep on hand a supply of sharpened tool bits, screw drivers in good repair, wire cutters that are sharp and operate well, etc., some plants endeavor to cover what they call tool handling or tool maintenance.

Some time is undoubtedly required to take care of this situation in many plants. Two approaches can be used to solve this problem. One is to establish precisely in the standard for each job the amount of time spent on these tasks and include it directly; or else, the time required can be estimated or in some other manner approximately determined to permit coverage as an allowance.

Where the allowance procedure is used, it will be found, in some cases, to be an educated guess or estimate; in others, it has been established in a practical manner by all-day time studies and/or ratio-delay studies.

SETUP TIME

Another time adjustment commonly made to the working standard is setup time. This is particularly appropriate where the operator changes tasks frequently and must rearrange his own workplace, tools, and materials. It also may arise when the operator incurs short waits while a setup man adjusts the operator's tools or machine(s) for a new task, for maintenance purposes, or to check their operating condition. Unless such time is included as a working element in the base standard, it is usually a stated allowance in the allowed time standard.

The time of the setup man, however, may be apportioned to the routed time for all processes or affected part numbers to give a truer cost standard. In this case, the setup time becomes a variance factor instead of an allowance. Sometimes setup time is treated both ways for the same cost routing to reflect both the time of the setup man and the time the machine operator must wait while the setup work is in progress. That is, the operator's time is covered by an allowance and the setup man's time by a variance factor in the costing for affected part numbers or processes.

CLEANUP TIME

It is a common practice in many plants for the operators to clean up their machines at the end of each shift. Normal procedure is to determine for each department the amount of time required for an operator to perform this task for the kinds of machines found in that department. The operators are then expected to stop productive work near the end of the shift to clean up their equipment. One way of compensating for this time is to introduce a variance factor for cleanup into the cost standard. For example, in a plant which works 460 minutes daily (480 minutes less 20 minutes rest period) and permits 4.6 minutes cleanup time, the allowance would be 1 per cent. In other cases, workers are responsible for cleaning or lubricating their equipment periodically. Such time may be covered as a non-cyclic element in the work standard or included as a special allowance in the basic or allowed standard.

MISCELLANEOUS MATERIAL HANDLING

This type of allowance or variance factor is normally encountered in plants utilizing standard data or its equivalent and where many operations of like nature are found.

The normal procedure is to process the job work elements, establish the time required for each element by referring back to standard data (if the element consists of manual motions this could be accomplished by using MTM), and then account for any material handling such as filling of material trays, disposing of boxes or pans full of finished parts, etc., by adding a direct time element or an allowance to cover the material handling. This is called material handling allowance or variance factor and, similar to others, could be determined for the average situation by means of all-day time studies and/or ratio-delay studies.

If the material handling is performed by a material handler instead of the operator, it is still often desirable to apportion the material handling cost to each operation, part, and/or assembly. This is done on the cost routing by the application of a variance factor against the allowed time with rest period; but this data is not given to the production operator, since it does not affect him.

INITIAL TRAINING

New parts being introduced into an assembly or a machining department will generally present new work elements to the operator. The operator cannot achieve full-speed production until he has performed the new sequence of work elements a sufficient number of times for the work to become automatic—requiring no apparent conscious thought as to the order of elements and exactly what must be done in each work element. This effect is greater in the assembly of such more complex apparatus as found in the radio and television industry than in most machine shop activities.

Many industries, universities, and independent physiologists have studied learning patterns and habits. They typically have developed learning curves which must be adapted to meet the requirements of standards work in the form of efficiency curves or training curves. A case in point is the MTM Learning Curve project described in Chapter 20. It does provide a means whereby the learning and the associated costs can be predicted—a unique and new situation in work measurement. Its continuation promises to yield practical procedures by which initial training variance factors can be easily established in industrial operations.

Most researchers generally agree that there is a very rapid rise in performance (reduction in cycle time) at the start of learning a new operation and that the rate of rise gradually tapers off as the number of cycles (units produced) increases. Figure 2 shows a typical efficiency curve. Some

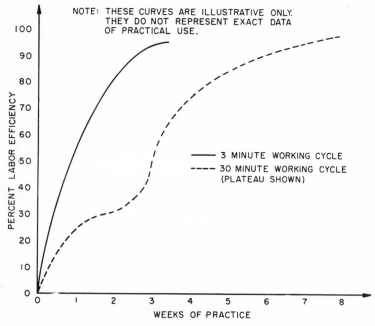

Fig. 2.   Typical efficiency curve for trainee on progressive assembly line.

researchers say this curve will exhibit one or more "plateaus of learning," such as is illustrated by the dotted curve in Fig. 2. The authors have observed both situations in actual practice, although the reasons for the plateau behavior were not clear and could not be determined.

The so-called learning or initial training variance factor is important to the plant or industrial engineering function that must estimate the cost of a limited run on a new product prior to actually putting it into production. Such plants, over a period of years, develop so-called training curves for various kinds of work situations and use these to determine the required initial training factor.   These curves are considered to be confidential company data and are protected from disclosure to competitive industries. They may be a series of curves for varying work cycles with the learning time shown in days on the abscissa plotted against operator efficiency on the ordinate, as is illustrated by Fig. 2.   Another approach is to develop a curve showing units lost on the ordinate versus the length of work cycle shown on the abscissa.   Still another approach, illustrated in Fig. 3, portrays total days operator training time as it varies with the length of the work cycle.   There are many variations from these and the decision on which system to use is usually based on very practical considerations as found in the concerned industry.

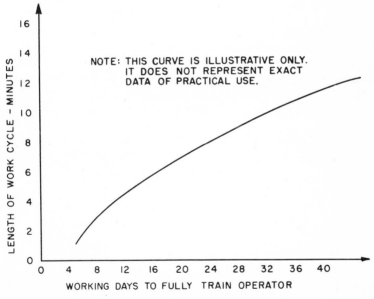

Fig. 3.   Typical training curve for trainee on progressive assembly line.

The initial training variance factor may be introduced into the work measurement as a daily or weekly adjustment, or it may be used merely to adjust the base standard for costing purposes.   In some plants, it is never reflected in either the labor standard or the basic standard cost of a part. This usually occurs in plants having relatively the same class of work as would be true for a press shop, a rolling mill, etc.   The cost department in such plants keeps historical records of variance from standard by plant and/or department and adjusts estimated standards by a percentage for the purpose of costing a product. This percentage adjustment then normally covers a multitude of causes and is not at all adaptable or satisfactory where the work cycles vary, quantities to be produced vary, complexity of work is not an approximate constant, etc.

RETRAINING

Many industrial plants have plant-wide employee seniority. In assembly industries, such plant-wide seniority can have a profound effect upon the cost of operations. Where female workers are involved, the turnover in a given department in the lower pay categories might be as high as 100 per cent every six to eight months.

As new operators are introduced to the job, they obviously require training. It is usual to find that the learning time for a new operator in a department that has been successfully producing a unit for two or three months is less than that required for each operator originally starting a job, because trained personnel are present who can assist the new worker to learn the operation. The new operator is also "spurred on" to catch up with the older operators, and this psychological factor has a profound effect on the length of time required for training. Therefore, this situation is often called retraining to give it a distinct identity.

The amount of retraining time required for a new operator can vary from 15 to 75 per cent of that required to initially train a new operator on a complex task when his co-workers are also all starting new on the job. The amount actually required depends upon the complexity of work, the length of the work cycle, the amount of assistance available to the new operator, etc. If the labor standards were established by applying MTM procedures, the information in Chapter 20 will be helpful in assessing the retraining time.

This retraining time adjustment practically never appears directly in the allowed standard. However, it will often be found as a stated variance factor in the routed time standard.

COMPLEXITY OF WORK

Although the underlying philosophy upon which this allowance or variance factor is based is clear cut, there is certainly no precise way to determine its magnitude. An example of complex work is that occasionally encountered in assembly industries having long work cycles involving orderly assembly of many parts that do not by their size or shape furnish clues as to their place in the assembly. The amount of learning and memory required for such work is far above normal.

Assume that work standards, based on a fully trained worker performing the operation, have been established for a long, complex manual task by applying MTM or standard data. Based on the concept that an operator on such a task never becomes trained enough to gain automaticity in his work, particularly when the repetitiveness of the task is low, a complexity-of-work allowance is sometimes used to increase or adjust the task standard. If each element in such a task averages 0.03 minute length, a 30-minute work cycle would contain 1000 work elements; if the task were not repetitive in nature, the memory requirement would obviously be of major magnitude. As much as six months might be needed to learn the operation to the point where it could be done automatically. In addition, the average operator in many assembly plants does not remain at the same task more than six months, which makes a complexity variance factor even more necessary.

In a sense, then, a complexity of work allowance or variance factor makes a time standard more realistically account for work which imposes definite mental activity over and above that normally required by similar manual motions. The thinking and decision time involved tends to slow the manual speed attained, or else it appears as operator hesitations caused by the necessity to occasionally stop and plan ahead or to refer to a lengthy written process. It might even be caused by pauses to refer to a finished model conveniently placed for reference.

This type of allowance or variance factor is usually based on experience in other similar operations where variations from the standards have been noted; that is, standards based on MTM or standard data as previously outlined.

Plants having an initial training variance factor sometimes pyramid the situation by also introducing a complexity variance factor into the routed standard. This usually occurs only where a limited number of assemblies is to be produced and the complete learning cost must be identified. Some engineers object to the complexity allowance or variance factor with the claim that it really is a multiple coverage of initial training. This is to a large extent true for highly repetitive operations. However, other psychological considerations sometimes justify a decision to split the so-called initial training variance factor into two parts: one part is called the initial training factor and the other is called complexity of work allowance or factor. The training might have required six to twelve months and actually may never have been complete enough due to the quantity to be produced, employee turnover due to transfers (in some industries with plant-wide seniority, the equivalent of a complete department turnover every six months is possible), labor contract clauses, etc.

Since the learning curve on very long cycles has a very small slope after the initial training, the validity and reason for a complexity allowance or variance factor is apparent. If an ordinary operator could never hope to meet the standard, there would be little justification for setting such a standard.

REWORK AND/OR REPAIR

Rework is often classified as that labor required to correct existing units in accordance with latest engineering changes. Repair is the labor required to correct production errors. Units are sometimes assembled lacking certain parts due to parts shortages; to correct this condition later requires a combination of rework and repair. All three reasons for excess labor expended are encompassed by adjustments to the time standards for rework and repair.

Rework and/or repair work may or may not be performed by special operators. It is practically never included in the allowed standard of the operators originally making or assembling the parts. The labor required, however, usually is covered by a so-called rework and/or repair variance factor applied to the allowed standard for making and/or assembling the part, or when developing the standard cost of the part or assembly. Such work also can be processed and a labor standard established for each concerned task. This is sometimes done and is very effective in securing good repair and rework performance. Such procedure, however, does not solve the problem of establishing a true actual cost and, to some extent, a true standard cost for each part or assembly.

SUMMARY

Outlined in this chapter are the more common types of allowances and variance factors, the theories underlying them, and the general method of computing, determining, and applying them. Specific details vary so greatly between industries that it would be futile to specify in detail the exact method of application and the various forms required for properly showing the method of application. Regardless of the amount and variety of time standard adjustments normally applied in a given industry, it is instructive to note that management policy usually governs. Executives have the right to interpret measurements and revise or overrule normal policy as determined by the exigencies of production. It is important, however, that firm policies be promulgated so that difficulty in the use of allowances and variance factors can be avoided and consistency of application can be attained.

CHAPTER 24

Mathematics in Work Measurement

Work measurement is concerned, primarily, with providing scientific management a quantitative measure of work performance. As a measuring tool, it is essentially a combination of scientific procedures coupled with the arts of observation and analysis. Mathematics is involved; and the industrial engineering profession has followed the older branches of engineering in adapting both traditional and advanced mathematical techniques to help solve its work measurement problems.

Since this text is primarily concerned with *practical* work measurement, only the *necessary* mathematical techniques are given with no attempt to display all the details of theory behind rules of application. Details of mathematical and statistical theories can be found in standard texts. Attention here is focused on such information as will broaden the outlook of the work analyst, orient him to the more common practical tools, and summarize the more important means of numerical analysis which will prove valuable in everyday work measurement.

The topics considered herein have all been referred to in earlier chapters: computation of workstudy data; statistical validity; workstudy analysis and synthesis; work sampling or ratio-delay; and time conversion. While much of the discussion directly concerns time study, reference will be made to pre-determined times such as Methods-Time Measurement where appropriate. The reason for this approach is obvious if the reader will refer to the latter portion of Chapter 22 regarding combining these techniques.

COMPUTATION OF WORKSTUDY DATA

Most of the everyday calculations connected with work studies—whether for time study or pre-determined study such as MTM—consist of simple arithmetic and algebra; however, there are areas where the use of statistical techniques can be of great help. To delineate these areas, consider the following problems.

Work measurement labor standards involve the measurement of constant and variable elements. Both elements contain numbers which may be more or less correct depending on the way they were measured, i.e., the precision of the measuring devices (including any human judgment or estimation that comprises part of the scheme of measurement), the procedure and interpretation attached to any numbers behind the one in question, and the assumptions (conscious or tacit) made prior to the measurement; all affect the end result. Statistical tools can play a large role in helping an analyst decide just how good are the numbers which appear in his constants and variables. The analysis of variables may be quite complex and often must include dimensional analysis. Stated more simply, constants can be analyzed by arithmetic and statistics, whereas variables involve the use of algebra and other higher forms of mathematics, plus knowledge of the physical system being measured as it interacts with its surroundings or other systems.

Although, generally, the reader is interested only in procedures or approximations that are economical to use and which consistently give reasonable answers, there are many aspects of the discussion in this chapter which will concern ideas which he needs to know, but which he may seldom apply or actively use in computing or interpreting the data with which he is working.

With these background ideas, it is well to examine both the sample time study and the example MTM analysis found earlier in this text. Following this, as the section headings show, some detail can be given which sheds light on the comments for each of the studies.

The Time Study

The time study of Fig. 2, Chapter 21, has been computed through to the total allowed minutes for the task. Note that this includes: (1) various actions and adjustments in the basic watch readings and elapsed times, (2) deletion of readings and elapsed times deemed improper, (3) averaging of the remaining "T" values, (4) application of a rating factor, (5) addition of an allowance, (6) adjustment for frequencies of certain elements, and finally (7) summation for the total standard per piece time. In so many steps, although they involve only straight arithmetic, there are many chances for error.

For example, what assurance exists with only one to ten watch readings for each element that the answer is within, say, 5 or 10 per cent of the correct value? Also, do the maximum and minimum "T" values indicate that the elements are adequately timed, or instead that some variable of major significance to the correct answer has been neglected or buried in the data? Are the frequencies for elements 13 and 14 correct? Should all watch times where the operator was talking to the cementer have been discarded? Although the final answer is probably acceptable to most time study men, no reasonable certainty of the mathematical correctness of the answer is possible without good answers to these kinds of questions. The practical man can, however, rely on the methods used to compute the standard in this case if he is assured by the statistician that they give the degree of precision the situation requires. Some of the means by which errors can be detected and handled are discussed in the section entitled Statistical Validity.

The MTM Study

To see where mathematical questions can be raised in an MTM analysis, refer to the study in Figs. 1, 2, and 3 of Chapter 19. Even though the measuring device used for this study (pre-determined times) is unquestionably more sensitive in reflecting the true situation than is time study, the same questions of validity and accuracy can be raised. In fact, this very sensitivity makes it easier to pinpoint where errors did or could occur. To enumerate a few, consider the following questions: Were the motions properly classified as to kind, distance, and/or case and class? Are the motion and element frequencies correct for the task under analysis? Were the time values correctly applied from the MTM data card and all calculations correctly done? Did the analyst correctly convert all TMU values to minutes? Obviously, the main possibility not present with MTM that looms large for time study, ignoring the question of rating,[1] is the question of whether a sufficient number of readings was taken for the accuracy desired, since only one good entry of data suffices for each MTM motion being analyzed. The MTM research has answered many of the questions that can be raised by the practical analyst as to how good are the time values for the individual MTM motions and whether they are really additive to get a total task time. Future research will further illuminate this area. It perhaps should be emphasized that MTM research makes *full* use of applicable mathematical techniques. The MTM analyst, therefore, starts his study with a tremendous advantage over the average time study analyst since neither, as individuals, can usually afford the time required to make a full statistical and mathematical analysis of each work study.

[1] Those familiar with the rating controversy will understand why the authors do not wish to veer from the subject at this point. Suffice it to say that rating problems enter both time study and pre-determined times, although in a somewhat different way—for each individual time study taken but only in establishing the original time data for a pre-determined system like MTM. The authors also feel they have given adequate information on rating in Chapters 2 and 6 of this text and therefore will not discuss it further here.

Other Workstudy Analysis Procedures

Chapter 22 described a number of means by which both methods and time data could be investigated and numbers expressing the situation developed. Chapter 23 also involved mathematical questions, in that the amount and method of applying allowances and determining variances both influence the precision and the validity of the time data which the work analyst gives to the cost accounting department. These further examples serve to show the complexity of any analysis of the precision of work measurement.

STATISTICAL VALIDITY

Mathematicians have developed many computational techniques, some rather complex, to apply to raw data of any kind and thereby determine its precision, and possibly its accuracy, which can help in ascertaining its validity with respect to what the data purports to represent. While greater use of these mathematical devices is being made by researchers and those developing more practical forms of work measurement techniques, most work analysts in their daily work will not concern themselves with new applications of theory, but rather with the practical application of procedures based on such advanced development work.

Accuracy may be defined as the degree to which a given value or set of data is a true measure of the quantity observed or evaluated. However, all measurements contain some degree of imperfection; and this is the reason statistics enters the picture. The science of statistics permits the analysis of numbers or data to ascertain the amount or range of departure of the numbers from the true value which would be obtained by measuring the entire population for the quantity in question. It also helps predict from imperfect data what the true value is within stated probability limits. Such techniques can be applied equally well to basic investigations and to particular data such as that resulting from a work measurement study.

With a sufficiently large sample for any valid measurement of a given property, the data obtained will plot into a normal distribution curve such as is shown in Fig. 1. Here the number of observations or occurrences are plotted against appropriate units on the vertical scale, with the measured or calculated value of the variable being tested for distribution on the horizontal scale. The sigma limits extend equally on both sides of the average value $(\bar{X}')$.

With smaller samples, as usually found in practice, statistical analysis provides the only means by which the distribution of a complete lot may be predicted without actually measuring each item in the lot. If the true distribution of a lot is known, the average value for all the measurements is the high point of the curve and the dispersion of the data can be seen readily.   The shape of the curve obtained from a plot of the data will give clues as to the validity of the data itself and will also suggest what corrections might be needed to make the data valid.   The normal distribution

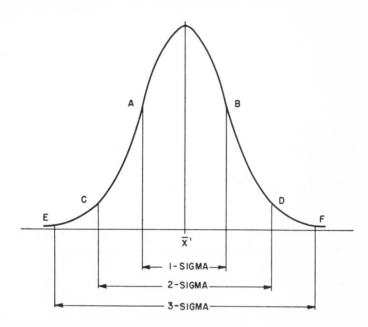

LIMITS	BOUNDS	PERCENT AREA* (POPULATION) COVERED	PERCENT REMAINDER	ODDS OF INCLUSION (COVERAGE ÷ REMAINDER)
I- SIGMA	A TO B	68.27	31.73	2.15 OR 2 TO I
2- SIGMA	C TO D	95.45	4.55	20.98 OR 21 TO I
3- SIGMA	E TO F	99.73	.27	369.37 OR 369 TO I

* SOMETIMES CALLED RISK FACTOR

Fig. 1.   The normal distribution curve.

curve, with attendant statistical measures, is therefore a practical tool if correctly applied to real problems.

From the few statistical terms already mentioned, it is obvious that the work measurement man of the future must know more and be more analytical in his approach to work problems.   While still keeping sight of the large picture, he must be able to understand and use detailed mathematical tools just to meet the demands of everyday business.   It is equally evident that work analysts must keep abreast of the rapid developments in the application of statistics and mathematics to work measurement.   The traditional pragmatic approach to problem solution, which can be exemplified by the often heard statement that "Whether it's right or wrong—it works!", will be abandoned with time and education. Work measurement engineers will tend to proceed more on knowledge than on improvising, with greater certainty that their recommendations will prove workable. However, these ideas in no way relieve the work analyst of the need to be practical.

To orient the reader to work that has already been done in the field, so that he will understand how far work measurement has already progressed along mathematical lines, some of the better known work and details connected with the statistical accuracy and validity of both MTM and time study are next presented.

Methods-Time Measurement

Unquestionably, statistical accuracy and validity is a vital MTM concern, having been a part of the MTM technique and research from their inception. The originators took special pains to state conservatively the limits of the data, its probable degree of validity, and even the need for further validation work. The research sponsored by the MTM Association has made full use of all available statistical techniques. Mathematical analysis is even more important for MTM now than ever before, as can be seen by studying any of the more recent MTM Research Reports.

An important case of the use of mathematical techniques in checking the accuracy and validity of MTM data is the Cornell Report described in Chapter 4 of this text. In addition, many of the consultants working in the MTM field have made extensive tests and checks of their own along similar lines. Much of the committee work of the MTM Association, particularly that of the Research Committee and the Training Committee, directly concerns mathematical investigations into the data, its application, improvement of both interpretation and correct usage, and ways and means to further employ statistics in MTM development. Noteworthy of the latter is the present usage of electronic data processing equipment in MTM research with a resulting increased capability of employing more sophisticated computer analysis in conjunction with the Electronic Data Collector (EDC) as described in Chapter 22. Increased application of statistics and mathematical analysis is also evident in each new research report published by the MTM Association. By such growth and attitudes, MTM is already much improved over its original version; the future promises even better things in its development and application.

Time Study

While this noteworthy mathematical progress in MTM was taking place, adherents of time study were also making great strides along similar lines.

They correctly felt that much of the difficulty with time study (refer to the critique of R. F. Hoxie in Chapter 1) could be alleviated or eliminated by application of statistical analysis and other mathematical tools. Of particular importance were the ways and means to determine and predict the required number of readings required for given limits of precision developed and published by many writers.

One of the most complete sources of information concerning the application of statistical measures to time study is an article[2] by John M. Allderige. He ably explored the entire question of mathematical procedures and statistical tools to develop a recommended five-step procedure which could be widely used to improve time study. The authors of this text definitely wish to recommend this article to the reader and have attempted to extract the procedure in this section, although not explaining the mathematical theories.

Many additional works and published material testify that scientific time study will depend increasingly on statistical procedures. Almost any industrial engineering, mechanical engineering, technical management, and college-sponsored conference today includes papers and speakers in this field. The proceedings and reports of such groups are another excellent source of data for more information on the topic. Some of the specific groups which can be contacted for this material are: Industrial Management Society, Society for Advancement of Management, American Institute of Industrial Engineers, American Society of Mechanical Engineers, and the Industrial Engineering Departments of many noted universities. Additional current developments appear almost monthly in the technical magazines. From the number of sources cited, it is obvious that time study has kept pace in applying mathematics to work measurement.

The procedure developed by Mr. Allderige, which follows next, answers in a practical manner the following basic measurement questions:

1. How many time study observations are required for each element or cycle?
2. Are the readings obtained consistent?
3. What is the precision of the final prorated cycle time?

Note that these are the questions most asked by time study analysts, and answers to them will help greatly to insure that the *measurement* aspect of the time study is properly accomplished. Basically, the first question is answered by Steps I, II, and III of the procedure by utilizing a statistically determined nomograph. Constructing and analyzing a control chart in Step IV answers the second question. The last question is next answered by a second reference to the nomograph under Step V of the procedure.

[2] "Statistical Procedures in Stop Watch Work Measurement," by John M. Allderige, *Journal of Industrial Engineering*, Vol. VII, No. 4, July–August 1956.

The symbols used in Mr. Allderige's procedure are as follows:

N The number of readings or observations taken or to be taken as required by the precision desired. Most important is that these observations must be *random* throughout the study

E Per cent precision of the calculated cycle time (based on 95% assurance)

A Subscript to identify main cycle

$B,C,etc.$ Subscripts to identify auxiliary elements

T Subscript for total cycle

u The number of auxiliary elements in the total cycle

F The frequency of auxiliary ("occasional") elements

k A constant accounting for the nature of frequency determination

X Observed time value in minutes

$\bar{X}$ Arithmetic time average for each group of four readings

$\bar{\bar{X}}$ Arithmetic time average for an element or the entire cycle

R The range for groups of four, that is the difference between the highest and lowest time value in the group

$\bar{R}$ Average range for the main cycle

R^* Range value for the complete, prorated cycle

$S_{\bar{x}}$ The value of one sigma or standard deviation of averages ($\bar{X}$) of groups of 4.

The procedure will be given in definite steps and an example used for the purpose of clarification. If, after reading this section, the reader wishes to investigate further, it is suggested that he consult the reference article and other writings on statistical procedures, especially as applied to work measurement.

Step I. Make a conventional preliminary time study of 16 observations in groups of four, combining all elemental values covering the constant portion of the work cycle, at the same time taking into account and recording all auxiliary elements.

The use of only 16 observations or readings is not an absolute requirement; this procedure will also work for any other multiple of four readings such as 20, 12, or 8. However, since the preliminary study will be used to determine the number of readings required for any specified or desired degree of precision it is important to note that there will be a progressive tendency to underestimate the total number of readings required for a given desired degree of precision as the multiple of the preliminary readings is reduced. The nomograph used for this determination can be entered for successive checks as more data are collected; therefore, the number of preliminary observations can be reduced below 16 without any real penalty other than the inconvenience of making repeated references to the nomograph. However, 16 observations has proved to be a practical number.

As will be seen later, a control chart is developed to test the consistency of the data. It is a very simple consistency test that would not have been possible if averages from groups of at least four observations were not used. "There are many possible frequency distributions of individual time values requiring equally as many possible tests of consistency if individual data were to be tested. Averages of groups of four conveniently form, in most cases, only one type of distribution regardless of the distribution of the individual values—a normal frequency distribution."[3] It is because of this that one consistency test can be employed on these averages of groups of four in the control chart.

Only the main, constantly repeating, cycle times are taken in groups of four. However, the frequency and time values for auxiliary elements (those that do not occur each time the main cycle repeats in the study) must also be shown in both the preliminary study and in the final version. How this is done is shown in the example in Tables 1 and 4.

Either raw data can be used in the procedure or it may be normalized by applying operator performance ratings to the element times prior to calculations. If raw data is used, an average operator rating can also be applied to the resultant answer to achieve normalization. The example in Tables 1 and 4 uses the first approach and processes only the raw data.

Random observations are readings taken without any intentional regularity in terms of clock times. Randomization reduces the probable error of the results of any sample of a total population. There are several reasons for this fact. In any process or series of events, there are natural variations which will tend to average out if the observations of the process are not grouped in a short, concentrated time span. Perhaps more important to work measurement, the workers (one of the major factors in the process) would soon realize when non-random checks were to occur. They would then depend on this regularity in case they wished to influence the results of the study by deliberately taking such actions as would cause the study to accord with their own desires. Obviously, this would introduce an extraneous variable which would make the study almost worthless in the statistical sense. It is, therefore, essential to assure that any observations taken are truly random in nature.

A random number table should be used to randomize the groups of four observations over the available time period if maximum accuracy is to be obtained. The preliminary study of the example in Table 1 shows that the four groups of four observations each were randomized over an available 3½-hour period. Randomization is not new in work measurement—it's the basis for work sampling or ratio-delay as illustrated later in this chapter.

[3] Allderige, *op. cit.*

Table I. Results of Preliminary Study— 16 Observations, Groups of 4

(Time in Minutes)

MAIN ELEMENT A

Random Clock Time	Time Values X_A	From Groups of 4	
		Average $\bar{X}_A$	Range R_A
8:15	.90	0.98	0.26
	.88		
	1.14		
	1.00		
9:30	.99	1.06	.47
	.90		
	.97		
	1.37		
9:45	1.09	1.04	.53
	.96		
	1.32		
	.79		
11:15	1.11	.92	.33
	.79		
	1.01		
	.78		
Totals	16.00	—	1.59

AUXILIARY ELEMENTS

Element B — Random occurrence	
Time Value X_B	0.57
	0.44
Total	1.01
Element C — Fixed occurrence	
Time Value X_C	2.16

SUMMARY OF ALL ELEMENTS

Element	Kind	Number of Observations, N	Total Time $\sum X$	Average Time $\sum X \div N$	Average Range $\sum R \div N/4$	Occurrence Frequency $N_A \div N$	Prorated Time $\bar{\bar{X}} \div \bar{\bar{F}}$
A	Main Cycle	$N_A = 16$	16.00	$\bar{\bar{X}}_A = 1.00$	$\bar{R}_A = 0.40$	$\bar{\bar{F}}_A = \frac{16}{16} = 1$	1.00
B	Auxiliary	$N_B = 2$	1.01	$\bar{\bar{X}}_B = 0.51$	—	$\bar{\bar{F}}_B = \frac{16}{2} = 8$	.06
C	Auxiliary	$N_C = 1$	2.16	$\bar{\bar{X}}_C = 2.16$	—	$\bar{\bar{F}}_C = 14$ (fixed)	.16
						Preliminary Prorated Cycle Time $\bar{\bar{X}}_T =$	1.22

Preliminary Range Value: $R^* = \bar{R}_A(1 + 0.12u) = 0.40(1 + 0.24) = \underline{0.50}$

Randomization does impose some requirements which are difficult to meet when using stop watch work measurement. This is especially true for short-run jobs or jobs with deadline requirements that drastically limit the time available to make the study or where the greater disturbance factor of a random study cannot be tolerated. As the time span of measurement is shortened, there is less adequate coverage of product variations, process variables, auxiliary elements, and the like. However, it is sometimes possible to make use of re-runs of the job to achieve a truly random study. While Mr. Allderige's procedure is based on random readings, it is possible to apply the five-step procedure to non-random data and still derive benefits from its use.

A random observation schedule can be developed in a number of ways. For maximum accuracy the observations should be based on a random number table, of which many are in print and available. By coding clock minutes available during the length of time permitted for the study (minute 1, 2 . . . 210 for the 3½-hour time available in the example study), the random numbers obtained from the table can be used directly to define the clock time for observations and will thereby automatically produce a random observation schedule. Another way is to draw from a hat slips of paper which bear the minutes available for the study (minute 1, 2, 3, etc., the same as previously mentioned) until the total number of readings to be taken are scheduled. Other ways of producing a random number display is to shuffle and deal cards bearing numbers, spinning a wheel such as used in games of chance, etc. The essential thing is to obtain a completely random schedule that states specifically a clock time when each observation or group of observations must be made.

The four readings or observations of any group of four are taken on successive work cycles. It is the time for the *start* of each group of four that should be randomized. The observer making this study ran a sample set of four observations and found that the time to take the group required about 15 minutes. The 3½-hour period he had available contained 14 periods of 15 minutes duration of which he needed to select four on a random basis. One way to do this, as previously outlined for general randomization, would be to code the possible beginning times as minute 1, minute 16, minute 31, etc., and then refer these to a random number table; otherwise one of the other randomization techniques described can be used. Table 1 shows the example study together with the necessary calculations. The groups of four observations were randomized over a 8½-hour period at the clock times shown.

In the example, the engineer extended the raw data from the continuous watch times taken on each group of four main cycles. First, however, he eliminated all data associated with methods not conforming to the right- and left-hand chart element descriptions covering the process. Besides the groups of four readings for the constantly recurring main cycle, the analyst also listed the time values for two auxiliary elements which occur at varying frequency in both the preliminary and final study. Auxiliary element B occurred twice during the study, but actually was estimated to occur once for every 8 occurrences of the main cycle. Its variable frequency could be fixed in value only by completing the full study, but an estimate was necessary for the preliminary study. On the other hand, element C is known to have a fixed frequency of one occurrence per 14 main cycles.

The example applies the procedure to one operator. However, it can be used just as effectively on a collection of operators. Ideally, the process for handling groups of operators would call for a random selection of four operators for one cycle each in each group of four observations. Whether this approach is taken on a job involving many operators depends on the engineer's eventual use of the measured value. It is sufficient to say that measuring a group of operators through the use of the procedure can be accomplished if such is desired.

A definite step in the procedure is the calculation of range values. Range is the arithmetical difference between the highest and the lowest values in any set of data or group of readings; statistically, it shows the degree of dispersion of individual readings from the average for the set. Obviously, the auxiliaries must be taken into consideration in this calculation. Exactly how they are considered is dependent upon what is known concerning the frequency of occurrence. If all of the auxiliary frequency ratios are known, then the rule for range (R^*) is expressed as

$$R^* = \bar{R}_A(1 + 0.1u)$$

where $\bar{R}_A$ is the main cycle average range and u is the number of auxiliaries. Such knowledge of the auxiliary frequency ratios would result from correct formal application of work sampling techniques or job knowledge, such as a constant number of pieces per tray. When the auxiliary frequency ratios are all estimated, the approximation rule

$$R^* = \bar{R}_A(1 + 0.15u)$$

is used to calculate the range. For any intermediate situation, where some of the frequencies are estimated and some are known, then use of

$$R^* = \bar{R}_A(1 + 0.12u)$$

is suggested as a compromise. This can be summarized as shown in Table 2.

Note in the example shown in Table 1 that the preliminary range value (R^*) was calculated using the compromise formula where the frequency ratios of the auxiliaries were only partially known.

Table 2. Determination of Range Value R*

For any one element $R^* = \bar{R}$
For the over-all, pro-rated cycle $R^*_T = \bar{R}_A(1 + ku)$ where $\bar{R}_A$ = the $\bar{R}$ for the main cycle u = the number of auxiliary elements in the study k = 0.1 if the auxiliary frequencies are all known or   0.15 if the auxiliary frequencies are all estimated or   0.12 if they are a mixture of known and estimated values.

All of the necessary work to be accomplished under Step I is listed in Table 3.

Step II. Determine the number of observations required for the desired precision E by using the Work Measurement Alignment Chart (Fig. 2) and establish a plan for obtaining them.

The nomograph for the procedure of Mr. Allderige, shown as Fig. 2, is basically an alignment chart which can be used as shown by the dashed

Table 3. Rules for Step I†

Rule 1A	Group the main cycle data in tabular form in groups of four, noting the observation time for each group, and summarize for total time.
Rule 1B	Calculate the range (R) for each group by subtracting the lowest reading for the group from the highest reading for the group, and then total these ranges.
Rule 1C	Tabulate each auxiliary in separate columns, indicating the frequency and its accuracy (exact or estimated), and total the element times.
Rule 1D	Calculate the average time $(\bar{X}_A)$ for the main cycle and each auxiliary $(\bar{X}_B, \bar{X}_C, \text{etc.})$. $\bar{X}$ is obtained by dividing the total observed time by the number of observations. (In the example, for instance, 16 minutes for the main cycle divided by 16 readings results in an $\bar{X}_A$ of 1 minute).
Rule 1E	Calculate the average range $(\bar{R}_A)$ for the main cycle. This is done by dividing the total range from Rule 1B by the number of groups of four.
Rule 1F	Compute the preliminary pro-rated cycle time $(\bar{X}_T)$ by adding to $\bar{X}_A$, the average time for the main cycle, the average time values for each auxiliary adjusted for its proper frequency. The adjustment is accomplished by dividing these values by their frequency of occurrence.
Rule 1G	Calculate R^* using the appropriate k constant as defined under the discussion of range value.

† Reference to Table 1, which illustrates the procedure to be used in handling the preliminary data, will aid the reader in accomplishing a full understanding of Steps 1A to 1G. Note that the example used the formula for range value applicable when the defined frequency of the occurrence of the auxiliaries is only partially known.

example. In this example, the analyst first decided what degree of precision (E) would be acceptable for the final study in order to establish the initial point on the left-hand scale. In the example, E was taken as ± 5 per cent. In effect, the engineer said he would be satisfied with the pro-rated cycle time of 1.22 minutes in the preliminary study if the actual time value was betwen 1.16 minutes and 1.28 minutes, a ± 5 per cent variation from 1.22 minutes.

Using the values $E = 5$ per cent, $\bar{X}_T = 1.22$, and $R^* = 0.50$, as the result of the preliminary study, he entered the work measurement alignment

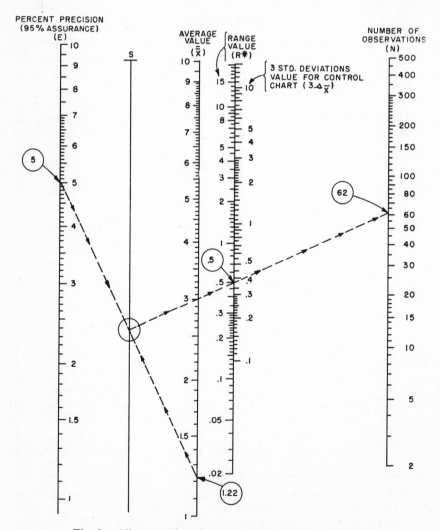

Fig. 2. Alignment chart for stop watch work measurement.

chart. He aligned E and $\bar{X}_T$ and noted the point of intersection on the S scale. For the statistically minded, this S scale is proportional to the desired precision expressed in absolute terms—$S = \bar{\bar{X}}_E$ for the data of the study. He next aligned this point of intersection on the S scale with the range value 0.50 and extended the line to the far right (N) scale, where he obtained 62 as the number of readings or observations required for the main cycle to produce the desired degree of precision. The nomograph is so constructed that these 62 readings will give the indicated 5 per cent precision limits, or thereabouts.

The final study can now be *designed* as follows, where design implies an observation plan: The engineer in the example had already made 16 observations, which left him with a problem of obtaining 46 additional observations to achieve the required total ($62 - 16 = 46$). Since the basic procedure calls for groups of four, he selected the next highest multiple of four or 48 as the number of additional observations to be made. The next problem involved randomly scheduling the 48 required observations in 12 groups of four each over the remaining available time. In the example, the available time was 2½ days, which period contained 80 of the required 15-minute periods—15 minutes being the approximate time required to make a group of four observations. He selected 12 of the 80 available periods of 15 minutes during 2½ days by using a random number table and thus set up his observation plan.

Step III. Take the required stop watch readings in accord with the study design, incorporate the data previously obtained in the preliminary study and then again tabulate and calculate the results as defined under Step I.

The completed example study, given as Table 4, shows all of the detail discussed under Step I, together with the calculation of the final pro-rated cycle time of 1.20 minutes and the final range value of 0.56 minutes. This table clearly shows the arrangement and method suggested by Mr. Allderige for a statistically valid time study, and it also includes the data taken in the preliminary study.

Step IV. Plot a control chart and analyze the study for consistency.

The control chart for the example study appears in Fig. 3A. This chart is made by following the series of rules next discussed.

    Rule IVA. On coordinate paper with appropriate scale distance, plot in sequence the $\bar{X}_A$ values for each sample set of four observations and then draw in the line representing the average value ($\bar{\bar{X}}_A$).

In the example, there are 16 sets for the required total of 64 readings. The $\bar{\bar{X}}_A$ value (the average of the $\bar{X}_A$ values) for the example was 1.01 minutes.

Table 4. Results of Complete Study
(Time in Minutes)

Main Element A				Random Clock Time	Time Values X_A	From Groups of 4		Auxiliary Elements	
Random Clock Time	Time Values X_A	From Groups of 4				Average $\bar{X}_A$	Range R_A		
		Average $\bar{X}_A$	Range R_A	Sub-Totals	32.70	—	3.81		Time Value X_B
8:15	0.90	0.98	0.26	8:00	.64	0.97	0.50	E	0.57
	.88				1.01			L	0.44
	1.14				1.14			E	0.60
	1.00				1.09			M	0.52
								E	0.33
9:30	.99	1.06	.47	10:45	1.02	1.05	.38	N	0.47
	.90				.81			T	0.40
	.97				1.18				0.34
	1.37				1.19				
								B	3.67 Total
9:45	1.09	1.04	.53	1:15	1.11	1.04	.44		
	.96				.76				Time Value X_C
	1.32				1.20				
	.79				1.10			E	
11:15	1.11	.92	.33	2:30	.90	.93	.52	L	
	.79				.68			E	2.16
	1.01				1.20			M	1.86
	.78				.93			E	1.83
								N	1.90
1:30	1.19	1.30	.26	8:45	1.26	1.00	.41	T	1.80
	1.36				.80				
	1.22				.92				9.55
	1.45				1.07			C	Total
2:00	.79	.97	.51	9:30	1.27	1.02	.46		
	.97				1.12				
	.82				.84				
	1.30				.81				
2:30	.82	.91	.29	11:00	1.17	1.00	.33		
	1.10				.84				
	.93				.97				
	.81				1.03				
3:30	.64	.99	1.16	3:45	.97	.97	.28		
	.66				.99				
	1.80				1.10				
	.84				.82				
Sub-Totals	32.70	—	3.81	Totals	64.59	—	7.14		

Table 4 (*Continued*)

SUMMARY OF ALL ELEMENTS

Ele-ment	Kind	Number of Observa-tions N	Total Time $\sum X$	Average Time $\sum X \div N$	Average Range $\sum R \div N/4$	Occurrence Frequency $N_A \div N$	Pro-rated Time $\overline{\overline{X}} \div \overline{\overline{F}}$
A	Main Cycle	$N_A = 64$	64.59	$\overline{\overline{X}}_A = 1.01$	$\bar{R}_A = 0.45$	$\overline{\overline{F}}_A = \frac{64}{64} = 1$	1.01
B	Auxiliary	$N_B = 8$	3.67	$\overline{\overline{X}}_B = 0.46$	—	$\overline{\overline{F}}_B = \frac{64}{8} = 8$	.06
C	Auxiliary	$N_C = 5$	9.55	$\overline{\overline{X}}_C = 1.91$	—	$\overline{\overline{F}}_C = 14$ (fixed)	.13
						Final Prorated Cycle Time $\overline{\overline{X}}_T =$	1.20

Final Range Value: $R^* = \bar{R}_A(1 + 0.12u) = 0.45(1 + 0.24) = \underline{0.56}$

Rule IVB. Determine and draw in the control limits for the chart. The limits are found by referring again to the nomograph in Fig. 2, where they are constructed on the same line with the range scale. To find the value to use, enter the range scale at the value for the average range ($\bar{R}_A$) as previously calculated for the main cycle and note opposite it the three standard deviations value ($3s_{\bar{x}}$). This value must be added to and deducted from the $\overline{X}_A$ of the chart to find the absolute values of the limits.

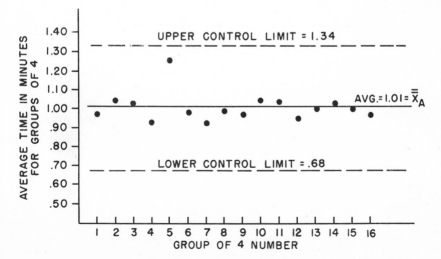

Fig. 3A.   Control chart analysis.

For the example study, $\bar{R}_A$ of 0.45 minute was found on the range scale and the value of three standards deviations (3-sigma) was read from the opposite scale at the same point as 0.33 minute as shown in Fig. 3B. Applying these limits to 1.01 minutes gives the statistical

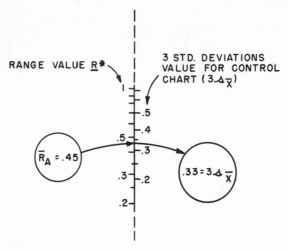

Fig. 3B. Determining three standard deviations for control limits of Fig. 3A. (Abstracted from Fig. 2.)

bounds of 1.34 minutes for the upper control limit and 0.68 minute for the lower control limit. Note that this step follows exactly the procedure used by statistical quality control analysts.

Rule IVC. Plot the control limits on the chart and note any inconsistency in the data.

The upper and lower control limits found under Rule IVB are shown plotted in Fig. 3A. These lines are usually drawn as dotted lines so as to contrast with the average line. They show the bounds within which all of the sample readings should fall as long as only normal chance causes were operating within the system during the time study. If any points exceed these limits, there is an assignable cause of variation operating which should be checked and corrected.

The second part of Step IV, analyzing for consistency, makes use of the chart just constructed in the same way as is done for statistical quality control. If all points fall within limits, as is the case for the example study, the study is consistent and any variation in the readings was due to chance causes. This whole technique of control charting depended and was based statistically on using a sample size of four to make the readings and using the nomograph to determine the limits.   The beauty of the procedure, therefore, is that it makes it possible for the analyst to chart and analyze his data without complicated control chart computation.

Any out-of-control data must be investigated to determine the cause which produced such data.   This condition means that something occurred not due to chance alone and the cause must be identified, all data associated with it eliminated, and the control chart recomputed.   It should be recalled that all data belonging to non-specified procedures should be eliminated at the time of observations by the engineer.   Because of this, the assignable cause for any non-typical occurrence detected by the control chart usually reflects a situation which justifies modification of the study by a separate allowance, a separate standard, or additional observations.   A few of the more obvious reasons for non-typical occurrences could be undetected changes in method by the operator, incorrect application of performance rating (if the data was rated), wrong watch readings, errors in computation, and plotting errors.

If the out-of-limit occurrence really appears to be part of the system (as the engineer chooses to describe the system), then the underlying distribution may be too skewed to be normalized by groups of four.   Larger groupings should then be made and appropriate limits set on those averages to test consistency.

Another possible type of out-of-control situation arises when the variation between random time periods at which the observations were made exceeds the variation within a time period (the time during which a sample group of four observations are made).   If this condition is important enough to the engineer, he should then investigate it for correction.   If such a variation is generally expected, however, then a different consistency test is proper.   This involves taking averages of groups of four themselves in groups of four, determining the range and average range, multiplying this value by two to get an adjusted range value, and then using the nomograph to determine appropriate limits.   Abruzzi has termed such consistency as "grand stability."[4]

Step V.   With the data in statistical control, again enter the Work Measurement Alignment Chart (Fig. 2) with the new values to determine the precision of the final answer.

This is accomplished by aligning N_A on the far right scale of Fig. 2 with the range value (R^*) and extending the line to the S scale, where the point of intersection is noted.   This point of intersection is next aligned with the $\bar{\bar{X}}_T$ value on the average value scale, the line then being extended to the far left scale (E), where the reading at the point of intersection indicates the per cent precision E.

[4] *Work Measurement,* by A. Abruzzi, Columbia University Press, New York, 1952.

In the example, the N_A of 64 on the chart is aligned with the final range value (R^*) of 0.56 and the line extended to the S scale. This point of intersection is then aligned with $\bar{\bar{X}}_T$ of 1.20 minutes and the line extended to the left, where it intersects the precision scale (E) at 5.6. This means that the example study has defined $\bar{\bar{X}}_T$ as 1.20 minutes to ± 5.6 per cent, which can be expressed as 1.20 ± 0.07 minutes. More specifically, it means that the interval of 1.13 to 1.27 minutes had an approximate probability of 95 per cent of containing the true average time—the time that would have been obtained from a continuous study on the operator over the entire three-day period during which the sampling data was collected. This was sufficiently close to the initial study specification of ± 5 per cent to consider the measurement phase of the example study as complete.

The advantage of using Mr. Allderige's or a similar statistically valid procedure is obvious. It makes it possible to lift time study from the realm of controversy and make it a substantially more powerful tool for management.

WORKSTUDY ANALYSIS AND SYNTHESIS

When a work analyst has completed one or more work studies, whether by stop watch or by a pre-determined time technique, he must then analyze the data and prepare it in the form(s) required, the form(s) of data presentation being dependent on the purpose for which the study or studies were taken.

The types or forms of data presentation are many and varied. However, the final choice of format almost always depends on the purpose— the two principal ones being (1) supplying labor and machine time standards, and (2) developing and/or reporting labor cost data. Of course, any report to an individual or group requesting data must be prepared with consideration of the technical background of the types of individuals who are expected to use the data. The more detailed and complex approaches often appropriate for the industrial engineers must generally be made simpler and less detailed for foremen, union stewards, cost accountants, etc. Due to the great variety of presentation methods, no attempt is made here to delineate each type of the possible combinations, but rather the more important and most used forms of data presentation are discussed and/or indicated.

To develop and present labor and machine time standards and/or labor cost data in a readily understandable and useful form, the engineer must consider at least three topics which involve mathematics or devices which have mathematical backgrounds. These are: (1) Identifying Constants and Variables; (2) Forms of Data Expression; and (3) Means of Combining Data. Obviously, other items involving mathematics, such as accounting procedures, company policy, etc., must be considered beyond the scope of this book.

Identifying Constants and Variables

To aid discussion of this subject, it is helpful to quote from A.S.M.E. Standard 106 "Industrial Engineering Terminology" the accepted definitions of constant and variable elements as follows:

Constant Element: 1. An element for which the leveled or normal time is always the same regardless of the characteristics of the parts being worked upon, as long as the method and the working conditions are unchanged. 2. An element for which, under a specified set of conditions, the standard time allowance should always be the same. *Example:* Raise spindle a definite distance on a drill press of a certain size and make.

Variable Element: An element for which the leveled or normal time, under the same methods and working conditions, will change because of the varying characteristics of the parts being worked upon; as size, weight, shape, density, hardness, viscosity, tolerance requirements, finish, etc.

A few guiding principles may be abstracted from these definitions regarding the matter of data presentation. First, note that a good report specifies or describes what methods and conditions are behind the data presented. Second, when reporting constant values, it is well to state this fact and whether they can change with other conditions and methods. Third, it is essential to list the salient physical and chemical characteristics of the parts involved—particularly those which are crucial to the validity of the data. Under very special conditions it is sometimes desirable as well to indicate certain possible physical changes and how they will cause the values reported to vary.

The discussion under this section will delineate the areas where variables are normally encountered. How to handle them in actual labor standard construction will be discussed in Chapter 27.

In the development of labor standards, the work measurement engineer must first be able to decide what is constant, what is variable, and the extent of any variation. The manner in which this is done will differ somewhat for MTM and time study.

A properly executed *MTM analysis* with its supporting information contains concise, complete data on the conditions and the method employed. This, as previously explained, makes it relatively easy to examine each motion and/or element to see whether the time standard does or can vary. One practical method of separating constants and variables in a motion pattern systematically is to analyze each motion in sequence and then checkmark the variable motions on the margins of the analysis form. It also is possible to estimate the probable extent of any variation in the time standard for the pattern with the variable motions highlighted.

It should be noted, however, that there will almost always exist in any work measurement situation some variable element that the practical analyst will treat as a constant. For example, the distance involved in tossing aside an object can vary and is also difficult to measure; hence a good estimate of the usual distance will normally be accepted by most analysts, with the actual variation being ignored. The time study analyst, as well as the MTM analyst, has the same kind of problem and uses a similar approach with his elapsed times to arrive at answers for the type of situation just described.

Typical of the questions that can be raised to help isolate variable motions or elements from an MTM pattern are the following: Would material variations require a different set of motions for the element from time to time? If so, the fact that different motions constitute a different method would dictate designating the element as variable and analyzing the variation. Does the element and/or motion within the element occur with the same frequency for each cycle of operations? Either the method can be variable for the element due to differing motion frequency or, even with the method constant, the element itself can be variable with respect to the cycle. Do changes in the kind, distance, case and/or class of motion take place or are they probable within the element? Such variations again mean that the method varies, and they can be isolated by examining each motion in sequence as suggested earlier. The manner by which constancy or variability can be determined from an MTM analysis should now be clear.

Determining whether *time study* elements are constant or variable is more difficult. Significant variations are often buried within elements simply because the element takes the same watch time even though the method by which it is performed is quite different from cycle to cycle. One reason for this condition is the need to select time study elements long enough to permit accuracy in reading the watch and recording the data, which often induces the time study analyst to choose elements too broad or vaguely defined to permit detection of method variations. Perhaps the most practical check, even with this characteristic, consists in comparing the elapsed times for each repetition of the element to see the extent of time variation. MTM training, obviously, would aid the time study analyst in further examining elements for which large time variations occur to discover if they point to a variable element. However, an even better way to evaluate the presence of other than chance variation would be to utilize one of the latest statistical procedures of time study, such as that developed by Mr. Allderige.

Forms of Data Expression

Much skill is needed by the industrial engineer in choosing the form in which data is to be expressed. For example, operating managers who request data are generally interested in answers, not preliminary detail. They want it in a form they can use directly and easily. This is true not only of managers, but of almost anyone else for whom data is prepared. The reputation earned by a work measurement engineer will depend to a large extent on the reports he submits, therefore he must know to whom they are going and tailor them to meet the user's requirements in the most effective manner.

All numerical data involves both numbers and dimensional units, and may consist in whole or in part of variable factors. These characteristics all influence the form in which work measurement data is expressed. Constants can be tabulated or stated as arithmetic numbers. Variables are more commonly expressed as algebraic formulae, or as graphs or curves. In any event, when reporting either constant or variable data, it is essential to either define the units and terms employed or else remind the recipient that previously established units and/or definitions are applicable.

Most data can be presented pictorially, and the more effective industrial engineering reports make frequent use of this device. For such pictorials as pie charts, histograms, bar charts, cartoons, etc., there is always the necessity to use mathematics either to determine the picture or to help construct it with reasonable proportions. Work analysts may find need for the help of specialists in illustrating and "glamorizing" their very often "dry" reports. Such visual aids as models, scaled parts, and photographs sometimes prove feasible adjuncts in emphasizing and highlighting the data being presented.

Means of Combining Data

General, cost, and special management reports normally require the industrial engineer to combine, condense, and simplify much of the data which appears in detail in his analysis. This also must be done before the engineer can use many of the presentation devices and forms of data expression described. To do this sometimes requires the use of higher mathematics and statistical procedures.

Tabulations, charts, and graphs are means of combining data that appear with regularity. An example of this approach which works well for the case involving a limited number of variables is shown in Fig. 4. This example covers a case where the routed time to test electrolytic capacitors varies with the two principal product configurations of can size and number of terminals. The main limitation of these data combination devices are that, basically, it is possible to show only a few major variables against the main data. In the example, the can size and number of terminals (with the secondary variables of capacity and resistance checks at each terminal) are found on the margins of the table and the intersection of these values gives the routed time.

Number of Terminals	Number of Tests Req'd.		Can Diameter, Inches			
			1		1⅜	
	Capacity	Resistance	Units per Hour	Minutes per Unit	Units per Hour	Minutes per Unit
1	1	0	1408	0.0426	1111	0.0540
	—	1	990	.0606	806	.0744
2	1	0	1063	.0564	877	.0684
	—	1	806	.0744	676	.0888
	—	2	653	.0918	559	.1074
	2	0	781	.0768	637	.0942
	—	1	632	.0948	521	.1152
	—	2	531	.1128	448	.1338
3	1	0	847	.0708	730	.0822
	—	1	675	.0888	585	.1026
	—	2	561	.1068	495	.1212
	—	3	483	.1242	431	.1392
	2	0	653	.0918	546	.1098
	—	1	543	.1104	459	.1308
	—	2	469	.1278	402	.1494
	—	3	413	.1452	358	.1674
	3	0	564	.1062	467	.1284
	—	1	480	.1248	224	.2682
	—	2	421	.1422	357	.1680
	—	3	375	.1596	323	.1860

Fig. 4. Capacitor test rates (All rates in *allowed* minutes).

When more than two variables influence the final time, a chart of this simple type will not suffice. The use of a multivariable chart, can then be employed. Multivariable charting is well described in an article[5] by T. R. Snakenberg and the authors recommend this article to the reader.

The multiple nomograph technique is another means of relating several variables in concentrated form. The nomograph presented in another section of this chapter is an example of this technique. Other examples may be found in technical articles in current publications which often consist solely of a nomograph and an accompanying explanation of its derivation and use. Another common approach is to develop an algebraic formula relating the various items or elements—the elements themselves usually being presented in summarized tabular form.

WORK SAMPLING OR RATIO-DELAY

One of the more promising mathematical tools by which the industrial engineer analyzing work can improve his results, principally in the areas of indirect standards and determining allowances without all-day studies, is known mainly as *Work Sampling* or *Ratio-Delay*. The reason these two names have the widest acceptance of the many used is that they best describe the procedure. Work Sampling denotes what is done and Ratio-Delay connotes the true mathematical nature of the underlying techniques. A rigorous mathematical treatment will be avoided in favor of explaining the procedure in the simplest possible terms, again referring the reader wishing detailed theory to specialized mathematical texts, technical articles, etc., as previously explained.

The normal distribution curve of Fig. 1, as previously explained, is a graphical representation of the distribution of natural variations to which the laws of probability and statistics can be applied. It is connected with the procedure being described here in much the same manner as it was with the statistical determination of time study accuracy covered in a previous section of this chapter. In essence, the work sampling procedure relies on statistical concepts related to probability theory to short-circuit the amount of work (number of readings or sample size) required to obtain an average value for a measurable unit to a specified degree of accuracy for the attribute being measured. Note from Fig. 1 that the average of all values in the "population" is the value associated with the highpoint of the curve.

The work sampling procedure can be used to predict, with only a limited number of observations, such things as percentage delay due to

---

[5] "The Use of Multi-Variable Charts to Simplify MTM Standard Data," by T. R. Snakenberg, *Journal of Methods-Time Measurement*, Vol. I, No. 5, December 1954.

one or more specified causes, frequency of occurrence of auxiliary elements (previous section mentioned this), and even approximate performance times for labor standards (although this is usually limited to work that is not highly repetitive). Actually, the techniques of ratio-delay can be used for many other purposes, but these are the main ones in which the work analyst is interested.

The remarks concerning randomness of readings and the problems of scheduling observations given in the discussion of statistical time study procedures in this chapter apply as well to ratio-delay. Emphasis in this section will be on the additional practical procedures and strategies needed for the engineer to perform and interpret work sampling studies.

The first major public announcement indicating the truly practical nature of work sampling or ratio-delay was made in an article[6] by Dr. Chester L. Brisley. Actually, Messrs. Ralph M. Barnes and Donald S. Correll authored an earlier article dated Sept., 1950; and Dr. Barnes authored a book[7] on the subject later.

The material in this section is based principally on an article[8] by John M. Allderige, author of the material earlier included on statistical time study. It contained the nomographs and suggestions of the procedure which are described here. In a manner similar to that employed for statistical time study, the procedure to be followed in making a statistically valid ratio-delay study without excessive computation will be given in definite steps. The reader who has unanswered questions after completing a study of this section is urged to investigate further by consulting the referenced material or other writings concerning statistical procedures.

Ratio-Delay or Work Sampling is defined in A.S.M.E. Standard 106 entitled "Industrial Engineering Terminology" as follows: "A statistical sampling technique employed to determine the proportion of delays or other classifications of activity present in the total work cycle." A simple example making it relatively easy to understand the working of this procedure follows.

Assume that an analyst must determine the proportion of the working day the chief clerk in an industrial engineering department spends in answering the telephone, taking dictation, and filing. A simple, condensed description of the application of this technique is that the observer would make randomized visits to the work area of the chief clerk a pre-determined number of times daily and tabulate on a prepared form, by merely checking

[6] "How You Can Put Work Sampling to Work," by C. L. Brisley, *Factory Management and Maintenance*, McGraw-Hill, New York City, July 1952.

[7] *Work Sampling*, by Dr. Ralph M. Barnes, W. C. Brown and Co., Dubuque, Iowa, 1956.

[8] "Work Sampling Without Formulas," by John M. Allderige, *Factory Management and Maintenance*, McGraw-Hill, New York City, March 1954.

the appropriate category, the activity she was engaged in at the time of observation. In other words, he would merely record which element was occurring at the instant of each visit; and, if she was doing something not defined in the categories, he would mark an occurrence under a "catch-all" classification such as "other activities."

At the end of 15 days, a summary of his tabulations might read as follows:

Activity	Observations	Per Cent of Total
Answering telephone	120	60
Taking dictation	36	18
Filing	20	10
Other activities	24	12
Totals	200	100 Per cent

The final percentage distribution of the various elements as calculated in the right column will tend to equal the exact percentage distribution that would result from a continuous observation of her activities. This, of course, depends on whether correct procedure was followed and observations were random.

The procedure for work sampling next advocated has a statistical background very similar to that for the time study procedure, and solves statistically the problem of the number of observations required to achieve a predetermined degree of accuracy required for the elements. To emphasize the similarity of the two procedures and to orient the reader in advance, the major steps of the ratio-delay procedure are listed as follows:

Step I. Specify and define the items or elements to be studied.

Step II. Estimate the final answer or make a preliminary one-day study of 50 or more random observations and summarize them.

Step III. Design the study by applying the alignment chart to the data of the preliminary study and/or estimate to determine the required number of observations, then schedule them randomly.

Step IV. Accomplish the study as designed, developing a control graph, analyze the data for statistical control by using the graph with the control limit chart, and revise the observation schedule if indicated.

Step V. Summarize the study and determine its final precision.

Each step of this procedure, and the principles governing them, will now be separately discussed in detail.

Step I. Specify and define the items or elements to be studied.

It is extremely important to state explicitly the content of each item or element that is to be studied. The elements must be so selected and defined as to leave no doubt in the mind of the observer into which category he should place what he sees. This means that, in addition to the categories which must be defined as to percentage of occurrence, he must always have one element in every ratio-delay study into which he can classify all occurrences which do not fit without question into one of the main categories. In the simple example previously given, this element was labeled "Other activities."

At first glance, the work covered by each element in the simple example regarding the industrial engineering clerk appears to be obvious. However, observation of the clerk's activities could be misleading, unless the content of each element is carefully defined.

Definition of element content is best illustrated by discussing one of the elements of the simple example—say, that of filing. Filing will normally include work performed both at the filing cabinets and at the desk of the clerk. At the cabinet, she may be at times engaged in work not properly called filing, such as removing papers or merely referring to them without removing them. At the desk, she will normally arrange in alphabetical or numerical order the papers to be filed as part of the task of filing; but she may also sort papers at her desk for other purposes, as well as performing other kinds of work on stacks of papers. With these possibilities, the observer would not likely be sure whether he was seeing filing work at either location unless he would ask the clerk if the work was filing. Since it is generally undesirable to disturb the operator during a ratio-delay study, the need for defining elements and providing recognition cues by which the observer can distinguish the elements so defined is now more apparent. In the example, one approach would arbitrarily define filing as all work at the filing cabinet, although this would perhaps mean another study to be taken later if *only* the filing activity were to be reassigned to another clerk.

As mentioned above, it is generally undesirable to disturb the operator(s) at work during a ratio-delay study. If the definition of the categories is such as to make this necessary, it means that the operator(s) can easily influence the results to accord with their own wishes. Obviously, the study would then lose its value in some measure. This points up a human relations problem in work sampling which is similar to that involved in any other work measurement procedure. Operators should always be made aware that they will be studied, and also for what purpose, if their confidence and cooperation is to be gained. When this is not done, they will discover the study soon enough anyway and will greatly resent not being trusted by being informed at the start.

The need to properly define the categories is true for the type of ratio-delay study being presented here. Another approach—one that makes the use of statistical procedures and validation extremely difficult—is to make random observations and list what is being done at the time of observation. This plan is followed unless a repeat of the same activity allows another tally under a previous listing. The elements, as well as their magnitude, are never finally determined with this approach until condensation of the data is made at the end of the study. In a sense, then, even this approach requires careful definition of element content, the task merely being deferred until the end of the study, which occurs when the analyst feels sufficient observations have been made to warrant ending them.

Since the specification of work content in an element can often be critical, it is important that the definition be in written form. This will fulfill the record keeping requirement of good workstudy. Another reason for writing the definition is that it helps avoid the introduction of statistical error due to the observer modifying his thinking, and hence his classifica-

		16 February 1956
Large Drill Press Section		A. Count Terr, Analyst
HOLBORE CORPORATION		Industrial Engineering

Purpose of Study: To guide the planning of a new layout for the drill press area, so as to minimize operator interference

Problem Studied: Determine per cent of operator time lost due to traffic in aisles with the present layout

Plan of Study: Ten random observations per shift to be completed in twelve days. There are three 8-hour shifts of 20 operators each

Results of Study: Per following tabulation and calculation.

Activity	Code	Observations Taken	Per cent of Total
Productive work	A	5,726	81.3
Delays not specified in study	B	998	14.2
Interference delays due to:			
Pedestrian traffic in aisles	C	163	2.3
Manual material handlers	D	17	.2
Truck material handlers	E	4	.1
Inspection delay	F	130	1.9
Totals		7,038	100.0%
Total Interference Delays (C through F)		314	4.5%

$$\text{Error} = \pm 2\sqrt{\frac{p(1-p)}{N}} = \pm 2\sqrt{\frac{0.045(1-0.045)}{7,038}} = \pm 0.0049 \text{ or } \pm 0.49\%$$

Answer: Interference Delay is 4.5% ± 0.5%. This means that the interval from 4.0 to 5.0% has about a 95% chance of containing the true value. It also shows the percentage of element tolerance to be: $\pm \dfrac{0.49\%}{4.50\%} = \pm 0.109 = \pm 10.9\%$

Fig. 5.   Interference delay summary

tion of observations, as the study progresses. When this error has occurred, it means that only part of the data is valid and/or the observer has recorded a mixture of data of questionable over-all validity. If he feels an original definition is incorrect, he should complete the study as defined, so that he has data consistent with that condition. He can then make an additional study to check the effect of his revised thinking by comparing it with the first for differences in element content.

The example ratio-delay study which will be used to illustrate the procedure is summarized in Fig. 5. It concerns the determination of interference delay due to specified causes in a large drill press section of a machine shop. The purpose of the study was to guide the planning of a new layout so as to minimize production time lost due to work interferences encountered by the operators. The major element in this study as to expected degree of occurrence was productive work, as will be true of most studies in which all observations taken must be classified in some manner. To categorize all other events, this study included elements for: (1) the delays due to interferences which were to be evaluated; and (2) all other non-productive delays not being investigated in detail. Note also the use of code letters to identify each of the elements. This was done for convenience in identifying the observations on the study form used by the observer. Figure 6 shows the observation form used for one day of the study, including the data taken.

The study not only determined the amount of delay in per cent of total time due to interference with the operator, but also classified the causes for the delay and determined the contribution of each cause to the total interference delay. This data was important to the purpose of the study, since the layout could be planned with more factual data at the planner's disposal. The necessity for such sub-classification is a feature often found in work sampling studies.

Step II. Estimate the final answer or make a preliminary one-day study of 50 or more random observations and summarize them.

The purpose of this step is to provide number values with which to enter the ratio–delay alignment chart in Step III. The procedure permits the magnitude of the final answer (total interference delay in the example) to be either estimated or based on a preliminary study. If a preliminary one-day study is taken, the engineer summarizes his counts or number of observations for each category and calculates the resultant percentage distribution for each category. This computation is made by dividing the total for a given element by the grand total for all observations taken. Using a preliminary study as described under this step, the total interference delay for the example study was indicated to be approximately 4 per cent of the operators' time, or 2 out of 50 observations.

INTERFERENCE DELAY OBSERVATION FORM   Date 2-12-56

Daily Shift	Clock Time	Incidence by Code						Total Taken
		A	B	C	D	E	F	
1st	0732	13	6	1				20
	0813	17	2				1	20
	0905	18	1	1				20
	1001	15	4			1		20
	1036	11	7	1			1	20
	1218	9	10	1				20
	1305	13	6				1	20
	1346	15	3	2				20
	1413	18	1	1				20
	1448	6	13				1	20
2nd — 1st Half	1512	19		1				20
	1603	17	2				1	20
	1658	16	3	1				20
	1742	19					1	20
	1823	11	8	1				20
Half-day Totals		217	66	10	0	1	6	300
% of Total		72.4	22.0	3.3	0	0.3	2.0	100%
2nd — 2nd Half	1908	18	1				1	20
	1951	19	1					20
	2021	18	1		1			20
	2145	19					1	20
	2231	16	3	1				20
3rd	2318	19	1					20
	2402	19					1	20
	2453	18	1	1				20
	0114	19	1					20
	0147	19					1	20
	0208	16	3	1				20
	0350	19					1	20
	0438	19	1					20
	0510	18	1	1				20
	0607	18	2					20
Half-day Totals		274	16	4	1	0	5	300
% of Total		91.4	5.3	1.3	0.3	0	1.7	100%
All-day Totals		491	82	14	1	1	11	600
% of Total		81.8	13.7	2.3	0.2	0.2	1.8	100%

Period	Interference — % Delay	3 Sigma Limits %	Upper Limit %	Lower Limit %	
1st Half 2nd Half	5.6% 3.3%	4.2% 3.1%	9.8% 6.4%	1.2% 0.2%	Analyst: *A. Count Terr*
All Day	4.5%	2.6%	7.1%	1.9%	

Fig. 6.   One day's observations for example ratio-delay study.

Whether the preliminary answer is estimated or results from a preliminary study under this step of the procedure, it is used with an alignment chart to determine the number of observations required as part of Step III.   Since this chart can be consulted as often as necessary, in a manner similar to that for the chart connected with the statistical time study procedure, there is no major penalty for beginning with an estimated answer.   The advantage of making a preliminary study, however, is that the result from the first entry into the alignment chart is more likely to provide the correct final answer as to the number of observations required without the necessity for further entries.   This is especially true when the observer initially has no reasonably good idea of what the final percentage distribution of elements is likely to be.   Preliminary study data can also serve to shorten the complete study, since validly it can and should be included as part of the complete data of the final study.

Step III.   Design the study by applying the alignment chart to the data of the preliminary study and/or estimate to determine the required number of observations, then schedule them randomly.

The alignment chart or nomograph used for this step, Fig. 7, is a work sampling alignment chart.   It is used to ascertain the number of observations required for the desired degree of precision and to check the actual precision upon completion of a work sampling study.   It is mathematically based on about 50 per cent assurance that the designated sample size will produce the specified precision interval with about 95 per cent probability of that interval containing the true value.   The indicated number of readings required depends on both the magnitude of the work element being measured and the degree of precision that is permissible.   Essentially, it is a graphical means of easily obtaining results which would otherwise require excessive computation.

It was mentioned that the chart provides 95 per cent assurance of being within the specified precision interval.   For those mathematically inclined, it can be stated per Poisson's equation that

$$\text{One standard deviation} = \sqrt{\frac{p(1-p)}{N}}$$

in which one standard deviation (1 sigma) is defined as the per cent of variation from the mean value permitted for a given reading if it is to be accepted or included in the final sample as being valid data, p is the percentage which the element being studied bears to the total observations, expressed as a decimal, and N is the number of observations taken in the sample.

To construct a nomograph like that used in this procedure, the statisti-

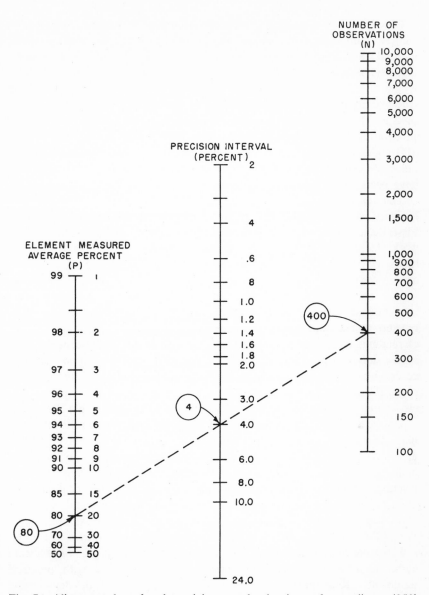

Fig. 7. Alignment chart for determining sample size in work sampling. (95% confidence level.)

cian takes account of one basic problem.   He must decide on an acceptable per cent assurance (the inverse of risk) that the actual average obtained from sampling is within the specified precision interval.   Because the alignment chart for this procedure was built with about a 95 per cent assurance (actually 95.45 associated with 2-sigma limits), the *average value* obtained by following the procedure specified in this section of this chapter will be within the specified per cent of the true average (the precision interval) and there is 95 per cent assurance of that being so. If the risk factor chosen had been defined as one-sigma limits, then the statistician would be selecting the chance of being within the specified per cent of the true average only 68.27 times out of 100 (this gives odds of 61.27/31.73 or 2 to 1). If 2-sigma limits are specified, as is true for the chart of this procedure, the chance of being right is increased to 95.45 times out of 100 (odds of about 21 to 1). Lastly, if this procedure had been built to reflect 3-sigma limits, it would mean that the chance of correctness would have been 99.73 times out of 100 (odds of about 369 to 1).

The result obtained from Step II, whether estimated or from a preliminary study, is used with the alignment chart in the following manner: First, decide what precision is desired (for example, ±5 per cent) for the work element being checked in the work sampling study. Next, multiply this selected precision by the element percentage found in Step II (4 per cent in the example) to obtain a "precision interval," which is 0.2 per cent for the numbers just given. It is a fact, however, that as the precision interval is decreased, the number of observations required becomes ever greater; an accuracy of ±5 per cent would require an exorbitant number of readings to assure validity, actually 24 million for 4 per cent delay to a precision of 5 per cent. Since this is out of the question, it was deemed acceptable for the sample study to have a precision of 10 to 15 per cent, say, 12½ per cent. Multiplying 4 per cent by 12.5 per cent yields a precision interval of 0.5 per cent, which was used for the study being illustrated.

On the alignment chart, the element percentage is found on the left-hand bar, and this point is aligned with the point on the middle bar corresponding to the precision interval. The resulting line when extended to the right-hand bar will intersect that scale at the number of observations required. Using a ruler to line up the element percentage of 4 per cent and the precision interval of 0.5 per cent, it is found on the right-hand scale that approximately 7,000 observations will be needed for the example study. With this information, the analyst is ready to design his study.

From the foregoing discussion it can be seen that the degree of precision and, therefore, the precision interval, must be selected with practical judgment. Remembering that one of the purposes of ratio–delay study is more economical use of the analyst's time, it obviously is essential to keep the number of observations to be made to a minimum consistent with the final use required of the sampling data. When the element to be measured is a large proportion of the total sample, say 20 per cent, the number of observations required for 5 per cent precision would be only 400, as shown in Fig. 7. In this case, therefore, a precision of 5 per cent is reasonable, whereas it was ridiculous for the data of the sample study;

rotating the ruler about the percentage for the element on the left-hand bar of the chart as a pivot, it is easy to see the interplay between the precision interval and the number of observations. The strategy just mentioned is a good one to use when applying this procedure, so as to keep the number of observations required within reasonable bounds.

Having determined the number of readings required, 7,000 or so for the example, the engineer is ready to plan or design his study. As noted in Fig. 5, it was decided to take 10 random observations per shift over a period of twelve days. Since there were 20 operators on each of 3 shifts, this meant that the analyst could obtain 600 observations or readings per day to get the total of 7,000 within 12 days. Actually, since he already had 50 readings in the preliminary study, somewhat less than 12 days were required.

As described earlier in this chapter under statistical time study, it is very important that the observations be randomized. The means for achieving this were amply described there, and are not repeated here for that reason.

The observation form used by the engineer should be as simple as possible. The one used in the example study, shown in Fig. 6, is typical of those used in a work sampling study. Since ratio-delay studies differ radically as to the number of elements to be studied, their definition, the period over which the observations are spread, etc., it is usually better to design a simple form specially for each study. That is, no standardized forms for work sampling studies are in general usage as is the case for time studies. The analyst can save himself much time and effort by devoting a little care to the design of his observation form.

Step IV. Accomplish the study as designed, developing a control graph, analyze the data for statistical control by using the graph with the control limit chart, and revise the observation schedule if indicated.

Having completed Step III, the engineer next carries out the study in accordance with the observation plan. It is possible to do this without knowing until the end of the study whether the data taken is statistically valid, which might necessitate additional study to correct bad data. The use of a control graph in this step of the work sampling procedure, however, will enable a check for statistical validity both at the end of the study and also at intermediate periods—it can even be applied for very short periods if desired, such as for each half-day interval, when the daily observations are large in number.

At the end of each day, or the period for which he is to check statistical control if it is less than a one day period, he summarizes his counts and calculates: (1) the percentage delay for each element and/or sub-element; and (2) the cumulative percentages for the same items, which includes the combined effect of all previous readings. He uses this data to plot a control graph as next described.

As soon as the summary computations are completed, the analyst should begin his control graph and continue to plot it until the completion of the entire study. An example control graph is shown in Fig. 8, although it does not depict data from the example study. The ordinate is graduated

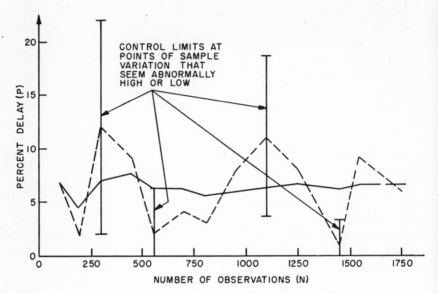

Fig. 8.   Representative ratio-delay control graph.

in percentage of interference delay (or other appropriate category) and the abscissa in cumulative number of observations. On this set of coordinates is plotted both the total percentage of interference delay (or other element being evaluated) for the period being plotted at the total number of observations up to that time and the cumulative value of the variable (interference delay in the example) up to that point. In the plot shown in Fig. 8, solid lines indicate the cumulative values and dotted lines connect the values for the period in question. Note that the cumulative curve tends to approach a constant value as the study progresses, showing only minor variation for the last few periods being plotted. This behavior indicates the variable being determined is nearing a stable value, whereas the dotted curve shows the continued normal fluctuation in each period.

At any particular time that the variation for a given period seems abnormally high or low, the consistency of the sample—set of observations —for that period may be checked by using the alignment chart for control limits shown in Fig. 9. With this chart, the upper and lower control limits for the sample of any given period may be found and applied to the graph as shown in Fig. 8 to see whether the study remains in statistical control. When points appear out-of-control in the plot, being either above the upper limit or below the lower limit, it means that some factor other than chance causes is influencing the set of observations. The data connected with this condition can then be examined for the assignable cause

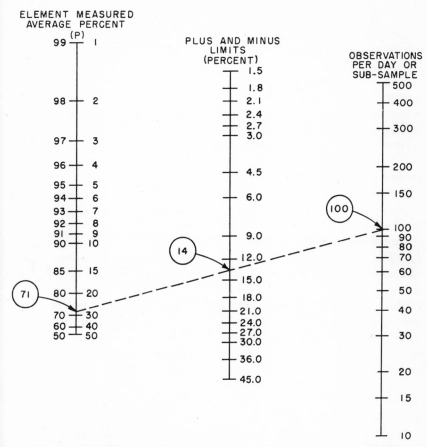

Fig. 9. Alignment chart for determining control limits in work sampling.

and either corrected, if possible, or eliminated as bad data. Good data must then be taken later in the study to replace any data eliminated for this reason.

The control limit alignment chart, Fig. 9, is used in the following manner. The number of observations taken per day or specified sample period (found on the right-hand bar) is aligned with the cumulative percentage (found on the left-hand bar), and the percentage control limit is read at the intersection of this line with the middle bar. An example is plotted on Fig. 9. It shows the control limits to be ±14 per cent (for 3 sigma tolerance) for 100 observations per day of an element being studied that has a cumulative average of 71 per cent. This means that the cumulative percentage for the readings obtained prior to and including the 100 observations is typical so long as none of the incremental averages calculated for sub-samples of the total observations exceeded 85 per cent (71 per cent + 14 per cent) or were less than 57 per cent (71 per cent − 14 per cent). In the example, the total number of observations included 10 sub-samples of 100 observations each. This means that the element in question should not occur more than 85 times nor less than 57 times (which are the percentage limits applied to the sub-sample size of 100) in each of the 10 sub-samples. Stated another way, if each sub-sample is within limits, then the total sample of 1,000 observations is valid. Also, when an individual sample within limits is added to any previous in-limit samples of a continuous study. the cumulative sample in turn is typical.

The reason for finding the control limits should now be evident. The control graph will reveal when the dotted curve varies greatly, and these points can be judged against the control limits. Where the variation is slight, however, the analyst may confidently proceed without taking this precaution. The cumulative curve, on the other hand, serves to help judge the extent of variation and also to give clues, by leveling off, regarding the approaching end of the study. Any points not in control require examination of the data for that point. If the trouble cannot be corrected, this data, and all data associated with the identified cause, should be discarded. If part of the data is correct, it may be retained and only that portion in error dropped. For example, readings taken in a department shortly after an operator has fainted can be chaotic; if they can be isolated in the study, they should be discarded, but the rest of the data for that period should be retained if sound.

Since 600 observations per day were taken in the example study, the analyst decided to apply the control procedure twice daily to 300 observations each time.

When the observations required during the study have all been taken and the control graph plotted, with any necessary checks and corrections being accomplished, the analyst has carried to completion the study as designed. He knows that he has a series of random observations correctly categorized and sufficient in number, within the limits of statistical variation as well, to give the desired degree of assurance that his sample is representative of the total population. In other words, he can use the resulting percentages as though he had the full number of readings required to produce the entire probability curve for the kind of data he was observing. He can do this because this work sampling procedure is based on scientific principles which accurately predict the correctness of his results. The only remaining task is covered in Step V.

Step V.   Summarize the study and determine its final precision.

Knowing that the data is in statistical control as a result of accomplishing Step IV, it is then possible to prepare the summary of the study which was shown as Fig. 5. This summary can assume various forms, depending on the nature of the study, the desires of the analyst as to how to express his results, policy or procedure standards in his company, etc. In general, however, it should include most of the topics noted in the sample summary because it comprises, in most cases, the report of the study to the authority who requested it. Normally, observation sheets and other papers connected with the analysis are retained by the analyst.

To determine the final precision attained during the study, the analyst may either calculate it as was done in Fig. 5, or he may re-enter the alignment chart in Fig. 7 as follows. The final average element percentage on the left-hand bar is aligned with the final sample size as found on the right-hand bar of the alignment chart. The intersection of the line joining these two points is noted on the precision interval scale on the center bar. In the example study, aligning 4.5 per cent on the left bar with 7,038 observations on the right bar produces a line whose intersection with the center bar shows the precision interval to be 0.5 per cent. This indicates that the total interference delay of 4.5 per cent was correct within ±0.5 per cent, as is shown calculated at the bottom of the summary for the example. Stating this another way, it means that there is a 95 per cent chance that the interval between 4.0 per cent and 5.0 per cent contains the true delay.

Another statistic that can be obtained is the per cent element tolerance. Dividing the precision of 0.5 per cent by the element percentage of 4.5 per cent (see bottom of summary) shows the element tolerance to be ±.109 or ±10.9 per cent. This compares favorably to the 12.5 per cent originally used to determine the number of observations required. Since the engineer had expected to be satisfied with a tolerance somewhere between 10 per cent and 15 per cent, he accepted this difference and was pleased with the results.

While there are many possible ways to take ratio-delay studies, and many minor variations of each of these, the authors feel that the procedure outlined above is a step in the direction of improving this work measurement tool. Certainly, it permits more confidence in applying the ratio-delay principles than is the case where no statistical control is kept or computed.

TIME CONVERSION

There is a tendency for industrial engineers and work analysts to think of time conversion as a topic that can be dismissed conveniently from serious consideration. This attitude of disinterest often leads to unnecessary computations, clerical bottlenecks, and sources of error; all of which indicates an internal weakness within the industrial engineering department.

If it is proper to consider any legitimate means by which to reduce direct labor on the factory floor, it is equally important to reduce labor within the industrial engineering activity—such engineers often need to take a dose of their own "medicine." Work analysts can set an example by expediting their own tasks and procedures by utilizing efficient methods. Much of the drudgery connected with translating work studies into practical cost accounting data consists of time conversions, application of allowances and variance factors, dollar computation, etc. This onerous chore can be minimized by eliminating unnecessary repetitive calculations.

Basically, two chief purposes are served by work study data—regardless of whether time study or a predetermined system was used to produce the data. The purpose internal to an industrial engineering department is to meet the need for time data with which to evaluate methods, processes, and, sometimes, performance; normally, minutes per piece and pieces per hour are the most convenient time units to use. The other major purpose is to supply the cost accounting department with time and/or dollars per piece or per one hundred pieces for such purposes as labor control, pricing, and wage calculation. The most convenient time units for this usage are hours per piece or hours per hundred pieces, with the inclusion of any or all of the proper allowances and variance factors in the figure submitted plus dollar information where applicable. The reason cost accounting is easier with hourly units, essentially, is because most labor rates are negotiated and applied in terms of dollars per hour. An additional possible requirement for accounting systems is the conversion of time units to production per hour, man-hours per specified quantity, or the number of operators needed to produce at a specified rate. It is plain that a work analyst can profitably expend some time and effort to simplify required calculations.

The utilization of pre-calculated tabular values to eliminate a continual recomputation of frequently required data is illustrated by Tables 5, 6, and 7. These tables contain the majority of the time and dollar conversion data normally needed in work study activities.

Table 5 lists the common time conversion factors which must be used within an industrial engineering activity. Its use can be illustrated by two examples.

Example 1: An operator takes 5 seconds to assemble several parts. Assuming 100% performance, determine the required select minutes and select hourly production for this operation.
Solution:
　Select minutes = 5 seconds $\times$ 0.0167 = 0.0833 minutes
　Hourly production = 3,600 $\div$ 5 seconds/piece = 720 pieces/hour.

Example 2: An MTM pattern, with 15% P.F. & D. allowances added, shows a task to merit an allowed time standard of 2,060 TMU. Compute the allowed minutes and the allowed time production per hour for this operation.

Solution:

Allowed minutes = 2,060 TMU × 0.0006 = <u>1.2360 minutes</u>

Allowed rate = 100,000 ÷ 2,060 TMU/piece = <u>48.5 pieces/hour.</u>

Table 5. Time Conversion Table

(Based on the defined value of 100,000 TMU per hour)

Having	Perform This Operation	To Get
Hours	Multiply by 60	Minutes
Hours	Multiply by 3,600	Seconds
Hours	Multiply by 100,000	TMU
Minutes	Divide by 60 (or multiply by 0.0167)	Hours
Minutes	Multiply by 60	Seconds
Minutes	Multiply by 1,667 (or 100,000/60)	TMU
Seconds	Divide by 3,600 (or multiply by 0.000278)	Hours
Seconds	Divide by 60 (or multiply by 0.0167)	Minutes
Seconds	Multiply by 27.8 (or 100,000/3,600)	TMU
TMU	Multiply by .00001	Hours
TMU	Multiply by .0006	Minutes
TMU	Multiply by .036	Seconds
Pieces per hour	Take reciprocal	Hours per piece
Pieces per hour	Divide into 60	Minutes per piece
Pieces per hour	Divide into 3,600	Seconds per piece
Pieces per hour	Divide into 100,000	TMU per piece
Hours per piece	Take reciprocal	Pieces per hour
Minutes per piece	Divide into 60	Pieces per hour
Seconds per piece	Divide into 3,600	Pieces per hour
TMU per piece	Divide into 100,000	Pieces per hour

Table 6 gives another type of tabular data often found useful and which eliminates unnecessary repetitive calculation. It provides pre-calculated minute and second values for almost the entire range of TMU time values normally encountered in work analysis. Similar tables could be developed for ranges of other time units, should such conversions prove frequently

Table 6. Conversion of TMU to Minutes and Seconds*

TMU Range	TMU	Minutes	Seconds
Thousands	10,000	6.000	360.00
	9,000	5.400	324.00
	8,000	4.800	288.00
	7,000	4.200	252.00
	6,000	3.600	216.00
	5,000	3.000	180.00
	4,000	2.400	144.00
	3,000	1.800	108.00
	2,000	1.200	72.00
	1,000	.600	36.00
Hundreds	900	.540	32.40
	800	.480	28.80
	700	.420	25.20
	600	.360	21.60
	500	.300	18.00
	400	.240	14.40
	300	.180	10.80
	200	.120	7.20
	100	.060	3.60
Tens	90	.0540	3.240
	80	.0480	2.880
	70	.0420	2.520
	60	.0360	2.160
	50	.0300	1.800
	40	.0240	1.440
	30	.0180	1.080
	20	.0120	.720
	10	.0060	.360
Units	9	.0054	.324
	8	.0048	.288
	7	.0042	.252
	6	.0036	.216
	5	.0030	.180
	4	.0024	.144
	3	.0018	.108
	2	.0012	.072
	1	.0006	.036
Tenths	0.9	.00054	.0324
	.8	.00048	.0288
	.7	.00042	.0252
	.6	.00036	.0216
	.5	.00030	.0180
	.4	.00024	.0144
	.3	.00018	.0108
	.2	.00012	.0072
	.1	.00006	.0036

* 1 minute = 1,666.7 TMU.   1 second = 27.8 TMU.

Table 7. Dollar Value of Time Units for Various Labor Rates

TMUs →	1,000	2,000	3,000	4,000	5,000	6,000	7,000	8,000	9,000	10,000
Minutes →	.60	1.20	1.80	2.40	3.00	3.60	4.20	4.80	5.40	6.00
Hours →	.01	.02	.03	.04	.05	.06	.07	.08	.09	.10
1.00	.0100	.0200	.0300	.0400	.0500	.0600	.0700	.0800	.0900	.1000
1.05	.0105	.0210	.0315	.0420	.0525	.0630	.0735	.0840	.0945	.1050
1.10	.0110	.0220	.0330	.0440	.0550	.0660	.0770	.0880	.0990	.1100
1.15	.0115	.0230	.0345	.0460	.0575	.0690	.0805	.0920	.1035	.1150
1.20	.0120	.0240	.0360	.0480	.0600	.0720	.0840	.0960	.1080	.1200
1.25	.0125	.0250	.0375	.0500	.0625	.0750	.0875	.1000	.1125	.1250
1.30	.0130	.0260	.0390	.0520	.0650	.0780	.0910	.1040	.1170	.1300
1.35	.0135	.0270	.0405	.0540	.0675	.0810	.0945	.1080	.1215	.1350
1.40	.0140	.0280	.0420	.0560	.0700	.0840	.0980	.1120	.1260	.1400
1.45	.0145	.0290	.0435	.0580	.0725	.0870	.1015	.1160	.1275	.1450
1.50	.0150	.0300	.0450	.0600	.0750	.0900	.1050	.1200	.1350	.1500
1.55	.0155	.0310	.0465	.0620	.0775	.0930	.1085	.1240	.1395	.1550
1.60	.0160	.0320	.0480	.0640	.0800	.0960	.1120	.1280	.1440	.1600
1.65	.0165	.0330	.0495	.0660	.0825	.0990	.1155	.1320	.1485	.1650
1.70	.0170	.0340	.0510	.0680	.0850	.1020	.1190	.1360	.1530	.1700
1.75	.0175	.0350	.0525	.0700	.0875	.1050	.1215	.1400	.1575	.1750
1.80	.0180	.0360	.0540	.0720	.0900	.1080	.1260	.1440	.1620	.1800
1.85	.0185	.0370	.0555	.0740	.0925	.1110	.1295	.1480	.1665	.1850
1.90	.0190	.0380	.0570	.0760	.0950	.1140	.1330	.1520	.1710	.1900
1.95	.0195	.0390	.0585	.0780	.0975	.1170	.1365	.1560	.1755	.1950
2.00	.0200	.0400	.0600	.0800	.1000	.1200	.1400	.1600	.1800	.2000
2.05	.0205	.0410	.0615	.0820	.1025	.1230	.1435	.1640	.1845	.2050
2.10	.0210	.0420	.0630	.0840	.1050	.1260	.1470	.1680	.1890	.2100
2.15	.0215	.0430	.0645	.0860	.1075	.1290	.1505	.1720	.1935	.2150
2.20	.0220	.0440	.0660	.0880	.1100	.1320	.1540	.1760	.1980	.2200
2.25	.0225	.0450	.0675	.0900	.1125	.1350	.1575	.1800	.2025	.2250

Labor Rate in Dollars Per Hour   Dollar Values

To cover the following time ranges in			Shift decimal in table value to the
TMUs	Minutes	Hours	
1 to 10	0.0006 to 0.006	0.00001 to 0.0001	Left three digits
10 to 100	.006 to .06	.0001 to .001	Left two digits
100 to 1,000	.06 to .6	.001 to .01	Left one digit
10,000 to 100,000	6 to 60	.1 to 1	Right one digit
100,000 to 1,000,000	60 to 600	1 to 10	Right two digits
1,000,000 to 10,000,000	600 to 6,000	10 to 100	Right three digits

needed. This type of table is used, essentially, to avoid repetitive multiplication. A method of utilizing this table is shown in Examples 3 and 4.

Example 3: Convert 912.8 TMU to minutes.
Solution:

TMU	Minutes
900	0.540
10	0.0060
2	0.0012
0.8	0.00048
Total 912.8	0.54768

Example 4: How many seconds is 247.1 TMU?
Solution:

TMU	Minutes
200	7.2000
40	1.4400
7	0.2520
0.1	0.0036
Total 247.1	8.8956

Both of these examples make use of simple addition which can be performed on a low cost adding machine or manually. The calculation of labor costs, most frequently required in conjunction with cost savings analysis and for product pricing, can often be simplified by using a tabulation of the type shown in Table 7. Although it covers the range of labor rates from $1.00 to $2.25 per hour, it could be extended to lower and higher values if desired; a work analyst might also find it convenient to develop a table with more rows and columns, which would reduce the amount of interpolation necessary.

Example 5: A worker earning $1.55 per hour performs a task which the work analyst believes can be retooled to save 420 TMU. What tooling cost will be the breakeven point?
Solution:
Referring to the bottom portion of the table, it is necessary to shift the decimal in the table one place to the left for TMU values between 100 and 1,000. A similar step is taken for the 20 TMU value. Then:

TMU	Dollars
400	$0.00620
20	0.00031
Total 420	$0.00651

A saving of $0.00651 per piece will result from retooling. If, say, 180,000 pieces per year are normally produced, the maximum tooling cost that could be paid for out of one year's savings would be:

180,000 pieces/year $\times$ $0.00651/piece = $1,171.80.

In addition to simple tabular schemes, other major computational savings involving both arithmetic and algebra can be effected by making full use of work-saving computing procedures.   Underlying the design of such procedures should be the knowledge that it is desirable to utilize addition and subtraction where possible, since simple office machines then can be used to partially mechanize the work.   Multiplication often, and division almost always, requires the use of such specialized and often unavailable auxiliary computing devices as slide rules (inaccurate), electric calculators, and comptometers to save time, to avoid errors (such as the most frequent one— incorrect placing of decimal points), and to reduce laborious longhand calculation.

It is assumed in this discussion that a large number of calculations are required in a short time, or that the number required will be large over a period of time.   To reduce total computing time, therefore, means that the number of sums, products, and quotients should be reduced by combining calculation steps.

An example will be used to illustrate the method and the economies to be effected by properly combining calculation steps.   It is assumed that many calculations of the nature shown are required daily for the conversion of time-study data into hours per piece with allowances and variance factors included.   A detailed discussion describing the content of allowances and variance factors can be found in Chapter 23.

The example is: The cost department has requested the total hours per piece required to produce a part, with all normal allowances and variance factors included.   The analyst has time studies on all five of the required operations that total 6.072 select minutes.   The allowances and variance factors he normally includes are shown in the detailed conversion steps (see next page).   Note that they pyramid in definite order.

The advantage of the combined factor method is obvious; it not only saves time but it reduces the chances for error, since it requires only one simple multiplication versus nine multiplications, one division, and four additions.   The over-all saving that can be effected by developing tables and/or graphs to cover the full range of allowances and variance factors in this manner (producing a factor sheet) can be considerable.   The main limitation to this idea is that any useful or pertinent information should not be buried in these combined steps so that it cannot be examined or audited.

Detailed Steps Ordinarily Used

Select Time	6.072 minutes/piece
6% Personal Time	0.364
5% Fatigue Allowance	0.304
4% Minor Delays	0.243
15%	
Allowed Time	6.983 minutes/piece
3.67% Rest Period	.256
Total	7.239 minutes/piece
3% Training Loss	.217
2% Setup Time	.145
5% Material Handling	.362
4% Major Delays	.290
14%	
Total	8.253 minutes/piece
Inspection 10%	.825
Total Time	9.078 minutes/piece

Hour/piece = 9.078 ÷ 60 = <u>.1513 hr./pc.</u>

Simplified Computation

Combine all allowances and variance factors into a single factor:

$$\frac{1.15(1.0367)(1.14)(1.10)}{60} = 0.0249 \text{ combined factor}$$

Multiply select time by combined factor:

$$6.072 \times .0249 = \underline{.1512 \text{ hr./pc.}}$$

It is essential that shortcut factors should not be used without obtaining agreement to the procedures and values among all parties who will have occasion to examine the calculations. If such agreement is not obtained, much valuable time of managers and technical personnel will be lost in endless explanations and proofs that the answer produced is correct, particularly if large sums of money are committed by the magnitude of the final answer to such an analysis. Also, not all parties who receive a labor cost analysis will be as familiar with the process, workstudy procedures, the assumptions made, and the general approach of industrial engineers to a specific problem as is the person who produces the analysis. Therefore, it may be necessary for psychological reasons, at times, to make the calculations in such a way as to permit the reviewer to see what values certain variables and/or constants attain on the way to the final answer. For instance, an analysis submitted to the foreman of a machine shop will be received better if allowed time is developed and shown as a separate item.

SUMMARY

The many mathematical tools already being widely employed in work measurement indicate the need for work analysts to become acquainted with them and to fully understand them if they are to fit themselves for the continuing development of analysis techniques.   There is an obvious trend toward ever greater use of mathematical and statistical tools in the solution of industrial engineering and management problems.   The techniques presented in this chapter, therefore, are core material that will some day be an absolute requirement for a person to qualify as a work analyst. Even today, the work analyst must know them to achieve any noteworthy status in the profession.

Some of the tools and techniques have been merely described and their nature indicated in this chapter.   At least two techniques—Statistical Time Study and Ratio–Delay—were deemed sufficiently basic and important to justify elaboration.   The reader should not, however, conclude that the subject has been exhausted.   He can profitably seek from other sources information on many other mathematical and statistical topics not even mentioned earlier.   To list some examples of such topics, the following areas and/or tools can be investigated by an alert student wishing to expand his knowledge: mathematical means (arithmetical, weighted, median, mode, geometric, and harmonic); dispersion (deviation, range, standard deviation, standard error, quadratic mean of deviation, coefficient of dispersion, coefficient of skewness, and critical ratios); the method of least squares to establish curves and trend lines; coefficient of correlation; Student's "t" test; Chi-Square test; confidence intervals and degrees of freedom; analysis of variance; and the theory of probability.   While it is presently true that most of these items are of concern and value mainly to the researcher in work measurement, the practicing work analyst must also understand them to intelligently apply the results of research to practical situations.

Clearly, then, the use of mathematics in work measurement should concern every student and practitioner of work analysis.

PART IV

Applications Engineering

CHAPTER 25

Control of Labor Costs Based on Standards

Substantial sums of money can be saved by establishing labor standards which can be used to manage and control the expenditure of funds for labor in productive enterprises. As an illustration of this fact, the experience of one of the authors is cited. He participated in the direction and installation, within a large industrial concern, of a dual program of methods correction and labor standards (including a standard cost accounting system) that was accomplished in less than a year. The combined program resulted in a *yearly* savings of well over one million dollars, with about half of this total resulting from each phase of the program. The impressive figure of one-half million dollars saved from establishing labor standards alone dramatically emphasizes the opening statement above.

Labor standards are normally used to best advantage in conjunction with either an incentive pay system and/or a standard cost accounting system.

The standards program mentioned did not involve wage incentives, rather it relied upon measuring performance against the standards in terms of individual operator efficiency and implementing any corrective action indicated. Incentives undoubtedly would have produced an additional 20 to 30 per cent increase in productivity; but not all of this could have been counted as a savings, since the operators would have received proportionate pay increases for performance above 100 per cent.

BASIC CONCEPTS OF INCENTIVE PLANS

Labor Standards with Incentive Pay

There are two basic kinds of wage incentives based on labor standards. One pays the operator in direct proportion to any performance above normal or 100 per cent. The other pays bonuses according to some sort of sliding scale, other than in direct proportion to any increase of performance. Early incentive installations often utilized the sliding scale approach. Most such installations have since been converted to a pay system that rewards the worker in direct proportion to performance above standard.

The method of computing an operator's pay under an incentive plan is based either on a price for each hundred parts produced or on a base rate for a standard hour's work. The basic procedure of computing an operator's pay under the price per hundred piece system is quite obvious and needs no elaboration. The fundamental procedure under a base rate system is almost as obvious.

One method is to calculate the operator's efficiency in terms of hourly, daily, or weekly efficiency by dividing actual production by standard production for the time involved. This efficiency is then multiplied by the base rate; of course, adjustment must be made for the number of hours he worked at the calculated efficiency on the particular incentive job.

A second method divides his actual total number of parts produced by the hourly standard (pieces per hour) for the operation to obtain the standard hours of work. These standard hours are then multiplied by the base rate to determine the amount of pay due the operator. The actual detailed procedure followed by any given plant varies according to the individual situation.

The American Society of Mechanical Engineers[1] in Standard No. 106 entitled "Industrial Engineering Terminology" defines labor efficiency in this manner:

1. The ratio of standard performance time to actual performance time usually expressed as a percentage.
2. The ratio of actual performance numbers (e.g. number of pieces) to standard performance numbers usually expressed as a percentage.

Note that the methods indicated for efficiency calculation are in accord with these definitions.

It is quite common for incentive installations to begin payment of the incentive 10 to 20 per cent below what is actually considered as normal performance. This policy utilizes a so-called incentive allowance which actually has the effect of adding time to the base or select time for the operation. Beginning payment of an incentive at a point below actual normal performance is based on the theory that an operator who begins to

[1] At this writing date, the American Society of Mechanical Engineers and the American Institute of Industrial Engineers are jointly developing a new A.S.A. Standard version of the terminology for the American Standards Association; this will supersede all previous standards and will undoubtedly enjoy pre-eminent authority status.

earn an incentive premium, will be further motivated to attain his best possible performance. Actual results in the field indicate some factual support of this theory and some benefits can be derived from this approach. Such policy is, of course, often reflected in the base rates—often they are lower than would be the case if payment of incentive began at normal or 100 per cent performance.

Many situations exist in industry where an operator works part time on an incentive job and part time on a non-incentive job. This type of situation can be handled by reporting practices connected with the daily time card system. Also often involved in such a case is a problem of two different base rates. The incentive job may have one base rate and the non-incentive job another base rate. However, it is normally undesirable to require operators to work under such conditions. An operator placed on an incentive job should be provided, wherever possible, such tasks that all of his work will be on an incentive rate, even though two or more different operations on different parts are involved.

Also encountered are situations where during a given pay period operators work on two or more incentive jobs that do not carry the same base rate or price per hundred pieces. Again, the time card system can take care of such situations. Operators are often paid average earnings when machine breakdowns occur, when taken off incentive jobs to instruct new operators or try out new machines, when their normal work is not available, or when they report for work at the beginning of a shift and for some reason cannot perform incentive tasks (parts are not available, etc.). The payment policy for such situations varies from plant to plant. While it may be questionable to pay average earnings for machine breakdowns, lack of parts, etc., the practice is unquestionably proper for temporary absence from regular work to instruct new operators or to try out a new machine. These latter two occasions obviously occur at management's discretion, so an operator should not be penalized for possessing acquired skills valuable to management.

It is generally conceded that an incentive pay system should never be started unless the majority of operators can be covered by the system. Sixty per cent would constitute a bare minimum, a much more practical and desirable coverage being 75 to 90 per cent. Once an incentive system is started, those not covered by incentives will normally begin demanding coverage. If it is obvious that the system cannot be extended to cover most of the direct labor operators, then it should never be started at all, since it will only cause labor difficulties within the plant when attempted under such conditions. An obvious solution under these circumstances is to set labor standards where possible and measure individual operator and/or department performance against them, which data can then be used as an aid in securing adequate performance.

Individual Versus Group Incentives

On individual operations, it is natural and easy to provide for an individual incentive. It is generally agreed that individual incentives are also the most effective and, therefore, desirable type; however, individual incentives cannot always be established. This is particularly true for progressive assembly operations where any particular operator's productivity depends upon the productivity of his team mates. Group incentives are logical in this type of situation. Group incentives are not as effective as individual incentives; however, some increased performance is usually obtained.

Under group incentives, particularly those involving progressive assembly lines, the maximum production is limited by the slowest operator. It is usual in these situations to find the more experienced operators aiding inexperienced persons, thereby reducing the earnings loss due to training of new operators introduced to the line. It is also true that they encourage laggard operators to strive for their best performance. This action by the laggard operator's team mates is often much more effective in obtaining maximum production than is pressure from the supervisory group.

Another beneficial aspect of such group incentives is the fact that when an operator obviously cannot keep pace with normal and/or superior operators, they will approach the foreman and actually request replacement. In non-incentive installations, on the other hand, a laggard operator's team mates often keep quiet or even insist that he be retained, since their pay is not affected and the amount of work expected of them is reduced.

Process Controlled Work and Incentives

Whether the operator is rewarded in direct proportion to his performance or on a sliding scale, one of the most controversial elements in an incentive plan is the procedure to be followed when all or a large portion of the work cycle is machine or process controlled. The greater the proportion of the work cycle controlled by machines or other process requirements not directly controlled by the operator's pace, the less is his opportunity and hence his reward for exerting maximum effort unless a special incentive plan is developed and used to compensate for this situation. Reference to the discussion of Man and Machine Charting in Chapter 22 will be helpful in what follows regarding the effect of such process controlled work on the time cycle.

With industry constantly increasing its use of mechanization and/or automation, the problem of incentive payment on such jobs is appearing to be ever more critical in relation to the maintenance of satisfactory labor relations and maximum output. Involved in this problem are the facts that a fair incentive plan must permit a reward for operator efficiency and that his performance above standard has two effects on the work including machine or process controlled elements. By maintaining a faster pace in the manually controlled portion of the cycle, the operator obviously accomplishes the manual work in less time (including both external and internal work); and *he also increases the machine utilization,* because it then performs its essentially constant cycle oftener per unit of time than would be the case if the worker merely sustained average or normal performance pace. In addition, when the operator continues the faster pace during internal work (refer to the discussion of Man-Machine Charting), he then becomes able either to rest enough during the idle time so that he can easily continue the higher pace without undue fatigue or to absorb extra machine assignments that will make his time more valuable to the management.

With an understanding of the facts just presented, the design of an incentive plan for wage payment on tasks not fully under operator control resolves itself into a decision on the rewards due the operator for superior performance and then a proper application of fundamental mathematics so as to yield the desired result. This is easier said than done as evidenced by the wide variety of apparent solutions found to this problem in industry. A survey study[2] which evaluated the practices with respect to a number of important criteria is rephrased by the authors as follows.

1. Is the plan simple and understandable? That is, are the calculations and ease of explanation such that the operator will be confident of it?
2. Does the plan afford adequate incentive earnings considering consistency, fair differentials, comparative attainment, and maintenance of proper attitudes by all parties to the plan?
3. Will the plan protect management's interests in regard to equipment performance, manual labor output, ease of developing and explaining labor standards, and simplicity and accuracy of standards calculation?

The approaches or solutions made by industry, from the source cited, can be classified as follows

A. Normal piecework or standard hour (previously discussed)
B. Constant machine incentive allowance combined with standard hour
C. Constant work incentive combined with standard hour
D. Empirical determination of work performance
E. Empirical determination of both work and equipment pertormance.

The first approach has been discussed already. It is unsatisfactory for process controlled work because it does not provide an adequate incentive opportunity on such work. Although the second solution can provide financial incentive, its inconsistencies undoubtedly tend to result in dis-

---

[2] "Incentive Wage Practice for Restricted Work," by Dr. John C. Scheib, Jr., *Journal of Industrial Engineering,* Vol. VIII, No. 3, May–June, 1957.

satisfaction by the workers. That is, although it might yield usable and reasonably correct results for a given task, it contains no adjustive feature for task variation.

Approach C appears to be the best over-all procedure, except for one factor—the pace adjustment used is a constant which yields exactly correct results only when the operator works at the forecast pace. It provides a generally satisfactory financial incentive with relative simplicity of mathematical computation for development of standards. The earnings computation is simple and straightforward, with the difficulty of explanation being slight. By using pre-calculated tables, etc. the slightly complex computations required for standards development can be greatly simplified also. The standard is developed by summing *all* manual work elements (both external and internal) and *adding to this the idle time which would be incurred if the operator would work at a certain pre-established level of performance.* Of course, this standard will be *exactly* correct only if the operator works at that pace, since too much idle time will be included in the standard if he works faster and too little when he works below the pre-established pace. Actually, this error normally tends to be small. The approach does allow or adjust for task differences, as well as providing the other benefits previously indicated. The authors feel it is the best practical solution to the problem for most situations at the present time.

The pay plans involved in Approach D are based on empirical determination of earnings by the use of tables, etc. *which depend primarily on the manual work time involved.* Since such tables can usually be constructed to provide a correct result only for a given task (in terms of percentages of external and internal manual work and idle man time), the standards and earnings calculations both become extremely complex if the plan attempts to adequately and properly cover a wide range and variety of tasks. This leads to a further major detriment—the operator will not understand it.

Although the last solution is the most complex, it is technically the best in that it can yield a precise answer to every task evaluated. However, its complexity tends to negate the fact that it provides satisfactory incentive earnings and adjusts well to differing tasks. This procedure attempts the admittedly desirable task of giving consideration to the maintenance of machine capabilities as well as to the manual work performance. While neither of the resulting dual standards—one covering the machine capacity and the other the performance of the worker himself—is too complex in its development or application, the time standard has little meaning to the average operator and the earnings calculations are of necessity very complex. This complexity results from the necessity to relate each of the two standards to actual time and then relating these two results to each other through the use of formulae or prepared tables. This plan therefore does not appear as practical as Approach C.

It cannot be too strongly emphasized here, however, that the success or failure of any wage system does not depend solely on its merits, but more importantly on how wisely and fairly it is administered. While undesirable features can be overcome, it is best to take full advantage of all possible benefits and/or features during the original design of the system. Hence, Approach C appears to offer the best solution to incentive payment for operations involving process controlled elements.

A more recent solution not included in the source cited but which is very close to Approach D is known as Multi-Factor incentives. Here, the incentive is based on combinations of job-related factors, some of which have no connection with the magnitude of the output from the work cycle. Rather, some of the factors concern product quality, composition, etc. All or only some of the factors may be controllable by the operator; therefore, others may be machine or process controlled. Multi-Factor incentives can be developed for most man-machine operations and for operations which are only partially process-controlled. Developing Multi-Factor incentives involves essentially the following steps:

(1) Determine those factors other than mere quantity of output which the operator can control, e.g. thickness of coatings, composition of mixtures, percentage of impurities, fineness of finish, brightness of polish, etc.

(2) Establish for each such factor in Step 1 its relative importance to the finished production

(3) Assign numerical "weights" by which each of the controllable factors may be allocated, i.e., the degree of effect controlling of the given factor should have on the amount of an operator's pay

(4) Isolate and measure the amount of machine or process controlled time in the work cycle

(5) Establish the time required by the manual portions of the operation

(6) Combine the data of Steps (4) and (5) to establish the basic work cycle time. The principles of Man-Machine Charting in Chapter 22 will assist in this step

(7) Synthesize the results of Steps (3) and (6) into a wage incentive formula for the given operation.

Such Multi-Factor incentives are the most sophisticated approach possible. They normally are used only when operator-controllable factors have a sufficient degree of economic importance to justify the development of this kind of incentive. This approach also can be used in a general way to set performance goals for such tasks as engineering and accounting if the work measurement engineer is creative and imaginative in applying this procedure to such work.

Job Evaluation with Incentives

Before initiating a program of labor standards, it is usually wise to couple it with a job evaluation program. Basically, job evaluation is a systematic procedure for determining proper differentials in pay between the various tasks in a plant. Note that it essentially determines *differentials* in pay and not the exact base rate for each job. A good industrial engineering course will cover the details of a job evaluation program and it is not the intent here to cover this procedure. The industrial engineer's attention is merely called to the procedure and the fact that it is wise to assure the establishment of proper pay differentials between the various jobs.

Job pay-rate differentials sometimes become quite distorted in plants where certain groups of employees performing certain key operations have been very aggressive in the management and direction of their labor union for many years. These groups then often achieve special benefits for themselves which makes their rate of pay out of proportion to that of others in the plant.

Similar disproportionate pay often results from changed conditions. For instance, special premiums are often introduced for performing operations involving exposure to heat or fumes which at some later date following installation of modern ventilation systems and/or cooling systems may be entirely unjustified. Yet the pay differentials originally established because of the poor conditions usually continue. Similar situations often exist when originally highly developed skills were required and later mechanization eliminated the need for such skills.

Summary of Incentive Pay

To summarize, maximum increase in productivity through the use of labor standards is attained when the standards are coupled with an incentive pay system. The increase in productivity above normal is approximately 20 to 30 per cent. A 20 per cent productivity increase does not mean that management has gained by 20 per cent, but rather by some factor less than the 20 per cent, since extra payment is made for production exceeding the normal. However, management gains in addition by somewhat more production at base cost because less floor space per unit of production is required; fewer machines are needed; fewer facilities in general are involved; and also the total cost of personnel services, insurance, and other similar practices are reduced. Incentives also provide management better control of production so that they can more accurately forecast completion dates of orders, etc. These benefits to management are quite tangible and substantial.

It is sometimes argued that production under an incentive pay system does not yield a high quality product. However, quality is not necessarily sacrificed because of an incentive installation; but it is quite important to maintain strong inspection and quality control organizations. Actually, this is important under either an incentive or non-incentive pay system; but it is somewhat more important to have such organizations under incentive conditions. Just how much more important is somewhat difficult to evaluate, since there are many instances of poor quality work in non-incentive plants. There is a greater *tendency* in incentive plants for the workers to neglect quality *if* they are not watched and/or know they are not being checked.

LABOR STANDARDS WITHOUT INCENTIVES

Labor standards systems without incentives are usually called "measured day work" systems. The problems involved in establishing standards are essentially the same as for incentive systems. The standards must be equally good for a measured day work system to be worth the effort required to establish and administer the plan.

To achieve satisfactory production, that is production approaching (but practically never equalling) that in an incentive plant, means that every known management technique must be utilized to the fullest extent. Having standards makes it relatively easy to detect below-average performance. The standards also provide a definitive goal for the operator. This is usually all they will do under a measured day work system, and it is up to the foreman and the supervisors to get adequate performance. This means that the foreman must be well trained and motivated to demand adequate operator performance. This is easier to say than to achieve; however, it is not beyond the realm of possibility—if management recognizes the problem and gears itself accordingly for the effort required. This applies to management at all levels from the factory manager down to the lowest supervisor.

Fortunately, most measured day work systems are coupled with a standard cost system that automatically generates reports showing variance from standard performance. The factory manager, supervisors, and industrial engineers must analyze these reports and determine reasons for any substantial variance from standard or normal performance. Industrial engineers, especially, will find that daily or weekly efficiency reports showing variance from standard performance are a necessity. In some cases, such reports can be in terms of departmental performance and in others they must be based on piece-part and/or individual operator performance if usable data is to be developed.

When a new job is started, operational performance reports are very desirable and in many cases a necessity. If over-all departmental type reports are utilized and there are many different kinds of operations in the department, it will be virtually impossible to detect which operators and/or which operations are causing any over-all low performance. It is only when the engineers and supervision are able to detect those operations most in need of corrective action that the necessary concentration on the problem can result.

These so-called efficiency reports are ordinarily produced by the factory cost accounting department and/or timekeeping department, but in some cases the industrial engineering department produces them. Under certain conditions, especially where a particular kind of job has been in operation for a long period of time, it is possible to resort to efficiency reports developed by foremen. This normally is not a good procedure because it makes it possible for the foremen to hide poor performance. However, it does have one beneficial effect in that it requires the foreman to take direct cognizance of the efficiency of his department. The usual approach, when having the foreman calculate his department's efficiency, is to have the industrial engineering department give him the number of standard hours credit per week that he should receive based upon the scheduled production or in terms of standard hours per unit of production. The foreman then needs only add up the number of actual hours expended by the personnel in his department and divide this sum into the number of standard hours to determine departmental efficiency.

TROUBLE SIGNALS

Low efficiency is always a "red flag" signal indicating a need for corrective action.

Low efficiency could indicate poor or insufficient training, low operator performance, incorrect methods, improper material, poor dimensional tolerance and/or specifications, improper parts, machines in poor condition, insufficient material, etc. This list could be continued ad infinitum. The industrial engineer's tasks, in cooperation with the other operating departments, are to locate the cause and to secure correction when and where required. Neither of these is an easy task.

Locating the cause of the trouble will often call into use all of the analysis skills and procedures at the command of the engineer. Generally, the problem should initially be tackled as follows if the probable cause is not already fairly well established:

1. Interview the production supervision involved
2. Interview the operator
3. Check with inspection and/or quality control personnel.

By this time, the probable reasons for the low efficiency will normally be fairly well established.

If the engineer dealing with departmental efficiency does not have operation efficiency reports available, he will be working under a great handicap and likely will not be able to isolate the cause of the trouble and secure correction. The reasons for this statement are multitudinous. One operator may be experiencing material delays, another is using incorrect methods, still another has a poorly operating machine, etc. Even if some bad conditions are corrected, new ones can develop without the engineer being aware of them, much less knowing their nature and location.

Once the general nature of the difficulty has been isolated, the engineer needs to select his analysis tools and proceed to finalize the exact cause of the difficulty. The various techniques mentioned in Chapter 22 will often help. Other hints involving work measurement analysis techniques have been given in other chapters, especially in Chapters 6, 18, 19, 21, 23, and 24. Common sense application of this knowledge usually yields a satisfactory answer as to what is wrong.

As soon as the *cause* of low efficiency is located, a major portion of the corrective task has been accomplished. Many hints and suggestions regarding the correction of work measurement difficulties have already been given. Others will be found in succeeding chapters, especially in Chapters 26, 28 and 29. .

Low efficiency is not the only indicator of trouble! Abnormally high efficiency is also a "red flag" indicator; in fact, it does not even need to be abnormally high. For example, assume that a new department has been established in a measured day work plant to manufacture a new product and that after two or three weeks some operations show efficiency of 40 to 50 per cent, the majority show 70 to 90 per cent, and about one-fourth of the operations show performances of 110 to 130 per cent. Obviously, the 40 to 50 per cent efficiency is too low and needs attention. In like manner, the 110 to 130 per cent efficiency operations also need attention. The high performance, while not out of line for operating an incentive installation, is not normal in a measured day work installation—especially not under the circumstances enumerated. The causes could be use of improved methods, poor standards, reduced quality requirements, above-average performance of operators, widened dimensional tolerances, better tools than those specified, etc. All of these may be desirable; however, all but one of the reasons indicate the need for a new labor standard. If such conditions are not corrected when and as they occur, the work measurement program soon deteriorates to being worse than useless; it really becomes a hindrance to operating personnel because no one believes in it and both labor and management try to use it to their individual benefit. Chaos is the final result. Work measurement programs must not only be carefully engineered in the beginning, but they need *expert* and *continuous* attention throughout their life. This concluding thought should always be remembered, not only by the industrial engineer but also by management.

CHAPTER 26

Fundamentals of Motion Economy

Most of the fundamentals underlying the principles of motion economy have already been discussed in the chapters covering the MTM procedure. The purpose of this chapter is to integrate that information with the sixteen laws or principles of motion economy as first stated by the Gilbreths. They are rules for achieving maximum motion economy and efficiency.

The usual approach in discussing motion economy is to divide the principles and their discussion into three main categories:

1. Motion economy as related to the use of the human body
2. Motion economy as related to the arrangement of the workplace
3. Motion economy as related to the design of tools and equipment.

This logical approach will be used here; but in addition to stating certain laws or rules, the authors will illustrate them with practical examples to make crystal clear the way in which they should be applied.

MOTION ECONOMY CONCERNING THE USE OF THE HUMAN BODY

1. *The Hands Should Be Idle a Minimum Amount of Time.*

To accomplish this objective will necessitate resorting to combinations of motions wherever possible. This subject has been fully discussed under motion combinations. The simultaneous motion table contained on the MTM data card and the set of more detailed tables included in the motion combinations chapter will be of great value to the industrial engineer in accomplishing this objective. When doubt arises concerning the specification of a particular motion combination as simo and the desired and/or exact answer is not evident by Table X of the MTM data card, reference should be made to the more detailed tables contained in the chapter on motion combinations, since those tables contain specific information which could not be included on the data card.

The desirability of achieving the goal set by this principle is obvious. If both hands are accomplishing *required* work, they will accomplish more than only one hand performing the same task under the same set of circumstances with the same tools. Clues to ineffective combinations of hand, arm, and/or body motions are readily available when MTM is being utilized. One such clue is the appearance of alternate blank areas in the right- and left-hand motion analysis forms. Such "dead" space highlights the possible presence of inefficient methods and motion sequences. Similar but less specific data can be developed by ordinary right- and left-hand motion analysis charts as outlined in Chapter 22.

Developing the most efficient work pattern for the manual portion of an operation often can be best accomplished by means of a cut and try analysis. There are usually several different ways to accomplish any given operation. An engineer will frequently need to employ this cut and try process, combined with common sense analysis, to develop as short a work cycle as possible.

2. Motions Should Be Confined to the Lowest Order Possible.

To accomplish this objective in processing an operation, an industrial engineer can achieve progress most readily by using the MTM procedure either directly, by writing an MTM pattern, or indirectly, by merely taking mental cognizance of the motion classifications when processing the task.

For Reaches required during an operation, the lowest order possible is a Case A, Type III Motion. The next lowest order is a Case A, Type II Reach. Also involved in this "order concept" would be keeping the motion distance as short as possible to minimize the total TMU required to accomplish a task. The fewer TMU required for a given basic motion, the lower is the order of the motion. This latter concept is universal and applies to any of the other basic motions identified in the MTM procedure. For example, the lowest order of Grasp is a contact, sliding, or hook Grasp involving zero TMU. The next lowest order of Grasp is a Case 1A requiring 2.0 TMU. Thus, MTM serves as an invaluable aid in implementing this well-established law of motion economy.

To attain the objective stated in this principle of motion economy will require ingenuity. For instance, careful attention to the design of the workplace is required to keep Reaches and Moves as short as possible, a subject separately treated in the original "laws of motion economy."

The required parts must be stored in a manner that permits an operator to get hold of them with the lowest possible classification of Grasp. For example, the normal procedure in presenting parts to an operator utilizes some sort of stock bin or tote pan, with the objects jumbled together in such a manner as to require a Case 4 Grasp. By using vibratory feed hoppers, such as have been developed in recent years and applied so successfully to automation projects, it is possible always to present to the operator one single part oriented to require only a Case 5 or, at the most, a Case 1A Pick-up Grasp. Such equipment, assuming a Case 1A Grasp would be required, will save a minimum time of 5.3 TMU per Grasp. If the object is small, it will save 10.9 TMU. Pre-orientation also helps to reduce any subsequent Position classification. Sometimes the same objective can be achieved without requiring the relatively expensive and complex vibratory feed hopper by feeding the part from a sliding chute in a manner such as to present only one part at a time. This latter approach is relatively inexpensive.

Similarly, each of the other basic motions required to perform an operation should be analyzed as to surrounding conditions so as to reduce motion classifications to a minimum. Reducing motion classification to a minimum does not guarantee sound economics—one can spend more to accomplish the objective than he can save. *When equipment is involved, a cost study to compare equipment costs to labor savings is essential!*

3. *Changes in Direction of Motion Should Be Kept to a Minimum.*

An experienced MTM analyst will recognize the worth of this statement. Involved in the understanding of this concept and its practical application is the fundamental concept that well-trained operators normally utilize gradual, mildly curved motions rather than either straight line motions or motions involving a high degree of curvature. *This is sometimes stated as a law or principle of motion economy* because it is virtually impossible to force a well-trained and efficient operator to use a straight line motion, except for heavy weights, since it is more natural for him to follow a curved path to his objective, but not one so sharply curved as that involved in an MTM "CD." Slightly curved paths are automatically achieved.

In connection with attempts to minimize changes in the direction of motion, it should be borne in mind that it is often possible to arrange a workplace so that the hand must travel a circular path—rather than move in broken paths—to two or three different points.

4. *Reduce Fatigue to a Minimum.*

This objective cannot be attained without giving attention to the effect of surroundings. Not only should engineers account for the motions made by the human body to perform an operation, but also the conditions surrounding an operator at his workplace.

Consider first the operator's motions. Proper use of his body members can often help reduce fatigue. To illustrate, if a lever having a high resistance to motion must be moved and the resistance cannot be eliminated through redesign of the apparatus, it is often possible to locate the lever where the operator can move it with a hip motion or a foot and/or leg motion. These particular body members are more capable of moving objects offering great resistance with less stress and strain than the hand and/or arm.

A wide variety of pneumatic, electrical, and mechanical devices are available to aid equipment designers to eliminate resistance to motion. Many of these devices are simple and actually make possible great economies in the expenditure of human energy. It will rarely happen that resistance to motion cannot be reduced by redesign of equipment.

It has been proven beyond all question that well-lighted, well-ventilated, and pleasant work surroundings aid in reducing fatigue and help put operators in a "frame of mind" to attain the best possible performance. These factors were adequately treated in Chapters 2 and 6.

The additional statements following encompass those rules of motion economy related to the human body which are normally found in discussions of time and motion studies.

5. *Arm Motion Paths Should Be Simultaneous, Symmetrical, and if Possible in Opposing Directions.*

6. *Both Hands Should Not Be Idle at the Same Instant.*

7. *Basic Motions* (a still common definition developed prior to MTM is Therblig) *Should Begin and End at the Same Instant.*

8. *Momentum Should Be Employed to Assist Operators Where Possible and Reduced to a Minimum When Muscular Action Must Check an Object Having Momentum.*

9. *Eliminate Controlled Movements Wherever Possible.*

10. *Motion Sequences Should Promote Automaticity.*

11. *Hands Should Be Relieved of Any Work That Can Be Done by Other Body Members.*

These are the more commonly found definitions of human body motion economy principles as developed by the Gilbreths and amplified by Dr. Ralph M. Barnes. They unquestionably can aid the industrial engineer. However, the earlier stated four principles or rules of motion economy as applied to the human body cover all the essentials and are very valuable when using the MTM procedure. Remember that the pioneers in time and motion study did not have available the results of research such as that exemplified in the MTM procedure.

The present body of knowledge resulting from MTM research definitely indicates that some of the earlier known motion economy rules sometimes lead to erroneous thinking. For example, it certainly is not necessary for both hands to begin or end their basic motions at the same instant or that they must be performing equal and opposite motions. Case A and E Reaches can be combined with virtually any of the other basic motions, and usually without any attendant difficulties. In general, the earlier laws are usable, but do not yield maximum results such as can be achieved by use of MTM data.

Statements regarding the validity of some of the more commonly stated principles of motion economy are not made to reduce any credit due the pioneers of industrial engineering, to whom we owe so much, but are intended rather to correct some of the slightly incorrect concepts which were developed due to a lack of adequate research facilities. Again, lest a false impression be gained, it is stated that the more commonly phrased principles of motion economy are still practicable, but there are valid exceptions to some of them under certain conditions.

One particular law admitting no quarrel is the principle that motions should be confined to the lowest possible classification. In fact, this law adequately covers the one stating that controlled movements should be eliminated. Knowledge of MTM makes this crystal clear. This law is one of the four most basic principles stated earlier in this section. Also, Rule 4 concerning fatigue underlies both Rule 8 concerning momentum and Rule 11 concerning the use of body members other than the arms and hands.

WORKPLACE ARRANGEMENT AND CONDITIONS SURROUNDING OPERATOR

Definite rules will be given to aid the industrial engineer in designing and locating the workplace so as to secure maximum production. These rules stem either directly or indirectly from the principles of motion economy for the human body previously considered in this chapter. Increased production achieved by following these rules is due, essentially, to greater economy of motion.

1. *Tools and Materials Should Be Located at Fixed Stations With the Individual Items Pre-positioned Whenever Possible.*

The ramifications of this particular rule have been covered already in Law 2 of body motion economy which states that motions should be confined to the lowest possible order. Reference to the MTM procedure, particularly those portions dealing with Reach and Grasp, will clearly show why this is a good rule to follow in designing workplaces.

Fig. 1.   Poorly designed workplace.
Courtesy of The Magnavox Company.

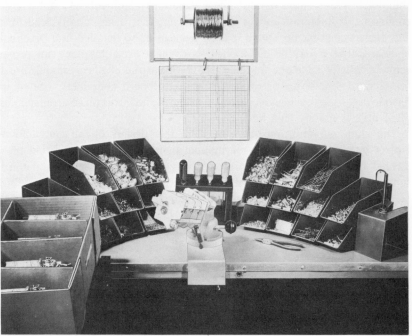

Fig. 2.   Improved workplace.
Courtesy of The Magnavox Company.

A poorly designed ineffective workplace is shown in Fig. 1. Observe that the parts being assembled are scattered over the bench and that the tools are lying loose, not being pre-positioned in fixed locations. It is a workplace that is relatively easy to improve. Merely putting the material into totepans permanently fixed in position and the tools into simple holders which pre-position them in a fixed location will greatly improve the situation. This is illustrated in Fig. 2.

2. *Gravity Feed Bins, Vibratory Feed Hoppers, etc., Should Be Used to Deliver Material to the Point of Usage Whenever Economically Feasible.*

Industrial engineers must always stress the economics of a given situation. If enough money is spent, most manual operations can be automated entirely; that is, all human motions can be eliminated or at least reduced to the point where they are relatively unimportant. Unfortunately, the volume of parts being produced is not always sufficient to justify automated equipment. In such cases it is essential for the industrial engineer to utilize relatively inexpensive equipment in devising efficient and effective workplace layouts.

There are occasions when the volume of work in conjunction with small cyclical savings is sufficient to justify the use of vibratory feed hoppers to completely pre-position parts. These situations admittedly are not overly common. It is almost always true, however, that using gravity feed bins will prove economically sound if the parts can be so handled in a practical manner. There may be a few instances where even this does not prove economically feasible and, in this case, the industrial engineer should resort to standard tote boxes or even common cardboard containers located in fixed locations for each given part. A well-designed workplace arrangement often utilizes gravity feed bins.

The authors were once involved in the design of an automation project intended to automate six manual operations that were being performed by twenty-four operators per shift (with partial second and third shifts required) when all work stations were fully manned. In investigating the economics of the problem, it soon became evident that all manual work could not be eliminated without extremely large expenditures of money to cover design and experimentation. However, it was determined that the twenty-four operators could be reduced to seven performing three separate manual operations; these seven also essentially eliminated any required second and third shift work for the tasks involved.

One operation involved positioning a rather complicated part into another which had been pre-positioned in a nest traveling on an indexing power conveyor. Because this position was non-symmetrical, a relatively lengthy time was required. If the part to be pre-positioned had merely been placed in a conventional parts pan, a P2NSE Position would have been required in addition to a Case C Reach and a Case 4 Grasp. Through the use of a vibratory feed hopper, it was possible to present the part in front of the operator in such a manner that the Reach could be reduced to a Case A, the Grasp to a Case 1A, and the Position to the equivalent of a semi-symmetrical one. The net effect of this procedure was to increase the productivity of the automation project by twenty per cent per year through the use of two vibratory feed hoppers whose cost would be recovered in less than one year's time.

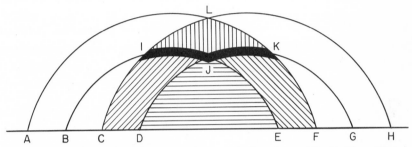

Fig. 3.   Normal and maximum work areas (refer also to Fig. 9, Chap. 7).

3. *Tools and Material Should Be Located Within the Normal Grasp Area and in Front of the Operator.*

The normal and maximum work areas for an operator are shown in Fig. 3. The distances and position of the operator which are here omitted for clarity and ease of discussion are shown in Fig. 9 of Chapter 7. Company policy, available space, and like reasons may modify these distances, but for motion economy and minimum fatigue distances should be proportional to those shown.

It is obvious that the operator can most effectively perform work at or near point *J*. This is particularly true if both hands must be utilized. Area *DJE* is advisable only for precision work with very small parts, where only finger and hand movements are used.

The area *EJKF* is quite satisfactory for right-hand activity and *CIJD* for left-hand activity, although the preferable locales are those portions of these areas nearest *IJ* and *JK*.

The area bounded by *ILKJ* is perhaps the next most valuable general area since it is directly in front of the operator.

Placing material in locations that confine the hand to the normal work area does not guarantee most effective use of the operator. This seemingly contradictory statement can easily be validated. For example, the left hand of the operator may need to procure a part located at point *C*, just within the normal work area for the left hand. To transport this part to a point directly in front of him near the base of area DJE will require a Reach greater than if the part is located in the area $ILKJ$ and near the base of this area identified by the curves IJK. In addition, if a visual action by the operator is needed to accurately Grasp the part, he obviously needs to turn his head to see a part located near point C whereas the same part will be within his normal range of vision if located directly in front of him in the area $ILKJ$.

Suffice it to say that use of the normal and maximum working areas requires practical interpretation for each particular situation. There are some exceptions to the general rules; however, it is generally good practice to confine the work within the normal right and left hand work areas. The key to practical interpretation is the fact that the parts should not only be located in the normal work area, but also directly in front of the operator.

4. *Tools and Material Should Be Located to Permit the Best Sequence of Work Elements.*

In order to fully accomplish this objective, detailed MTM work patterns must be developed to help determine the best sequence of work elements. Once the sequence has been developed, it is relatively easy to locate the tools and material so as to require the shortest possible motions and/or lowest classifications of work elements.

Full use of this technique involves such action as placing the first part required near the point of disposal of the finished part and similarly locating the rest of the tools and parts in a manner that provides for the shortest possible Reaches and Moves for the hands involved. Parts used by the left hand should obviously be on the left side of the workplace and vice versa. In addition, parts used by the left hand should be arranged in a regular or systematic manner around the front of the operator so that the first part would perhaps be located near the point I on the diagram in Fig. 3, and succeeding parts sequentially placed nearer point J along curve IJ. If this does not allow enough room for parts, they can be placed in double rows along IJ, stacked in bins along IJ, or located further from I along IC.

It is not to be deduced from the above statement that parts should necessarily be located toward point C. If only a few parts are involved, it is best to stock the left-hand parts along the path IJ and the right-hand parts along the path KJ. The main point being made is that the parts should be located in an inward sequence corresponding with usage, while at the same time arranged so as to get them as close as possible to the work area and, in addition, in front of the operator.

5. *Make Use of Drop Delivery or Ejectors for Disposal of Parts.*

Unless finished parts are fragile and/or otherwise easily damaged, it is often possible to dispose of parts by drop delivery or mechanical ejection.

This does not mean that drop delivery or ejectors should be used in each and every case where parts are not fragile.   There are many occasions when this approach is not the economical one.   For example, if the operator has produced a finished part which is to be packed, it is quite often possible to arrange empty packing cartons before the operator.   He can then take the finished part and place it in an empty carton.

If the part had been dropped into a box and thereby jumbled with other finished parts, its placement in a carton would require another operator to use a Case C Reach to the part plus a Case 4A Grasp to obtain control. These extra motions thus would have been added to the packing of the part. On relatively low volume production for the above example, utilization of drop delivery would have added unnecessary labor to the packing operation. On high volume production, this is not necessarily a fact, since drop delivery to a moving conveyor could have been utilized with the conveyor raising the part to a point directly in front of a packing operator who would complete the packing of the part.

It is again emphasized that the various principles or rules concerning the workplace layout must be interpreted in a practical manner and each situation analyzed.   An industrial engineer should be extremely careful not to make his viewpoint too narrow and merely consider each operation by itself.   He must, of necessity, consider related operations, if maximum economy in production is to be achieved.

6. *Under Normal Conditions the Height of the Workplace and Chair Should Be Such That the Operator Can Either Sit or Stand While Performing Required Work.*

Please note that this rule is prefaced by "under normal conditions." Some operations do not lend themselves to standing.   One of these would be coil winding.   Another would be the normal paper work performed by a clerk. In the time of our grandfather or great-grandfather, it was common to see clerks seated on high stools to work at high desks and at times standing before these high desks performing clerical work.   It has been found from actual practice that clerks can work best when seated and that they will not stand unless forced to do so.   Forcing an operator to do anything not normal to a particular task is not conducive to maximum performance.

The kind of operations normally performed in a sitting position are those that are more precise and exacting and/or those which require the operator to reason and think.

The operations that lend themselves best to this rule are those requiring work of a less precise nature and for which the motions are relatively broad. When the parts are relatively heavy in weight, standing should be possible while the parts are being manipulated.

7. *Chairs Should Be of the Posture Type.*

Obviously, the reason for having chairs of the posture type is to reduce fatigue. Most modern plants utilize posture chairs in both the plant and in the office.

8. *Illumination of the Proper Quality and Intensity Should Be Provided.*

This subject has been discussed in connection with reducing fatigue. However, restatement will emphasize the importance of this subject. The industrial engineer would do well to consult a lighting specialist when it is obvious that favorable sight conditions are relatively difficult to accomplish.

There is no one best source of light or lighting fixture. Many sources of light are available as well as many different kinds of lighting fixtures. When properly applied, the net result is maximum chance for vision and minimum eye strain.

9. *The Color of a Workplace Should Aid Visual Perception and Reduce Eye Fatigue.*

This concept was discussed under the subject of reducing fatigue to a minimum in earlier chapters. The general approach to this objective is to paint the immediate work area in a light color and the surrounding areas in somewhat darker but restful shades.

10. *Provide for Proper Ventilation, Temperature and Humidity Control.*

It is often claimed that five to ten per cent greater production can be obtained when using air conditioning. This subject was discussed in earlier chapters. There is no doubt that air conditioning does provide many benefits; but the exact amount of extra productivity possible is variable, depending on many conditions. Each case must be analyzed on its own merits.

In regard to ventilation, the authors think many psychological factors affect its value. They believe that almost as much benefit is obtained by merely impressing on the operators' minds that ventilation is being supplied as from the ventilation itself. In many cases, unless the operator can see and hear the fans operating or feel the air blowing, he will not be convinced that sufficient ventilation is being provided.

In the ordinary factory area, elaborate and expensive air distribution ducts installed solely to provide ventilation are not believed to be economically sound by the authors. Part of this is due to the psychological factors mentioned; and, second, elaborate ductwork goes a way toward paying for air conditioning, particularly if self-contained air conditioning units of three- to ten-ton size can be used.

DESIGN OF TOOLS AND EQUIPMENT

Various rules or principles have been listed under this general subject to aid the industrial engineer in achieving maximum production via maximum motion economy and efficient utilization of the human body.

1. *Combine Tools Wherever Possible.*

This common sense rule requires a practical outlook to utilize it effectively. A common example of this would be the combining of a torque indicator with a screw driver or wrench. Not only will such a tool tighten the screw, nut, or bolt; but it will also indicate the degree of tightness by a torque scale if this is required.

Obviously, even more sophisticated approaches to this subject are possible. Many of these, however, require specialized machines designed for the particular task involved. Here the economics of the situation must be carefully examined before embarking on an elaborate project of machine design and construction.

2. *Hand-Operated Devices Should Be Designed to Distribute the Load Among the Fingers and Provide for Maximum "Purchase" Area.*

This very practical rule needs to be considered when buying tools and equipment requiring the operator to exert considerable force through the use of his hands. In a very practical way, it means that screw drivers, for example, should have a relatively large grasping surface for the hand if considerable force will be required to tighten a screw. Presenting a relatively large surface for grasping to the hand provides for maximum "purchase," minimizes the possibility of injury to the hand, and helps to lessen fatigue.

3. *Crossbars, Levers, Hand Wheels, Etc., Should Be Positioned to Minimize the Reaches and Moves Required of the Operator.*

When purchasing machine tools, the industrial engineer should closely examine the machine from this viewpoint. At times, the choice will lie between two machines having very similar performance specifications. The choice then should favor the machine that will provide the greater motion economy.

GENERAL DISCUSSION

The basic rules of motion economy presented have been augmented by very practical supplementary rules concerning the operator's workplace, tools, and equipment. They generally apply equally well for all operations, whether in an office or on the production floor. It remains for the industrial engineer to utilize maximum ingenuity in achieving maximum work or motion economy. Each operation analyzed should be approached with a completely open mind and various approaches tried before reaching a final conclusion. Almost any operation can be performed in several different ways, but the method that is most economical obviously is the one to use.

From a practical viewpoint, psychological factors often enter the decision of which method to use in performing an operation. Although an engineer could devise a rather unique method that he is convinced is somewhat better than any other that could be utilized, if this particular method does not appeal to the supervisor and/or the operator and cannot be "sold," it is sometimes wise to use a compromise method. Merely because a method is better than others does not insure its success in application. If it is not given a fair chance by the supervisor and/or operators, the results can be sabotaged to such an extent that the compromise method might have yielded better results.

Do not misunderstand the authors' meaning in regard to the above situation. Under no circumstances are they recommending merely "giving in" to operators or the supervisory group when differences of opinion exist. Rather, the necessity for the engineer to sell the results of his efforts produces occasions when compromising to get some of the benefits is better than to insist upon a particular point and perhaps achieve nothing as a final result. This kind of situation is mentioned to illustrate the kind of practical approach that must be used by the successful industrial engineer. Industrial engineering is not all science; it also involves a lot of applied psychology, human relationships, and human engineering.

CHAPTER 27

Standard Data and Time Formulas[1]

The justification of standard data and time formulas is simple: if it is proper to consider any legitimate means by which to reduce labor and increase productivity on the factory floor, it is equally essential for industrial engineers and work analysts to set an example by utilizing efficient methods and procedures to accomplish their own tasks. One of the best ways to do this is by the employment of standard data and time formulas for determining individual job standards.

It was explained in previous chapters that any work can be progressively subdivided into shorter categories to suit various aims of the work analyst. For example, the progression might be as follows: major tasks, task operations, operation sequences, sequence elements, and basic motions. Although examining the smallest category, basic motions, permits detailed attention to all factors of the work with units universally applicable to any kind of work (as with manual work analysis with a predetermined time system such as MTM), this approach tends to be expensive and cumbersome when applied to each and every task for which a time standard must be set. Better use of the analyst's time for the latter purpose results by developing, instead, standard data for one of the larger types of categories and applying this data to ascertain the time standards for similar tasks on a given line of work, say, drill press work. The increased ease and rapidity of standards application with this approach is justified even though it permits less attention to detail and limits the applicability of the standard data. This is the approach used by Carl Barth, Harrington Emerson, Dr. Ralph M. Barnes, and others as mentioned in Chapter 3.

Except for the size, nature, and factors included in analysis elements for standard data of this type, the mechanics and study approach are very

---

[1] In the First Edition, the authors thanked Mr. Richard E. Awbrey for assisting with this chapter. However, the extensive revisions in this edition are solely our own.

similar to that used in applying pre-determined time systems. Throughout this chapter the reader will profit from recalling the concepts, approach, usage, advantages, and disadvantages of MTM and other pre-determined time systems. Many of the remarks previously made concerning these topics apply directly to standard data as discussed in this chapter.

To establish the time standard for a task requires the addition of all elemental times for each part of that task. As these elements and their accompanying time values are made larger, the number of elements needed to encompass a given task is progressively reduced. Since the amount of study and effort required of the work analyst to apply a standard frequently is in direct proportion to the number of work elements with which he must deal, the advantage gained by classifying work elements into the largest *practicable* increments is obvious. Conversely, the isolation of shorter elements for study during development of standard data makes easier determination of a more precise standard, since all aspects of the work then can be analyzed with better coverage of the variations and closer scrutiny of fewer ideas at a given time. To exploit both aspects of element length to the best advantage, with proper emphasis to each, this chapter offers a procedural approach for developing standard data.

THE NATURE OF STANDARD DATA

Once a time standard has been developed for a given job, the job obviously need not be re-analyzed for its standard time on each occasion it is performed; and it is logical to keep a systemized record of the time for that job. In this way, the need to direct attention to the fine details of that job on repeated occasions can be avoided; effectively, the analyst is freed to study other jobs and thus enlarge the coverage and scope of his efforts. The practice of motion economy as applied to the work analyst himself is further enhanced by maintaining systematic records or schedules of times for work elements common to many tasks frequently performed. This philosophy is the basis for both standard time data and time formulas.

There are many reasons for developing standard data and time formulas in work measurement activities. Economy of time and effort by the industrial engineering department is the most important reason. In most industrial plants, new jobs or variations of existing tasks are created daily. The work content of these jobs may not differ radically from that of other jobs, nevertheless each new or revised task must be assigned a standard time for cost control purposes since production costs are gaged against such standard times, scheduling activities use them for work loads, workers and management use them as goals, etc. It is obvious that this activity is important. The time and manpower needed to determine and establish labor time standards can be greatly reduced with standard time data.

As stated earlier in this book, work measurement is not an exact science; the fact that it entails the development and use of certain skills and arts means that practical judgment on the part of analysts cannot be avoided. Obviously, such skills and judgment can vary from one person to another; so the results of work analysis can, and often do, vary to a measurable degree. The use of standard data and time formulas minimizes the skill and judgment required to set a standard and thereby yields results having a higher degree of consistency.

The development of good standard data and time formulas requires analytical thinking based on full usage of an engineering approach tempered by practical experience in time study and/or predetermined times. Conversely, having such data available, the skill and experience required to specify labor time standards is greatly reduced. With good standard data, the routine of setting standards may be delegated to junior engineers and less experienced work analysts, or even to clerks and timekeepers properly trained for the work. In fact, much of this work can be programmed for accomplishment with an electronic computer. In this manner, the best-trained and experienced talent is liberated for developing further standard data or time formulas.

The development of good standard data requires the work measurement engineer to devote much greater attention to the underlying causes and factors affecting the times for various elements than is the case when individual job rates are being set. In setting individual job standards, whether based on collecting data by using a stop watch or with pre-determined times, a comprehensive view of the work involved is often difficult to achieve because the time demands of this approach with available manpower do not normally permit a broad analysis of all preceding and following processes. Often, the analyst fails to "see the forest for the trees" and consequently overlooks important factors which deserve attention and either should be considered in standards or else changed to effect economies. Since attention must be concentrated on related jobs when developing standard data, the engineer usually will locate related problems and recognize areas in which improvement might be possible.

The most important use of standard data is in determining production time standards for industrial jobs in advance of production. This usually must follow a study of the design blueprints and/or product specifications and, whenever possible, reference to a working model. Standard data can also be used to set or check standards for tasks by actual observation after the start of production. Other uses include methods improvement, job design, labor cost estimates, cost savings proposals, plant layout, production scheduling, machine loading, and job evaluation.

Definitions

STANDARD TIME DATA consists of systematic schedules of performance times pertaining to classified elements of work.

Note that this definition fits the MTM system of pre-determined times. However, as used in this chapter, standard data pertains to elements requiring larger increments of time and a pattern of fundamental motions as contrasted to MTM elements, and these larger work units often include machine time and/or other process time as well. Standard data elements are essentially different from pre-determined time elements.

To orient the reader's thinking, it is worthwhile to note the definition of a standard found in A.S.M.E. Standard 106 entitled "Industrial Engineering Terminology" as follows:

2. Any established or accepted rule, model, or criterion against which comparisons are made.

This same source also defines Standard Time Data as:

A compilation of all the elements that are used for performing a given class of work with normal elemental time values for each element. The data are used as a basis for determining time standards on work similar to that from which the data were determined without making actual time studies.

A Time Formula is defined in A.S.M.E. Standard 106 as:

A collection of standard time data arranged in the form of an algebraic expression for determining the standard time of an operation.

Perhaps this latter definition might be modified to cover cases where the time values to be obtained from such formulas are expressed as multivariable charts, nomographs, or ordinary graphs. The authors would prefer the following:

A TIME FORMULA is an expression of the procedure required to determine production time for a task from standard time data, the expression being one, or a combination of: (1) a mathematical equation; (2) a multivariable chart; (3) a nomograph; or (4) an ordinary graph.

It is important to note that all standard data and time formulas should be accompanied by: (1) a written definition of the work covered by the data, (2) a description of the pertinent factors pertaining to the time standards (on occasion, important exclusions should also be stated), and (3) a set of instructions for proper application of the data.

Standard data, then, provides a schedule of times, and a time formula can serve as a means of properly applying such times expeditiously. In addition, it is possible to express concisely with formulas some time data that would be difficult to express clearly in any other fashion. This chapter describes many practical techniques and considerations involved in developing standard data and time formulas.

Two differing element lengths associated with pre-determined time systems and standard data were previously discussed, as well as differences in their basic nature. There are various other possible ways to categorize these two important subjects. For instance, time data can be classed as *microscopic* or *macroscopic*.[2] An example of microscopic data is that contained in the MTM system which consists of well-defined, discrete, minute parts that are added and/or combined to make the total standard. An example of macroscopic data might be a time study standard based on a study of a total operation with no breakdown to elemental constituents. The point is that standards (provided identical methods of job performance are evaluated) produced using either system can be equally correct, the basic difference being in the size, nature, and definition of the building blocks. Similar special descriptions of other ways to categorize standard data and time formulas have been written to accord with the interpretations and aims of many other authorities. This text chooses one definite approach, but many alternate approaches exist.

Orientation

Besides the manually controlled portion, many industrial jobs also involve machine time or other process time as an integral part of the work cycle. When automatic feeds are employed in machining operations, the machine time to be determined for a standard depends on the speeds and feeds selected, and these are not always easy to specify or choose. When hand feeds (controlled by the operator) are used, the problems become even more involved. Time standards for many other types of process-controlled elements (e.g., spray painting) are also frequently difficult to evaluate in objective terms, since they often involve variable factors having a direct bearing on performance times.

When time studies are made of individual jobs to develop time standards, it is all too often the practice to assign the least experienced men to this task. In many such cases, they are neither sufficiently qualified nor allowed enough time to carefully analyze all factors influencing the process-controlled elements. For these reasons, process element times are often inconsistent and inaccurate when determined by studying individual jobs. The standard data approach, however, more frequently results in careful analysis of process—and machine—controlled elements by experienced and trained personnel.

[2] These terms were originated by Dr. William Gomberg and the concept was stated in Vol. V, No. 4 (July, 1954) of the *Journal of Industrial Engineering*.

Standard data that has been accepted by both management and labor reduces the probability of labor troubles resulting from time standards. Under this condition, disputes can be most frequently traced to misapplication of the data rather than to errors in the agreed time values. This advantage favors standard data over the procedure of determining standards by individual job studies.

The development of good standard data is often time consuming and expensive due to the engineering man-hours required, and is therefore not always economically justified. The expenditure of engineering time should be carefully balanced against the benefits to be derived. Unfortunately, many industrial engineering departments often overlook this aspect of developing standards.

Specialized standard data applicable to only one type of work is rarely justifiable for long-cycle, non-repetitive or infrequently performed job cycles. However, it is often the case that work elements that are a part of an infrequent job are also common to other jobs. When this is true, the standard time for the infrequent job, or parts of it, often may be determined from data existing on other jobs. Another possible solution to providing standard data for such jobs is to develop standards for the basic motion combinations found in many classes of manual work. This is the approach used in developing basic MTM-GPD (horizontal) standard data, which is described later.

At the other extreme are short-cycle, long-run, large-volume jobs which almost dictate the use of detailed analysis in preference to using standard data. Short cycle jobs often are difficult to evaluate with standard data that has been designed to cover a variety of situations, since the amount of residual error may be so large as to introduce intolerable percentage errors in relation to the total work cycle. This same residual error is generally of small consequence on medium and long cycle operations, since the individual elemental errors will tend to counterbalance one another. Standard data, if used at all, on high-volume, short-cycle work (e.g., 1 to 2 minute operations), should be developed with extreme care and precision because there will be little chance for elemental errors to cancel each other.

Long-run or large-volume jobs ordinarily justify extensive, detailed methods studies that allow standards to be established with great precision and accuracy. Therefore, individual studies on such jobs are usually more advisable than the application of standard data. Often, a preliminary process for such jobs is established by using standard data for the time evaluation; the job is then reprocessed with either MTM or time study after the "debugging" and training periods have been completed.

On "toolroom" jobs, on which only job lots are produced, the method of developing and applying standard data is usually not too refined. On the other hand, the development and application of data for mass production assembly lines normally demands great care and accuracy.

There are no invariable rules to use in determining whether standard data should be developed. It is safe to say, however, that when all other factors are equal, standard times that are as accurate as can be justified economically should be developed.

Prior to any standard data work, a preliminary survey should be taken to establish the type of data needed and what limits of accuracy can be tolerated. Most engineers know that the cost of a machined part increases in proportion to any decrease in permissible tolerances. This same principle applies to standard data work. For manual work, the ultimate in precise standard data might result from direct application of carefully analyzed MTM and/or statistically validated time study data, while the roughest type of data would consist of merely estimated times for entire job cycles. The latter type of standards are often referred to as total task time standards, although this term does not imply estimation of the standard time. Most industrial applications of standard data are a compromise between these two extremes.

The Importance of Method

Bearing in mind the nature and attributes of standard data just discussed, it is helpful to return to the unifying theme of this text—the importance of method in managerial control. Basically, the Gilbreths felt that if the best method (e.g., use of the best, least involved motions for manual methods) were always used to perform tasks, the time and expense of doing the work would approach a minimum that could not be further reduced. In other words, time is in a sense extraneous in standards if their method content is the basis for concerted action and supervisory control, since the cost of labor would then automatically be minimal. Taylor emphasized that the time was meaningless without attention to the methods employed, although he insisted that time standards should be based on the minimum time performance of qualified experts in the work. The common thread in these remarks is that methods are the determinants of time, rather than the reverse.

For standard data and time formulas to be meaningful, therefore, several well-defined requisites are essential. The method reflected in a standard should be the best that can be devised within economic bounds; it should be carefully taught; and it should be enforced. With this being true, it is possible to evaluate the prescribed method timewise. Finally, unless the specified method is maintained, the standard will not reflect accurately the prevailing situation and its attendant costs.

As the procedure for developing standards is studied it is important to bear in mind the methods basis for the steps taken and how the details given are all oriented to determining, evaluating, instituting, and maintaining the method on which a time standard is based. If the correct method is instituted for the standard being determined, little difficulty will arise concerning the proper time for the tasks covered by that standard. When this is not the case, any resultant standards are a waste of analysis time—this being true regardless of the procedure or system used to define the time standard.

EXISTING STANDARD DATA

Before presenting the traditional procedure for developing standard data, various existing sets of MTM-based standard data will be identified. They may be considered for application on the basis of adequacy and economy. Developing original standard data is an economically sound, but often very expensive and time-consuming procedure. It uses many techniques, some of which require special training and/or long experience. Also, it demands the concentrated attention of competent industrial engineers who can be assigned to the development project for a significant period of time. These factors suggest that in many cases it is better to use an existing set of standard data instead of expending manpower to develop standard data by traditional methods.

Practically all standard data are established with the "building block" concept. This concept is that, with some acceptable loss of accuracy and a tolerable reduction in methods improvement capability, progressively larger time elements are derived for more rapid and less expensive direct rate setting usage. Such elements can be coded to greatly reduce analysis time and data recording requirements when determining an operational standard for a particular task.

However, most existing standard data are *vertical* in nature. That is, the various "building blocks" are based on actual work task elements and are therefore restricted to one kind or class of work. Extensive coverage therefore results in huge masses of relatively inflexible blocks. These are difficult to locate with even the best of coding schemes, and they frequently are not clearly applicable to all cases where an operational standard is desired.

A more recent approach is known as *horizontal* standard data. Here the various "building blocks" are based upon motion sequences common to many kinds and classes of work. Extensive coverage results from careful design of the blocks as regards the included range of variables, averaging of motion frequencies to minimize accuracy loss, and generality of application. With an efficient coding and data filing system, such elements can be used to produce desired operational standards which do not exhibit the defects of operational standards based on vertical data. Therefore, each horizontal element has greater universality of application with a lower cost of usage.

Of direct interest are certain existing sets of standard data based directly on MTM, partly due to their historical relation to MTM-GPD as later discussed. The following are not in any particular order so far as their date of origination is concerned:

(1) USD—Universal Standard Data. Developed by and available from H. B. Maynard and Company.

(2) UOC—Universal Office Controls.[3] Developed by Harold B. Maynard, William M. Aiken, and John F. Lewis. Available from H. B. Maynard and Company.

(3) UMS—Universal Maintenance Standards. Developed by and available from H. B. Maynard and Company.

(4) MSD—Master Standard Data.[4] Developed by Richard M. Crossan and Harold W. Nance. Available from Serge A. Birn Company.

(5) MCD—Master Clerical Data.[5] Developed by Serge A. Birn, Richard M. Crossan, and Ralph W. Eastwood. Available from Serge A. Birn Company.

(6) ISD Integrated Standard Data. Developed by Richard M. Crossan, Martin T. Mobach, and Harold W. Nance for International Business Machines Corporation. Not available, but used as the basis of Autorate.

(7) Autorate—A computer program version of ISD developed by and available from the Service Bureau Corporation, an IBM subsidiary.

(8) Tapco Data. This data was developd by the Tapco group within the Thompson Ramo Wooldridge Company for their own usage.

As these various methods of applying MTM appeared, there arose a problem which was well-stated by Dr. H. B. Maynard at a December, 1961 meeting of the MTM Association as follows:

Although MTM provides basic motion time data which are the same for every company in every industry, the industrial engineers in each company use it independently to solve afresh the same problems over and over again. Every company develops its own time formulas and standard data, something which could easily be done just once for many different machines and processes if there were a central agency working on this problem. The cost of all this dupli-

---

[3] *Practical Control of Office Costs* by Harold B. Maynard, William M. Aiken, and John F. Lewis, Management Publishing Corp., Greenwich, Connecticut, 1960.

[4] *Master Standard Data* by Richard M. Crossan and Harold W. Nance, McGraw-Hill Book Company, New York City, 1962.

[5] *Measurement and Control of Office Costs* by Serge A. Birn, Richard M. Crossan, and Ralph W. Eastwood, McGraw-Hill Book Company, New York City, 1961.

cation of effort represents a tremendous waste which could easily be avoided. . . . In an age which has seen the development of computers and electronic data processing, this method of accomplishing work measurement is far behind the times.

As a direct result of this suggestion, the MTM Association for Standards and Research of the United States and Canada responded by developing (see Chapter 5) its version of MTM-based standard data called MTM General Purpose Data (MTM-GPD). This set of basic horizontal-type standard data benefited from being established by persons experienced with the MTM-based standard data versions cited above. The MTM-GPD data represents the combined experience of its developers with the above data and other private data plus the infusion of new ideas needed to produce a common, unified set of data.

The existing data synthesis into MTM-GPD resulted in data with a greater degree of element coverage and more universal applicability. To meet the central agency idea, the MTM Association with a full-time staff coordinates efforts to maintain existing MTM-GPD data and to develop further data. Very importantly, the MTM-GPD manuals are kept current and are organized for easy access to the basic MTM motions behind any given element; this permits methods work at any level of complexity while gaining the rapidity of time determination. In many other respects, the data are faithful to the original MTM concept of true methods design; basically they are an efficient extension of the Detailed MTM Data tailored to application needs.

In accordance with the "building block" concept, MTM-GPD involves several levels of data. The first two levels are leased in two volumes, together with a data card for each level. Currently, the second level is being enlarged by the addition of more categories. When this is completed, higher levels will be considered. Another future project is to explore the development of a computer program version. The existing levels may be described as follows:

(1) B—Basic or elemental level. All of these data elements consist of either individual MTM motions or frequently used basic MTM motion sequences. They are the foundation of the MTM-GPD system, with accuracy very close to that of Detailed MTM Data. The key to this data is the particular combination of MTM motions included and the motion frequencies of occurrence. In determining the latter, the wealth of experience among the members of the compiling committee and analysis of actual industrial motion patterns submitted by association members were used. This means that the data design and frequency features reflect a truly representative sample of industrial motion variation.

(2) M—Multipurpose level. When basic level and/or other multipurpose elements are consolidated into longer elements which occur in a wide variety of operations, they are called multipurpose elements. Such elements are general enough to apply to widely different classes of work, yet specific enough to provide definitive time values. Again the data depends on elemental frequencies which were a consensus of the developers.

Also to be considered later are higher levels of data for special or single purpose usage based on appropriate combinations of the B and M levels. These could be tailored to fit specific needs of given industries, types of products, service fields, etc. Possible examples of each of these might be electronic assembly, precision mechanical products, and warehousing.

Another facet of many existing sets of standard data which has been included in MTM-GPD is the element coding technique. For example, alpha-mnemonic coding as discussed later in this chapter offered experience to the compilers of MTM-GPD when they were devising the coding system, which is alpha-numeric with a mnemonic (memory jogging) design.

MTM-GPD uses a three-group, seven-position element coding. The groups are separated by hyphens and each position in the group has a definite connotation. In the first group of three alphabetical positions, the first letter represents the data level by a B or M (and probably S for special purpose when it has been developed). The next two letters identify the element category, such as GT for get, PL for place, EL for elemental, BM for body motion, AC for actuate, etc. The second group of two letters denotes subcategories or variables of the element. For instance, AL for approximate location, EA for easily grasped additional object, LP for letter printed, etc. Note that all of the position coding previously described is alpha and mnemonic in nature. The last group of two digits is numerical to represent variables such as distance, case of motion, amount of variation, range of time values, etc. For example, the numbers 02 could indicate: 1"–3", Case 2 Apply Pressure, upper case writing, etc. The coding is apparent from the MTM-GPD data cards and leads directly to details of motion and method in the appropriate volume of MTM-GPD data.

A complete symbol like BPL-CS-06 not only shows a basic data place of an object with a close and symmetrical fit following a 3" to 9" move, but also locates in the data manual the precise motions and time analysis for this element. Another example would be MGT-JL-18 to show the multi-get of an object jumbled loosely about 18" away. The obvious descriptive power of such condensed element coding permits greatly increased efficiency in recording work elements. Due to the conciseness of coding, MTM-GPD analyses are much shorter and more quickly written than are Detailed MTM analyses. It is fairly common to see MTM-GPD patterns with approximately half of the analysis lines required for a Detailed MTM pattern on the same task. Also, the efficiency of code selection is increased by the mnemonic feature and the reduction of choices between variables as compared to Detailed MTM analysis.

Finally, the accuracy of MTM-GPD is very close to that of Detailed MTM. The Application Training Course Manual of the MTM Association indicates that, for 95 percent of the cycles considered, analysis showed an accuracy within five percent of the actual cycle time for all but very short cycles; and the accuracy increases as the cycle time becomes greater. Actually, MTM-GPD already has proved adequate as to accuracy in hundreds of applications. The subject of MTM-GPD accuracy has even been investigated with a computer simulation[6] which showed satisfactory results. Therefore, from almost any practical standpoint, the reader may well consider using MTM-GPD for his standard data system. Further useful information on this point may be found at several places in Chapter 5.

Still another set of MTM-based standard data was adopted June 11, 1965 at the Managing Board meeting of the International MTM Directorate in Munich, Germany (as this text was going to press). It is called MTM-2.

This set of combined MTM-based data was developed from an outline presented to the International MTM Directorate at Stockholm, Sweden during October, 1964 by Svenska MTM-Foreningen (Swedish MTM Association). The directorate referred this outline and other pertinent data to the International Applied Research Committee. Their efforts reported at Munich resulted in the action noted above.

The particular format of MTM-2 and training requirements will be available through the various national associations when they approve it in behalf of their membership. As is true for MTM-GPD, proper application of this new data depends on a thorough understanding of the Detailed MTM Data; therefore special procedures are stipulated by the International Directorate and by the member national associations to qualify for its usage. The MTM-2 data therefore is another development from the increasing cooperation between participating national MTM associations working through the International MTM Directorate to further the international acceptance of scientific management.

Various features of MTM-2 are as follows. It utilizes a highly condensed data card and greatly abbreviated element coding. Decision models are provided to aid in classifying occurrences to the proper coding. The data was designed by using the results of motion frequency research coor-

---

[6] "Accuracy of MTM-GPD" by William K. Hodson, *Journal of Methods-Time Measurement*, Vol. IX, No. 1, MTM Association, Ann Arbor, Michigan, September-October 1963.

dinated through the International Applied Research Committee of the Directorate. It has categories for Get, Put, Apply Force, Regrasp, Eye Time, Crank, Step, Foot or Leg Motion, and Body Motion. Each of the Get and Put categories is divided into three types and each type has five distance groupings, thus making possible 15 choices of time values for both Get and Put. In addition, special codings are used to indicate the application of a static weight factor to the Get category and a dynamic weight factor to the Put category. Therefore, with 15 codes and 39 time values, the MTM-2 data is a much compressed version of MTM. It is anticipated that this feature will greatly speed the setting of time standards, although at a major sacrifice of detailed methods information in the final motion pattern. The development is, however, another milestone on the path to more efficient specification of time values for manual work.

In establishing more economical work measurement standards for areas outside of the traditional industrial bounds, MTM-based standard data offers a potentiality of bringing the benefit of labor standards to such diverse activities as shipping, transportation, retailing, business offices, financial institutions, hotels, hospitals, publishing, entertainment enterprises, etc. Admittedly, many of these will not be covered for quite some time in the future; but the data techniques and analysis approaches already are available.

PROCEDURE FOR DEVELOPING STANDARDS

The following steps are usually required to develop standard time data and time formulas:

1. Preliminary survey of existing conditions
2. Standardization of the task by methods engineering
3. Definition of the work to be covered
4. Determination and coding of all required work elements
5. Classification of work elements
6. Determination of manual element times
7. Development of process element times
8. Summarizing of all data and formulas
9. Testing of the data for validity
10. Preparation of the final report
11. Final approval of the data
12. Maintenance and audit of the data.

In general, the sequence of steps can be followed in the order shown; however, some overlapping and change of sequence may be required. In certain cases, it is also possible to eliminate some steps. Understanding of many of the steps may be clarified by re-reading the discussion of element variability and frequency determination in Chapter 19.

(1) Preliminary Survey

A preliminary survey should precede actual development of any standard data and formulas. One purpose of the survey is to determine whether the methods, facilities, etc., are standardized or if corrective action should be taken before beginning to collect data. Standard times will apply, strictly speaking, only for the given set of conditions under which they were developed and they will be meaningless if this set of conditions does not exist. *The main reason for any failure of standard data is a lack of proper standardization of job methods,* techniques, layouts, etc. In other words, the times are inappropriate for application if the methods which the data reflects are not actually used for the task covered. The preliminary survey establishes the amount of work to be done prior to the actual start of the standard data work. This means determining the items requiring attention, assigning responsibility for corrective action, and estimating the total man-hours required to prepare the standard data and/or time formula. A report on these findings should be prepared for the management. A word of caution—management's decisions, as well as its evaluation of the work done later, will be influenced by this report. Too great optimism will cause trouble near the end of the development, whereas it will probably never get started with too pessimistic an outlook.

During the preliminary survey, the approximate cycle times, the volume of work involved, and other characteristics that will affect the degree of refinement justified should be checked. This will permit more realistic planning for the development work.

The preliminary survey may reveal so many variations in techniques, methods, and existing conditions as to make standard data development inadvisable until these things are under control. This could mean a thorough study of the layout, workplace facilities, tooling, machines, material flow and handling, methods, job techniques, and personnel requirements. Obviously, analysis of and change in these things are preliminary to standard data development rather than a part of it, but they must be under control before valid data can be developed.

(2) Standardization of Method

It is rarely possible or practical to approach perfection by standardizing all factors which affect job conditions. Since human beings are involved, compromises in some phases must be made. Also, industrial jobs are not static but rather are continuously changing; improvements in tools, methods, techniques, etc., will occur. And regardless of the care with which standards for procedures and methods are established, there will always be exceptions!

Since it is impractical or uneconomical in many cases to make radical changes in methods of doing a given type of job, some undesirable factors must be accepted in an existing status. However, this does not mean that they cannot be standardized. It cannot be overemphasized that standard data will apply only within the limits of the conditions which are established and/or prevail.

All of the remarks regarding good MTM and/or time study procedures made previously apply especially to developing standards intended to be used as standard data. Because of their extreme importance in this case, they bear repeating. In addition, a few extra items must be included. The engineer desiring to produce practical, realistic, and usable standard data must concern himself with the following:

(1) Definition of the work covered
(2) Drawings and/or photographs of the workplace layout
(3) Lists of tools and fixtures to be available
(4) A procedure for using the tools and equipment
(5) A dimensioned sketch of the area layout
(6) The procedure for assigning personnel to jobs, and the number of people to be used
(7) Details on machine utilization
(8) Scheduling of jobs and machine loading (often it is inadvisable to run a certain job unless another can be run simultaneously)
(9) Material handling methods and equipment
(10) Quality and inspection requirements.

Although this preliminary work may appear to the uninitiated to be extraneous, an experienced industrial engineer knows it pays. The preliminary information serves as a ready reference and guide while the data is being developed. Even more important is the fact that the final data must include complete descriptions, definitions, sketches, etc., to support the time information; after all, these factors are direct evidence of the method which the time covers. Also, when the completed data is tested for validity, such back-up information is consulted many times; it can also eliminate many arguments over ambiguities when the conditions covered or assumed to be covered become a vitally important factor in labor disputes.

(3) Definition of Work Coverage

Another important item is the precise definition of the work to be covered by a given standard. The real work of data development cannot begin unless the tasks to be included have been determined and *defined as to their limits*. The established limits should be carefully reduced to writing. For example, consider the task of winding coils used in electronic gear. Assume the task of developing data to cover the winding of single-layer, linear wound coils having solid cylindrical ungrooved cores. Although this seems to be a sufficient description, an experienced analyst of coil winding standards knows that any standard for this operation would be vague without other established limits such as the following:

1. Minimum and maximum diameter and length of core
2. Core materials and surface finishes
3. Minimum and maximum wire gages to be used
4. Types of wire and wire insulation
5. Wire spacing, if any, and the accuracy required
6. Wet (varnish or adhesive) or dry winding conditions
7. Dimensional tolerances.

These and other basic factors affecting the time to wind the coils will have an effect on the time standards. Obviously, the workplace, tools, winding machine, tension devices, and other methods and process factors are also involved to a major degree. Even for this relatively simple example, a little exercise of the imagination will emphasize the need for complete and precise definition of the limitations on the time values. In actual work situations, it becomes necessary frequently to use a "trial and error" approach to establish many of the limitations; it will usually be found that no one bothered to determine them precisely in the past.

(4) Determination and Coding of Work Elements Required

Once the preliminary work is completed, including a definition of the work to be covered, the first step in actual data development work is listing of all the work elements. This means a determination, within the defined limits, of all the work elements required to perform jobs covered. Great aid in this step is afforded the analyst by any familiarity he may have with the jobs in question or similar tasks on which he has developed standard data.

Among several methods of determining the list of elements are these:

1. Examine existing time studies or other work measurement studies on specific, related jobs.
2. Observe typical jobs being performed, especially those similar.
3. Visualize all the steps required to perform the jobs covered.
4. Recheck procedure and method records made during the standardization phase described earlier.
5. For factory jobs, discuss the work with the process engineer, production foreman, operator, and others familiar with the work. For office jobs, discuss the work with the systems and procedures analyst, office

supervisor, office personnel, and others familiar with the work. They often possess information about the task that cannot be obtained in any other way. However, be cautious to avoid being misled, rather use the data they give as a basis of further investigation.

6. Arrange experiments or "dry runs" for jobs not being performed currently. This resort may be necessary to assure accuracy in the listing.

7. Take and analyze motion pictures of the job. These can also serve as methods records and proofs of the data analyzed.

Terminology used in naming the elements should be consistent with terms used throughout the plant. This will promote understanding of the standards by people other than those who develop them. In fact, standardization of terms should be an integral part of standard data work. Whenever possible, the analyst should apply approved terms which may be found in numerous authoritative standards, technical glossaries, or nomenclature lists. Foremost among these are publications of the American Standards Association. Other widely accepted sources are available from: American Management Association, Management Division of the American Society of Mechanical Engineers, American Institute of Industrial Engineers, Systems and Procedures Society, and many defense agencies of the federal government.

At this point it is unnecessary to be overly concerned about all details of the work content interior to these work study elements, since they can be analyzed in detail during the next step in this procedure. It is more important to *be extremely careful to define precisely the endpoints of each element to be measured*. Remember the discussions on this subject in conjunction with basic MTM motions. Incidentally, revisions in the elements listed are to be expected as the development work progresses.

It is generally a good idea to define all standard data elements in writing. This means identifying the starting and stopping points of these elements as they will be used in the standard data as well as brief descriptions of what occurs. Such data may then serve as an essential reference for the application engineer.

A set of coded symbols, letters and numbers, should be assigned to each element. This serves several purposes: (1) It aids the filing of data of either the developmental or final type; (2) It provides a cross-reference for similar or identical elements on other jobs; and (3) It minimizes ambiguities arising from the exclusive use of element names.

One of the best approaches to element coding the authors have seen is the alpha-mnemonic system devised by Richard M. Crossan and Harold W. Nance. These consulting engineers found that many clients developed standard data which was either not used at all or misused mainly because it was cumbersome and difficult to apply. To quote their verdict[7]: "One of the truisms in this business is that *standard data is no better than the human memory*. Or put another way: 'You can't economically *use* a standard element if you can't economically *find* it'." The typical standard data manual becomes so comprehensive that it is often easier and less expensive to develop a new standard than to find the needed elements in the manual. Alpha-mnemonic coding helps the analyst to communicate efficiently with the manual. It is an alphabetical (alpha) coding system which triggers the analyst's memory (mnemonic) and thereby reduces the time needed to carry out the coding process and to locate or identify previously coded elements.

The element coding problem is the routine need to assign codes when developing data and then to readily identify the assigned code meaningfully when referring to it later. Since the problem arises from the limitations of the analyst's memory, its solution should be based on a reasonable recognition of his inherent capacity to process, store, and recall pertinent information. Psychologists have delved deeply into the human attention span and memory span, which vary with an individual's natural aptitude. However, although this is by no means a limit, a conservative range of these sensory and mental spans is three alphabetical and five numerical symbols. Alpha-mnemonic coding utilizes this range to facilitate the coding process and efficient coding recognition.

The alpha-mnemonic coding system of Crossan and Nance therefore is based on three practical rules[8] as follows:

1. No code symbol should be made up of more than three letters of the alphabet.
2. Each code letter must be the first letter in a word which describes all or part of a given element.
3. No alpha letter can be used more than *one* time in the first field; more than once in a subcategory in the second field; nor more than once in a subcategory in the third field.

The first rule recognizes the memory span and establishes only three positions or "fields" of the element code to assure reasonably economical coding. Each of these fields must have a specific assigned meaning or purpose to meet the second rule. The third rule prohibits ambiguous coding duplication within each field.

The first field designates broad general classes or categories of activity. This is done most effectively when the analyst specifies action verbs rather than object nouns. Since the second field denotes less general subcategories of activities, it may require the use of either objective verbs or

---

[7] *Master Standard Data* by Richard M. Crossan and Harold W. Nance, McGraw-Hill Book Company, New York City, 1962.

[8] *Ibid.*

descriptive adjectives and nouns. The third field, which identifies specific information further delineating the final element or time data, is seldom expressed by a verb. Rather, the code letter should be the initial of a word connected with the basic measuring unit, dimension, order of measurement (such as first, second, etc.), differences in type of object, etc. To keep the final coding within the other requirement mentioned earlier, namely a five digit span, no more than two additional fields may be included. These normally will be numerical to identify such variables as distances, fits, types or classifications of subcategories, etc. If letters must be used, the relative violation of the first rule which results should be minimized by restricting the number of letters used, say to two or three at most, and limiting their meaning to a dual choice of variables which is clear-cut.

Another general guide is that the coding process should not be started until the analyst has become thoroughly familiar with the activity to be coded. This concept reduces errors and shortens coding time by avoiding the need for later corrections and recoding due to a lack of essential data being available during the original coding. The coding process itself consists of four progressive steps which are described in the following paragraphs.

STEP ONE in coding is to establish the first field for most effective, least restrictive coverage of the range of operations a set of standard data is to cover. Keep in mind that if the data is for an activity where multi-purpose elements predominate, such as machining or fabricating operations, the required categories necessarily will be broad and general; whereas an activity comprising mainly single-purpose elements can be defined more specifically.

The routine is to make a columnar list of all letters of the alphabet except X or Z, which are excluded to avoid confusion with the "times" sign and the number "2" when the code is applied. Then consider each letter *sequentially* and associate with it a word beginning with that letter which describes a broad class of the work to be covered. At this stage, do not linger at each letter to think of more than one word and choose between them; but defer consideration of alternates until after the first list is completed. Also, do not randomly enter words in the list as they occur, rather proceed in order to the next letter and skip any letter which presents difficulty. Avoid worrying about each letter and its associated word or detailed meaning, since the first list seldom is the final version adopted. Just apply this procedure and the steps following it as directed, and the final result will automatically include consideration of all necessary factors at the proper time.

For example, the first list for machine shop data might appear as follows:[9]

[9] *Ibid.*

A	Assemble	I	Inspect	Q	
B	Body motions	J		R	Remove
C	Clean up	K		S	Set up
D		L	Loosen	T	Tighten
E		M	Material handling	U	
F	Fasten	N		V	
G	Gauge	O	Obtain	W	Wrenches
H	Hammers	P	Place	Y	

Examination of this first attempt easily discloses some changes that must be made. For example, Assemble is too broad, because it includes so many variables that they cannot be fully covered by a three-letter code. These variables might be kind of object, type of object, size of object, method of handling object, alternate usages of the object, etc. all of which must be expressed by the limited symbols in an unambiguous manner. Of course, using the fourth and fifth fields might be feasible if numbers could express some of these differences. In a sense, even the element time value itself could be used as an extra field; but only if there would be no duplications of element times with respect to the preceding fields within one total code symbol. Thus the Assemble element should be revised. An example of a category in the field which is too narrow or specific is Hammers. This being a specific tool, its use will be easily covered by the code; but this will use up a letter possibly needed to express a more general category, which could include hammering elements. A similar objection applies to the category Wrenches. Also, the Hammers and Wrenches categories are not verbs for an action, but nouns which greatly restrict the extent of the code coverage.

By considering such difficulties, the code letters can be reassigned one or more times to generate a new result such as the following[10]:

A	Actuate	I	Instruction	P	Place and
C	Clamp and unclamp	J	Job preparation		remove parts
F	Finish	L	Layout	S	Set tools
G	Gauging	M	Machine	T	True up
H	Handling		handling		

This list bears little resemblance to the first attempt. It has three less categories, but they now cover virtually the complete range of machine shop manual elements.

STEP TWO of the coding process is to determine the second field by a somewhat different approach. Here more specific questions are answered for each of the primary fields. Again the most direct procedure is to make

[10] *Ibid.*

a rough list based on the alphabet, but this time each list should consider both the first field and what the third field might need to represent. Such a list[11] for the primary field of Gauging might appear as follows:

CI	Caliper	Inside per dimension
CO	Caliper	Outside per dimension
F	Female and male thread	Per occurrence
GR	Gauge Radius	Per radius
H	Hole—small	Per hole
II	Indicator	Install and remove
IU	Indicator	Use for inspection with Jo blocks
J	Jo blocks	Assemble and disassemble
MD	Micrometers	Depth
MI	Micrometers	Inside
MO	Micrometers	Outside
P	Plug—male	Per hole
RS	Rule—scale	Per occurrence
RT	Rule—adjustable steel tape	Per occurrence
S	Screw thread pitch	Per occurrence
T	Telescope	Per hole
V	Vernier	Per occurrence
W	Wires	Per dimension

The general guiding principle in making the second field list is to assign the most meaningful code letters to those elements with the greatest frequency of occurrence. For example, the desire to classify male and female thread gauges with an M or T (for male and thread) is overruled by this principle. Micrometers are used much more frequently than thread gauges, so they pre-empt the M code letter. Also T is the only possible designator for telescope gauges without violating General Rule 2. Therefore, the F for Female is the only possible letter to associate with male and female thread gauges. While these decisions sometimes seem tedious, there is usually some logical way to express all necessary subcategories within the coding rules. Patience at this point will pay dividends in the final coding structure.

STEP THREE of the coding process is to assign the coding for the third field. This will be partially accomplished during consideration of the second field. The most direct approach therefore is to review the tentative assignments to either confirm them or to devise better alternates. A key to this review is concentration on the various methods by which the objects named in the second field may be used. This procedure is illustrated by the following partial extension of the gauging code (note that all three fields are shown in this listing):

---

[11] *Ibid.*

GCI	Caliper, Inside
GCO	Caliper, Outside
GFF	Female and male thread, Female thread
GFM	Female and male thread, Male thread
GGR	Gauge Radius
GGH	Gauge Hole
GII	Indicator, Install and remove
GIU	Indicator, Use for inspection with Jo blocks
GJA	Jo blocks, Assemble and disassemble
etc.	

At this point, there is an ambiguity in the third field where I is used to mean both "Inside" and "Install and remove." Since the "Inside" usage is more general, the best change would be GII to GIA. This is all right because the A has the same meaning of "Assemble and disassemble" as used for the GJA category.

STEP FOUR in coding considers the fourth and fifth fields simultaneously. It answers the query of whether any further element identification is needed or desirable for easy application. It should further consider the element time to be developed. If only the element time remains for a given coding in the first three fields, the coding need not be enlarged provided there will be no ambiguity due to differences in the numerical time values. However, to allow for frequency problems, differences in linear distance or other discrete measurements, etc. a one- or two-digit number may be added to the code. At times, General Rule 1 may need to be relaxed for simplicity, if the fourth field letters used are common to all classes of the first field. This could result in a further field in the Gauging coding as in the following partial example:

GCIF	Caliper, Inside, First dimension
GCIA	Caliper, Inside, Additional dimension
GCOF	Caliper, Outside, First dimension
GCOA	Caliper, Outside, Additional dimension
GFFF	Female and male thread, Female thread, First thread
GFFA	Female and male thread, Female thread, Additional thread
etc.	

The substantial advantages of using alpha-mnemonic coding are more apparent when data catalogues other than the previous example of machine shop data become familiar. A first field list for furniture upholstering[12] is the following:

[12] *Ibid.*

A	Apply	H	Handling	P	Position
B	Body motions	I	Inspect	R	Regulate
C	Cut and trim	J	Join (manual)	S	Stretch
F	Fasten (mechanical)	M	Measure and	T	Tear
G	Get and aside		mark	U	Unfold and fold

Another example is the first field list[13] for sewing:

A	Align	H	Handle parts	R	Realign
B	Bundle	I	Inspect	S	Stack
C	Cut and break	M	Machine handling	T	Trim
F	Fold	O	Obtain and aside parts	U	Unfold
G	Get and aside objects	P	Place		

In both of these lists, the coding is very mnemonic (memory jogging) in that it immediately causes the reader to instinctively visualize the class of work operations included.

(5) Classification of Work Elements

The *first* step of classification is examining the element listing to discover elements common to work in other areas of the plant that may have been covered previously by standard data. Developing standards for such elements can be then eliminated from the task. Some sort of cataloging and filing system should be used to facilitate cross-referencing of elements. *Care must be taken to assure that elements bearing the same name are actually equal and/or identical in work content!* Unless this is true, the standards will not be valid because they reflect different methods, although the element name might be identical.

The *second* step of classification is separating all manually controlled elements from the process- or machine-controlled elements. Each type will involve different handling in subsequent development steps. A simple example may help to illustrate here. Consider dialing a telephone:

1. Reach to dial and insert finger.
2. Rotate dial to the stop and release.
3. Wait for return of dial to normal position.

The first two elements are manually controlled but the third involves the process control caused by the wait for the dial spring to act.

The *third* classification step is identifying each element as to its constancy or variability. Constant elements are those whose performance time will not vary within the defined limits of the element. Variable elements are those which vary in time value or are dependent on the magni-

[13] *Ibid.*

tude of variable factors in the job. Refer to Chapter 24 for a detailed discussion of variability. An element of the same name may be constant for one work task but variable for another. For example, the element "pick up part" for the task of loading a moving conveyor in a given department as part of a defined process would be essentially constant if the operator was located at the end of an automatic processing machine delivering parts having the same physical dimensions and orientation one at a time. This same element "pick up part" would be variable, however, if the operator were tending a turret lathe where the required time to obtain a given part could vary with the type of containers used and with the various sizes of parts (from small to large, etc.) associated with this type of work. It may not be readily apparent whether to class some elements as constants or variables. When this happens, the identity can be delayed until the detailed measurement analysis is made later in this procedure.

(6) Determination of Manual Element Times

Two methods commonly used to measure manual element times have been covered in previous chapters—they are MTM and time study. Detailed information on these techniques is not repeated here, since they can be studied elsewhere in this text. However, a few restatements and additional observations will be given.

Time Study Considerations

As a tool for developing standard data for manual elements, time study has some definite disadvantages. It may take several months to observe and time a sufficient variety of jobs to obtain a good sample of data, since the jobs must be in operation to permit timing at all. Frequently, time studies made in the past cannot be used because of wide variations in elemental breakpoints; also it is not unusual to find old time studies lacking vital details regarding the methods used during the study. The best elemental breakpoints for standard data purposes may be extremely difficult to detect when making a time study, and a later decision to revise breakpoints necessitates either additional timing or retiming. Added to these disadvantages, perhaps of a more crucial nature, is the inherent uncertainty regarding leveling or performance rating.

The biggest advantage for time study versus pre-determined time systems is that elements or portions of elements are less likely to be overlooked, since all required time is accounted for, especially when the continuous observation method is used. Another advantage with the continuous method of time study is the required recording of all delays occurring during the study; this factor helps isolate unavoidable delays which can be the basis for establishing proper allowances. The frequency of occurrence for elements not an integral part of the regular cycle will also be revealed by the time study.

MTM Considerations

Methods-Time Measurement is actually a highly refined form of standard data. This really means that standard data is used to develop standard data. Because MTM elements normally span small time increments, its direct application to develop time standards for individual jobs is time-consuming and costly. Its use is more economical, however, in developing standard data because it requires less total time and cost than with time study. This is true primarily because one *good* MTM pattern for an element suffices, whereas a *valid* time study element time requires a statistically correct number of readings as shown in Chapter 24.

Among the additional advantages of using MTM to develop standard time data is the flexibility with which element breakpoints may be revised, both at the time of observation and at any subsequent time in the development. Elements may be written to begin and end at whatever point best suits the given situation, and changes are easily made. Another MTM advantage is that standard data and time formulas may be developed in much less total time than with time study because it is unnecessary to actually observe a wide variety of jobs over a period of time when they can be found running in collecting valid data. The variations inherent in the work are more obvious when proper MTM analysis is followed, and they can be evaluated timewise in a logical, defensible manner.

Another MTM advantage is the capability of using MTM-GPD either alone or in conjunction with detailed MTM and/or time study to develop specialized standard data.

A disadvantage of using MTM is the chance for untrained and/or careless engineers to fail to record all of the MTM elements necessary to a task, thereby reflecting an erroneously "tight" time allowance. Care must be exercised so that the patterns realistically and fully cover the method prescribed for the process.

(A) *Constant Manual Elements*

To prepare *time study* data for analysis, each identical element from all the studies should be tabulated and summarized on a spread sheet. Of course, it is desirable that only elements taken by statistically valid procedures (see Chapter 24) be accepted. If highly accurate and precise standards are desired, some additional statistical methods available (note the summary of Chapter 24) should be employed to test the validity of the individual values averaged for constant purposes. The constant element times may be determined by averaging all accepted values. It is desirable at least to determine the mode, median, and mean for comparison. This will suffice for many standards, but the extra tests mentioned may often be justified.

The times for constant elements *based on MTM* require merely the writing of one valid pattern for the proper method and assigning the MTM element times. Minor pattern variations due to variance of part size, distance, etc., should be checked carefully and, if the time effect is small, such variation can be effectively ignored by striking a workable average and using this for the standard. The error permitted should be held to about 5 per cent of the element time, which is the commonly accepted limit for statistically validated time study values. When the effect of the variations is too great, however, the entire element may justifiably be reclassified as a variable element—note the greater insight possible with MTM.

(B) *Variable Manual Elements*

Conventional methods for handling variable *time study* elements consist of plotting values from all the pertinent time studies on a graph with time as the ordinate and a suspected variable factor as the abscissa. To the resulting plot, if the variation is apparently due to the abscissa used, a curve may be fitted visually or by use of such statistical devices as the Method of Least Squares. This curve or an equation of it then becomes the variable standard data.

When more than one variable factor is involved, the method for handling the data is more complex. Although various engineering and mathematical techniques may be employed, completion of the graphical and/or statistical analysis normally results in an equation or formula expressing the time as a function of all variable factors. The final formula should be in the simplest form with the meaning of symbols clearly identified. Also, the variable factors should be expressed in terms of the job conditions. It is important to bear in mind that all significant information required to use the formula must be readily available to the person applying the data.

The first step with *variable MTM elements* is to write the MTM pattern, just as with constant elements. However, the pattern should be written for the general case, leaving variables as unknowns. Where Reach and Move distances vary, a symbol such as X or Y may be substituted in the time expression. If the case of Reach or Move also is subject to a variable condition, provision should be made for this fact. Similar tactics, such as reference to the Position table, provide a way of writing a formula that can be evaluated with only the MTM data card.

All of the conditions under which the elements may vary should be listed. A schedule of times then can be developed for the various conditions. Just as for data established by time study, it is important to keep in mind what information will be available to the person using the data. All variable factors should be expressed in objective terms of such nature that they may be readily identified.

To clear up any doubts, an example on this point may be in order.

Consider the element "load part in fixture" for which the MTM element pattern is:

TMU	RH	DESCRIPTION
11.5	R10B	To part on table
2.0	G1A	Pickup part
13.5	⎛ M10C	Bring part to fixture
—	⎝ G2	Shift to orient
T_p	P____	Insert part in fixture
		(See Position table)
2.0	RL1	Release part

Total = $(29.0 + T_p)$TMU

This element varies with the type of Position required. The TMU value represented by T_p could be left for the user to determine by reference to the MTM Position data. This would mean that the person using the data must know MTM in order to determine the type of Position involved before he can determine the total element time. Furthermore, since many applications of the data may be made at a desk with only the blueprint of the part available, another complication has been added. It would be difficult to apply the MTM data without further information regarding the fixture and workplace.

Perhaps a better method of summarizing the element time would be to determine the relationship between the shape of the part and fixture, as well as the fit tolerances, and the class of Position required. A schedule of times versus the shape and size of the part and hole as variable factors can be developed from this. These factors could be readily evaluated by any engineer, not just one trained in MTM. Working out formulas in this manner to cover many variable elements is relatively easy with MTM. Algebraic expressions for the element times are usually most advantageous, although alignment charts, curves, or tabulations may be easier to handle.

(7) Develop Process Time Schedules

The process time for machining operations involving automatic or semi-automatic equipment can be established by mathematical calculation as soon as the feeds and speeds are known. However, determining the optimum feeds and speeds is often difficult, since they can be greatly influenced by such factors as the composition of the material, the finish required, the amount of stock removed, the capacity of the machine, the type of cutting tool, the method of holding the tool and/or workpiece, the type and amount of coolant employed, the tolerances to be held, and others.

While many handbooks list recommended feeds and speeds for various conditions, these recommendations are guides only. Another source of suggestions is the instruction book or manual for the machine, whether it is found in the factory or in the office. A schedule of the actual feeds and speeds for given machines required for various conditions should be determined by experience coupled with experimentation. This may require an analyst to supervise or execute controlled "trial and error" experiments on a number of jobs and machines. This is the best method of collecting valid data on machine performance.

Handbooks may also be used as guides for operations involving machines utilizing hand feeds; however, the exercise of an analyst's experienced judgment then becomes even more important in arriving at a basis for time schedules. The use of the term "experience" here does not imply blind acceptance of actual times established with a stop watch. Very often, hand feeding rates can be increased by the operator significantly when not being studied with little effect on the quality of the work or tool life. At times consultation with product engineers, process engineers, tool engineers, and production foremen will prove helpful in evaluating hand feeds. Even with this advice, it may still be necessary to undertake experiments and validation studies prior to exercise of the experience factor.

Many process-controlled elements can be established only with a stop watch. Such operations as polishing, welding, deburring, and soldering contain elements of this type. These kind of elements can be controlled to some extent by the operator. For example, the time to polish a metal surface on a buffing wheel may be varied by changes in pressure exerted by the worker.

(8) Summarize and Formulate Data

All application data should be summarized in a manner permitting convenient usage. Ideas on this topic can be found in Chapter 24. When possible, the elements should be listed in chronological order. Combinations should be made wherever possible and practical. For example, a series of elements which invariably occur in consecutive order should be combined, assuming the frequency of occurrence for each element is the same in the combination. Such recapitulation ("recap") is an essential task for successful standards development.

A *mathematical formula* can probably be written for almost any type of work. Since many jobs would require too complex an expression, however, sole reliance on this method would defeat the purpose of practicality and simplicity. A formula covering the entire time cycle should be used only when the component expressions are reasonably simple. In other cases, several alternate methods of expressing the final data are available.

One commonly used method is listing or tabulating all the elements, along with their performance times, on a *data sheet* which is used to select time values on a reference basis. A form of data sheet known as *an appli-cation check sheet* is actually an expendable work sheet. It combines a listing of all elements and times with spaces for checking and/or extending the times to develop standards for given jobs. A set of rules may also be included.

A separate set of instructions for applying standard data, along with examples, is often necessary. Although the *instruction sheet* need not include elaborate detail, it should list all of the information needed by the application engineer. This could include the element and task definitions, development data, method standardization data, and the sources where additional information may be found. The location of details backing up this information for reference should also be indicated in some manner. The instructions should clearly define the limits of application, with a notice that the validity of answers obtained by extension or extrapolation of the data beyond these limits has not been verified.

In addition, instruction sheets should describe how to apply the data and formulas and, briefly, how they were derived. It is also important to include an itemized list of all pertinent job facts and information needed to develop standards by the formula, table, or graph. Usually, one good example of application that includes a sketch or photograph of the parts or materials will make the data and formula usage clear.

(9) Test the Validity of the Data

Although valid procedures and validation of data used should be an integral part of every step for producing standard data and/or time formulas, it is worthwhile or even essential to make a final check on the veracity of the finished results. Several typical jobs should be selected and the data applied to determine the standard time. These same jobs then can be analyzed by time study or detailed MTM analysis, and the resulting time standards compared against the answer from the standard data. Application of the data and formulas to specified examples by someone other than the development engineer may also bring to light points not made clear on the summary sheet as well as tending to eliminate bias. These results can be compared to those obtained for the same examples by the development engineer.

The results of any comparison methods should agree within approxi-mately 5 per cent or within the normal permissible error which has been established for the standard data or formula in question. The main purpose of such tests is to determine: (1) Have elements been omitted from the standard data? (2) What is the effect of known cumulative errors on individual elements? and (3) Does the data lend itself to rapid, easy appli-cation? Any discrepancy revealed by validation procedures is good reason to restudy or revise the standard data or time formula concerned.

(10) Prepare Final Report

The final report should explain the scope of the project, summarize what was accomplished, suggest the results anticipated, and recommend any action to be taken. It should include all the summarized data, the instruction sheets, and other pertinent information. The results of the verification tests should also be included. The various anticipated uses for which the data may be employed should be explained. One widely used format for the final report on a time formula, developed by Methods Engineering Council, is shown in Fig. 1. Details regarding this format are given on pages 252–257 of "Methods-Time Measurement" by Maynard, Stegemerten, and Schwab, McGraw-Hill, 1948.

(11) Obtain Final Approval

Final approval procedure varies extensively. In some plants, it may be only a formality. In other situations, especially where incentive pay systems are in effect, the approval of standard data and time formulas may involve review by several management men as well as meetings with labor union representatives. In most cases, the development engineer must thoroughly explain the data and formulas and be prepared to clarify any development details that are questioned. Even though a genuine engineering job has been done, it is still frequently necessary to sell the results. It pays to plan the presentation in advance and to have available examples illustrating how the data is applied.

(12) Maintain and Audit the Data

In discussing the nature of standards earlier, attention was directed to the dynamic quality of industrial jobs. The fact that jobs are subject to change with time and new technology necessitates a periodic restudy of work covered by standard data. Changes in methods and job conditions seldom come promptly to the attention of the industrial engineering department for restudy unless the supervision is unusually conscientious or labor difficulty arises. Jobs not on standard data, however, are often routinely observed from time to time, so that changes are more readily noticed.

When tools are improved, machines replaced, or myriad other possible changes occur, the standard data and time formulas concerned should be reviewed for appropriate revisions in the data. Maintenance is a very important phase of standard data work that is too often neglected. In the long run, obsolete standard data and formulas will engender labor difficulties, poor control of production costs, loss of faith in the industrial engineering functions, and a distrust for standards among the supervisory staff.

Effective maintenance programs must be planned. Schedules for the periodic review of all work under standard data should be developed and

Formula No. _____

PART: (Specific part or class of parts covered)

OPERATION: (Simplified key description or title)

MATERIAL: (Basic stock or pieces to be assembled)

WORK STATION: (Specific identity of tools and equipment, including a
workplace layout)

ALLOWED TIME: (Statement of the time formulas and to which part of the
operation they apply, including time tables and application
rules)

APPLICATION: (Limitations on the coverage of the formula, with important
exceptions, together with factory location and date required
to legally establish the prevailing conditions of coverage).

ANALYSIS: (Statements of responsibility for various aspects and adjuncts
of the work done at the station, the allowances permitted and/or
applied. and the characteristics of the part or process the
analyst who applied the formula must determine)

PROCEDURE: (Description of the work elements required for the task)

METHOD AND SYNTHESIS: (The work patterns and/or time studies taken to
establish both the method and the time, plus the
analysis steps accomplished to synthesize the time
formula in sufficient detail to permit restudy or
validation of the work measurement and formulation)

INSPECTION: (The quality requirements of the work and/or responsibility
of the inspector in connection with it)

PAYMENT: (All data and information needed to determine and explain how
the time formula affects and is used to determine the pay of
the operator, with any precautionary clauses regarding changes
in methods and/or method of payment being included)

APPROVAL: (Signatures required to make the formula official and effective)

Date: _____   _____   _____
                          (Signature)   (Signature)

Fig. 1.   Time Formula Report form.

enforced as a regular, unquestioned policy. Not only will this practice
afford and allow an opportunity to check standards, but it will also help
determine whether the methods originally established are being followed
or are still applicable at all.

The application of standard data and/or time formulas must not be performed carelessly or improperly. The person using the data must fully understand or appreciate what it means. The available details of the development, definitions, instructions, etc., deserve careful reading. Otherwise, especially if the work is complex, errors may be introduced unknowingly. Of course, this will result either in "tight" or "loose" standards. To minimize the effects of improper application of standard data, the periodic maintenance audits should include checks on the application of the data. The auditing engineer should familiarize himself with the work and the data prior to selecting a sample of jobs where the data was applied and making a recheck of all figures.

The results of audit findings should be reported to the proper authorities with favorable comments or recommendations for corrective action. These reports provide management with facts and data leading to effective means by which to achieve control of labor and other costs. Enhancing the competitive position of the enterprise in this way leads to the maximizing of profits, which is in the ultimate best interest of labor and management and which is the real justification for standard data and time formulas.

AN EXAMPLE OF STANDARD DATA AND TIME FORMULAS

To help illustrate some of the principles discussed in this chapter, a simple example consisting of the development of standard data for a gaging operation which follows the tapping of blind holes in small metal parts is presented. The steps follow the suggested procedure. Although most actual applications of the procedure will be more complex than this example, they might involve distracting details which would hinder understanding the approach which is being illustrated clearly and simply.

Preliminary Survey

This survey will reveal the basic facts of the operation, of which the following are typical. The task involves checking Class 2 threads of tapped blind holes in small metal parts with a double-end, threaded plug, "GO"-"NOT-GO" gage illustrated in Fig. 2. The part was previously secured in a fixture for tapping the drilled holes. When all holes in a particular part have been tapped and the chips cleared from the holes, the operator checks the threads by using the "GO" end of the gage to discover if the minimum size has been held and the "NOT-GO" end to find out whether the maximum allowable size has been exceeded.

During this step, other data included in later steps will have been noted and possibly some factors measured, especially if they are constant and will be needed later. Further ideas for this step were previously discussed and will not be repeated here.

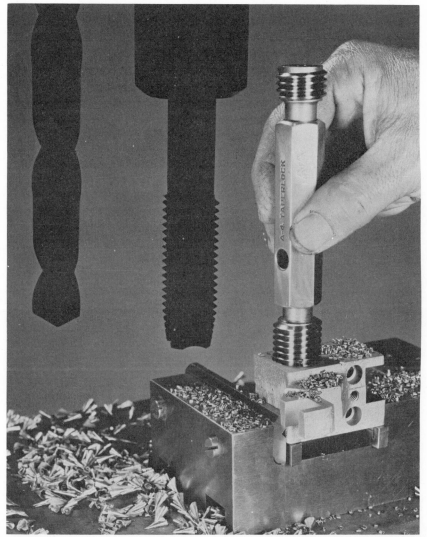

Courtesy Greenfield Tap & Die Corp.

Fig. 2.   Thread-gaging operation.

Standardize Method

To select a standardized method implies that a number of alternates have been evaluated either roughly or in sufficient detail to arrive at the method to be specified.   In this example, it is assumed such work has resulted in the method described.

As previously emphasized, it is necessary to specify the workplace layout on which the method depends. Figure 3 shows the layout for this example. When not in use, the gage is kept within easy reaching distance on the bench to the right of the operator since all of the gaging work is performed with the right hand. When all holes in a particular part have been tapped, and the chips have been blown away with the air hose, the

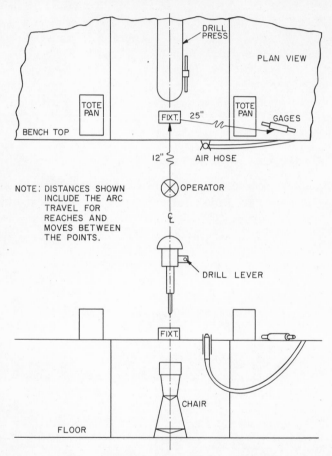

Fig. 3. Workplace layout for example study.

gaging operation begins with the worker picking up the gage and bringing it to the workpiece.

With the gage at the hole, the operator inserts the "GO" end into the first hole and screws it in to the bottom of the hole (this is possible only if the minimum size has been held). The gage must travel freely the full depth of hole on the "GO" end. The next step is to remove the gage from the hole while counting the threads engaged, rotate it end-for-end, and then check the same hole with the "NOT-GO" end.   If the threads are properly sized, only one thread will engage on the "NOT-GO" end. After removal from the hole following "NOT-GO" checking, the gage is either brought to the next hole for checking with the "GO" end (if there is more than one hole to be gaged) or else it is laid aside where specified in the lay-out to permit resumption of other work.   To inspect for the correct number of threads, it is a required feature of the method (as already mentioned) that the operator pause to count every thread as each full revolution is completed while removing the gage.

Although the standardizing procedure has been given in a narrative manner in this section, the net result of actual application normally will consist of written job processes, workplace layouts, part number lists, material descriptions, etc., which show the work of standardizing the method and the final method chosen.

Define Work Coverage

Spelling out the limitations placed on the time standard follows rather easily from consideration of the features of the prescribed standard method. For the example, it was determined that the following limitations would apply—note that they are logical in relation to the previously specified data.

1. Gaging of Class 2 threads in metal parts only
2. Gage must be of the "GO"-"NOT-GO", double end, thread plug type
3. The operator must count the threads engaged while removing the gage
4. No variation in nominal thread size or nominal depth of hole in any particular part
5. Center-to-center spacing of holes in a given part must not exceed 4 inches
6. Standard applies only to parts held in the fixture in which tapped
7. The workplace layout specified in Fig. 3 must be used for the time standard to apply
8. Only blind tapped holes are covered by this standard
9. The number of holes per part may vary from 1 to 10
10. The nominal diameter of hole may range from ⅛ to 1 inch
11. Holes may range in depth from ⅛ inch to 1½ inches
12. The handling and/or allowance for rejects is not covered in this standard.   It is for base performance time only.

Determine and Code Work Elements Required

This step involves listing all required work elements, assigning a code and indicating the variation in frequency of occurrence as follows:

CODE*	ELEMENT DESCRIPTION	FREQUENCY PER PART
1	Obtain gage	1
2	Locate "GO" end to hole	1 to 10
3	Screw "GO" end into hole	1 to 10
4	Unscrew "GO" end from hole	1 to 10
5	Reverse gage, check "NOT-GO" entry	1 to 10
6	Reverse gage, move to next hole	0 to 9
7	Lay gage aside	1

* Note that the coding is kept to simple numerical in this example due to space limitations in this book.

Obviously, elements 1 and 7 will be performed for each part, while the others will vary in frequency of occurrence depending on the number of holes per part. In addition, the motion content of elements 3 and 4 will vary with the number of threads checked per hole; which, in turn, depends on the diameter and pitch of thread. Finally, element 6 will not be required if there is but one hole in the part and will occur a maximum of nine times per part according to Item 9 of the work coverage limitations.

Classify Work Elements

The elements just isolated must next be classified as to variability, together with the cause of any variation, in the following manner:

CONSTANT ELEMENTS	
ELEMENTS	CONTROLLING FACTORS
1. Obtain gage	Reach and Move distance vary slightly but will be considered constant for the standardized layout
2. Locate "GO" end to hole	Positioning and seating the first thread is a true constant for the given conditions
5. Reverse gage, check "NOT-GO" entry	The method of performing this is also a true constant
6. Reverse gage, move to next hole	Regrasping controls. Distance to next hole always less than 14″ it would take to control this element
7. Lay gage aside	Distance of Move to aside may vary slightly but will be considered a constant for the layout specified

(*continued*)

(*continued*)

VARIABLE ELEMENTS	
ELEMENTS	VARIABLE FACTORS
3. Screw "GO" end into hole	Hole diameter and number of threads per hole
4. Unscrew "GO" end from hole	Hole diameter and number of threads per hole

Note that classification of an element as constant or variable depends on whether that element varies in time required for any of the limits and/or conditions of the standard previously mentioned. Listing of the constant and variable elements as shown above is essential, even on a simple job, to help the analyst comprehend the measurement problem involved in the development of particular data.

For the practical accuracy required in this example, the time variation involved in elements 1, 2, 5, 6, and 7 due to the specified conditions will be slight, which justifies classifying them as constant elements. While the distance to the next hole may differ in element 6, for instance, consideration of the limit given (4-inch center spacing of holes) leads to the conclusion that this difference will not be greater than 1 or 2 inches at most, with corresponding small time effect that safely can be neglected. It is seldom that variations of this small amount will be considered significant in standards development.

The performance time for elements 3 and 4 varies significantly with the variable factors listed because as the handle of the gage becomes larger with increasing nominal hole diameters, more finger motions are needed to engage each thread. Also, since each thread will require a complete revolution of the gage to account for the screwing time, the time for elements 3 and 4 must obviously be multiplied by the number of threads in the hole. This can be determined either by the analyst or a person applying the standard by multiplying the depth of hole in inches by the number of threads per inch. This will be the only preparatory calculation required in order to apply the standard formula to be shown later.

Determine Manual Element Times

Assume for this example that no previous data exists for any of these work elements, because none of the elements are common to jobs previously studied. Also, assume this task to be entirely under manual control, with no time determination for process-controlled or machine-controlled elements involved. Since the manual time could be determined by either time study or MTM, each will be discussed separately in the following sections. In concluding the example, however, the MTM patterns have been used as the basis for manual element times.

Time Study: Using this approach, the analyst would need to make a large number of time studies to cover the entire range of variables and conditions required by the statements made earlier. Other difficulties are: (1) The job would have to be running for each of these cases, which could mean that collection of the data would take quite some time; (2) Careful analysis of the time data would be necessary to determine the true variables; and (3) It would be necessary to follow the principles of statistical validity presented in Chapter 24 to avoid errors in the large number of computations required.

In spite of these difficulties, however, this approach, with care and integrity on the part of the analyst, can yield valid standard data.

An example study covering one of the many case possibilities is shown in Fig. 4. This study is synthetic rather than actual, but it illustrates very well the nature of such time determination. Note that the lack of a readily recognized breakpoint between elements 2 and 3 as set up for the standards being developed necessitates combining them when using the stop watch to record times. Data gained by such time studies, all of which would be similar to this typical example, would

Date
Study No. TG-8
Sheet No. 1 of 1 Sheets

TMU WATCH-CONTINUOUS TIMING
3/8" NOMINAL DIAMETER
6 THREADS PER HOLE

Methods Engineering Council Form No. 100

Elements	Obtain Gage		Check with "Go" End		Remove "Go" End		Reverse Check "Not-Go"		Reverse, Move to Next Hole		Lay Gage Aside		
Number	1		2-3		4		5		6		7		
Line	T	R	T	R	T	R	T	R	T	R	T	R	
1	50	50	162	212	250	462	110	572	18	590	–	–	
2	–	–	170	760	238	998	98	1096	20	116	–	–	
3	–	–	158	274	240	514	102	616	12	628	–	–	
4	–	–	156	784	247	2031	93	124	16	140	–	–	
5	–	–	157	297	252	549	100	649	–	–	24	2893	← FIRST CYCLE 2893 TMU
6	48	48	165	213	247	460	104	564	13	577	–	–	
7	–	–	155	732	251	983	96	1079	21	100	–	–	
8	–	–	161	261	238	499	90	589	18	607	–	–	
9	–	–	158	765	248	2013	98	111	14	125	–	–	
10	–	–	160	285	250	535	108	643	–	–	28	2671	← SECOND CYCLE 2671 TMU
11	53	53	154	207	245	452	102	554	15	569	–	–	
12	–	–	167	736	258	994	107	1101	16	117	–	–	
13	–	–	162	279	252	531	99	630	17	647	–	–	
14	–	–	151	798	241	2039	91	130	14	144	–	–	
15	–	–	165	309	238	547	93	640	–	–	23	2663	← THIRD CYCLE 2663 TMU
16	51	51	160	211	240	451	95	546	19	565	–	–	
17	–	–	162	727	242	969	98	1067	12	1079	–	–	
18	–	–	164	243	249	492	105	597	11	608	–	–	
19	–	–	155	763	254	2017	101	118	18	136	–	–	
20	–	–	152	288	246	534	97	631	–	–	20	2651	← FOURTH CYCLE 2651 TMU

Summary

	1	2-3	4	5	6	7	
Totals "T"	202	3194	4926	1987	254	95	10,878
No. Observations	4	20	20	20	16	4	4
Average "T"	50.5	159.7	246.3	99.4	15.9	23.8	2719 TMU AVG. CYCLE
Minimum "T"	48	151	238	90	11	20	
Maximum "T"	53	170	258	110	21	28	
Rating (S.E.C. Cy.)	DDDD →						
Leveling Factor	1,000 →						
L.F. x Ave. "T"							
% Allowance							
Time Allowed	50.5	159.7	246.3	99.4	15.9	23,8	→ STANDARD TMU PER ELEMENT

Foreign Elements

Sym	R	T	Description
A			
B			
C			
D			
E			
F			
G			
H			
I			
J			
K			
L			
M			
N			
O			

	Skill			Effort	
	A1 A2	Super		A1 A2	Excessive
	B1 B2	Excellent		B1 B2	Excellent
	C1 C2	Good		C1 C2	Good
✓	D	Average	✓	D	Average
	E1 E2	Fair		E1 E2	Fair
	F1 F2	Poor		F1 F2	Poor

	Conditions			Consistency	
	A	Ideal		A	Perfect
	B	Excellent		B	Excellent
	C	Good		C	Good
✓	D	Average	✓	D	Average
	E	Fair		E	Fair
	F	Poor		F	Poor

General Rating for Study	Skill	Effort	Cond.	Consy
	D	D	D	D

Study Started A.M. P.M. — Study Finished A.M. P.M. — Overall Time HRS

Fig. 4. Time study of thread-gaging operation.

next be subjected to graphical and statistical analysis. Figure 5 shows for the example study one means by which the constant elements of the standard can be determined, element 5 being the one covered. Plotting and analysis of the nature shown in Fig. 6 would be needed for the variable elements in order to cover the range of data from all the studies and also permit analysis into standard times.

To use the time study approach for development of standard data requires a great deal of skill and effort on the part of the analyst. Even for the simple example under consideration, this should be obvious by examining the work and detail required in Figs. 4, 5, and 6. Insofar as data for manual elements is concerned, the use of pre-determined

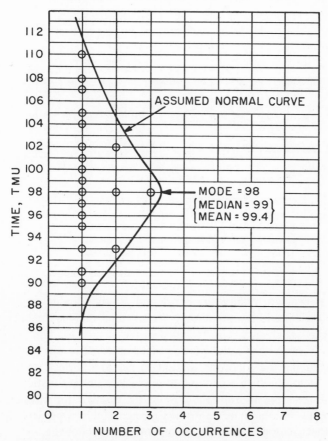

Fig. 5. Graphical analysis of a constant element.

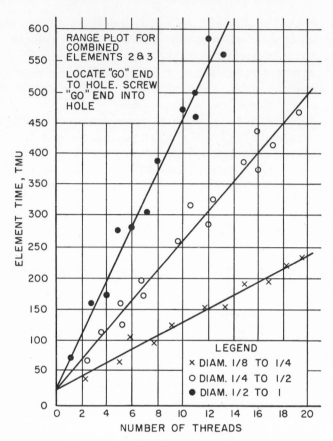

Element 2 Time = Intercept = 22.0 TMU
Element 3 Time = TMU per thread = Linear Slope:
   Diam. ⅛″ to ¼″ = 11.0 TMU per thread
   Diam. ¼″ to ½″ = 23.5 TMU per thread
   Diam. ½″ to 1″ = 44.0 TMU per thread

Fig. 6.   Range plotting for variable elements and analysis of plot.

times appears to reduce the effort and remove doubts as to coverage
of the variables in the situation; however, time study is the only recourse
when process elements are included in the standard.   The reader could
profitably review the latter portion of Chapter 22 at this point and also
after studying the following section to get a confirmed orientation on
the problem of which technique to apply in a given situation.

Methods-Time Measurement: Since the example for this procedure is
based only on manually controlled elements, this approach has advantages that are apparent in the example patterns following.

In the patterns for *constant elements,* it is possible to introduce slight variations to account for differences in gage sizes, part sizes, placement of the gages, etc. These variations were considered to be trivial for the intended usage of the example development. Thus, these patterns represent average conditions for the range of conditions covered in the constant elements.

Element 1.   Obtain gage

22.2	R25B	to gage on bench
2.0	G1A	pickup gage
26.4	M25C	bring gage to part
—	G2 3	orient "GO" end
—	T90S	

50.6 TMU

Element 2.   Locate "GO" end to hole

| 16.2 | P2SE | locate "GO" end to tapped hole |
| 4.6 | M2B | rotate CCW to align threads |

20.8 TMU

Element 5.   Reverse gage, check "NOT-GO" entry

4.0	D1E	lift "GO" end from hole
4.3	mM4B	bring gage to clear
16.8	G2 3	shift end in fingers
9.2	M5C	bring gage to hole
16.2	P2SE	locate "NOT-GO" end to hole
4.6	M2B	rotate CCW to align threads
4.6	M2B	
2.0	RL1	
4.0	R2B	screw in one thread
2.0	G1A	
2.9	M1B	
10.6	AP2	force-check travel
4.6	M2B	
2.0	RL1	
4.0	R2B	unscrew gage from hole
2.0	G1A	
2.9	M1B	
4.0	D1E	lift "NOT-GO" end from hole

100.7 TMU

Element 6.   Reverse gage, move to next hole

| 16.8 | G2   3 | shift end in fingers |
| — | M5C | bring to next hole |

16.8 TMU

Element 7. Lay gage aside

21.2	⎛ M25B		carry gage to bench
—	⎜ ~~G2~~ 3 ⎞		⎫ orient end of gage
—	~~T90S~~ ⎠		⎬
2.0	RL1		let go of gage

23.2 TMU

The patterns for the important *variable elements* have been written for only one revolution of the gage, that is, for one thread. Since the second and succeeding threads will merely require repetition of the same pattern, a standard can be found by multiplying the time per thread by the number of threads involved per hole. Note that the hole in the gage handle through which the "GO" end plug is secured provides a good reference point for counting the number of threads engaged as removal is effected. In element 4, a P2SE is assigned for the "pause and count" action. Using an MTM "equivalent" motion in this way to cover the performance time was discussed under the heading *Synthetic Elements* in Chapter 19. The correctness of the time data developed using this equivalent motion was checked by time study before applying it regularly every time the element covered occurred.

The patterns have been written for each of three hole-diameter ranges to account for the variation of nominal hole size and for the variation in the size of the gage handle which the operator will manipulate. For simplicity in this example, the motions assigned for increasing diameters have been simplified as compared to the actual motions which occur. Actually, the finger motions required increase gradually in length (for Reaches and Moves) and number as the diameters increase. The grouping of ranges given here is also too simplified for accurate standards work, since it is obvious that the diameters at the breakpoints could fall into either of two groups which differ greatly in time value assigned by the choice made. However, this being only an example to illustrate principles, this discrepancy will be ignored in this presentation.

Element 3. Screw "GO" end into hole (Variable-per thread time)

⅛″ to ¼″ diameter		¼″ to ½″ diameter			½″ to 1″ diameter		
2.9	M1B	2.9	M1B	1	4.6	M2B	1
2.0	RL1	4.6	M2B	1	11.4	M3B	2
4.0	R2B	4.0	RL1	2	6.0	RL1	3
2.0	G1A	8.0	R2B	2	15.9	R3B	3
10.9 TMU		4.0	G1A	2	6.0	G1A	3
		23.5 TMU			43.9 TMU		

Element 4. Unscrew "GO" end from hole (Variable-per thread time)

⅛" to ¼" *diameter*		¼" to ½" *diameter*			½" to 1" *diameter*		
3.4	M1C	5.2	M2C	1	13.4	M3C	2
16.2	P2SE	3.4	M1C	1	5.2	M2C	1
2.0	RL1	16.2	P2SE	1	16.2	P2SE	1
4.0	R2B	4.0	RL1	2	6.0	RL1	3
2.0	G1A	8.0	R2B	2	15.9	R3B	3
27.6 TMU		4.0	G1A	2	6.0	G1A	3
		40.8 TMU			62.7 TMU		

Develop Process Element Times

Since the illustrative example does not include any process-controlled elements, this step of the procedure is not illustrated. It would normally be accomplished, however, by application of the principles in Chapter 21 and other places in this text. Time study is the usual approach to determining such elements.

Summarize and Formulate Data

Recapping the MTM elements developed to cover the gage operations, since all further work on this example will be based on the MTM analysis, the following time values emerge for the constant and variable elements:

Constant Elements

A. Per part   Elements 1 and 7 = 50.6 + 23.2 = 73.8 TMU
B. Per hole   Elements 2 and 5 = 20.8 + 100.7 = 121.5 TMU
C. Per hole less one Element 6   = 16.8 TMU

Variable Elements (Per thread for one hole)

D1. ⅛" to ¼" diam. Elements 3 and 4 = 10.9 + 27.6 = 38.5 TMU
D2. ¼" to ½" diam. Elements 3 and 4 = 23.5 + 40.8 = 64.3 TMU
D3. ½" to 1" diam. Elements 3 and 4 = 43.9 + 62.7 = 106.6 TMU

This data comprises the times available to express standard data for the gaging operation. A number of methods are possible by which to summarize the data into a form that can be readily applied to set individual time standards. Figure 7 shows a partial tabulation for one of the diameter ranges, and three tables of this general nature could be used to present the data over a wide range of holes per part and threads per hole to make full use of the tabular or tabulation method. Another possibility, the application check sheet, is very convenient provided the person who sets the individual standards is properly instructed in its use. This method of summarizing is illustrated in Fig. 8, and the manner of using this check sheet should be obvious to the reader upon careful examination.

Perhaps the most general method of summarizing converts the data into a *time formula* for each of the diameter ranges. The example permits illustration of standard time formulas in very simple form as follows:

Let N = the number of holes per part
T = the number of threads per hole
Then NT = the number of threads per part

The formula will then be expressed as:

$$\text{TMU per part} = \text{Constant elements} + \text{Variable elements}$$
$$= (A + B + C) + x$$

where $x = D1, D2,$ and $D3$ in turn multiplied by NT and

$$(A + B + C) = 73.8 + 121.5N + 16.8(N - 1)$$
$$= 73.8 + 121.5N + 16.8N - 16.8$$
$$= 57.0 + 138.3N$$

Holes per Part	Threads per Hole					
	4	5	6	7	8	9
1	349.3	387.8	426.3	464.8	503.3	541.8
2	641.6	718.6	795.6	872.6	949.6	
3	933.9	1,049.4	1,164.9	1,280.4		
4	1,226.2	1,380.2	1,534.2			
5	1,518.5	1,711.0				
6	1,810.8	2,041.8				
7	2,103.1	2,372				
8	2,395.4					
9						
10						

Fig. 7. Partial tabulation of gaging time in TMU for nominal hole diameters of from ⅛ to ¼ inch.

Hence, by substitution and combination:

⅛″ to ¼″ diameter:	TMU per part = 57.0 + 138.3N +	38.5NT
¼″ to ½″ diameter:	TMU per part = 57.0 + 138.3N +	64.3NT
½″ to 1″ diameter:	TMU per part = 57.0 + 138.3N +	106.6NT

To apply these formulas, it is necessary to know N for the part in question, determine T as indicated earlier, and multiply these to determine NT. For instance, letting $N = 1$ and $T = 12$ for a $\frac{5}{16}''$ diameter hole, the time would be:

$$\text{TMU per part} = 57.0 + 138.3(1) + 38.5(12) = \underline{657.3 \text{ TMU}}$$

This answer could be converted to a select time of .39438 minutes.

GAGING TIME
("GO" - "NOT-GO" THREAD PLUG)

Code Number	Element Description	Unit Time, TMU	Apply per	Freq.	Total Time, TMU
1 - 7	Obtain and Lay Aside Gage	73.8	Part	*1*	*73.8*
2	Locate "GO" end to hole	20.8	Hole	*4*	*83.2*
3 - 4	Screw in and unscrew "GO" end		Threads	*5*	
	1/8" to 1/4" diameter	38.5	Thread per Hole	–	
	1/4" to 1/2" diameter	64.3	Thread per Hole	*20*	*1,286.0*
	1/2" to 1" diameter	106.6	Thread per Hole	–	
5	Reverse gage, check "NOT-GO" entry	100.7	Hole	*4*	*402.8*
6	Reverse gage, move to next hole	16.8	Hole less one	*3*	*50.4*

Total Select Time, TMU	*1,896.2*
Allowance, *20* %	*379.2*
Allowed Time, TMU	*2,275.4*
Conversion Factor to *HRS*	*.00001*
Routed Time, *HRS* per Pe.	*.0228*

Fig. 8. Application Check Sheet.

Test Data for Validity

The analyst could assure the correctness of his MTM work by having another engineer check his patterns and calculations. A very practical method of validating data developed by either MTM or time study consists of taking check studies on a reasonable range of representative parts on the floor with a stop watch and comparing the *select times* to those obtained from the formulas and/or development data. Of course, the check timing would need correction for operator performance level and steps would be required to assure that the check timing was being made on the method in the standard data. With a reasonable number of random checks against the results of the formulas, the analyst can assure himself of the correctness of the standard data and time formulas developed.

Prepare Final Report

As discussed under the procedure earlier in this chapter, it is essential to the records phase and administration of the standard data and times formulas developed in the industrial engineering department to prepare adequate final reports. This would include the various definitions, limitations, layouts, tables, formulas, application rules, etc.

After the standards have been developed, the elements can be completely defined in the report in a manner similar to that used for the following two elements:

1. *Obtain gage.* Starts with the reach to the gage on the bench, includes picking up the gage and any regrasps needed to improve the hold and/or regrasps in conjunction with turns to orient the "GO" end in the general direction of the hole, ends when the gage has been moved to the hole in the part.

5. *Reverse gage, check "NOT-GO" entry.* Starts with disengage of "GO" end of gage from last thread checked, includes turning the gage over end for end and trying the "NOT-GO" end in the first few threads, ends when the "NOT-GO" end is disengaged from the hole.

Obtain Final Approval

The requirements of this step, depending on the company policies, usually involve submission of the final report to the proper parties, clarifying and explaining anything they question, and obtaining their signatures. This approval action also includes any steps which must be taken administratively to place into effect the methods on which the standards are based, revisions in the cost department records and timekeepers' procedures, and such similar action.

Maintain and Audit the Data

This step becomes a cooperative effort between the floor supervision, the administrative staff personnel, and the industrial engineering department.

Clues as to whether a given standard needs attention will be given by such signals as the variation in efficiencies reported by the cost department, out-of-line earnings, complaints by the foremen, union requests for review, and discrepancies between standard and actual conditions noted when the analyst makes a required periodic audit. Remember, methods change with manufacturing conditions and technology, and should therefore be considered periodically to see whether the data still holds. Good standard data and time formulas have often fallen into disrepute due to inattention to the maintenance and audit phase which should be considered as an integral part of the development procedure.

SUMMARY

Standard data and time formulas are very basic in relation to the industrial engineering field and scientific management. Mechanical and electrical design engineers as compared to industrial engineers differ fundamentally in the knowledge they command for determining the time required to produce and the attendant costs, which are absolutely essential to the practice of scientific management. To arrive at such data, a coordinated view of the men, materials, and machines in productive processes is required. During the development of standard time data and time formulas, the analyst evaluates much of the factual material on which this viewpoint must necessarily be based. Scientific managers rely on work analysts for more than just the time aspect of such work; indeed one of their richest sources for managerial information exists in the standards activity of industrial engineering.

In developing standard data and time formulas, employing a predetermined time system such as MTM has many advantages over time study analysis. A recapitulation of these would include the facts that:

(1) Less time would be required
(2) Element changes for a more convenient breakdown are facilitated
(3) It is easier to isolate and separate constant and variable elements
(4) Tabular data for variable elements can be more easily and quickly derived
(5) Short elements can be determined more accurately.

The development of standards is a job well worth tackling, as it can lead to great financial benefits. The resulting data, when properly used, can save production dollars, aid intelligent management, lead to better cost estimates, help to bring in additional and new business, and promote higher profits. This last idea is, after all, the real aim and the one which should be kept in mind.

CHAPTER 28

Application Areas for
Work Measurement Techniques

The application of work measurement techniques for direct determination of labor and cost standards was presented rather completely in previous chapters. Other important areas of application were mentioned briefly and/or partially discussed. Enlarging the reader's knowledge of some of these areas is the purpose of this chapter. The many possible variations in applying work measurement to these areas precludes complete discussion; however, the basic concepts and approaches are delineated to facilitate their application to the diverse problems encountered in industry, business, and government.

Obviously, no field of knowledge is ever complete, and this is vitally true of possible applications of work measurement. The relative newness of the work of industrial engineers causes newer and better approaches to be found to old problem areas; also, as entirely new problem areas are isolated from the industrial complex, the techniques must often be changed to solve such problems. This is not surprising when one witnesses the astonishing expansion of the technology and the art in even the oldest fields of engineering. The need for continual broadening of the interests and abilities of industrial engineers is a foregone conclusion; therefore, any discussion of their technology must necessarily be incomplete. The material in this chapter should be studied with this orientation in mind.

Insofar as work measurement is concerned, any benefits of its application depend most directly on the industrial engineer's ability to: (1) get the facts, (2) arrange the facts, (3) apply the proper techniques to arrive at answers, and (4) formulate, recommend, and/or effect appropriate courses of action. In other words, the only way to get results in work measurement is to analyze correctly the particular situation and then to achieve a practical result that pays for the effort of all concerned parties. That this is no easy task does not excuse shoddy work or expediency, nor does it justify investigation to the point where any cost recovery will be overbalanced by the cost of analysis. To give proper attention to and work within the framework of the economic picture is, therefore, a prime duty of anyone practicing work measurement. In considering the application areas, the reader should bear in mind this necessity to make any application of the technique pay for itself.

METHODS IMPROVEMENT

The ideal methods improvement technique is the one which provides a means of determining the best way to do a task before the task ever begins. This is an ideal, however, which cannot usually be attained for several reasons. For one thing, as industrial technology changes, newer materials become available, more adequate tools are invented, etc., so that it is always possible to improve a method in some degree provided enough time and money are devoted to this aim. Also, there are practical limits to the ingenuity of industrial engineers as of a given moment which forces a modification of their concept of the ideal to include the effect of time. Put in the form of a statement, *As of a given moment, it is possible to design the best method under prevailing conditions: the ultimate method is never found.* Obviously, the greater the amount of information and data available bearing on a certain problem, the more possible it is to approach the ultimate. For example, it is often possible with a pre-determined time system such as MTM to achieve prior to production a method which cannot later be improved upon within the bounds of economic expenditure. In most cases, however, methods in existence can be improved and the new method made to pay by proper usage of work measurement.

Methods improvement and work measurement are inseparable. Before a labor standard is established through *any* work measurement technique or procedure, the method to be used should practically always be analyzed for possible improvement. The degree of such analysis and subsequent improvement should, of course, be tempered by the quantity of items to be produced, their economic value, etc. The greater the quantity, the more methods analysis and improvement can be justified. Justification is largely a question of economics—will the cost of analysis, the applicable tool and equipment cost, etc., be paid for by reduced labor, less material waste, better quality, etc.?

To help the engineer answer this question, most companies develop standard forms by which to compare the economics of one method against an alternate. The typical form shown in Fig. 1 contains an actual example

COST SAVINGS REPORT

DEPT. AFFECTED ___1100 Riveting___ DATE ISSUED ___7-27-56___

ASSEMBLY OR PART NO. AFFECTED ___96453-2___ I. E. LOG NO. ___11-982-56___

PERIOD OF SAVINGS BASED ON ___Annual Production Rate___

TYPE OF CHANGE ___Reprocess per new method, beginning at next release.___

DESCRIPTION OF CHANGE * ___See attached MTM analyses. Process tooled with holding___

___fixture to replace purely hand assembly. Also, fixed stackbins and drop dis-___

___posal through hole in work table replaces operating from and disposing to any___

___available cardboard container. The new method is completely SIMO in hand usage.___

___This change will increase operator output.___

COST SAVINGS COMPUTATION:

A. LABOR SAVINGS PER UNIT**	$	.00558
B. MATERIAL SAVINGS PER UNIT**	$	------
C. REJECT REDUCTION SAVING**	$	------
D. GROSS SAVING PER UNIT (A + B + C)	$	.00558
E. TOTAL UNITS CONSIDERED**		128.000
F. GROSS SAVINGS (E X D)	$	714.24
G. COST OF EFFECTING CHANGE**	$	33.20
H. TOTAL COST SAVINGS (F - G)	$	681.04

DEVELOPED BY ___C.I.Kno___ , IND. ENGR. DEPT. APPROVED BY ___U.R. TWO___ ACCTG. DEPT.

    * Attach sketch if required.

  ** See reverse side for analysis of these units.

Fig. 1A.   Cost savings report.

where the proposed method change is economically sound. Note that the form does not provide for applying overhead against direct labor, since only rarely does measurably less supervision or other real overhead cost reduction result from methods improvement in direct labor. This is the usual attitude taken by industry on this question.

An MTM analysis of the old method can be seen in Fig. 2; the new method is fully illustrated by Figs. 1, 2, and 3 of Chapter 19. These are

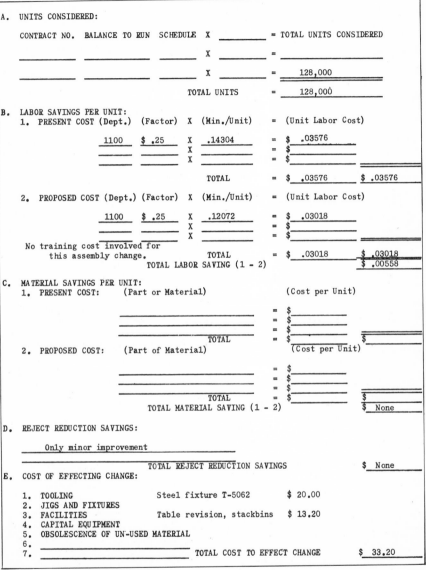

Fig. 1B.   Reverse side of cost savings report.

the two methods being compared in the example cost savings report in Fig. 1.   Variations of this form can be developed to reflect methods improvement projects in such other areas as office work, stockrooms, toolrooms, shipping departments, maintenance activities, etc.   Note the statement in the cost savings analysis that no training cost was involved.   The

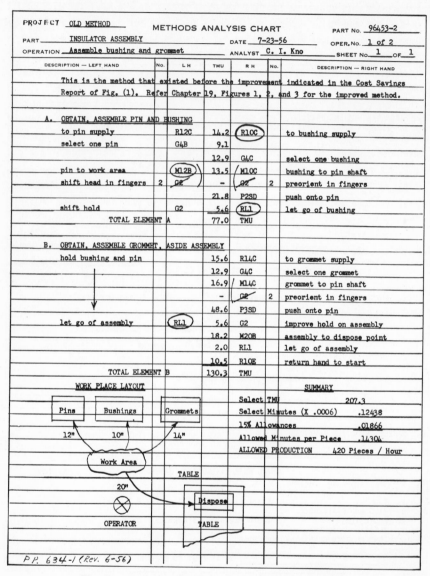

Fig. 2. Analysis of old insulator assembly method.

reason was that the new method was initiated with new operators at the beginning of a new production quantity, and these workers were merely trained in the new, rather than the old method. Their training would have been necessary anyway, and its cost was not due to a change in method. An extra training cost which would reduce the amount of savings might have been chargeable if the new method was installed near the end of the preceding run with operators already trained and practiced in the old method.

This example of methods improvement illustrates the kind of analysis possible with MTM which would be more difficult by other techniques. Note that the small difference in the per piece cycle time would be difficult to catch with the ordinary decimal minute stop watch. To determine and evaluate a method believed to be an improvement with time study would require timing of a large number of cycles for *each methods change* which could be devised by a trial and error process and with repeated retraining of the operator required for each change in method. The smaller the improvement, the more difficult and expensive it is to isolate using time study. With the MTM approach, however, the only effort and expenditure involves paper work and visualization at a desk; although the final method would deserve later testing for its practicality. However, that the economic aspect of any proposed methods improvement almost always requires evaluation is re-emphasized, since appearances can be deceiving.

The laws of motion economy are a useful guide for methods improvement when the analysis can be of a comparatively broad nature and a result near the ultimate is not sought. They will not, however, generally permit the extent of improvement of manual operations possible with MTM. Re-reading of Chapter 19 on Motion Patterns will remind one of the reasons for this fact.

COST REDUCTION PROGRAMS

Most industrial firms either support a continuing program of cost reduction or else launch one or more cost reduction drives each year. Usually, the principal recipients of the training and promotional activity associated with such efforts are the supervisors.

Traditionally, the ordinary cost reduction program and/or drive consists of presenting typical methods improvements (preferably ones developed in the same plant at which the program is given), associated training in the analysis and improvement of production problems through usage of the five popular industrial engineering questions (What? Why? Where? When? and Who?), plus remarks about the theory and application of the laws of motion economy.

The two basic flaws in many such cost reduction efforts are: (1) they do not appeal to and reach all levels in the productive team; and (2) the general information given, although good and proper, does not provide a dynamic tool to attack the problems isolated nor does it adequately provide enough means for isolating the problems in the first place. The advent of MTM has added a powerful tool that can be directed to solving the latter deficiency especially. It makes possible analysis and considerable improvement of methods by relative novices to work measurement. The traditional approach is fine as far as it goes, but it fails to meet all the demands of modern technology.

The most noteworthy aspect of modern technology, reflected in increasingly complex processes and machines in the most modern industrial plants, is its dependence more and more on the team approach to solving production problems. It is not enough, as with the traditional approach, to improve the simpler production processes and solve the ordinary types of problem. Major improvements usually require the coordinated services of teams of specialists. To cite only one example, the more outstanding major productivity increases today usually result from usage of more advanced machines and/or automation techniques. Such activities, particularly automation projects, can seldom be carried on even by the services of a single specialist. More often, they demand a team of specialists composed of production personnel, industrial engineers, tool engineers, automation engineers, product engineers, and occasionally even those versed in operations research. The situation is similar in office cost reduction programs, the only real difference being the composition of the team. Hence, cost reduction and methods improvement programs that are to meet today's needs should recognize the necessity to bring teamwork action to bear on complex problems, while continuing the traditional approach on simpler problems.

OPERATOR TRAINING

The minimum productive labor cost tends to be incurred on any product if the operators' initial training can be based on the right work methods. To achieve this desirable goal means that the correct methods must be established *before* starting the production run. One of the advantages of MTM is that it permits establishing correct methods on *manual* work prior to production. Further aid toward establishing correct methods in advance of production—next to MTM in importance—is afforded by consideration of the laws of motion economy coupled with any specialized standard data available. Section II of this text contains many clues regarding work measurement techniques that bear directly on operator training. Initially training the operator to use correct methods has the additional advantage of being considerate of the feelings and motivation of all parties involved in the training effort.

Not only is it desirable to establish correct manual methods prior to production to minimize operator training costs, but it is also valuable to apply work measurement techniques to establish the correct equipment, workplace layout, hand tools, cutting tools, machine tools, grinding wheels, etc. It usually pays, especially if techniques new to the plant are to be used, to take the additional step of having the process engineers, tool engineers, production supervisors, and a small group of experienced operators try out and "debug" the proposed methods, tools, and equipment prior to bringing in the production operators. Then the methods established, together with all the factors on which they must necessarily be based, will be proved so that the initial training of production operators can proceed.

Training of the worker to do his task, or retraining of older operators to improve their performance, has long been a recognized difficulty in the struggle of industry toward better results from the investment in men, materials, and machines. Industrial psychologists and personnel workers have most often been responsible for this area and normally work through the foremen, often in conjunction with a training school for new workers. This effort frequently is a general attack on the improvement of labor skills and abilities. Much good has resulted from this approach, but the one problem that has consistently proved most vexing is that of providing concise, clear information to the foreman and his operators regarding the proper detailed methods that should be used. It is in this area that industrial engineers, relying on work measurement techniques, can offer to all of the parties involved in the training problem a much needed helping hand. While the personnel department probably should still be responsible for providing the required training, it should work closely with the industrial engineers who can discover and express the detailed training information needed in a readily understandable form. Fortunately, this has become standard procedure in many plants.

WORKPLACE LAYOUT

Proper arrangement of the workplace, together with insuring that all the tools and materials required are present in proper condition, will unquestionably provide maximum opportunity for effective production performance. Application of the laws of motion economy and work measurement permit the best results in providing good workplace layouts. The kind of detailed methods analysis described earlier in this chapter, particularly with MTM, is the key to discovering both better arrangements and the effect any given arrangement has on the time required, the skills needed, and the tools that are most effective.

This is evident in Figs. 1 and 2 in Chapter 26. MTM was employed to achieve a superior layout and at the same time reduce the labor standard for the operation performed at this workplace. The reduction of lost time in assembling the large number of parts into a relatively complex electronic chassis—approximately 20 per cent—resulted from application of MTM which spotlighted the relatively long Reaches and Moves, high order Grasps, difficult Positions, idle periods of either hand, etc. A good methods engineer always looks for precisely these clues as to which items he can improve. The improvement does not, of course, result from the MTM alone, but MTM certainly provides a systematic and reliable procedure by which to determine quickly what should be done.

No claim is made that Figs. 1 and 2 in Chapter 26 illustrate the ultimate in methods improvement, as further application of work measurement would undoubtedly reveal additional improvements to be possible; but even the usage of the simpler rules of MTM in this instance produced a striking result. Older techniques, again, might well give equal results; but they definitely would not come as quickly or with as little analysis cost.

PLANT LAYOUT

In a very real sense, the arrangement of an entire plant may be considered as the "workplace layout" of the entire factory operation and its personnel. In essence, the functions of other groups such as material handlers and inspectors along with those directly concerned with fabricating and assembly tasks must be subjected to work measurement, if the most effective flow of materials and products through the plant is to be achieved. With this broader base of application and outlook, however, there is not much difference between improving plant layouts and workplace layouts.

Transporting of material from station to station, reduction of walking time by personnel, the use of material handling devices, simplified gaging, conveyors, etc., all involve manual labor which must be evaluated. The laws of motion economy, time study, MTM, etc., can be used to establish the individual operations which, when totaled, constitute a plant. Work measurement can then be reapplied to evaluate what happens between operations and to integrate them into the most efficient pattern. The manufacturing facility which results from this approach can be achieved most easily by making the results available to the Plant Engineering department and cooperating with them before, during, and after revisions in plant layout. In fact, the results themselves should reflect teamwork between industrial engineering and plant engineering personnel.

ASSEMBLY LINE BALANCING

One of the paradoxes of the "age of automation" is that unit operations in the fabricating and machining areas of product manufacturing have yielded the more outstanding successes while final assembly operations have remained largely manual. In fact, a tendency to use the labor force displaced by such successful automation to assemble the increased output has often led to proportionately greater manual labor content in the assembly of the product. This trend has focused attention on improvement of an often neglected traditional industrial engineering technique—line balancing.

The concept of assembly line balancing is relatively simple, but its successful attainment in a rigorous manner has proved to be a sophisticated problem. A progressive assembly line consists of an integrated flow of parts and materials into a functioning whole as a result of coordinated operations performed by workers and machines under cyclic control. Transfer of the materials and subassemblies between working stations occurs either automatically, e.g. by a moving belt, or by the operators passing them along to the next station. Each station worker must finish his assigned work elements within the same total cycle time, which is controlled by the conveyance speed, a timing signal, or the receipt of material from the previous work station. This necessity for all line workers to meet the cycle time, which must equal the task time at the slowest time station, is the key to economical assembly line operation.

The cycle time may be determined by or be dependent upon a number of such factors as the completion speed of the slowest working station (more than one operator may work as a team at the same station), limitations of technical and machine processes at various line stations, and arbitrary or essential run rate decisions by the factory managers. Regardless of how the cycle time is established, it imposes a working limitation on every station in the line.

Line balancing is the art and science of assuring, within the cycle time constraints, that every line station attains the highest possible efficiency of manual and machine time. One purpose of line balancing, therefore, is to determine the most economical run rate, whether or not this is the cycle time employed. Another purpose is to reassign working elements (MTM is excellent for this task) as necessary and possible to reduce to the minimum any idle time during the working cycle at every line station. However, this cannot be done without detailed knowledge of the process, precise information on the motions performed at a given station, and close attention to the necessary precedence (order of assembly) relationships between assembly sequences.

The attack on line balancing thus requires usage of coordinated management techniques. Engineers and technologists must design and control the technical processes. Production control personnel and factory staff who are responsible for the functioning and quality of the product must specify and check the order and care of assembly. But without doubt, the industrial engineering staff armed with work measurement techniques—particularly those capable of detailed motion design, such as MTM—is best equipped to determine and maintain superior working methods. Also, in the necessity to smoothly integrate the efforts of these various members of the management team, the work measurement engineer can provide the most effective leadership as a result of his professional capability. For example, his process charting skills lead to organization and control of precedence problems and quantitative description of the technical processes which are indispensable.

While space does not permit more detailed treatment of this important application area for work measurement, the reader undoubtedly realizes the direct utility of the data and techniques covered in this textbook as a means of achieving the balanced line. The need for line balancing is not restricted to manufacturing. Indeed, it is needed in hospitals (e.g. the tray and food assembly line in the dietary department), warehousing (e.g. a spare parts packing line), postal handling (e.g. continuous sorting lines), transportation (e.g. airline baggage handling and reservation procedures), shipping (e.g. sequential loading routines), and in many more instances where manual and machine operations must be smoothly coordinated to assure a sustained flow of output. That these kinds of operations have successfully resisted massive automation efforts to the present time attests the fact that conventional line balancing offers a broad and continuing field of work measurement activity. Actually, line balancing skills frequently have been the key which enabled many of the automatic assembly lines now existing to become successful.

LABOR ESTIMATES

There are many possible approaches to this task. One set of conditions could involve variables indicating the need for specially developed estimating standards while another set might justify the use of detailed MTM to estimate labor content. Since this broad and complicated subject cannot possibly be discussed in full detail, it would probably be best to review the ordinary procedures for estimating labor and the reasons for such estimates. Some of the more typical basic reasons for estimating labor are: (1) Product costing; (2) Preparation of bids; (3) Labor forecasts; (4) Method comparison; and (5) Determination of machine requirements.

The labor associated with each of the reasons listed can range from that concerned with a very simple task or part to that connected with a very complicated device having many parts and involving applications of physics, mechanics, electronics, heat, pneumatics, hydraulics, etc. The quantities involved may range from a few units to production runs extending through a number of years, with the rate of production varying from extremely low to extremely high levels. Essentially, the labor involved could be overhead (indirect), direct, contracted from an outside organization, or some combination of these.   By now, it should be apparent that an entire book could easily be written on the subject of estimating; therefore, only the more common approaches to labor estimation will be given here.   These are (1) guessing, (2) weighted normal times—as exemplified by estimating standards, and (3) detailed study.

Estimating by guess—often called "guesstimating"—is an approach that can always be used.   Obviously, the accuracy of the guess is problematical, although the art of guesstimating can be developed to the point where amazingly close answers are achieved.   The authors know one person of long experience with guesstimating whose labor estimates on complicated assemblies almost invariably fall well within five to ten per cent of the actual total labor required as later determined by processing after the order is received.   Such persons are rare; most estimators are very erratic in their time guesses, especially without extensive experience to temper their impulses.   In any event, guesstimates always leave the recipient with the uncomfortable situation of having no quick means of analyzing the forecast for probable accuracy.

Do not undervalue the guesstimating approach.   Many situations arise where a properly stated guess is the best possible means of estimating—in fact it may be the only possible approach if estimating time is short and sufficient knowledge of the item estimated is not available to make a detailed estimate.   However, this approach should obviously be avoided if any reasonable degree of certainty concerning the accuracy is desired. Guesstimate answers can be improved greatly through comparison of the task to a similar one for which a good labor figure is known and/or to standard labor and/or cost data available regarding similar parts.

The second approach, weighted normal times, is that usually meant when "estimating standards" are referred to in industrial engineering writings.   These are usually found in plants making many different varieties of the same product or many different items in a family of products that must be costed on a rapid basis.   For example, an electronic plant offering its services to others, including the government, must often cost and bid items on very short time schedules.   To cope with such necessity, the plant develops a specialized set of standard data adapted to solving the estimating problem.

A major point in connection with weighted normal times is that, even though quite accurate times for portions of the estimated tasks could be and often are developed or available, the estimating standards contain "experience factors" that reflect the results of analyzing later performance based on bids or else adjust the standards for known or supposed variations that could occur should the bid be successful in getting business.   Estimating standards are not of necessity inaccurate.   It is also important that they be simple and easy to use.   These latter criteria sometimes impose oversimplification that requires modification in some degree through detailed analysis on problems not normally encountered.

A simple example of such data would be the developed time required to solder the average wired terminal in an electronic apparatus. This time would represent the labor cost for a wide variety of kinds and types of terminals for simplicity. The standard would be of little value in actual processing work, since a given kind of terminal might require two or three times as much soldering time as another. However, if the right weighted average (with consideration given to types, sizes, and quantities of each normally encountered) is determined, it can be used with reasonable accuracy for estimating. All the estimator need do is to count the number of solder joints and multiply this by the standard to calculate the total soldering labor in the unit being estimated. The advantage of this procedure is obvious, since it is both fast and easy, and it usually produces a sufficiently accurate result.

The third estimating approach can be very refined, or it can be limited to a more rapid approximation of the labor cost. One way to keep it simple is to use MTM-GPD or a simplified version of some other pre-determined time system to attain rapidly a reasonable estimate, with the work being done mentally or with a very minimum of writing and record keeping. This strategy often pays and is perhaps one of the best ways to get a relatively good answer on short notice. Another refinement would consist of using the simplified data but keeping full written records of the work done to permit later verification and examination.

The ultimate in estimating labor would consist of using either detailed MTM and making a full analysis of the tasks by visualization or standard data developed from MTM and/or time study. Naturally, the more familiar the estimator is with the product and the processes by which it is produced, the better this approach can be. Having sufficient knowledge and judgment, it is even possible to pre-determine the tasks so well that the finished analyses can later be used to order tools, set up the workplace, and even as a labor standard for production of the unit which was bid and received. Or at least, with this extent of estimating, the analyses could be the basis of pilot run processes that would permit rapid revision, based on how the pilot run showed errors and the need for other kinds of revision, into the finished production process that would later apply as the standard.

MACHINE, TOOL, AND EQUIPMENT DESIGN AND SELECTION

Industrial engineers are always concerned with the over-all effectiveness and operating ease of the machines, tools, and equipment used by the workers. They frequently guide the design of such items or else aid in their selection from standard designs commercially available. In such practice, the aim is to reduce the manual labor required to a minimum; both the laws of motion economy and MTM are helpful in achieving this aim.

Many firms have begun to train tool and/or machine designers in an appropriate version of MTM. The methods consciousness resulting from such training is alone sufficient oftentimes to bring about noticeable improvements in design. The experience of the authors has been, however, that to get the best results from the average designer it is necessary to require that he submit MTM analyses with his preliminary designs. Following approval of the design supervisor and the process man responsible for the project, the designer can then complete his work with confidence that the best tool is being specified and that it contains the best features possible. The value of this approach to reduction of production costs often can be surprising.

Another advantage of training designers in MTM is that they can better understand the language and aims of the industrial engineer and converse with him on an equal basis regarding the use of his designs. Where MTM training is not provided, the minimum training that will approach this aim is the kind normally associated with cost reduction programs as discussed earlier.

A very simple example of machine design making use of work measurement techniques is that of a machine having the various feed levers operated by body, leg, and/or foot motions in order to free the hands to do other productive work. MTM or other types of analysis could show the . advantages of designing in this way. As a word of caution, the need for special operating attachments of this kind is, of course, nil if the hands cannot be productive when other body members are activating the machine.

In tool design, fastening devices are often prime targets for methods improvement efforts and are therefore excellent places for the designer to apply MTM knowledge. For example, a conventional way to design a drill jig with its clamp is shown in Fig. 3, along with an MTM analysis of the method for closing and clamping the jig. The hinged cover is closed and a handwheel is screwed tight against the cover. Note in Fig. 4, however, that clamping the same jig with a lever bar results in less than one-third the operating time to get the jig ready for drilling. Even this simple analysis, therefore, shows how MTM can achieve substantial savings in the design of tools.

PRODUCT DESIGN

The application of work-measuring techniques to product design should be fairly obvious, as it is similar to that discussed for designing machines,

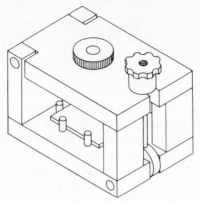

Description	No.	LH	TMU	RH	No.	Description
jig lid		G1A	2.0	G1A		handwheel
lower lid		M3A	4.9			wait for lid down
hold jig			3.6	M2A		engage clamp bolt
			5.6	G2		adjust grip
			10.8	M2A	3	tighten handwheel
			6.0	RL1	3	3 twists
			12.0	R2A	3	
			6.0	G1A	3	
			3.6	M2A		final twist
			16.2	AP1		final tighten
let go of jig		RL1	2.0	RL1		let go of handwheel
Total			80.7	TMU	or	0.04842 minutes

Fig. 3.   MTM analysis of closing a conventional drill jig.

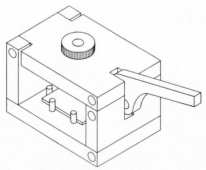

Description	LH	TMU	RH	Description
jig lid	G1A	2.0	G1A	bar clamp
lower lid	M3A	8.1	M6A	engage clamp
		10.6	AP2	seat clamp
let go of jig	RL1	2.0	RL1	let go of clamp
Total		22.7	TMU	or 0.01362 minutes

Fig. 4.   MTM analysis of closing an improved drill-jig design.

tools, and equipment. The remarks concerning training apply equally well to product designers, although it is more usual that an industrial engineer is assigned to work along with a group of product designers in arriving at a design which can be economically manufactured. The same approaches can be applied to considering the product design from the viewpoint of the production tools, processes, and labor content required to manufacture the design. Insuring that a minimum of labor is required to make the parts and assemble them into the final product is one of the best possible ways to meet the competition that usually exists for any product. The point at which to make maximum production savings is often at the original design of a part, since the characteristics demanded frequently dictate in a large degree the processes and methods required to produce it.

This type of thinking has begun to influence even the sales and advertising literature that accompanies products, particularly when the products are the type used by other manufacturers. The advent of MTM has provided a common basis for developing and stating data relative to the operation of a product. Brochures containing MTM analyses or statements that MTM was used to design the product are being circulated in increasing numbers. At present, such data is of value principally to other engineers in the buying concern that can understand and use the data; but it is not hard to envisage the day when even salesmen and purchasing agents will find it advantageous to have training in simplified or detailed MTM so they can also evaluate such brochures. It is interesting, at least, that the method of operation can be so clearly shown by MTM that it is obvious to qualified readers of such brochures.

The authors anticipate that one of the most profitable future uses of MTM and other types of work measurement will occur in the field of product design.

HUMAN FACTORS DESIGN

Perhaps the broadest application area for work measurement techniques of all those included in this chapter is human factors design. Often called human engineering, this activity is in the vanguard of both engineering and sociological advances of today. It draws heavily on such interdisciplinary arts and sciences as physiology, psychology, econometrics, ergonomics, physics, chemistry, electronics, etc. For this reason, it offers a unique opportunity for work measurement and industrial engineers to collaborate with professional advantage to all concerned.

The human factors design activity arose from a military necessity for devising weapons systems with proper regard for the human being operating the system. His capacity limits often are equalled or exceeded by the demands of technological warfare and the limitations of time and speed on his proper performance. As was true of many other wartime developments, human factors design has been utilized increasingly to meet more peaceful needs. In the transition, however, it passed from the realm of "price is no object" into the economic sphere. Therefore, a new dimension of economic justification and profitability has been added to the parameters of human factor design. Thus, its application now demands the unique abilities of work measurement personnel and other specialists in industrial engineering.

To put the subject in perspective, human factors design concerns the specification and selection of operating components of devices, equipment, and the operator's environment to maximize the efficiency of the human-machine interface or the human-workplace combination. This attention to the man-machine system involves deeply the need to know human capabilities and how they may be safely used to attain desired states of system function. Therefore, the current need for industrial engineering in the field concerns the basic and applied research required to develop practical design criteria and application data. More particularly, the application of human factors design needs both to draw on existing methods-time technology and, in turn, to influence advances in that technology.

A final important idea in this application area is that it is inherently involved in all the other application areas mentioned in this chapter. Methods improvement demands consideration of both the work and the worker. Cost reduction programs can succeed best when they solve human needs in an economical way. Operator training will be greatly enhanced when human factors are better known, this idea being a motivating purpose of the current MTM research (see Chapter 20). Workplace layouts directly involve the human capacity of the operator. Plant layout is an integral part of the human working environment. Assembly line balancing can be limited or facilitated, depending on the attention to human factors involved. Labor estimates should properly include evaluation of the human factors in new business and the new technology new products may include. Machine, tool, and equipment design and selection already can be directly enhanced by the human factors application data from military technology. Lastly, product design which adequately considers the user of the product will be achieved only by the application of human factors data in the design process. The literature on many of these applications of human factors already is extensive and is growing rapidly. Work measurement analysts can ill afford to neglect this potential area of professional service.

PART V

Organization and Management

CHAPTER 29

Management Aspects of
Work Measurement[1]

The American Institute of Industrial Engineers has defined its profession as follows:

Industrial Engineering is concerned with the design, improvement, and installation of integrated systems of men, methods, and equipment. It draws upon specialized knowledge and skill in the mathematical, physical, and social sciences together with the principles and methods of engineering analysis and design to specify, predict, and evaluate the results to be obtained from such systems.

Another frequent assertion by industrial engineers is that they are responsible for obtaining the most effective utilization of manpower, machinery, material, space, and general facilities.

This chapter considers the essential question of manpower utilization within the industrial engineering department and the department's relation to general management objectives. Space available in this text does not permit a complete discussion of industrial engineering; rather the remarks are concentrated upon those aspects of industrial engineering involved in the usage of work measurement techniques.

DYNAMIC CHANGES IN ENGINEERING

Twentieth century progress in the industrial and economic spheres has been largely based on accomplishments of engineering which are well

[1] This chapter combines concepts and material appearing in separate chapters of the First Edition and in several chapters of: *Managing Engineering and Research*, by Delmar W. Karger and Robert G. Murdick, The Industrial Press, New York City, 1963. The reader is urged to pursue the subject matter in that reference.

known to the general public. Among these achievements are the practical conversion of many inventions and scientific discoveries into useful devices and services, the development of power and its distribution, the volume of power equipment and machinery used for production, and—perhaps not yet fully appreciated—the application of management skills to make such progress possible. The consequent outpouring of goods and services which could never have been attained by hand production alone permitted a transition from preoccupation with production problems to needed assaults upon the problem of satisfying consumer desires. Thus developed the modern phenomenon of economic change typified by the plethora of new products and services which have been necessary to remain competitive in business.

These developments, in turn, have profoundly affected the nature and role of engineering in its growth to meet the challenge of change. For instance, engineering must now be much more concerned with considerations beyond mere production, such as marketing and customer requirements— because industry has become market oriented. These concerns directly affect the work of industrial engineers and work measurement personnel. For example, they are frequently involved with value analysis. In this activity, marketing considerations indicate that they must not overemphasize utility value and thereby lower the esteem value below the point at which the customer will cease to buy. Another factor related to the new emphasis is the need for continual estimates and re-estimates of the cost to produce prospective new products. Often this must be done with very little information available from the product designers. Therefore, industrial engineers and work measurement analysts must develop new skills to meet the problem.

The life cycle of a new product is shown diagrammatically in Fig. 1. Characteristically, the successful development of new products and new technology follows an extremely hazardous path. Typically, about 40 new ideas are required to successfully produce one which can be sold in the marketplace for a profit. The progressive elimination of new product ideas does not occur only at the start of the development process but continues throughout the period of development. Also, the costs involved increase progressively with each succeeding stage of the process. Obviously, responsible managers must constantly examine new ideas from the economic viewpoint and eliminate the poor risks and failures as soon as possible. This is the main reason they continually require current estimates, often before complete engineering data is available and without the freedom of waiting until the estimators can be fully informed on all phases of the design or planning. A predetermined time system such as Methods-Time Measurement offers distinct, important advantages to estimators who must develop the labor costs under the conditions just outlined. Although initial cost estimates may indicate the elimination of an idea, subsequent

Fig. 1.   The life cycle of a new product.

re-estimates frequently permit the successful introduction of a new product. Even with relatively little additional or revised information, the current estimate can result in a radically different verdict from earlier estimates. This is another reason justifying management's requests for re-estimates.

Modern engineering projects have so grown in scope, size, and complexity that it might well be impossible for one person working alone to complete a large project in a lifetime. The often incredible coordination required for such projects is due not only to the magnitude of individual phases of the project, but also to the fact that other similar projects and activities must be accomplished concurrently. Not only has technology in all fields of science and engineering, including work measurement, been advancing at a breathtaking rate, but also the *techniques of managing* the complex activities thereby generated have been following closely—as indeed they must, if the achievements are to be realized. Because of this explosion of knowledge and technology, and due to the rise in the employment of project teams representing many disciplines, the manager of industrial engineering and his staff face new demands and must employ new approaches. Often the chief engineer, since he cannot hope to become expert in all of the knowledge areas involved, can only use his technical competency as a basis of tempering otherwise subjective judgments concerning the work of his staff. Similarly, the staff member charged with detailed accomplishment of the chief's objectives must increasingly learn the value of close cooperation with his peers on the team and how to enhance the team effort to reach the goals of the project.

Both the engineer already a manager and the engineer aspiring to that status need to be aware of the expanding dimensions of management. They must learn to recognize management problems and to study ways and means of handling them. Even more vital is their need to realize that managerial, not technical, skills are the major determinants of job success in executive positions. Precisely because their training is primarily in the technical areas, their appreciation of human skills frequently is underdeveloped or even lacking. The typical industrial engineer has been trained in cost accounting to a degree, understanding of the various forms of organization to a higher degree, and the design and operation of management control systems most of all. However, work measurement personnel usually lack real educational depth in the areas of finance, marketing, personnel relations, psychology, anthropology, sociology, and many other disciplines associated with understanding the human resources they are charged with mobilizing. Therefore, an engineer who would succeed as a manager usually needs to expand his outlook and viewpoints to meet the dynamic changes with which he hopes to cope.

The preceding general discussion leads logically to the subject matter presented in this chapter. After clarification of the broader aspects of industrial engineering management, the remaining material provides specific information bearing on the successful attainment of work measurement goals.

OBJECTIVE INDUSTRIAL ENGINEERING PLANNING

Planning is creative thought in advance of action. It is concerned with formulating objectives, alternative courses of action, and choices of alternatives. In proportion to the monetary stakes involved, the importance of planning increases with the complexity of an enterprise. Any engineering manager should participate in the over-all company planning for his own organization and function. This planning must be directly related to the company objectives and over-all plans. Unity of objective is a basic principle of management.

No manager can plan as though his own organization were a separate part of the company and hope to meet his objectives independently. Manufacturing, distribution, marketing, finance, and engineering must be unified. Planning requires more than a thorough knowledge of one's own field. It demands an *understanding* of the problems in all areas of the company. Nevertheless, the planning of industrial engineering and work measurement activities are important in their own right and should not be neglected. Indeed, if they are properly planned, this will facilitate company planning for other areas and perhaps other functional managers can borrow ideas which would otherwise be missed from the industrial engineering staff.   Unity implies a flow of ideas between and among all organizational units of the company, each unit contributing its unique capability.   In the management area, the industrial engineering department should make itself indispensable as a source of planning capability.

Another planning requirement which has become increasingly common is the greater length of the included period.   Managers have found it essential to work in terms of long range planning toward objectives that are five to twenty years in the future.   Short range planning covering one or two years is no longer adequate to meet the competition.   Actually, short range plans must be an outgrowth of long range plans and represent only a clearer definition of the more immediate aspects of long range plans.   To fit the current planning trends, the industrial engineering manager needs to know how to plan in detail with precision for the year ahead and with imaginative foresight for many years into the future.

All of these general guiding principles should be remembered while the reader considers the following material on organizational, performance, and resource factors which bear on the success of industrial engineering and work measurement activities.

Organizational Factors

The principal dimensions of planning and developing the organization are discussed under the following five headings: Department Responsibilities and Structure, Staffing Requirements, Training and Development of Technical Personnel, Creative Staff Management, and Financial Requirements.

Department Responsibilities and Structure revolve about the assigned functions to be performed within the department.   The first seven listed below are prevalent in seventy-five per cent or more departments, while the remainder are less prevalent although many departments include one or more in their list of responsibilities:

1. Time study and/or predetermined time system application
2. Standard data and time formula development
3. Standard data and time formula application
4. Where appropriate, development of wage incentive plans
5. Where appropriate, application of wage incentives
6. Methods development and motion study
7. Labor standards and processing
8. Job evaluation
9. Plant and office layout
10. Cost estimating
11. Jig, fixture, and tool engineering

12. Suggestion system
13. Paperwork systems and procedures
14. Plant engineering.

As an example of how all these functions can be structured into the same industrial engineering department, Fig. 2 depicts the actual organization chart of an electronics plant department where the authors once worked. It will aid the reader in understanding some of the remarks to follow.

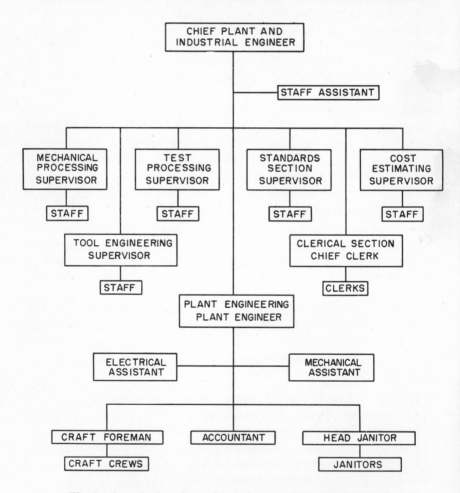

Fig. 2.   Organization chart of an industrial engineering department.

Staffing Requirements are met by determining the qualifications and number of technical personnel plus supporting co-workers needed to carry the existing or planned workload and operating schedules.   The training and experience of most industrial engineers and work measurement analysts generally equips them to understand the concepts and implications in this area. However, a lasting and successful relationship between an engineer and his company requires that the following four principles be kept in mind:

1. His personality, educational, and professional qualifications must fit the requirements for the job.
2. He should like the kind of work involved.
3. He needs a mutual agreement with the company that he fits well with his co-workers and associates.
4. He and his family need to enjoy the kind of living environment found in the community where the company is located.

Much has already been stated about the desirable qualifications of both industrial engineers and work measurement analysts—especially those concerning personality characteristics. However, for clarity and amplification, the general and educational requirements, work experience, and knowledge criteria for a senior industrial engineer are outlined in Fig. 3. Actual requirements will vary with the company and will differ for other positions in the department; however, the requirements shown are considered typical and are stated in the form normally used for position descriptions. The professional status of industrial engineering is obvious from Fig. 3. While all of these items cannot be discussed in the available space, remarks on the more important ones follow.

Age is deemed by many to be of least importance. Some engineers attain senior status when relatively young while others never really reach this level because of inherent lack of ability, technical knowledge, personality, drive, etc. The physical condition and home environment of an engineer are important. Industrial engineering work involves heavy pressures from levels both above and below in the organizational scheme; it is also often frustrating work. In general, an industrial engineer must maintain a pleasing personality and almost continuously "sell" himself and his work. One cannot succeed in this profession if he is ill or robbed of a major portion of his vitality because of conditions at home. Remarks concerning appearance are almost unnecessary—a successful salesman is always well-groomed and presents the best possible appearance. Good engineers have lost chances for advancement because this item was neglected.

The generally approved educational requirements have been stated; however, these must be flexible, depending somewhat on the industry and/or industrial engineering function involved. If the principal objective is standard data development, the qualification should be an industrial engineering degree or a bachelor's degree with a major in industrial management and

1. General and Educational Requirements

Age: 30–45.

Physical Condition: Good.

Home Environment: Good to excellent.

Appearance: Good to excellent.

Education: College graduate or equivalent. Industrial Engineering preferred. Business Administration—2nd choice. Electrical Engineering or Mechanical Engineering with Industrial Engineering experience satisfactory.

Motivation: Should have an intense desire to succeed.

Personality (important): Must be excellent. Man must have the personality that makes it possible for him to sell: (A) Himself; (B) His department; and (C) His work.

Stability: Must be able to perform well under consistent and extreme pressure.

Report Writing: Must be good to excellent. The ability to develop concise, to-the-point, reports is essential.

II. Work Experience: Five years minimum experience, the greater portion to be Industrial Engineering; however, he should have a good combination of the following:

(A) Time study experience (some essential, but much more than a majority of time study experience desired)

(B) Factory or equivalent work simplification experience

(C) Plant lay-out

(D) Processing

(E) Paper work simplification

(F) Procedure writing

(G) Training

(H) Job evaluation

(I) Cost accounting

(J) Production control

(K) Supervision of personnel

(L) Organization planning

(M) Quality control.

III. Knowledge: He should have a reasonable understanding and knowledge of all the various items mentioned under work experience.

Fig. 3.   Position description for Senior Industrial Engineer.

courses in work measurement and statistics. A staff member should also like using this knowledge, or he will soon become bored and seek other work. Processing machine shop operations, on the contrary, requires considerable machine shop practice plus knowledge of advanced machine tool techniques. This latter experience is frequently found in individuals who have completed their apprenticeship in toolmaking or machining and then entered industrial engineering via their practical experience in processing. This practical knowledge should be supplemented by courses in work measurement, motion analysis, MTM, etc. if such a man is to achieve true senior status. On the other hand, technical requirements of the work often dictate very stringent educational requirements. For example, the test processing section shown in Fig. 2 dealt with electronic apparatus which required complicated testing. To determine the tests needed and to process them required a high order of technical knowledge in electronics. Here the absolute requirement was a bachelor of science degree in electrical engineering with a major in electronics or communications.

Production foremen often can be trained to become good industrial engineers, specializing in processing assembly or machinery work. In fact, it is a good practice to bring production foremen into the industrial engineering department, even if for only a three- to six-month indoctrination period. Those who do not remain in the activity and return to supervision generally become better supervisors because of the knowledge gained. Also, they usually cooperate better with industrial engineers assigned to work in their department.

Motivation—the desire to succeed—is another prime requisite. A person may be technically competent, likable, etc., and yet not succeed in the profession merely because he lacks real motivation. It is this attribute which causes people to exert maximum effort toward doing a good job, doing it quickly, and finding new tasks which need to be done on their own. Such individuals, if technically competent, etc., require minimum supervision. Intense motivation means more than "lip service" to the idea; for although many persons claim they have such desire, their performance shows it to be merely wishful thinking. The need of the industrial engineer for personal stability and for report writing ability, however, requires no elaboration.

The work experience required is a variable that must be established as dictated by circumstances. Obviously, the test process engineer previously mentioned needs work experiences different from those shown in Fig. 3. To complete a partial qualification description like that in Fig. 3 for a senior industrial engineer for any given plant, it is merely necessary to define any special technical requirements, work experience, etc., and add duty and responsibility statements. Similar procedures would result in position descriptions for each of the departmental sections shown in Fig. 2 or each of the functional responsibilities listed earlier.

Training and Development of Technical Personnel is a management necessity which cannot be neglected if their initial qualifications are to be maintained or enhanced as they must be for the department to succeed in meeting new challenges and competition. The ultimate effectiveness of the engineering manager and his organization largely rests on the functional competence of the individuals who actually do the work, not on the technical competence of the chief. Hence, it is to the manager's advantage to train and develop his staff so that they are truly expert in their fields.

Since all successful upgrading depends directly upon individual self development, the necessity for motivating and encouraging the staff is ever present. People cannot be forced to learn, but constant persuasion in this direction coupled with reminders of the advantages—or even occasional mention of the adverse effects which could result—of upgrading themselves will tend to assure their attention to enlightened self interest. As a direct outgrowth of the explosion of technology, even the most capable personnel will become technically obsolete in about five years unless they continue to acquire and use the new knowledge and techniques. Technical survival is a very real challenge to professional people today, and it merits attention from both themselves and their managers. The manager is responsible for not only providing the opportunity to his staff for training and development, but also for encouraging and motivating them to take advantage of the opportunities offered.

As far as training is concerned, the opportunity can be either formal or informal. Formal training implies credit courses either internally or under company auspices at educational institutions. The latter can range from degree programs pursued under a variety of conditions to special seminars or short courses covering specific techniques deemed desirable for the work to be done by the trainee. Informal training also can be either internal or external. Internally, it can take the form of individual guidance upon the appropriate occasions or specific assignment to work with staff members who already are expert in the area to be covered. Externally, one of the best avenues of technical upgrading is membership and active participation in one or more of the many technical societies, trade associations, or cultural groups typically found within reach of the staff. While training can take many forms and be facilitated in many ways, one of the best strategies for the manager is to provide the example himself and insist that the staff emulate him.

Development implies a somewhat different type of activity. Although much of it is a natural outgrowth of training and educational pursuits, these will not of themselves assure that development will ensue. Essential to effective development is the placement of the individual in situations in which he must apply his knowledge, be responsible for his own decisions, and observably contribute to the progress of his company. While a staff member often can "worm" his way into such situations, the only sure route to accomplishing these aims is the conscientious action of his manager in both providing the opportunity and insisting on its acceptance. Also, continual advice and counsel during the course of such developmental exposure is most effective when it comes from the manager himself.

The mutual benefits to the company, the department, and the individual himself all provide adequate incentive toward training and development when they are wisely enunciated by the responsible manager. The current urgency for training and development within almost any organization cannot be overstressed. It is an organizational factor of paramount importance.

Creative Staff Management is the factor responsible for most scientific and engineering "breakthroughs". Creative thinking differentiates the routine plodder from the valuable contributor. For example, MTM resulted from a creative approach to the problems of work measurement. Creative engineering has the fortunate attribute of minimizing the time and cost of solving almost any engineering problem, and this is true for problems in the area of work measurement. It is indeed unfortunate that creativity is far easier to stifle or kill than it is to foster.

The truly creative engineering organization requires *both* a creatively oriented top management *and* a sensitive, creative engineering management. The industrial engineering manager must fully understand the creative process and be willing to withhold judgment of the creative solution until its validity can be established by engineering analysis. Deriding or even hindering the creative individual even only once or twice may ruin him as a creative contributor to the organization—often forever.

While it is easy to describe the necessity for creative management, the specific steps a manager can take to achieve it are less often defined. To meet this need, the following guidelines for both old and new managers of industrial engineering and/or work measurement are quoted as a checklist of valuable suggestions:

FROM ENGINEER TO MANAGER[2]

Now You're a Manager

SET UP THE ORGANIZATION

Get a charter which spells out your duties and relationships with other individuals and departments.

Be sure that your department is well organized, with all subordinate jobs well defined.

Make sure that your immediate subordinates, and also the next lower echelon, understand their responsibilities.

If there are any cliques, former manager, etc., make it plain that all major decisions are to be yours.

In hiring subordinates, place a premium on a combination of experience and potential, rather than on experience alone.

Be sure the people in lower echelon management spots are capable of managing properly. Personality and psychological tests are often misleading.

EXPECT A GOOD JOB

If the people you hire are not doing a satisfactory job, tell them. Outline the standards you expect, and let them know that if they fail to deliver, you have no choice but to replace them.

[2] *Managing Engineering and Research,* by Delmar W. Karger and Robert G. Murdick, The Industrial Press, New York City, 1963.

Don't supervise your lower level managers too closely, but meet with them individually for a short time each week.

Make it plain you expect a good job. In most cases your men will live up to your expectations.

Be "tough", but don't be brutal.

LEARN TO HANDLE PROBLEMS

Keep your own superior notified of what problems arise, but don't call him unless necessary. If you think a problem warrants his attention, leave a message for him. This gives him the option of getting in touch with you or not, as he sees fit.

When an urgent problem comes up, move in fast and follow the details closely. Leave no doubt that you have taken charge. If necessary, work yourself and your men around the clock.

Don't be afraid to ask questions when problems come up.

Learn to evaluate accurately any information that comes your way. A good manager doesn't have to be a good engineer, but he should be able to sift evidence and come up with a decision.

GET THE JOB DONE RIGHT

When a new job comes up, analyze it and start making your plans. See that current jobs are carried on by delegation, and spot check to see that things keep running smoothly.

Keep in touch with major reports on manufacturing, finance, marketing, etc., which may have an effect on engineering. Try to find areas where engineering's contribution may be extended.

Anticipate problems. Avoid the possibility of having to push the panic button.

See that jobs are done on schedule. Be sure that all specifications are met and that nothing is shipped out that doesn't meet engineering specifications.

TREAT YOUR MEN RIGHT

Don't short-circuit or override your men—work with them.

Don't criticize a man in front of others; feel free to *reward* a man in front of others.

Try to get your men advanced in salary and responsibility as rapidly as they deserve it. Don't hang on to a man who is offered a better opportunity than you can offer him.

Accept full responsibility for the mistakes of the group; don't unload them on to the individual when discussing these errors.

Don't let yourself become obligated to your subordinates through outside favors.

Keep your men informed and let them know where you stand with respect to them.

Application of these ideas will be particularly valuable to a new engineering manager or to one just assuming a new position. They outline an organized approach to creative management.

Financial Requirements of the well-organized department basically must consider both people and things. It is relatively easy to meet the needs and usually the cost of physical equipment, supplies, facilities, etc. In fact, a great deal of aid and advice are available from many sources both within and outside the company on such matters. However, meeting the true financial and other compensatory needs of the staff frequently becomes one of the prime problems of the manager. Failure in this area usually is more expensive in the long run than temporary shortages of physical needs, although there may be an interrelationship among these elements.

In compensating and rewarding his personnel, the manager must consider both the economic and non-economic needs of his people. Both monetary and non-monetary rewards should play their part in the compensation program. Here the industrial engineer or work measurement analyst has a broad background to draw upon, even though it is oriented to the level of the direct and indirect personnel of the production function. It is therefore indeed surprising to find so few managers in this area who apply these principles to their own staff compensation. Many reliable surveys have shown conclusively that professional personnel, in particular, value recognition of their accomplishments equally or even more than monetary rewards. However, this conclusion inherently depends on the monetary rewards being at least adequate to provide a standard of living commensurate with professional living.

Performance Factors

With well-defined objectives and all organizational factors planned to meet them, the next step in management is the executive function. The execution of plans, after all, is the real purpose of the plans. Thus many of the dimensions of the engineering manager's job circumscribe the functional aspects of "getting the job done", what may be termed performance factors. In the following discussion, the manager's attention is directed to five more basic concepts headed: Project Programming, The Design Process, Technical Parameters, Measures of Effectiveness, and Coordination and Control.

Project Programming refers to the sequential ordering in real time of all the events to be accomplished or necessary for attaining the goals of a plan. It provides a schedule for the application of executive routines and the expenditure of manpower, money, and materials to accomplish the steps required by objective planning. Programming has grown to be a very complex field drawing heavily on the disciplines of statistics, higher mathematics, operations research, and other sophisticated subjects with which the manager and his staff must become increasingly familiar if they are to achieve desirable goals. Because of this complexity, it will not be possible here to elaborate properly on programming; rather the remarks are confined to salient ideas.

New programming techniques typified by PERT, PERT/Cost, and CPM are gaining wider usage and can be used effectively on work measurement and other industrial engineering projects. Many such techniques are in the vanguard of management of the future, but current technology of the executive function already is necessary to apply if only to permit reaping the benefits to be derived from the increased effectiveness possible with modern electronic computers and computer algorithms. Modern programming techniques exemplify, in many cases, the only feasible means by which to allocate resources and permit management-by-exception. As such, they constitute a most important dimension of the executive function in engineering management.

The Design Process is a conspicuous component of the official industrial engineering definition quoted at the start of this chapter. Indeed, the design of "integrated systems" emphasizes the common bond between industrial engineering and the more traditional fields of engineering associated with the designs of products and other physical evidences of the application of scientific principles to enrich mankind. To the degree that industrial engineers lack familiarity with the design process, they are less than true to the professional calling of an engineer. Engineering executives need to mold their organization's activities in conformance with the design process.

What is the design process? What are the functional steps involved in designing either a system or a product? Which steps are creative? Which steps merely represent the processing of information? What and where are the feedback loops of the design circuits? Many of these questions can be answered by careful study of the generalized concept of the design process depicted in Fig. 4. Space does not permit further elaboration here on the process itself. However, thinking through the questions raised above will enable the engineering manager to lead his organization with fewer fumbles, less rambling down the byways of cut-and try, and a reduced reliance upon guess-and-hope. Understanding the basic design process is an intrinsic requirement for successful technical management.

Technical Parameters inherently place limitations on the performance of engineering and production. Actually, their success is largely determined to the extent that they economically meet the technical parameters which gage their output. Executive skill of a high order is demanded by such parameters in modern business. The principal parameters of interest here are reliability, standardization, and producibility.

It is as necessary to design an inherently reliable work measurement system as it is to design a reliable areospace system or weapons system. Reliability has a dual nature in that while it does increase costs, it also actually provides a necessary intrinsic value of the system or product. Unreliability in work measurement cannot be afforded any more than the "blow-up" of a new space rocket on the launching pad. By the same token, improve-

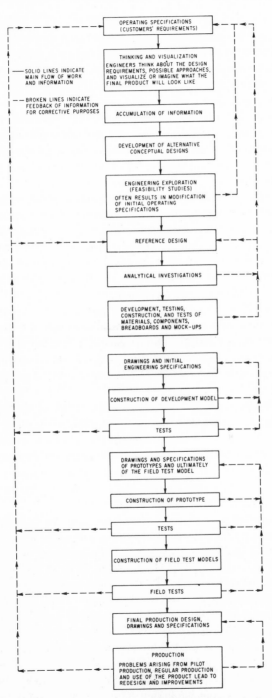

Fig. 4. Graphic portrayal of the system and product design process.

ments in a system which has attained initial reliability will tend to assure lower net over-all costs in the long run. Management's task in this area is to recognize the stage of development in relation to the cost. By avoiding the initially cheaper solutions to a problem, astute managers can reap the dependable long term performances which will eventually prove to be less expensive and much more satisfactory.

Standardization of products, components, and processes has received increasing attention because of its impact on cost and time as well as on both reliability and producibility. Standards, including those of work measurement, are fundamental to the prevention of duplication of effort, waste of economic resources, and confusion caused by lack of uniformity and interchangeability; they are a key principle of all engineering. Not only must standards be established, but they must also be disseminated and enforced. The engineering manager also needs to realize that standards should be revised to reflect changes in technology, lest his staff become shackled by the leashing of their creativity. For example, MTM represents not only a creative system, but also a series of standards relating to the performance of manual work. When changes in the standards become appropriate as a result of research or experience, adoption of the revisions is vital to maintaining and enlarging the benefits to be gained from the system.

Producibility is a relatively new concept of engineering and manufacturing teamwork. It concerns the production problems associated with the fact that the product designer largely fixes the cost of the product. His design frequently so circumscribes the selection of production alternatives that relatively little potential for cost savings remains during production. This contravenes the fact that basic process selection is the province of the industrial engineer which offers him the greatest chance to affect the cost of production. The lesson to be learned here is that all engineering executives should promote cooperation among the industrial engineers, cost estimators, and product designers during the design of the product, not just afterwards.

Measures of Effectiveness are essential to gaging the attainment of planned objectives. Managing and control are completely and permanently linked, and control requires measurement against standards. While almost all industrial engineering and work measurement managers know this is true for the direct labor in the plant, it is surprising to observe the number of them who fail to *really* recognize that it extends to their own activities, since they are a function within a managed enterprise. If the manager does not determine and establish suitable standards of measurement for his own staff, others will do it for him in a manner ordinarily not palatable or satisfactory.

The manager must therefore continually seek the most effective means of measuring the output of his organization and apply these methods. The measures can be objective, usually numerical in form, or subjective, based upon opinions or value judgments, or both.   If he cannot find and establish suitable objective measures, both he and his functional organization will be vulnerable to biased subjective measurement by others.   While the desirability of objective numerical measurements has been emphasized, the necessity of also developing and applying qualitative—usually somewhat subjective—measures cannot be ignored.   There is a great tendency to rely solely on quantitative measures, if such measures are used at all; and these often do not yield the best measurement, especially for an engineering-oriented activity.   A combination of measures is usually preferable, with some favoring of the objective type.

Measurement should be applied at three principal levels: (1) the individual, (2) the managed sub-units of the department, and (3) the department as a whole in relation to their contribution to the total business of the firm.   Results of measurement should not be used primarily to criticize any of these levels, nor to display to general view the problems of any level.   This is particularly true for the individual level.   Rather, the measurement should be used as a means of informing the responsible manager concerning variances and problems which require his corrective action.   The person having immediate responsibility for the level measured should be the first to know the results of measurements.   No one is in a better position to achieve the required changes in cooperation with the manager than this person.

This discussion of the measurement of industrial engineering highlights a major work measurement problem still not satisfactorily solved.   Although the discussion focused upon engineering, the same remarks apply to any functional area of any organization with only slight modifications.   Measurement of performance at all levels is necessary for management to achieve control—a fact emphasized early in this textbook.   This problem should challenge all industrial engineers and work measurement analysts. It will eventually be solved, and the solution probably will include some of the concepts outlined for establishing a multi-factor incentive system (see Chapter 25).

Coordination and Control are terms which can be used synonymously when the interrelations between departments are considered.   "Coordination" means bringing elements into common, concerted action.   Since professional personnel are the heart of any engineering function, the emphasis probably should be on coordination rather than control.   The word "control" has semantic overtones which are generally unacceptable to professionals.

It is not enough to formulate good plans, to organize and staff with the best personnel, and to understand the job at hand.   When the job is underway, divergence of action from the plans inevitably occurs.   To "control" after variance is detected (the true nature of control) is not good enough; rather, the key to effective execution of complex technical work is "coordination" or continuous alignment of all factors.

Resource Factors

During the consideration of Organizational Factors and Performance Factors, it was tacitly assumed that all resources required existed within the company. However, as is true for any engineering manager, the manager of industrial engineering is not limited by the organization at hand or the specialties available within the company. He should be aware of the uses and sources of outside engineering services and technical data. He must objectively examine not only the costs, but also the net gains to be obtained from outside assistance. Some typical outside resources are consultants, academic personnel and organizations, technical societies, trade associations, and technical information services. Many of these resources are free for the asking, but most involve monetary considerations which may be quite proper for achieving a planned goal.

The industrial engineering manager must clearly define the reasons for obtaining help from outside his company. A few of these are economy, the need to get the right people, facilities unavailable in his own company, overflow workloads, and specialized information not available within the company. Underlying some of these reasons is the fact that under certain circumstances it is uneconomical or impractical to staff and facilitate the engineering function internally. Even for industrial engineering and work measurement, outside assistance may be the best way to meet peak loads or to satisfy demands for special kinds of service which are desired only occasionally. In that event, the expenditure may be worthwhile.

MANAGEMENT OF METHODS AND LABOR CONTROL

To begin, labor control should be distinguished from cost reduction. Think of control as the maintenance of previously attained levels of performance, with cost reduction representing those activities which seek to definitely change such levels of performance and manufacturing costs by methods improvements, new tooling, revised layouts, better processes, superior motivation, etc. All labor control problems, in general, involve the following few basic steps:

1. Definition of the task or work to be performed, establishment of definite methods
2. Establishment of standards, i.e., a budget or goal of performance, time and cost "yardsticks"

3. Provision for measurement against such standards, efficiency computations
4. Analysis of departures from such performance standards, determining where corrective action is needed
5. Allocation of responsibility for bringing about improvements, assignment of specific corrective action to all management levels
6. Follow-up to assure performance on assigned tasks, expediting or revision of the corrective steps as needed.

The first two of these steps, relating directly to the material covered in this textbook, should be integrated properly. Valid standards can be established only by careful description of the work to be performed and the method of accomplishment. This is an important precept.

When labor standards are mentioned, people too often hastily conclude that wage incentives are involved. Standards and incentive payment are not necessarily synonymous. Some businesses should have wage incentives; but, in many other cases, such payment plans might not be appropriate. However, it is indeed a rare situation that will not justify some form of work measurement.

No supervisor at any organizational level can do a proper job with his personnel while lacking a fairly clear mental concept of the quality and quantity levels that represent satisfactory performance. Many plants, particularly small ones, have labor controls based upon nothing more than a fuzzy idea of what constitutes a fair day's work in the minds of the supervisors. In most of these cases, however, the supervisors were once capable workmen on the same machines using the same or very similar processes; they have confidence that the tasks are attainable, and they are willing to demonstrate this. Unfortunately, changed conditions including the growth of labor organizations, the increased formalization of labor relations, and the failure of top management to sufficiently back its line supervisors on labor matters have undermined such self-confidence and/or made it impracticable to demonstrate task performance. The truth is that such standards are quite subjective and often are far from correct. Under these conditions, supervisors may be reluctant to openly state their opinion of what represents a fair day's work, especially if their opinion conflicts with engineered standards.

These changing conditions have caused an increase in the use of what is frequently called "engineered" standards that are based on such techniques as time study, standard data, and predetermined elemental times like MTM, etc. Such studies include ratio-delay analyses and all-day production studies to determine the proper allowances to be included in the standard times. The determination of such standards has been discussed in prior chapters of this text.

It is true that the majority of existing measurement systems are associated with some form of monetary incentive, particularly so on direct labor operations. However, a large number of measured daywork installations in existence are either being changed for an incentive pay system or have proved to be entirely satisfactory in securing the advantages of labor measurement without the problems inherent in an incentive system. A successful measured daywork system requires substantially the same quality of standards, care in their maintenance, and most of the expense involved in running an incentive program of comparable quality. Accordingly, the basic discussion here concerns those steps inherent in a successful incentives program. The reader should remember that most of the items mentioned apply equally well to a good work measurement program without wage incentives, so reference to related problems in a daywork plant will be given only for better understanding of this material.

Desirable Practices

The practices which are best pursued to obtain adequate labor control can be considered under two headings: Standards of Performance and General Policies.

Standards of Performance

1. Standards of performance should be determined and applied only after conditions affecting the job are reasonably standardized. The standards should reflect the time for doing a specific operation under existing conditions by definite methods.
2. Standards of performance should clearly define the conditions affecting the performance of work on the job being measured.
3. Standards should be based on factual information obtained by the best techniques available.
4. Standards of performance, once set, should be guaranteed except for changed conditions which affect the amount of work required. While the individual or union obviously must have recourse through grievance procedures, settlements should always conform to the facts involved—in other words, the facts should determine the result of any dispute concerning labor standards. Compromises based only on the desire to "get along" will inevitably result in distorting the labor standards so that the essential opportunity or potential for uniform earnings for equal work will be destroyed.
5. Standards should be changed promptly to reflect changes in conditions which affect the amount of production required. This principle of promptness should also apply to changes in allowances, variance factors, special temporary (out-of-standard) practices, and the

like. Necessary changes in standards should be made promptly regardless of the source of the change, or of what needs changing in the standard. When an improvement suggestion originates with the operator, his reward for initiating a cost reduction should be paid as a direct reward. He should not be rewarded indirectly by not changing the labor standard, thereby allowing him to earn an excessive incentive bonus, if the basic purpose of the incentive plan is to be fulfilled. Such direct payment normally is accomplished through a suggestion plan which compensates him for accepted suggestions in some proportion to the savings achieved. The normal range of awards is ten to fifty per cent of the first year's savings.

6. Standards should express the level of performance required to earn "base rate". This level of performance should permit the qualified and experienced operator working under standardized conditions at an incentive pace to earn from twenty to thirty per cent above his base rate. Exceptionally skilled operators should be expected to earn more than this range, while less skilled and/or inexperienced operators would earn less.

7. Standards of performance should be expressed in a common unit of time per unit of production. Pieces per hour is the unit most generally employed.

8. Standards of performance should be expressed in units of production which accurately indicate the work performed on the immediate job being measured. That is, the meaning of "piece" must be defined for each particular job.

General Policies

1. Good timekeeping must accurately isolate daywork and delay time from productive time worked against the standard time. Delay time should be compensated at the operator's base rate; since this is the only fair payment method when an incentive standard is not being met temporarily because of delays, especially when the delay is not controllable by the operator. In addition, it is very worthwhile to isolate such time so that conditions causing it may be eliminated.

2. Policies and practices governing the administration of the incentive plan and/or daywork wage program should be clearly and adequately prepared in written form so that they will be applied consistently over a period of time.

3. Limitations of coverage under any incentive plan should be clearly defined in the statement of policies and practices.

4. Basic principles and policies of the particular payment plan and its

accompanying standards program should be understood and actively supported by the entire management.

5. Basic principles and policy provisions should be continuously explained and "sold" to all employees.

6. Once a payment plan and the included standards program has been installed, management has an obligation to administer and rigidly maintain it. Means to assure a periodic audit will assist in keeping the rates (labor standards) up-to-date. Limiting decisions on technical aspects of the payment plan and/or standards program to qualified personnel in the industrial engineering department will also help to maintain satisfactory standards and basic policies.

7. The plan and its operation should be as simple and as easily understood by both management and employees as is practically possible. Many otherwise excellent plans have foundered by inattention to this essential feature.

Practices to be Avoided

Incentive systems will fail if the desirable practices previously enumerated are not followed. When this is the case, it is easy to list many bad situations which can exist. Standards frequently are established with too little time permitted for the necessary methods work. Methods are poorly defined. Production counts are careless or even falsified. Timekeeping is lax and incorrect accounts are charged. The industrial engineers are poorly trained and inadequately supervised. Policies and practices are not adequately defined and management tries to bribe the cooperation of labor by yielding to all their demands. A prime axiom to combat such conditions is: *"Rates of pay and working conditions can be negotiated and arbitrated; but time standards should be established only on the basis of factual data"*.

Consistency is probably the one characteristic which, above everything else, is necessary for a satisfactory incentive system of any type. Standards can be too "loose" or they can be too "tight", provided they are consistently so. Consistent standards can easily be adjusted up or down; but once thousands of standards are in existence without relative consistency, a new start is unavoidable.

Having an incentive system in poor condition does not imply a need to discard the incentive plan in favor of daywork. In almost every case where this has been done, such action has resulted in increased costs. The proper solution, therefore, when an incentive plan is not working properly is to evaluate the situation and initiate the necessary corrections as soon as possible. In some cases, accomplishing the needed corrections may require a long time, but the wait during revision will be justified by the results from a properly functioning incentive plan.

A FORWARD LOOK AT WORK MEASUREMENT
AND INDUSTRIAL ENGINEERING

The slow, uncertain development of work measurement has been traced through the era of the "efficiency expert" to the more recent rise of methods engineering and predetermined time systems. Today, work measurement has an accepted and respected place in the economic life of industrial enterprises. The multiplicity of new techniques presently appearing in industrial engineering, however, vividly emphasizes the relative infancy of work measurement as a science. An attempt to envison the future environment of work measurement and/or labor control may serve to guide industrial engineers in surer paths toward the fuller extent of professional development they must achieve to successfully maintain their stature and more widely serve the aims of scientific management.

At the outset, it is relatively certain that the same, effective fundamental principles and policies as have been determined by long years of trial and error will continue to apply in developing and/or maintaining effective work measurement and wage payment plans. It is equally true that attention and devotion to a regard for the human factors in work measurement will become ever more essential to improvement in the productive efforts of industry, as well as to distinguishing industrial engineers as scientific artisans in the design of integrated systems of men, machines, and materials. This thesis was clearly stated by one of the leading management men of the world in the October 1956 issue of "Manage" magazine as follows:[3]

The improvement of human relations on a world-wide basis is not something that can be left to government, to the clergy, to industrial relations experts in industry. If we are to have better management from the viewpoint of human relations, we must have better managers. We must have people who temper their applications of management techniques with a deep understanding of the human problems involved. Our management leaders must give leadership in the creation of human values as well as material values.

It is sometimes easy to forget these most basic truths when surveying the large number of predictions currently fashionable in many public information sources. To enumerate a few of these possibilities which industrial engineers have helped to create for the future, a number of statements are offered. The wholly automated or semi-automatic factory will be a reality for the manufacture of most major products, although small shops will continue to exist and might indeed become even more numerous and specialized. The forerunners of robots to assist workers already are in existence today. The most complex machine of today will seem simple in

---

[3] Dr. Harold B. Maynard, President, Maynard Research Council, quoted in the magazine of the National Management Association, Dayton, Ohio.

comparison to those of tomorrow. Men will almost certainly surmount the confines of this planet to explore the worlds beyond. All of these will raise problems of such scope and complexity that it will be essential to bring to bear all the scientific, engineering, and human skills of which the human race is capable. This broad vista, if somewhat breathtaking, points out the great need for the intelligence, character, and determination that will be required in the man of the future.

When trying to solve a very complicated situation involving the expenditure of substantial sums of money, one should bring all possible techniques to bear upon the solution. This is not to say, however, that establishing work standards in a plant where a large number of man-hours are involved necessarily justifies the most minute and analytical technique possible. This approach to the problem may not yield an economic solution for the simple reason that the greater accuracy and preciseness may not be required, and therefore the extra time spent in applying such techniques could result in wasted money. Scientific knowledge and information should be applied with common sense. Saying this in another manner, the engineering application of scientific knowledge involves a consideration of economics; and the most effective, least costly satisfactory solution is the one that should be utilized.

The basic problems of industrial engineering will not change, nor will the fundamental principles now being used to develop successful solutions. The main difference, as the industrial engineer's environment continues to become more complex, will be his need to extend the boundaries of his knowledge and further refine the known techniques he now uses to develop solutions. He must become conversant and adept in the fields of work measurement, methods engineering, automation, systems and procedures, computers, mathematical programming, operations research, and many such similar activities that already exist in some form today. They are the forerunners of techniques yet unborn which will tax every power the industrial engineer can command to advance himself and his profession if they are to survive in the world of tomorrow. However, there is no need for pessimism, since industrial engineering is meeting the challenge courageously today and advances steadily on many fronts. The future of industrial engineering cannot fail to be bright, if only the emphasis on human values that has marked its past work remains as a cardinal guidepost to progress.

Bibliography

To conserve space in this listing, calendar months are abbreviated and certain of the entries are coded. When the symbol ( )* appears, the asterisk footnotes the entry within the parentheses. The footnote directs the reader to the following codes:

Code	Entry Signified
AIIE	American Institute of Industrial Engineers, Inc.; United Engineering Center; 345 East 47th Street; New York, New York 10017 (formerly located in Columbus, Ohio). Also designates local chapters and conference locations which are identified in the listing.
JIE	*Journal of Industrial Engineering:* American Institute of Industrial Engineers (see above).
ASME	American Society of Mechanical Engineers; United Engineering Center; 345 East 47th Street; New York, New York 10017.
MECH	*Mechanical Engineering:* American Society of Mechanical Engineers (see above).
MTMA	MTM Association for Standards and Research; Suite 101-B, Huron Towers; 2200 Fuller Road; Ann Arbor, Michigan 48105 (formerly located in Pittsburgh, Pennsylvania). Also designates conference locations which are identified in the listing.
JMTM	*Journal of Methods-Time Measurement:* MTM Association for Standards and Research (see above).
FACT	*Factory Management and Maintenance:* McGraw-Hill Publishing Company, Inc.; New York, New York 10036.

ÅBERG, ULF. "Frequency of Occurrence of Basic MTM Motions," *Research Committee Report No. 1,* Svenska MTM-Foreningen, Stockholm, Sweden, Aug 1962. Also published in: (JMTM),* Vol. VIII, No. 5, July–Aug 1963.
———. "Sequence of Motions in Manual Workshop Production," *Research Committee Report No. 2,* Svenska MTM-Foreningen, Stockholm, Sweden, July 1963. Also published in: (JMTM),* Vol. IX, No. 2, Nov–Dec 1963.
ABRUZZI, ADAM. "Formulating a Theory of Work Methods," (JIE),* Vol. V, No. 4, July 1954.
———. "The Quest for Certainty," (JIE),* Vol. IX, No. 5, Sept–Oct 1958.
———. "Time Study Rating Procedures," (JIE),* Vol. V, No. 1, Jan 1954.

* See code at start of Bibliography.

ABRUZZI, ADAM. *Work Measurement: New Principles and Procedures,* Columbia University Press, New York City, 1952.

———. *Work, Workers, and Work Measurement,* Columbia University Press, New York City, 1956.

(AIIE).* "In Tribute to Frank and Lillian Gilbreth," (JIE),* Special Reprint, May 1962.

ALBERTY, B. E. and F. J. DAY. "Photos Aid in Understanding Methods-Time Measurement," (JMTM),* Vol. I, No. 3, Aug 1954.

ALLDERIGE, JOHN M. "Designing Control Systems in Work Measurement," (JIE),* Vol. IX, No. 1, Jan–Feb 1958.

———. "Statistical Procedures in Stop Watch Work Measurement," (JIE),* Vol. VII, No. 4, July–Aug 1956.

———. "Work Sampling Without Formulas," (FACT),* Vol. 112, No. 3, Mar 1954.

ANDERSON, ARTHUR G., MERTEN JOSEPH MANDEVILLE, and JOHN MUELLER ANDERSON. *Industrial Management,* The Ronald Press Company, New York City, 1942.

ANDERSON, C. A. and G. L. THUERING. "Mirrors Extend the Scope of Cameras," *Advanced Management,* Vol. 16, Aug 1951.

ARMSTRONG, FRANK. "Universal Measurement," *Proceedings—15th Annual National Conference,* (AIIE),* Philadelphia, May 1964.

ARNOLD, D. C. and M. A. TINKER. "The Fixation Pause of the Eyes," *Journal of Experimental Psychology,* Vol. 25, 1939.

(ASME).* "Operation and Flow Process Charts," *ASME Standard 101,* 1947.

———. "Industrial Engineering Terminology," *ASME Standard 106,* 1955.

BAILEY, GERALD B. "Basic Motion Timestudy," *Proceedings—8th Annual Time Study and Methods Conference,* (ASME)* and Society for Advancement of Management, Apr 1953.

———. "Comments on 'An Experimental Evaluation of the Validity of Predetermined Elemental Time Systems'," (JIE),* Vol. XII, No. 5, Sept–Oct 1961.

BAILEY, GERALD B. and RALPH PRESGRAVE. *Basic Motion Timestudy,* McGraw-Hill Book Company, New York City, 1958.

BARANY, JAMES W. "The Nature of Individual Differences in Bodily Forces Exerted During a Simple Motor Task," (JIE),* Vol. XIV, No. 6, Nov–Dec 1963.

BARANY, JAMES W. and JAMES H. GREENE. "The Use of Self-Paced Tasks for the Evaluation of Work Methods," (JIE),* Vol. XI, No. 5, Sept–Oct 1960.

BARNES, RALPH M. "Are We Asking Workers to Do More Work?," (FACT),* Vol. 108, No. 7, July 1950.

———. "Industrial Engineering Survey," *Industrial Engineering Report No. 101,* University of Iowa, 1949.

———. *Motion and Time Study,* John Wiley & Sons, New York City, 5th Edition, 1963.

———. *Motion and Time Study Applications,* John Wiley & Sons, New York City, 2nd Edition, 1953.

———. *Work Sampling,* W. C. Brown and Company, Dubuque, Iowa, 1956.

BARNES, RALPH M. and ROBERT B. ANDREWS. "Performance Sampling in Work Measurement," (JIE),* Vol. VI, No. 6, Nov–Dec 1955.

BARNES, RALPH M. and HAROLD T. AMRINE. "The Effect of Practice on Various Elements Used in Screwdriver Work," *Journal of Applied Psychology,* Vol. 26, No. 2, Apr 1942.

BARNES, RALPH M. and MARVIN E. MUNDEL. "A Study of Hand Motions Used in Small Assembly Work," *Studies in Engineering Bulletin 16,* University of Iowa, 1939.

———. "A Study of Hand Motions Used in Small Assembly Work," *Studies in Engineering Bulletin 17,* University of Iowa, 1939.

———. "Studies of Hand Motions and Rhythm Appearing in Factory Work," *Studies in Engineering Bulletin 12.* University of Iowa, 1938.

* See code at start of Bibliography.

BARNES, RALPH M. and J. S. PERKINS. "A Study of the Development of Skill During Performance of a Factory Operation," *Studies in Engineering Bulletin 22,* University of Iowa, 1940.

BARNES, RALPH M. and J. BRYAN SULLIVAN. "Production Management Survey;" Bureau of Business and Economic Research; Southern Section, University of California, 1950.

BARNES, RALPH M., J. M. MACKENSIE, and MARVIN E. MUNDEL. "Studies of One- and Two-Handed Work," *Studies in Engineering Bulletin 21,* University of Iowa, 1940.

BARNES, RALPH M., J. S. PERKINS, and JOSEPH M. JURAN. "A Study of the Effect of Practice on the Elements of a Factory Operation," *Studies in Engineering Bulletin 22,* University of Iowa, 1940.

BARR, J. H. and DEXTER S. KIMBALL, *Elements of Machine Design,* John Wiley & Sons, New York City, 3rd Edition, 1935.

BAYHA, FRANKLIN H. "A Short Course of MTM Techniques," *Proceedings—1st Annual Management Conference,* (AIIE),* Fort Wayne, Indiana, May 1955.

———. "Fundamental MTM Techniques," *Proceedings—2nd Annual Management Conference,* (AIIE),* Fort Wayne, Indiana, Apr 1956.

———. "Progress Report on Development of New Simplified Data," *Proceedings— 5th Annual MTM Conference,* (MTMA),* New York City, Oct 1956.

———. "Research Techniques—An Analysis," *Proceedings—6th Annual MTM Conference,* (MTMA),* New York City, Sept 1957.

———. "What's New in MTM?," (JMTM),* Vol. IV, No. 2, May–June 1957.

———. "Your Standards Are As Good As Your Training!," *Proceedings—7th Annual Chapter Conference,* (AIIE),* Detroit, Michigan, Feb 1965.

BAYHA, FRANKLIN H. and JAMES A. FOULKE. "Application Training Supplement No. 7 —Position and Apply Pressure," (MTMA),* June 1964.

BAYHA, FRANKLIN H. and DELMAR W. KARGER. "Installing MTM—A New Approach," (JMTM),* Vol. I, No. 2, June 1954.

———. *Methods-Time Measurement Manual,* The Magnavox Company, Fort Wayne, Indiana, 1953, revised 1956.

BAYHA, FRANKLIN H., JAMES A. FOULKE, and WALTON M. HANCOCK. "Application Training Supplement No. 8—Position," (MTM),* Jan 1965.

———. "Application Training Supplement No. 9—Apply Pressure," (MTMA),* Jan 1965.

———. "Supplementary Data on Position and Apply Pressure," (JMTM),* Vol. X, No. 2, Mar–Apr 1965.

BEGEMAN, MYRON L. *Manufacturing Processes,* John Wiley & Sons, New York City, 1942.

BERELSON, BERNARD and GARY A. STEINER. *Human Behavior,* Harcourt, Brace, & World, New York City, 1964.

BERNER, G. E. and D. E. BERNER. "Relations of Ocular Dominance, Handedness, and the Controlling Eye in Binocular Vision," *Archives of Opthalmology,* Vol. 50, 1953.

BIEL-NIELSEN, H. ERIK. "Universal Maintenance Standards," (JMTM),* Vol. VII, No. 4, Nov–Dec 1960.

BIRN, SERGE A. and WILLIAM F. HYDE. "The Consultant's Contribution to Industrial Engineering," (JIE),* Vol. XV, No. 6, Nov–Dec 1964.

BIRN, SERGE A., RICHARD M. CROSSAN, and RALPH W. EASTWOOD. *Measurement and Control of Office Costs,* McGraw-Hill Book Company, New York City, 1961.

BLOCK, STANLEY M. "An Evaluation of Work Measurement Techniques," *Proceedings—7th Annual Chapter Conference,* (AIIE),* Detroit, Michigan, Feb 1965.

———. "Effects of Visual Requirements Upon Certain Simultaneous Hand Motions," *Ph.D. Dissertation,* University of Minnesota, July 1956.

———. "Newest Motion Timer and Recorder," (FACT),* Vol. 116, No. 9, Sept 1958.

* See code at start of Bibliography.

BLOCK, STANLEY M. "SEMTAR, Automatic Electronic Motion Timer," (JIE),* Vol. XII, No. 4, July–Aug 1961.

BRISLEY, CHESTER L. "How You Can Put Work Sampling to Work," (FACT),* Vol. 110, No. 7, July 1952.

BROUHA, LUCIEN. "Physiological Aspects of Work Measurement," *Proceedings—3rd International MTM Conference,* (MTMA),* New York City, Sept 1963.

———. "Physiological Assessment of Job Stress," *Proceedings—15th Annual National Conference,* (AIIE),* Philadelphia, May 1964.

———. *Physiology in Industry,* Pergamon Press, New York City, 1960.

BROWN, RAY E. "Administration Is Not a Numbers Game," *Modern Hospital,* Vol. 103, No. 5, Nov 1964.

BROZEK, J. "Personal Factors in Competence and Fatigue," *Industrial Hygiene and Toxicology,* Interscience Publishers, New York City, Vol. 1, 1948.

BRYSON, W. D. "Are You Getting the Most from Your Industrial Engineers?," *Proceedings—7th Annual MTM Conference,* (MTMA),* New York City, Sept 1958.

BUFFA, ELWOOD S. "The Additivity of Universal Standard Data Elements," (JIE),* Vol. VII, No. 5, Sept–Oct 1956.

———. "The Additivity of Universal Standard Data Elements, II," (JIE),* Vol. VIII, No. 6, Nov–Dec 1957.

———. "The Electronic Time Recorder: A New Instrument for Work Measurement Research," (JIE),* Vol. IX, No. 2, Mar–Apr 1958.

———. "Toward a Unified Concept of Job Design," (JIE),* Vol. XI, No. 4, July–Aug 1960.

BUTCHER, PHILIP J. "Predetermined Motion Times," *M. S. Thesis,* University of Kansas, 1953.

CAMPBELL, L. R. "The MTM of Learning," *Proceedings—11th Annual MTM Conference,* (MTMA),* New York City, Sept 1962.

CAMPBELL, W. A. "Managing Manpower in a Changing Economy," *Proceedings—9th Annual MTM Conference,* (MTMA),* Toronto, Canada, June 1960.

CAPLAN, STANLEY H. and WALTON M. HANCOCK. "The Effect of Simultaneous Motions on Learning," (JMTM),* Vol. IX, No. 1, Sept–Oct 1963.

CARLSON, JOHN G. "Production Standards for Small Lot Manufacturing," (JIE),* Vol. XIII, No. 6, Nov–Dec 1962.

CARMICHAEL, COLIN (Editor). *Kent's Mechanical Engineers' Handbook,* John Wiley & Sons, New York City, Design and Production Volume, 12th Edition, 1950.

CARMICHAEL, L. and W. F. DEARBORN. *Reading and Visual Fatigue,* Houghton-Mifflin Company, Boston, 1947.

CARSON, GORDON B. (Editor). *Production Handbook,* Ronald Press Company, New York City, 1948, 2nd Edition, 1958.

CARSON, R. G., JR. "Consistency in Speed Rating," (JIE),* Vol. V, No. 1, Jan 1954.

CHAPANIS, A., W. R. GARNER and C. T. MORGAN. *Applied Experimental Psychology,* John Wiley & Sons, New York City, 1949.

CHRISTIAN, ROGER W. "Personal Obsolescence," (FACT),* Oct 1964.

CLIFFORD, ROBERT R. "Tests to Predict Worker Total Performance," *Proceedings—12th Annual MTM Conference,* (MTMA),* New York City, Sept 1964.

CLIFFORD, ROBERT R. and WALTON M. HANCOCK. "An Industrial Study of Learning," (JMTM),* Vol. IX, No. 3, Jan–Feb 1964.

COCHRAN, E. B. "New Concepts of the Learning Curve," (JIE),* Vol. XI, No. 4, July–Aug 1960.

COHEN, L. and L. STRAUSS. "Time Study and the Fundamental Nature of Manual Skill," *Journal of Consulting Psychology,* Vol. 10, 1946.

CORRELL, DONALD S. and RALPH M. BARNES. "Industrial Application of the Ratio-Delay Method," *Advanced Management,* Vol. XV, No. 8 (Aug 1950) and Vol. XV, No. 9 (Sept 1950).

COWDEN, DUDLEY J. *Statistical Methods in Quality Control,* Prentice-Hall, Englewood Cliffs, New Jersey, 1957.

* See code at start of Bibliography.

CRANDALL, RICHARD E. "Time Allocation—A Staff Department Problem," (JIE),* Vol. XIV, No. 6, Nov–Dec 1963.

CROSSAN, RICHARD M. "A New Approach to Clerical Work Measurement," *Proceedings—7th Annual MTM Conference,* (MTMA),* New York City, Sept 1958.

———. "Let's Simplify MTM Application," *Proceedings—8th Annual MTM Conference,* (MTMA),* Detroit, Michigan, Oct 1959.

———. "Master Standard Data—A Step Toward Economic MTM Application," *Proceedings—10th Annual MTM Conference,* (MTMA),* New York City, Oct 1961.

CROSSAN, RICHARD M. and HAROLD W. NANCE. *Master Standard Data,* McGraw-Hill Book Company, New York City, 1962.

CROSSMAN, E. R. F. W. "A Theory of the Acquisition of Speed-Skill," *Ergonomics,* Vol. 2, No. 2, Feb 1959.

———. "The Measurement of Perceptual Load in Manual Operations," *Ph.D. Dissertation,* University of Birmingham, England, Oct 1956.

DALE, EDGAR. *Audio-Visual Methods in Teaching,* The Dryden Press, New York City, 1946.

DAVIDSON, HAROLD O. *Functions and Bases of Time Standards,* (AIIE),* 1952.

———. "On Balance—The Validity of Predetermined Time Systems," (JIE),* Vol. XIII, No. 3, May–June 1962.

———. "Work Sampling—Eleven Fallacies," (JIE),* Vol. XI, No. 5, Sept–Oct 1960.

DAVIS, BENJAMIN G. "Executivism: How to Climb the Executive Ladder," (MECH),* Vol. 86, No. 7, July 1964.

DAVIS, L. E. "A Study of Two-Handed Work with Variations in Weight Transported and in Transport Distances," *M.S. Thesis,* State University of Iowa, 1942.

DAVIS, LOUIS E. and CHARLES SCHLEGEL. "The Effects of Auditory Visual Rhythmic Disturbances on Work Measurement Performance Rating," (JIE),* Vol. XI, No. 3, May–June 1960.

DAVIS, R., R. F. WEHRKAMP, and KARL U. SMITH. "Dimensional Analysis of Motion: I. Effects of Laterality and Movement Direction," *Journal of Applied Psychology,* Vol. 35, 1951.

DeGARMO, E. PAUL and RICHARD K. SUGITA. "New Responsibilities for Industrial Engineers in Regard to Productivity," (JIE),* Vol. XIV, No. 6, Nov–Dec 1963.

deJONG, J. R. "The Effects of Increasing Skill and Methods–Time Measurement," *Time and Motion Study,* Feb 1961.

———. "The Effects of Increasing Skill on Cycle-Time and Its Consequences for Time Standards," *Ergonomics,* Vol. 1, 1957.

DIXON, W. J. and F. J. MASSEY. *Introduction to Statistical Analysis,* McGraw-Hill Book Company, New York City, 1951.

DODGE, R. and T. S. CLINE. "The Angle Velocity of Eye Movements," *Psychology Review,* Vol. 8, 1901.

DORLAND, W. A. NEWMAN (Editor). *American Pocket Medical Dictionary,* W. B. Saunders Company, Philadelphia, 1940.

DYER, DICKEY. "Mathematical Aspects of Work-Factor Allowances for Simultaneous Standard Elements of Work," (JIE),* Vol. IV, Feb 1953.

EARLE, SAMUEL W. "Industrial Progress with Memo-Motion Study," *Proceedings—7th Annual Chapter Conference,* (AIIE),* Detroit, Michigan, Feb 1965.

EMERSON, CHARLES PHILLIPS, JR. and JANE ELIZABETH TAYLOR. *Essentials of Medicine,* J. P. Lippincott Company, Philadelphia, 1940.

EMERSON, JAMES F. "Multiple Factor Incentives for Process Industries," (JIE),* Vol. VII, No. 4, July–Aug 1956.

EVANS, C. L. *Principles of Human Physiology,* Lea & Febiger, Philadelphia, 11th Edition, 1942.

FAIRSERVICE, THOMAS G. "Autorate—Computer Aid in Industrial Engineering," *Proceedings—15th Annual National Conference,* (AIIE),* Philadelphia, May 1964.

* See code at start of Bibliography.

FAIRWEATHER, OWEN. "Management and Labor Look at MTM," *Proceedings—8th Annual MTM Conference,* (MTMA),* Detroit, Michigan, Oct 1959.

———. "The Use of Predetermined Times in Labor Negotiations," (JMTM),* Vol. II, No. 3, July–Aug 1955.

FRANKHAUSER, G. "A New Point of View on the Leveling Procedure," (JMTM),* Vol. VIII, No. 4, May–June 1963.

FISHER, R. A. *Statistical Methods for Research Workers,* Hafner, 11th Edition, 1950.

FOULKE, JAMES A. and WALTON M. HANCOCK. "Industrial Research on the MTM Element Apply Pressure," *Research Report 111,* (MTMA),* Dec 1961.

FRANZ, DONALD and GERALD E. NADLER. "New Measurements to Determine the Effect of Task Factors on Body Member Acceleration Patterns," (JIE),* Vol. XII, No. 5, Sept–Oct 1961.

FULLER, FRANK H. "The Human Machine—Work &. Environment," (MECH),* Vol. 85, No. 12, Dec 1963.

FREEMAN, H. A. *Industrial Statistics,* John Wiley & Sons, New York City, 1947.

GEISEL, JOHN M. "White Collar Work Measurement—A Management System for Professional and Technical Work," *Proceedings—15th Annual National Conference,* (AIIE),* Philadelphia, May 1964.

GEMANT, A. *Frictional Phenomena,* Chemical Publishing Company, 1950.

GEOFFRION, ARTHUR M. "The Origin and Significance of Perceptron Theory," (JIE),* Vol. XII, No. 6, Nov–Dec 1961.

GEPPINGER, HELMUT C. *Dimensional Motion Times,* John Wiley & Sons, New York City, 1955.

GILBRETH, FRANK B. *Motion Study,* D. Van Nostrand Company, New York City, 1911.

GILBRETH, FRANK B. and LILLIAN M. GILBRETH. *Applied Motion Study,* Sturgis and Walton Company, New York City, 1917.

———. "A Fourth Dimension for Measuring Skill for Obtaining the One Best Way to do Work," *Society of Industrial Engineering Bulletin,* Vol. 4, Nov 1923.

———. "Classify the Elements of Work," *Management and Administration,* Vol. 8, 1924.

GILBRETH, FREDERICK M. "Crossing the Bridge—Some Pointers on Getting Action," (JMTM),* Vol. VII, No. 2, May–June 1959.

GILBRETH, LILLIAN M. "From Therbligs to Today," *Proceedings—1st Annual MTM Conference,* (MTMA),* New York City, Oct 1952.

———. "Scientific Control of Management," *Proceedings—5th Annual MTM Conference,* (MTMA),* New York City, Oct 1956.

GOCKEL, THOMAS R. "Building Block Concept of Standard Data," *Proceedings—11th Annual MTM Conference,* (MTMA),* New York City, Sept 1962.

GODWIN, G. A. "Basic Principles of the Work-Factor System of Time and Motion Study," *Machinery,* The Industrial Press, New York City, Vol. 85, Oct 1954.

GOLDMAN, JAY W. and HYMAN EISENBERG. "Can We Train More Effectively?," (JIE),* Vol. XIV, No. 2, Mar–Apr 1963.

GOLDMAN, JAY W. and L. W. HART, JR. "Information Theory and Industrial Learning," (JIE),* Vol. XVI, No. 5, Sept–Oct 1965.

GOMBERG, WILLIAM. *A Trade Union Analysis of Time Study,* Prentice-Hall, Englewood Cliffs, New Jersey, 2nd Edition, 1955.

———. "Some Developments in the Relationship between Collective Bargaining and Industrial Engineering," (JIE),* Vol. VIII, No. 5, Sept–Oct 1957.

———. "What Are the Specifications for an Effective System of Standard Data?," Vol. V, No. 4, July 1954.

GOODE, HARRY H. "Complexity, Research, and Industry," *Proceedings—3rd Annual MTM Conference,* (MTMA),* New York City, Oct 1954.

GOODMAN, BARBARA ETTINGER. "A Laboratory Study of Apply Pressure," (MTMA),* July 1959.

GOODMAN, BARBARA ETTINGER and JAMES A. FOULKE. "Instrumentation Used In A Laboratory Study of Apply Pressure," (JMTM),* Vol. V, No. 3, May–June 1958.

* See code at start of Bibliography.

GOTTERER, MALCOLM H. "Training Refresher and Research Integration," *Proceedings—7th Annual MTM Conference*, (MTMA),* New York City, Sept 1958.

GOTTLIEB, BERTRAM. "A Critical Analysis of Predetermined Motion Time Systems," *Proceedings—16th Annual National Conference*, (AIIE),* Chicago, May 1965.

GOULDEN, C. H. *Methods of Statistical Analysis*, John Wiley & Sons, New York City, 2nd Edition, 1952.

GRAHAM, BEN S. *Work Simplification*, The Standard Register Company, Dayton, Ohio, 1955.

GREENE, JAMES H. and W. H. M. Morris. "The Design of a Force Platform for Work Measurement," (JIE),* Vol. X, No. 4, July–Aug 1959.

———. "The Force Platform: An Industrial Engineering Tool," (JIE),* Vol. IX, No. 2, Mar–Apr 1958.

GREENE, JAMES H., W. H. M. MORRIS, and J. E. WIEBERS. "A Method for Measuring Physiological Cost of Work," (JIE),* Vol. X, No. 3, May–June 1959.

GRILLO, ELMER V. and C. J. BERG, JR. *Work Measurement in the Office*, McGraw-Hill Book Company, New York City, 1959.

HALSEY, JOHN J. "A New Model for Work Sampling—the GREDS Theory," (JIE),* Vol. XI, No. 6, Nov–Dec 1960.

HAMBLIN, HARRY M. "Union Participation in Industrial Engineering," *Proceedings—7th Annual MTM Conference*, (MTMA),* New York City, Sept 1958.

HANCOCK, WALTON M. "A Laboratory Study of Learning," *Proceedings—11th Annual MTM Conference*, (MTMA),* New York City, Sept 1962.

———. "New Research Techniques in Work Measurement," *Proceedings—12th Annual National Conference*, (AIIE),* Detroit, Michigan, May 1961.

———. "Pinpointing Operator Learning Time," *Proceedings—3rd International MTM Conference*, (MTMA),* New York City, Sept 1963.

———. "Progress Report on Learning Curve Research," (JMTM),* Vol. IX, No. 2, Nov–Dec 1963.

———. "Results of Industrial Phase of Research on Learning," *Proceedings—12th Annual MTM Conference*, (MTMA),* New York City, Sept 1964.

———. "The Effects of Learning on Short-Cycle Operations," *Proceedings—10th Annual MTM Conference*, (MTMA),* New York City, Oct 1961.

———. "You Can Reduce Training Losses," A. T. Kearney & Company Seminar, Chicago, Nov 1963.

HANCOCK, WALTON M. and JAMES A. FOULKE. "A Description of the Electronic Data Collector and the Methods of its Application to Work Measurement," *Research Information Paper No. 1*, (MTMA),* 1961. Also published in: (JIE),* Vol. XIII, No. 4, July–Aug 1962.

———. "Effects of Learning on Short-Cycle Operations," *Research Information Paper No. 2*, (MTMA),* 1961.

———. "Learning Curve Research on Short-Cycle Operations: Phase I. Laboratory Experiments," *Research Report 112*, (MTMA),* 1963.

———. "The Effects of Learning on Short-Cycle Operations," *Proceedings—10th Annual MTM Conference*, (MTMA),* New York City, Oct 1961.

HANCOCK, WALTON M., ROBERT R. CLIFFORD, JAMES A. FOULKE, and LEONARD F. KRYSTYNAK. "Learning Curve Research on Manual Operations: Phase II. Industrial Studies," *Research Report 113*, (MTMA),* July 1965.

HANES, BERNARD and EDWIN B. FLIPPO. "Anxiety and Work Output, (JIE),* Vol. XIV, No. 5, Sept–Oct 1963.

HARRIS, SCHELBY J. and KARL U. SMITH. "Dimensional Analysis of Motion: VII. Extent and Direction of Manipulative Movements as Factors in Defining Motions," *Journal of Applied Psychology*, Vol. 38, No. 2, 1954.

HASSELQVIST, OLLE, PER SÖDERSTRÖM, and ALF WIKLUND. *MTM:s Grundrörelser;* Utgivare, Svenska MTM-Gruppen, AB; Stockholm, Sweden; 1962.

HAVILAND, G. S. "Engineering Contributes to Company Decisions," (MECH),* Vol. 87, No. 3, Mar 1965.

* See code at start of Bibliography.

HECKER, DONALD, DONOVAN GREEN, and KARL U. SMITH. "Dimensional Analysis of Motion: X. Experimental Evaluations of a Time-Study Problem," *Journal of Applied Psychology,* Vol. 40, No. 4, 1956.

HEILAND, ROBERT E. and WALLACE J. RICHARDSON. *Work Sampling,* McGraw-Hill Book Company, New York City, 1957.

HILDRETH, G. "The Development and Training of Hand Dominance," *Journal of Genetic Psychology,* Vol. 75, 1949.

HITCHCOCK, FRANK J. "Do You Use Table X Correctly?," *Proceedings—8th Annual MTM Conference,* (MTMA),* Detroit, Michigan, Oct 1959.

HODSON, WILLIAM K. "Accuracy of MTM-GPD," (JMTM),* Vol. IX, No. 1, Sept–Oct 1963.

———. "Industrial Engineering in an Era of Changing Concepts," *Proceedings—16th Annual National Conference,* (AIIE),* Chicago, May 1965.

———. "The 'Solid State' Industrial Engineer," *Proceedings—10th Annual MTM Conference,* (MTMA),* New York City, Oct 1961.

———. "Universal Maintenance Standards," *Proceedings—7th Annual MTM Conference,* (MTMA),* New York City, Sept 1958.

HOEL, P. G. *Introduction to Mathematical Statistics,* John Wiley & Sons, New York City, 1947.

HOLMES, WALTER G. *Applied Time and Motion Study,* The Ronald Press Company, New York City, 1938, Revised 1945.

HONEYCUTT, JOHN M. JR. "Comments on 'An Experimental Evaluation of the Validity of Predetermined Elemental Time Systems'," (JIE),* Vol. XIII, No. 3, May–June 1962.

———. *The Basic Motions of MTM,* The Maynard Foundation, Pittsburgh, Pennsylvania, 1963.

HOXIE, ROBERT FRANKLIN. *Scientific Management and Labor,* D. Appleton and Company, 1921.

HUISKAMP, JANET, ROBERT C. SMADER, and KARL U. SMITH. "Dimensional Analysis of Motion: IX. Comparison of Visual and Non-Visual Control of Component Movements," *Journal of Applied Psychology,* Vol. 40, No. 3, 1956.

HUNTER, M. C. "Static and Clinging Friction of Pivot Bearings," *Proceedings—Institution of Mechanical Engineers,* London, England, Vol. 151, 1944.

INGENOHL, INGO. "Measuring Physical Effort," (JIE),* Vol. X, No. 2, Mar–Apr 1959.

ISCHINGER, E. "Analysis of Some Differences Between One- and Two-Handed Industrial Work," *M.S. Thesis,* Purdue University, 1950.

JOHNSON, WENDELL. *People in Quandaries,* Harper and Brothers, New York City, 1946.

JONES, W. DALE. "New Time Study Tool," *Advanced Management,* Vol. 18, Apr. 1953.

KANE, DON. *Planned Multiple Machine Assignments,* Argus Cameras, Ann Arbor, Michigan, 1956.

KARGER, DELMAR W. "Background of Predetermined Time Systems," (JMTM),* Vol. III, No. 2, May–June 1956.

———. "Developing Your MTM Training Program," *Proceedings—3rd Annual MTM Conference,* (MTMA),* New York City, Oct 1954.

———. "Dividends from Research," *Proceedings—3rd International MTM conference,* (MTMA),* New York City, Sept 1963.

———. "Electronic Development," *Proceedings—6th Annual MTM Conference,* (MTMA),* New York City, Sept 1957.

———. *The New Product,* The Industrial Press, New York City, 1960.

———. "Work Measurement Application and MTM," (JMTM),* Vol. X, No. 1, Nov–Dec 1964.

KARGER, DELMAR W. and ROBERT G. MURDICK. *Managing Engineering and Research,* The Industrial Press, New York City, 1963.

* See code at start of Bibliography.

KARPOVICH, P. V. and E. C. SCHNEIDER. *Physiology of Muscular Activity*, W. B. Saunders Company, Philadelphia, 3rd Edition, 1948.

KEACHIE, E. C. "Cost and the Learning Curve," *American Association of Cost Engineers Bulletin,* Vol. III, No. 2, June 1961.

KENNEY, J. F. *Mathematics of Statistics*, D. Van Nostrand Company, New York City, 2nd Edition, 1947.

KIMBER, DIANA CLIFFORD, CAROLYN E. GRAY, and CAROLINE E. STACKPOLE. *Textbook of Anatomy and Physiology*, The Macmillan Company, New York City, 1938.

KIRWIN, RALPH S. "Maximum Performance in a Daywork Plant," *Proceedings—3rd Annual Management Conference*, (AIIE),* Fort Wayne, Indiana, May 1957.

KINCH, ROBERT E. "Human Factors in the Measurement of Total System Effectiveness, (JIE),* Vol. XIV, No. 6, Nov–Dec 1963.

KLING, JULIUS (Contributor). *Funk & Wagnalls Standard Reference Encyclopedia,* Standard Reference Works Publishing Company, New York City, 1961.

KNOBLE, RICHARD H. "Measurement and Control of Indirect Costs," *Proceedings—7th Annual Chapter Conference*, (AIIE),* Detroit, Michigan, Feb 1965.

KOCH, WILLIAM C. "Correlation of Purdue Pegboard Dexterity Test Scores with Short-Cycle Operations," *(Unpublished) Report*, University of Michigan, 1964.

KOEPKE, C. A. and L. S. WHITSON. "Power and Velocity Developed in Manual Work," (MECH),* Vol. 62, 1940.

KOTTLER, JULIAN L. "The Learning Curve—A Case History in Its Application," (JIE),* Vol. XV, No. 4, July–Aug 1964.

KRICK, EDWARD V. "An Investigation of Simultaneous Motions as Treated in the Methods-Time Measurement System," *M.S. Thesis*, Cornell University, Ithaca, New York, 1955.

———. "Hyperenthusiastic and Hypercritical Writings on Predetermined Motion Times," (JIE),* Vol. IX, No. 3, May–June 1958.

———. *Methods Engineering*, John Wiley & Sons, New York City, 1962.

LAMBERT, P. "Practice Effect of Non-Dominant vs. Dominant Musculature in Acquiring Two-Handed Skill," *Research Quarterly*, Vol. 22, Mar 1951.

LANG, ANDREWS M. "An MTM Analysis of Performance Rating Systems," *Research Report 104*, (MTMA),* Apr 1952.

———. "A Research Report on Standards for Reading Operations," *Research Report 102*, (MTMA),* July 1951.

———. "Latest MTM Research Developments," *Proceedings—1st Annual MTM Conference*, (MTMA),* New York City, Oct 1952.

———. "MTM Newsletter," (MTMA),* Nos. 1 through 5, circa 1950–51.

———. "Methods-Time Measurement Bulletin," (MTMA), Oct 1951 and Feb. 1953.

LANG, ANDREWS M. and H. ERIK BIEL-NIELSEN. "Preliminary Research Report on Disengage," *Research Report 101*, (MTMA),* Feb 1951.

LANSBURGH, RICHARD H. and WILLIAM R. SPRIEGEL. *Industrial Management,* John Wiley & Sons, New York City, 1940.

LAVIGUEUR, LAWRENCE L. "Standard Data for Eye Time," (JMTM),* Vol. II, No. 1 Jan–Feb 1955.

LAZARUS, IRWIN P. "A System of Predetermined Human Work Times," *Ph.D. Dissertation*, Purdue University, 1952.

LEERBURGER, B. A., JR. "Scientific Management: Story of a Revolution," (FACT),* Oct 1960.

LEVIN, ROBERT. "Using MTM for Operator Training," *Proceedings—2nd Annual MTM Conference*, (MTMA),* New York City, Oct 1953.

LIKERT, RENSIS. *New Patterns of Management*, McGraw-Hill Book Company, New York City, 1961.

LOMICKA, ROY F. and JOHN M. ALLDERIGE. "Mathematical Man-Machine Analysis," (JIE),* Vol. III, No. 3, May–June 1957.

LOUDEN, J. KEITH. "The Manager—Today and Tomorrow," *Proceedings—6th Annual MTM Conference*, (MTMA),* New York City, Sept 1957.

* See code at start of Bibliography.

LOUDEN, J. KEITH. *Wage Incentives,* John Wiley & Sons, New York City, 1944.

LOWRY, STEWART M., HAROLD B. MAYNARD, and GUSTAVE J. STEGEMERTEN. *Time and Motion Study and Formulas for Wage Incentives,* McGraw-Hill Book Company, New York City, 3rd Edition, 1940.

LUCKIESH, M. and F. R. MOSS. "The Extent of the Perceptual Span in Reading," *Journal of General Psychology,* Vol. 25, 1941.

LYNCH, H. "Basic Motion Timestudy," (JIE),* Vol. IV. Aug 1953.

MABRY, JOHN E. "MTM-GPD General Purpose Data Original Development and Future Expansion," (JMTM),* Vol. IX, No. 1, Sept–Oct 1963.

MAYNARD, HAROLD B. "Design for Leadership," *Proceedings—3rd International MTM Conference,* (MTMA),* New York City, Sept 1963.

———. (Editor-in-Chief). *Industrial Engineering Handbook,* McGraw-Hill Book Company, New York City, 1956, 2nd Edition 1963.

———. "Industrial Engineering—Training for Management," (JIE),* Vol. X, No. 1, Jan–Feb 1959.

———. "The Ever-Growing Value of MTM," (JMTM),* Vol. VII, No. 4, Nov–Dec 1960.

———. "The Future of MTM," *Proceedings—1st Annual MTM Conference,* (MTMA),* New York City, Oct 1952.

———. (Editor-in-Chief). *Top Management Handbook,* McGraw-Hill Book Company, New York City, 1960.

———. "When Top Management Supports MTM," *Proceedings—9th Annual MTM Conference,* (MTMA),* Toronto, Canada, June 1960.

MAYNARD, HAROLD B. and GUSTAVE J. STEGEMERTEN. *Guide to Methods Improvement,* McGraw-Hill Book Company, New York City, 1944.

———. *Operation Analysis,* McGraw-Hill Book Company, New York City, 1939.

MAYNARD, HAROLD B., WILLIAM M. AIKEN, and JOHN F. LEWIS. *Practical Control of Office Costs,* Management Publishing Corporation, Greenwich, Connecticut, 1960.

MAYNARD, HAROLD B., GUSTAVE J. STEGEMERTEN, and JOHN L. SCHWAB. *Methods-Time Measurement,* McGraw-Hill Book Company, New York City, 1948.

McALLISTER, G. ERIC. "Random Ratio-Delay," *Research Report No. 12,* Management Sciences Research Project, University of California, Los Angeles, 1953.

McCORMICK, BROOKS. "Management and the Industrial Engineer," (JMTM),* Vol. III, No. 1, Mar–Apr 1956.

McCORMICK, E. J. *Human Engineering,* McGraw-Hill Book Company, New York City, 1957.

McCUGH, R. M. "Time and Energy Relationship of One- and Two-Handed Activity," *M.S. Thesis,* Washington University, 1932.

McKECHNIE, D. F. "Short Run, Long Cycle Operations Can Be Measured," *Mill and Factory,* Oct 1959.

McPHERSON, J. H. "How to Manage Creative Engineers," (MECH),* Vol. 87, No. 2, Feb 1965.

MEREDITH, G. P. "Theory of the Therblig," *Occupational Psychology,* London, England, Vol. 27, July 1953.

MILLER, GEORGE A. "The Magical Number Seven, Plus or Minus Two," *Psychological Review,* Vol. 63, 1956.

MIRER, STEVEN J. "Clerical Work Measurement," *M.S. Thesis,* Rensselaer Polytechnic Institute, Troy, New York, 1963.

MOOD, A. M. *Introduction to the Theory of Statistics,* McGraw-Hill Book Company, New York City, 1950.

MOTYCKA, JOSEPH. "Learning Curves—Pricing and Controlling," *Proceedings—16th Annual National Conference,* (AIIE),* Chicago, May 1965.

(MTMA).* "Application Training Supplements Nos. 1 through 5," Mar 1955.

———. "Application Training Supplement No. 6—Position," Oct 1960.

———. "MTM Basic Specifications," (JMTM),* Vol. V, No. 4, Nov–Dec 1958.

———. *Proceedings—1st Annual MTM Conference,* New York City, Oct 1952.

* See code at start of Bibliography.

(MTMA).* *Proceedings—2nd Annual MTM Conference,* New York City, Oct 1953.
————. *Proceedings—3rd Annual MTM Conference,* New York City, Oct 1954.
————. *Proceedings—4th Annual MTM Conference,* Chicago, Oct 1955.
————. *Proceedings—5th Annual MTM Conference,* New York City, Oct 1956.
————. *Proceedings—6th Annual MTM Conference,* New York City, Sept 1957.
————. *Proceedings—7th Annual MTM Conference,* New York City, Sept 1958.
————. *Proceedings—8th Annual MTM Conference,* Detroit, Michigan, Oct 1959.
————. *Proceedings—9th Annual MTM Conference,* Toronto, Canada, June 1960.
————. *Proceedings—10th Annual MTM Conference,* New York City, Oct 1961.
————. *Proceedings—11th Annual MTM Conference,* New York City, Sept 1962.
————. *Proceedings—3rd International MTM Conference,* New York City, Sept 1963.
————. *Proceedings—12th Annual MTM Conference,* New York City, Sept 1964.
————. *Proceedings—13th Annual MTM Conference,* New York City, Oct 1965.
MUCKSTADT, JOHN A. "Independence of MTM Elements," *Proceedings—12th Annual MTM Conference,* (MTMA),* New York City, Sept 1964.
MUNDEL, MARVIN E. "Allowing in Time Standards for Weight Handled," (JIE),* Vol. VIII, No. 4, July–Aug 1957.
————. *Motion and Time Study,* Prentice-Hall, Englewood Cliffs, New Jersey, 1950, 2nd Edition, 1955.
MUNDEL, MARVIN E. and IRWIN P. LAZARUS. "Predetermined Time Standards in the Army Ordance Corps," (JIE),* Vol. V, No. 6, Nov 1954.
NADLER, GERALD E. "How Many Time Study Readings to Take," (FACT),* Vol. 113, No. 2, Feb 1955.
————. *Motion and Time Study,* McGraw-Hill Book Company, New York City, 1955.
————. "Time Study Rating Evaluation," (JIE),* Vol. IV, No. 4, Nov 1953.
————. "Work Design: A Philosophy for Applying Work Principles," (JIE),* Vol. X, No. 3, May–June 1959.
NADLER, GERALD E. and DONALD H. DENHOLM. "Therblig Relationships: I. Added Cycle Work and Context Therblig Effects," (JIE),* Vol. VI, No. 2, Mar–Apr 1955.
NADLER, GERALD E. and JAY W. GOLDMAN. "Operator Performance Studies: II. Learning Analysis from Three-Plane Motions," (JIE),* Vol. XIV, No. 5, Sept–Oct 1963.
————. "The Unopar," (JIE),* Vol. IX, No. 1, Jan–Feb 1958.
NANCE, HAROLD W. "There Is a Need for Guided Application," *Proceedings—9th Annual MTM Conference,* (MTMA),* Toronto, Canada, June 1960.
NASH, A. E. "Ratio-Delay—A Prize Tool," *Proceedings—1st Annual Management Conference,* (AIIE),* Fort Wayne, Indiana, May 1955.
NICHOLS, D. EDWARD and HAROLD T. AMRINE. "A Physiological Appraisal of Selected Principles of Motion Economy," (JIE),* Vol. X, No. 5, Sept–Oct 1959.
NIEBEL, BENJAMIN W. *Motion and Time Study,* Richard D. Irwin, Homewood, Illinois, 1955.
NIEBEL, BENJAMIN W. and G. L. THEURING. "Let's Have More Accurate Time Standards for Basic Motions," (FACT),* Vol. 103, Sept 1951.
NINCKE, KLAUS H. "MTM Versus Time Study for Formula Construction," (JMTM),* Vol. VI, No. 4, Sept–Oct 1959.
NISSLEY, HAROLD R. "Effects of Weight and Distance on Short Cycle Work," *Mill and Factory,* Vol. 49, Nov 1951.
————. "The Importance of Learning in Setting Job Shop Standards," *Mill and Factory,* Vol. 47. May 1949.
OAKLEY, G. and SIDNEY J. FECHT. "How to Take Industrial Motion Pictures," *Proceedings—14th Annual National Time and Motion Study and Management Clinic,* Industrial Management Society, Chicago, 1952.
OBERG, ERIK and FRANKLIN D. JONES (Editors). *Machinery's Handbook,* The Industrial Press, New York City, 17th Edition, 1964.

* See code at start of Bibliography.

PAINE, RUSSELL R. "Experiment in Operator Learning at TRW," (JMTM),* Vol. IX, No. 4, May–June 1964.

PATERSON, D. G. and M. A. TINKER. "Eye Movements in Reading Type Sizes in Optimal Line Widths," *Journal of Educational Psychology,* Vol. 34, 1943.

————. "Influence of Line Width on Eye Movements," *Journal of Experimental Psychology,* Vol. 27, 1940.

————. "Influence of Size of Type on Eye Movements," *Journal of Applied Psychology,* Vol. 26, 1942.

PAXTON, JOHN S. "ACCRO-FAC," *Proceedings—7th Annual Chapter Conference,* (AIIE),* Detroit, Michigan, Feb 1965.

PRESGRAVE, RALPH. *Dynamics of Time Study,* McGraw-Hill Book Company, New York City, 1945.

PUNTON, JOHN W. "An Analysis of Research Into Position," (JMTM),* Vol. IV, No. 2, May–June 1957.

QUICK, JOSEPH H., JAMES H. DUNCAN, and JAMES A. MALCOLM, JR. *Work-Factor Time Standards,* McGraw-Hill Book Company, New York City, 1962.

RAND, CHRISTIAN. "A Hyper-Audio Pulse Triggered Input Device for Work Measurements, Standard Data Sampling, and Biological Response Studies," (JIE),* Vol. VII, No. 2, Mar–Apr 1956.

RAPHAEL, DAVID L. "A Basic Introduction to Methods-Time Measurement," *Proceedings—1st Annual Management Conference,* (AIIE),* Fort Wayne, Indiana, May 1955.

————. "An Analysis of Short Reaches and Moves," *Research Report 106,* (MTMA),* Sept 1953.

————. "A Research Methods Manual," *Research Report 107,* (MTMA),* Apr 1954.

————. "A Study of Arm Movements Involving Weight," *Research Report 108,* (MTMA),* Mar 1955.

————. "A Study of Positioning Movements: I. The General Characteristics; II. Special Studies Supplement," *Research Report 109,* (MTMA),* 1957.

————. "A Study of Positioning Movements: III. Application to Industrial Work Measurement," *Research Report 110,* (MTMA),* Nov 1957.

————. "MTM Research Activities," (JMTM),* Vol. III, No. 5, Jan–Feb 1957.

————. "Position Application," *Proceedings—6th Annual MTM Conference,* (MTMA),* New York City, Sept 1957.

————. "Position Research," *Proceedings—5th Annual MTM Conference,* (MTMA),* New York City, Oct 1956.

————. "Recent MTM Research Developments," *Proceedings—2nd Annual MTM Conference,* (MTMA),* New York City, Oct 1953.

————. "Research and MTM," (JMTM),* Vol. II, No. 5, Jan–Feb 1956.

————. "Research — An MTM Application," *Proceedings—4th Annual MTM Conference,* (MTMA),* Chicago, Oct 1955.

————. "Research Developments in Move with Weights," *Proceedings—3rd Annual MTM Conference,* (MTMA),* New York City, Oct 1954.

————. "Short Reaches and Moves—A Summary of the Complete Report," (JMTM),* Vol. I, No. 1, Apr 1954.

RAPHAEL, DAVID L. and GRANT C. CLAPPER. "A Study of Simultaneous Motions," *Research Report 105,* (MTMA),* Sept 1952.

RATNER, R. A. "Effect of Variations in Weight Upon Move Times," *M.S. Thesis,* Iowa State College, 1951.

RICHARDSON, WALLACE J. "Work Sampling Today," (FACT),* Sept 1959.

RICHARDSON, WYMAN R. "RAWS Multiple Regression Analysis," *Institute of Science and Technology Report 5432-4-R,* University of Michigan, Ann Arbor, Michigan, Aug 1963.

RIDER, P. R. *An Introduction to Modern Statistical Methods,* John Wiley & Sons, New York City, 1939.

ROWE, A. J. "A Useful Tool for Time Measurement Problems," (JIE),* Vol. V, Mar 1954.

* See code at start of Bibliography.

SCHEIB, JOHN C., JR. "Incentive Wage Practice for Restricted Work," (JIE),* Vol. VIII, No. 3, May–June 1957.

SCHMID, MERLE D. "Work Measurement Sampling," *Proceedings—7th Annual Chapter Conference,* (AIIE),* Detroit, Michigan, Feb 1965.

SCHMIDTKE, HEINZ and FRITZ STIER. "An Experimental Evaluation of the Validity of Predetermined Elemental Time Systems," (JIE),* Vol. XII, No. 3, May–June 1961.

———. "Response to the Comments on 'An Experimental Evaluation of the Validity of Predetermined Elemental Time Systems'," (JIE),* Vol. XIV, No. 3, May–June 1963.

SCHUTT, WILLIAM H. *Process Engineering,* McGraw–Hill Book Company, New York City, 1948.

———. *Time Study Engineering,* McGraw-Hill Book Company, New York City, 1943.

SCHWAB, JOHN L. "The Measurement of Human Effort—Part II," *Proceedings—15th Annual National Conference,* (AIIE),* Philadelphia, May 1964.

SCHWAN, HARRY T. "Maintenance Costs Can Be Reduced," *Proceedings—3rd Annual Management Conference,* (AIIE),* Fort Wayne, Indiana, May 1957.

SCHWARTZ, SHULA. "The Learning Curve and Its Application," *Library Bibliography No. 20,* Chance Vought Aircraft Company, Dallas, Texas.

SCOUTTEN, E. F. "MTM Versus Union Goals," *Proceedings—11th Annual MTM Conference,* (MTMA),* New York City, Sept 1962.

SELLIE, CLIFFORD. "Comments on 'An Experimental Evaluation of the Validity of Predetermined Elemental Time Systems'," (JIE),* Vol. XII, No. 5, Sept–Oct 1961.

SHAPERO, A. "Studies in Multiple Grasping and Positioning of Small Parts," *Proceedings—3rd Annual Industrial Engineering Institute,* University of California, Berkeley, 1951.

SIEGLER, N. "A Study of Some Factors Affecting Element Time in Manual Work," *Ph.D. Dissertation,* University of Minnesota, 1954.

SIMON, FRED. "Management and Labor Look at MTM," *Proceedings—8th Annual MTM Conference,* (MTMA),* Detroit, Michigan, Oct 1959.

SMADER, ROBERT C. and KARL U. SMITH. "Dimensional Analysis of Motion: VI. The Component Movements of Assembly Motions," *Journal of Applied Psychology,* Vol. 37, 1953.

SMALLEY, HAROLD E. "Comments on 'An Experimental Evaluation of the Validity of Predetermined Elemental Time Systems'," (JIE),* Vol. XV, No. 1, Jan–Feb 1964.

SMITH, B. J. "Validation of Certain Tests of Ocular Dominance," *Ph.D. Dissertation,* University of Minnesota, 1954.

SMITH, KARL U., et. al. "Dimensional Analysis of Motion: III. Complexity of Movement Pattern," *Journal of Applied Psychology,* Vol. 36, Aug 1952.

SMITH, KARL U. and GERALD RUBIN. "Principles of Design of the Sequential Interval Recorder," *Perceptual and Motor Skills,* Vol. 4, No. 1, Mar 1952.

SMITH, KARL U. and R. F. WEHRKAMP. "A Universal Motion Analyzer Applied to Psychomotor Performance," *Science,* Vol. 113, 1951.

———. "Dimensional Analysis of Motion: II. Travel Distance Effects," *Journal of Applied Psychology,* Vol. 36, 1952.

SMITH, PATRICIA ANN and KARL U. SMITH. "Effects of Sustained Performance on Human Motion," *Perceptual and Motor Skills,* Vol. 5, 1955.

SNAKENBERG, TED R. "The Use of Multi-Variable Charts to Simplify MTM Standard Data," (JMTM),* Vol. I, No. 5, Dec 1954.

———. "Time Saving Standards with Multi-Variable Charting," *Proceedings—3rd Annual Management Conference,* (AIIE),* Fort Wayne, Indiana, May 1957.

SNEDECOR, C. W. *Statistical Methods,* Iowa State College Press, 4th Edition, 1946.

* See code at start of Bibliography.

SOCIETY FOR ADVANCEMENT OF MANAGEMENT. "How to Use Performance Rating Films," New York City, 1952.

SOLBERG, R. B. "Time Allowances for the Handling of Weights for Use in Stopwatch Time Studies," *M.S. Thesis,* Purdue University, 1946.

STOHLMANN, DONALD G. "Development and Charting of Predetermined Time Data," (JIE),* Vol. IV, May 1953.

————. "How to Reach Your Cost Reduction Goal," *Proceedings—1st Annual Management Conference,* (AIIE),* Fort Wayne, Indiana, May 1955.

STOLL, RICHARD F. "Future of MTM Research or More Specifically Basic Motion Research," *Proceedings—6th Annual MTM Conference,* (MTMA),* New York City, Sept 1957.

————. "General Purpose Data (MTM-GPD)—The Standard Data System the MTM Association Developed and Sponsors," *Proceedings—15th Annual National Conference,* (AIIE),* Philadelphia, May 1964.

————. "The MTM Association and Its Work," *Proceedings—1st Annual Management Conference,* (AIIE),* Fort Wayne, Indiana, May 1955.

STUKEY, ARTHUR E. "Work Measurement in Perspective—Universal Time Data," (JIE),* Vol. XV, No. 1, Jan–Feb 1964.

TAGGERT, JOHN B. "Comments on 'An Experimental Evaluation of the Validity of Predetermined Elemental Time Systems'," (JIE),* Vol. XII, No. 6, Nov.–Dec 1961.

TAYLOR, FREDERICK WINSLOW. *Shop Management,* Harper & Brothers, New York City, 1919.

————. "The Present State of the Art of Industrial Management," *Transactions,* (ASME),* Vol. 34, 1912.

THOMPSON, DAVID A. "Information Theory in Mental Work Measurement," *AIIE Western Regional Conference,* San Francisco, California, Oct 1963.

————. "The Development of a Quantified Difficulty Measure for Precision Work," (JMTM),* Vol. VIII, No. 5, July–Aug 1963.

THOMPSON, DAVID A. and MARTIN ACKER. "A Detailed Physiological Difficulty Analysis of Manual Work," (JMTM),* Vol. VII, No. 3, Sept–Oct 1960.

THORSON, P. J. "Work Sampling—Sample Size," *Industrial Engineering News,* Department of Mechanical Engineering, Michigan State University, No. 29, Summer 1956.

TICHAUER, E. R. "Human Capacity, A Limiting Factor In Design," *Institution of Mechanical Engineers,* London, England, July 1963.

TINKER, M. A. "Time Taken by Eye Movements in Reading," *Journal of Genetic Psychology,* Vol. 48, 1936.

TINKER, M. A. and D. G. PATERSON. "Eye Movements in Reading Black Print on White Background and Red Print on Dark Green Background," *American Journal of Psychology,* Vol. 57, 1944.

TOWNSLEY, CLAUDE J. "MTM Usage—Procedure and Examples," (JMTM),* Vol. II, No. 3, July–Aug 1955.

TRAVIS, K. C. "The Latency and Velocity of the Eye in Saccadic Movements," *Psychology Monograms,* Vol. 47, 1936.

TYLER, LEONA E. *The Psychology of Human Differences,* Appleton-Century-Crofts, New York City, 1947.

URWICK, LYNDALL. "The Value of MTM to Top Management," *Proceedings—1st Annual MTM Conference,* (MTMA),* New York City, Oct 1952.

VANCE, STANLEY. *Industrial Administration,* McGraw-Hill Book Company, New York City, 1959.

VON TREBRA, PATRICIA and KARL U. SMITH. "Dimensional Analysis of Motion: IV. Transfer Effects on Direction of Movement," *Journal of Applied Psychology,* Vol. 36, 1952.

WADDELL, HARRY LEE (Editor). "Work Sampling," (FACT),* July 1952.

WALKER, R. Y. "The Eye Movements of Good Readers," *Psychology Monograms,* Vol. 44, 1933.

* See code at start of Bibliography.

WELFORD, A. T. *Ageing and Human Skill,* Oxford University Press, Cambridge, England, 1958.

WERKMEISTER, W. H. *An Introduction to Critical Thinking,* Johnsen Publishing Company, Lincoln, Nebraska, 1948.

WHITE, KENDALL C. "MTM-A Keystone for Standards," *Proceedings—11th Annual MTM Conference,* (MTMA),* New York City, Sept 1962.

——. "Predetermined Elemental Motion Times," *Paper No. 50-A-88,* (ASME),* Nov 1950.

WILKES, J. W. "The Effect of Job Difficulty Factors on Time, Energy, and Acceleration of Motion Patterns," *Sc.D. Dissertation,* Washington University, 1954.

WILLIAMS, J. A. C. "A New Conceptual Approach in Work Study," (JIE),* Vol. VII, No. 4, July–Aug 1956.

WINKELMAN, CHARLES. "The Positive Approach to Wage Incentives," (JMTM),* Vol. VI, No. 2, May–June 1959.

WOLFBERG, STANLEY T. "Standard Data—Catalysis or Catastrophe," *Proceedings— 10th Annual MTM Conference,* (MTMA)*, New York City, Oct 1961.

——. "Topsy-Turvy Control Concept," (JIE),* Vol. XV, No. 2, Mar–Apr 1964.

WOODSON, W. E. *Human Engineering Guide,* University of California Press, Los Angeles, 1956.

WOODSON, WILLIAM S. "Creative Techniques—A Comparative Analysis," (JIE),* Vol. XV, No. 2, Mar–Apr 1964.

Work-Factor Company. *Information About the Work-Factor System,* New York City, 1950.

YARD, ROGER L., SR. "GPD—Latest Development of the MTM Association," (JMTM),* Vol. VIII, No. 5, July–Aug 1963.

YOUNG, H. H. "The Relationship Between Heart Rate and the Intensity of Work for Selected Tasks," (JIE),* Vol. VII, No. 6, Nov–Dec 1956.

* See code at start of Bibliography.

Index